Course 3

21st Century Assessments

connectED.mcgraw-hill.com

Send all inquiries to:
McGraw-Hill Education
8787 Orion Place
Columbus, OH 43240

ISBN: 978-0-02-143953-9
MHID: 0-02-143953-2

Printed in the United States of America.

1 2 3 4 5 6 7 8 9 QVS 22 21 20 19 18 17 16 15

21st Century Assessments

Contents

Teacher's Guide

Assessment Item Types

Countdown

Chapter Tests

Performance Tasks, by Chapter

Benchmark Tests

Answers and Rubrics

Teacher's Guide to

21st Century Assessment Preparation

Whether it's the print ***21st Century Assessments*** or online **ConnectED**, *Glencoe Math* meets all of your assessment preparation needs.

How to Use this Book

21st Century Assessments includes the core assessment preparation materials needed to prepare students for upcoming online state assessments. Additional assessment preparation can be found in the interactive Student Edition or online **ConnectED**. See page vi for details.

Assessment Item Types

- Familiarize students with commonly-seen item types on online assessments.
- Each type comes with a description of the online experience, helpful hints, and a problem for students to try on their own.

Countdown

- Prepare students in the 20 weeks leading up to the state assessment.
- Each week consists of a two-page countdown that contains five problems, addressing multiple CCSS domains.
- **Ideas for Use** Assign each weekly countdown as in-class work, homework, a practice assessment, or a weekly quiz. Assign one problem per day or assign the five problems all at once.

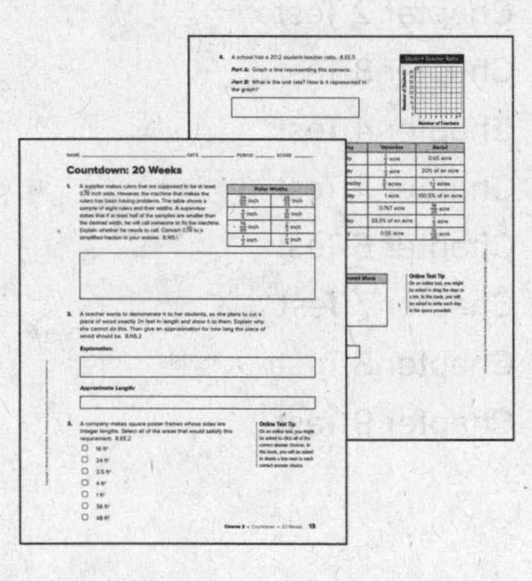

Chapter Tests

- Each six-page test contains 20 problems that assess all of the CCSS presented in the chapter.
- All problems mirror the item types found on online assessments, including several multi-part problems.
- **Ideas for Use** Assign as in-class work, homework, a practice assessment, a diagnostic assessment before beginning the chapter, or a summative assessment upon completion of the chapter.

Performance Tasks, by Chapter

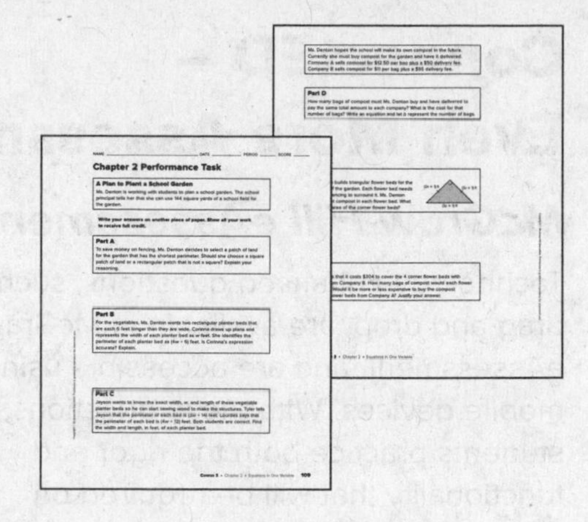

- Each two-page performance task measures students' abilities to integrate knowledge and skills across multiple standards, which help prepare them for college and future careers. Each rubric comes with samples of student work for correct or partially-correct responses.
- **Ideas for Use** Assign as in-class work, homework, a practice assessment, or as part of the summative assessment upon completion of the chapter.

Benchmark Tests

Four benchmark tests are available in this book. All problems on each test mirror the item types found on online assessments, including several multi-part problems. Each benchmark test includes a performance task.

- The ***first*** benchmark test is an eight-page assessment that addresses the CCSS from Chapters 1–3.
- The ***second*** benchmark test is similar in format to the first benchmark test, but addresses the CCSS from Chapters 4–6.
- The ***third*** and ***fourth*** benchmark tests are each twelve-page assessments that address the CCSS from the entire year, Chapters 1–9.
- **Ideas for Use** Assign each benchmark test as a diagnostic assessment prior to instruction or as a summative assessment. Assign the third and fourth benchmark tests as end-of-course assessments, using each one as a different version, or assign one as a diagnostic assessment prior to starting the school year. To score the performance tasks, refer to the rubrics located in the **Answers** section.

Go Online to Find More!

Charts for additional question analysis are available online for each countdown, chapter test, and benchmark test question in this book. These charts provide DOK levels, CCSS standards and mathematical practices correlations, and more.

Student scoring rubrics are available online for each chapter and benchmark performance task in this book. These student rubrics include a description of tasks students should perform correctly aligned with the task's maximum number of points.

- **Ideas for Use** Use the Student Scoring Rubric as a guide for student expectations, a student self-evaluation tool, as well as a final teacher evaluation tool.

ConnectED – Even More Assessment Preparation!

McGraw-Hill eAssessment

Technology-enhanced questions, such as drag and drop, are available in McGraw-Hill's eAssessment, and are accessible using mobile devices. With these questions, your students practice both the rigor and functionality that will be required on an online assessment.

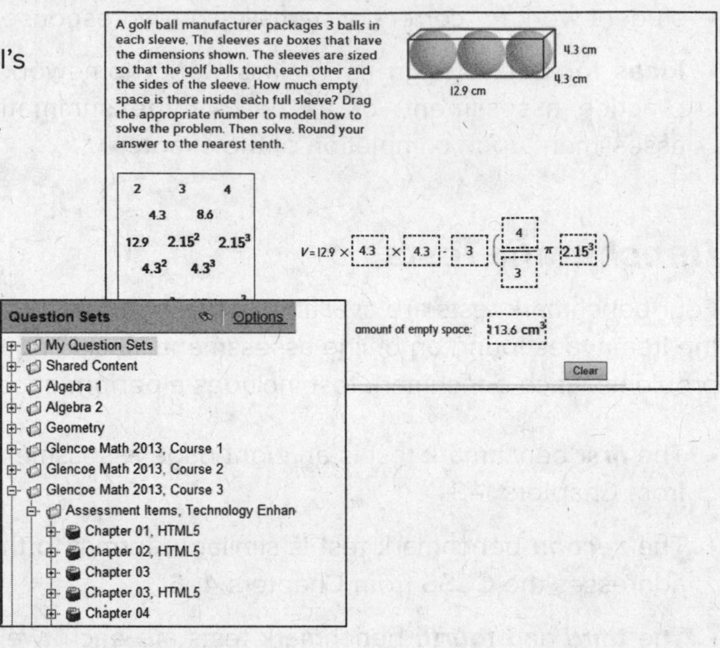

- Go to McGraw-Hill eAssessment.
- Expand your course folder.
- Expand the **Assessment Items, Technology Enhanced** folder.
- Drag selected chapter question sets into the test generator. HTML5 question sets are accessible using mobile devices.

Even More Performance Tasks!

Find additional performance tasks online. These tasks are also located in the interactive Student Edition, at the end of each chapter. Detailed rubrics are located in the Teacher Edition and online.

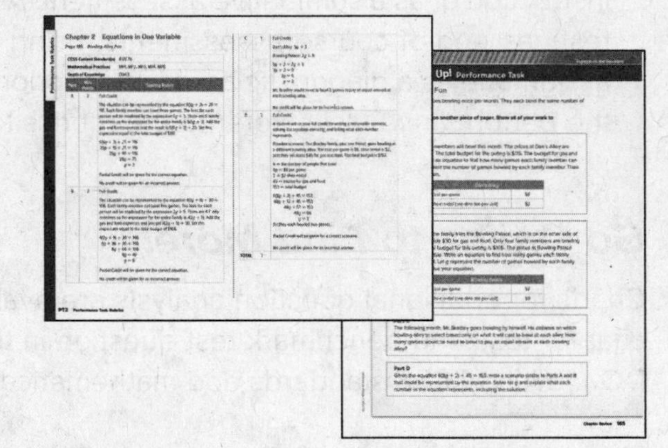

Assessment Item Types

You will encounter selected-response, constructed response, and technology-enhanced item types when taking an online assessment. Use these next several pages to become familiar with these item types. With each type, there is one for you to try on your own.

Selected-Response Items

You will be asked to select one or more given responses for a set of options.

Multiple True/False or Multiple Yes/No

Look at each real number. Select whether each statement is true or false. 8.NS.2

True	False	
☐	■	$0.\overline{72}$ is irrational.
■	☐	$\sqrt{4 + 9}$ is irrational.
■	☐	0.123456789 is rational.
☐	■	0.194194194... is irrational.

ONLINE EXPERIENCE

Click the appropriate box for each statement.

HELPFUL HINT

There are usually several statements, as opposed to one true-false statement. *All* of the statements must be selected correctly.

Try On Your Own!

Kelly knows that the seventh- and eighth-grade girls basketball teams scored a total of 81 points. She also knows that the seventh-grade team scored twice as many points as the eighth-grade team. She sets up and solves a system of equations using x as the number of points the eighth-grade team scored and y as the number of points the seventh-grade team scored. Select the appropriate box to identify whether the answer to each question is yes or no. 8.EE.8, 8.EE.8a, 8.EE.8b

Yes	No	
☐	☐	Does the equation $x = 2y$ represent a relationship between x and y?
☐	☐	Does the equation $x + y = 81$ represent a relationship between x and y?
☐	☐	Is the point (27, 54) found on the intersection of the graphs of the equations in the system?
☐	☐	Does this system of equations have an infinite number of solutions?
☐	☐	Did the seventh-grade team score 54 points?

Another example of a selected-response item is shown below.

Multiple Correct Answers

A series of transformations maps triangle ABC to triangle $A'B'C'$.
8.G.1, 8.G.1a, 8.G.1b, 8.G.2

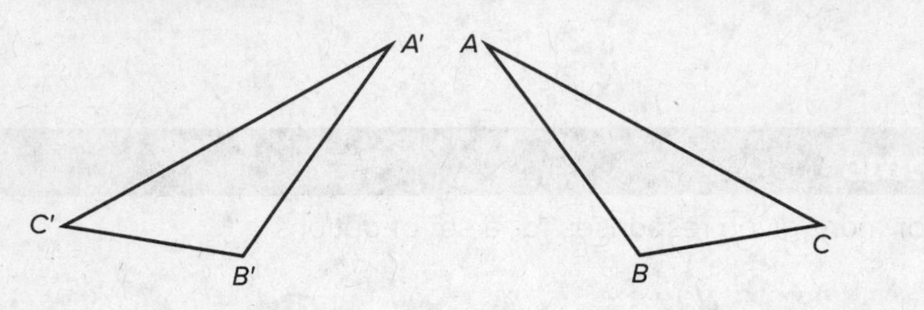

Select all of the statements that are valid based on the figures.

- [x] $AB = A'B'$
- [ ] 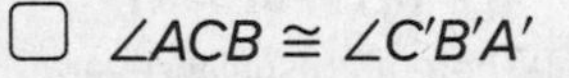 $\angle ACB \cong \angle C'B'A'$
- [ ] Because a dilation was used, the sum of the angles in ABC is greater than the sum of the angles in $A'B'C'$.
- [x] The areas of the triangles are the same.
- [x] Triangle ABC could have been translated, rotated, and/or reflected to be mapped onto triangle $A'B'C'$.

ONLINE EXPERIENCE Click *all* of the correct answer choices.

HELPFUL HINT Read *each* answer choice carefully. There is often more than one correct answer, as opposed to a single correct answer for a traditional multiple-choice problem.

Try On Your Own!

A cone and a cylinder have the same radius, 8 centimeters, and the same volume. The slant height of the cone is 17 centimeters. Select all of the statements that are valid based on the solids. 8.G.7, 8.G.9

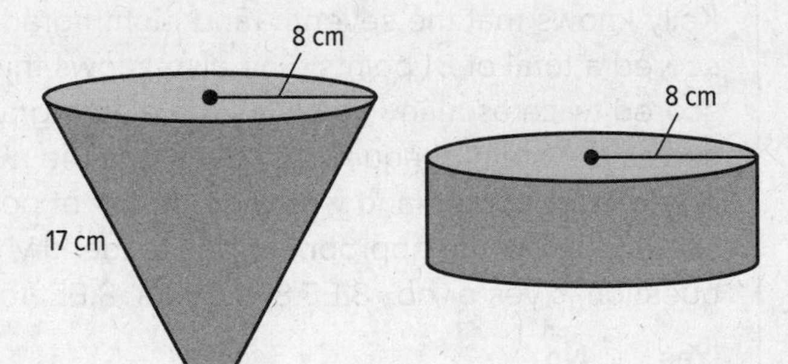

- [ ] The height of the cone is 15 centimeters.
- [ ] The height of the cylinder is three times the height of the cone.
- [ ] The volume of each solid is 320π cubic centimeters.
- [ ] The volume of the cone is $\frac{1}{3}$ the volume of the cylinder.
- [ ] The area of the base of the cone is equal to the area of a base of the cylinder.

Constructed-Response Items

You will be asked to generate a response, using letters, numbers, and mathematical symbols.

Type Entry

The circumference of a sphere is the same as the circumference of a circle that is on a plane containing the center of the sphere. The circumference of one sphere is shown. What is the volume of the sphere in cubic units? 8.G.9

$C = 6\pi x^2$ units

$36\pi x^6$

ONLINE EXPERIENCE
Use a keypad or keyboard to enter a response that may or may not contain variables and math symbols.

Try On Your Own!

Harlan downloads movies and pays a yearly membership fee plus a cost for each movie. Let x represent the number of movies Harlan rents. The graph shows Harlan's costs. Write an equation in the form $y = mx + b$ that represents the graphed function. 8.F.4

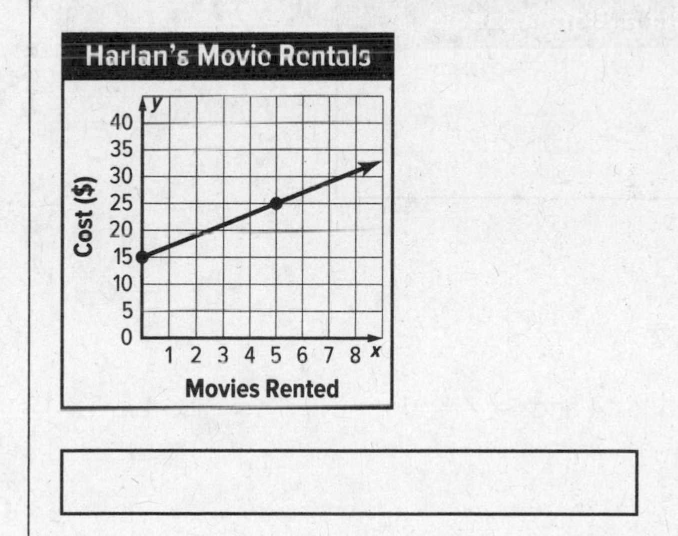

Technology-Enhanced Items

Many of the items on online tests are technology-enhanced items. In these items you will be asked to use computer-based technology, such as dragging and drawing objects, to solve the problem presented.

Bin Sort

Sort the equations listed at the bottom into the category that correctly shows the solution of the equation. 8.EE.7b

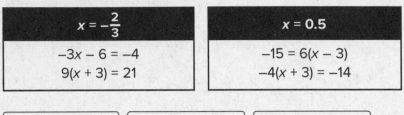

$3(x - 1) = 2$	$16x - 10 = 32$	$-4(x + 3) = -14$
$-15 = 6(x - 3)$	$-3x - 6 = -4$	$9(x + 3) = 21$

ONLINE EXPERIENCE
Sort objects by dragging them into their appropriate bins.

HELPFUL HINT
Depending on the actual problem, every bin may not have an associated object to which it is dragged. Read each problem carefully.

Try On Your Own!

Sort the triangles into the category that correctly describes whether or not the triangle is a right triangle. Assume all measures are in inches. 8.G.7

Right Triangle	Not a Right Triangle

Triangle 1	triangle with sides 4, 8, and $4\sqrt{3}$
Triangle 2	triangle with sides 9, 9, and $9\sqrt{2}$
Triangle 3	triangle with perimeter 13 and sides 4 and 5
Triangle 4	triangle with sides 8, 24, and 25
Triangle 5	triangle with perimeter 72 and sides 18 and 30

Another example of a technology-enhanced item is shown below.

Drag and Drop

Emilio has read some pages in his summer reading book. After two hours he is on page 96. After 5 hours he is on page 204. Assume that Emilio reads the same number of pages each hour. Drag a number into each box to show the initial value and the rate of change for the function that would represent this situation. 8.F.1, 8.F.4

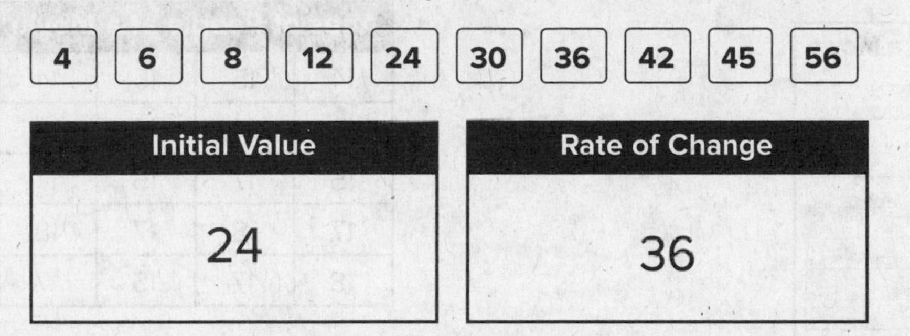

ONLINE EXPERIENCE
Drag objects to their appropriate locations, not necessarily in bins. In this book, write or draw the object in its appropriate location as opposed to dragging it.

HELPFUL HINT
Depending on the actual problem, not all of the objects are dragged to complete the problem correctly. Read each problem carefully.

Try On Your Own!

A wading pool with a water fountain inside is being designed for a city park. The pool will be shaped like a triangle and have an extended bench along one side. Drag angle measures to the boxes to make a possible triangle *ABC* for the wading pool. 8.G.A.5

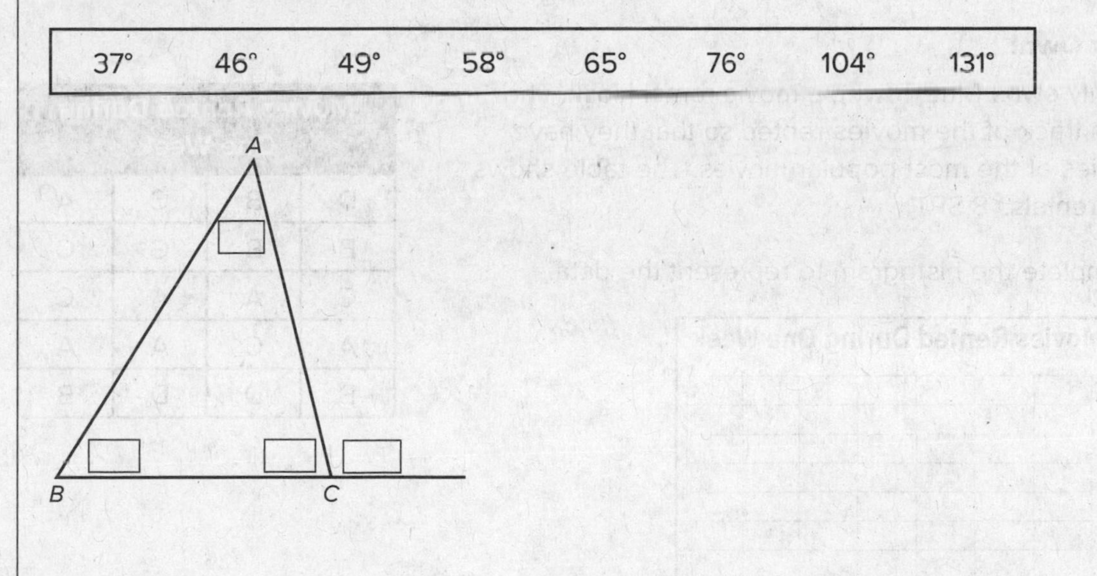

Some problems on an online assessment will require you to complete multiple parts. One or more parts may be technology-enhanced. An example is below.

Construct Statistical Graphs

ONLINE EXPERIENCE
Click to shade sections of the graph. If you make a mistake, click to deselect a section that you selected.

A movie theater manager surveyed the people in the audience about their ages. The table shows the results of the survey. 8.SP.1

Part A: Complete the histogram to represent the data.

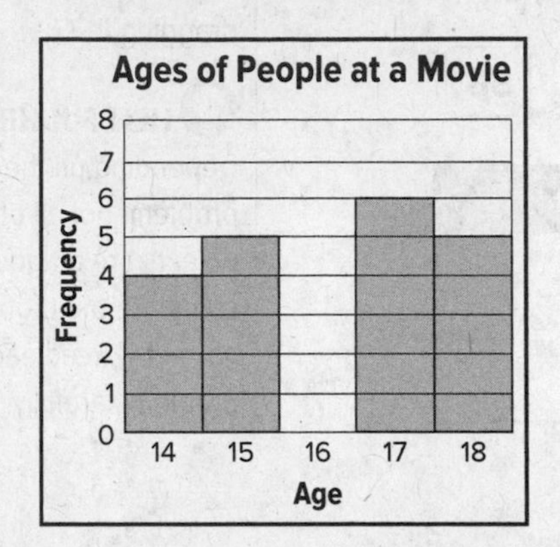

Ages of People at a Movie			
14	15	15	14
18	14	14	18
15	17	15	17
17	18	17	18
18	17	15	17

Part B: Identify any gaps or outliers in the data.

There is a gap between 15 and 17, but no outliers.

Try On Your Own!

Xavier's family owns Blue Tower, a movie rental kiosk. The family keeps track of the movies rented so that they have enough copies of the most popular movies. The table shows one week's rentals. 8.SP.1

Movies Rented During One Week			
D	B	C	A
B	B	G	C
C	A	A	C
A	C	A	A
B	D	D	B

Part A: Complete the histogram to represent the data.

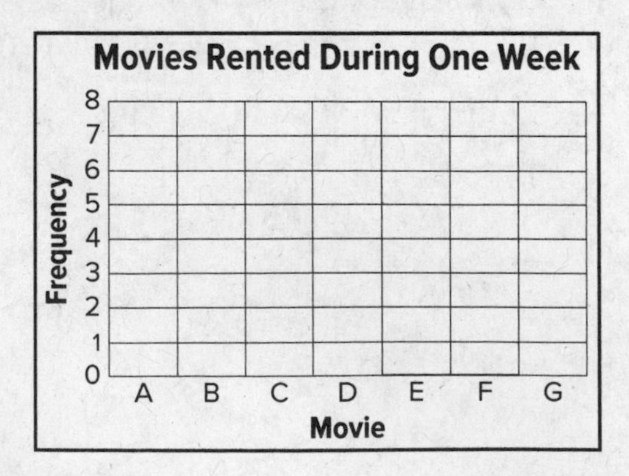

Part B: Identify any gaps or outliers in the data.

Another example of a technology-enhanced item is shown below.

Coordinate Plane

Click the buttons **Add Point** and **Connect Line** to plot points and draw lines on a coordinate plane.

Six minutes before game time, Keegan was stuck in slow traffic 9 miles away from the gym. He moved 1 mile every 2 minutes. Let $x = 0$ be game time. Graph the ordered pairs that show how far away Keegan was from the gym 12 minutes before the game, 2 minutes before the game, and at game time. 8.EE.5, 8.F.4

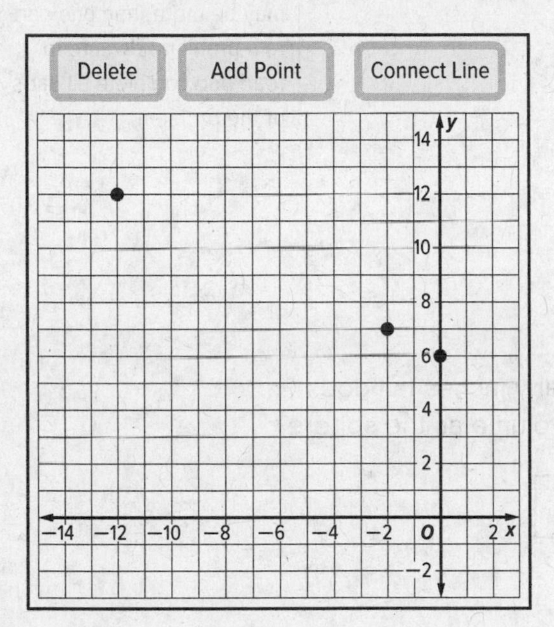

Try On Your Own!

Consider the graph of an equation that passes through the points (0, −5) and (4, −2). Graph the equation of the line that has the opposite rate of change and the same initial value as the original equation described. 8.F.4

Delete | Add Point | Connect Line

Another example of a multipart technology-enhanced item is shown below.

Volume of Solids

To make part of a sand castle, Teisha is given a ball filled with sand. She pours the sand into a cylinder to add a column to the castle. The ball and the cylinder each have a radius of 9 inches. 8.G.C.9

Part A: Shade the cylinder to show the same volume as the sphere.

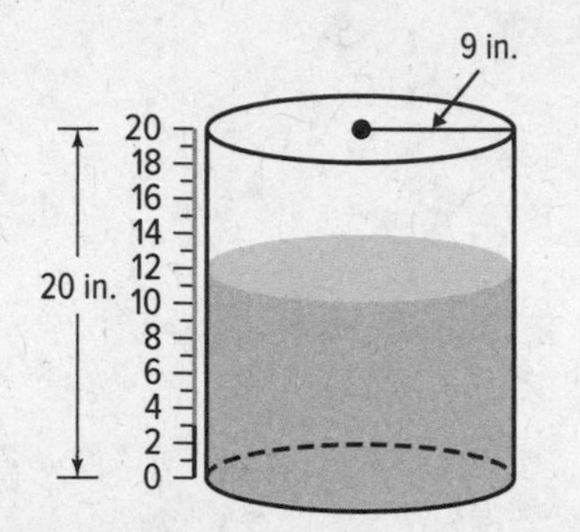

Part B: The radius of each solid is doubled. How many inches tall does the cylinder need to be so that it still has the same volume as the sphere?

24

ONLINE EXPERIENCE Click to shade sections of a solid. If you make a mistake, click to deselect the sections you selected.

HELPFUL HINT There may be more than one part to a problem. Be sure to read and complete all parts of the problem.

Try On Your Own!

Hank pours blue gel into the top of a cone with a radius of 8 centimeters, as shown at the right. The gel does not fill the cone completely. Hank notes that the top surface of the gel is circular and has a radius of 3 centimeters. 8.G.C.9

Part A: Shade the number of sections in the cone to represent the height, in centimeters, of the gel in the cone.

Part B: What is the volume of the gel in cubic centimeters? Round to the nearest hundredth.

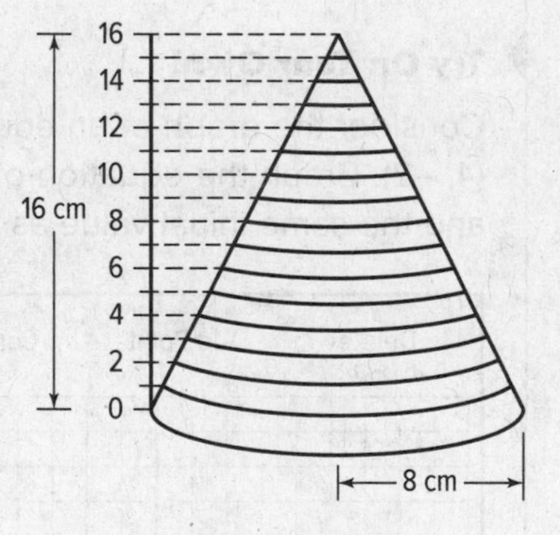

Performance Tasks

These tasks measure your ability to integrate knowledge and skills across multiple topics, which helps prepare you for college and future careers. An example of a performance task is shown below, with guidance about how to complete it.

On the Road Again

8.EE.5, 8.F.1, 8.F.2, 8.F.3, 8.F.4, 8.F.5, 8.G.8, 8.SP.1, 8.SP.2, 8.SP.3

For economic and environmental reasons, Ronaldo has chosen to use his bike to get around town rather than a car.

This performance task has 5 parts, Parts A–E. Read each part and follow the guiding instructions for how to complete it.

Part A

Ronaldo uses a coordinate plane to map his town. Each gridline represents 1 mile. How far is the park from the grocery store? Explain how to find the distance. How does your solution relate to the Pythagorean Theorem?

Park

Grocery Store

How far is the park from the grocery store? Round to the nearest tenth.

Explain how you found the distance.

How does your solution relate to the Pythagorean Theorem?

Part B

As Ronaldo travels from the park to the grocery store, he notes that after 1.5 hours he is still 1.8 miles from his destination. After 2 hours he would have gone 4.7 miles too far.

Write a function to relate Ronaldo's distance y to his time x. Show how you found the equation.

Is this a linear function? Justify your answer.

How long will it take Ronaldo to get to the grocery store from the park? Explain.

Part C

Another day, Ronaldo leaves home on his bike. He goes to his friend's house, which is halfway to work, at a slow pace. Ronaldo stays at his friend's house and then realizes that he left his bag at home. He quickly rides home to get it. He then bikes three times faster than his initial pace to get to work on time.

Sketch a graph that matches the scenario.

Identify whether each part of the graph is increasing, decreasing, or neither.

HELPFUL HINT
Questions may have more than one answer. This one requires four answers, one for each part of the graph.

Is this graph a function? Explain.

Part D

While Ronaldo rides his bike, his friend drives a car. She keeps track of how far she drives after filling the gas tank and how much gasoline is left in the tank after she drives. The table shows her results.

Distance Driven (mi)	20	40	100	120	160	240	300
Gas in the Tank (gal)	19	12	16	14	11	7	3

Use the data to construct a scatter plot of the distance driven and the amount of gas left in the tank.

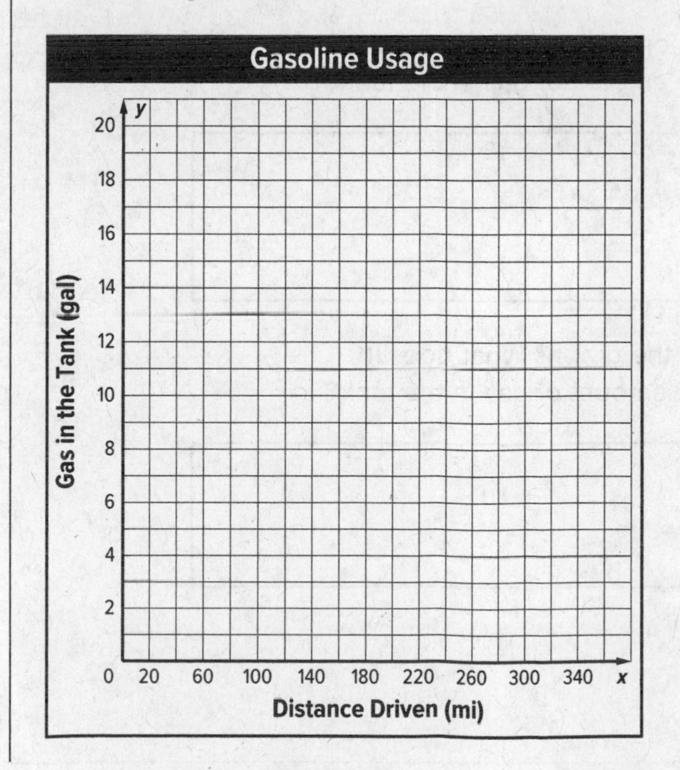

Are there any outliers? If so, which point(s)? Explain your answer.

What kind of association, if any, is there with the data? Explain your answer.

Part E

Draw a line of best fit on the scatter plot. Write an equation for your line of best fit. What is the rate of change? What does it represent about the distance driven and the amount of gas left in the car? What is the initial value? What does the initial value represent about the distance driven and the amount of gas left in the car?

Draw a line of best fit for the data on your scatter plot.

Write an equation for your line of best fit.

What is the rate of change? How is it shown on the graph? What does it represent about the distance driven and the amount of gas in the tank?

What is the initial value? How is it shown on the graph? What does it represent about the distance driven and the amount of gas in the tank?

NAME ______________________ DATE ____________ PERIOD ________ SCORE ________

Countdown: 20 Weeks

1. A supplier makes rulers that are supposed to be at least $0.\overline{78}$ inch wide. However, the machine that makes the rulers has been having problems. The table shows a sample of eight rulers and their widths. A supervisor states that if at least half of the samples are smaller than the desired width, he will call someone to fix the machine. Explain whether he needs to call. Convert $0.\overline{78}$ to a simplified fraction in your answer. 8.NS.1

Ruler Widths	
$\frac{39}{50}$ inch	$\frac{26}{33}$ inch
$\frac{4}{5}$ inch	$\frac{9}{10}$ inch
$\frac{76}{99}$ inch	$\frac{2}{3}$ inch
$\frac{1}{2}$ inch	$\frac{7}{9}$ inch

2. A teacher wants to demonstrate π to her students, so she plans to cut a piece of wood exactly 2π feet in length and show it to them. Explain why she cannot do this. Then give an approximation for how long the piece of wood should be. 8.NS.2

Explanation:

Approximate Length:

3. A company makes square poster frames whose sides are integer lengths. Select all of the areas that would satisfy this requirement. 8.EE.2

- ☐ 16 ft^2
- ☐ 24 ft^2
- ☐ 2.5 ft^2
- ☐ 4 ft^2
- ☐ 1 ft^2
- ☐ 36 ft^2
- ☐ 48 ft^2

Online Test Tip

On an online test, you might be asked to click all of the correct answer choices. In this book, you will be asked to shade a box next to each correct answer choice.

4. A school has a 20:2 student-teacher ratio. 8.EE.5

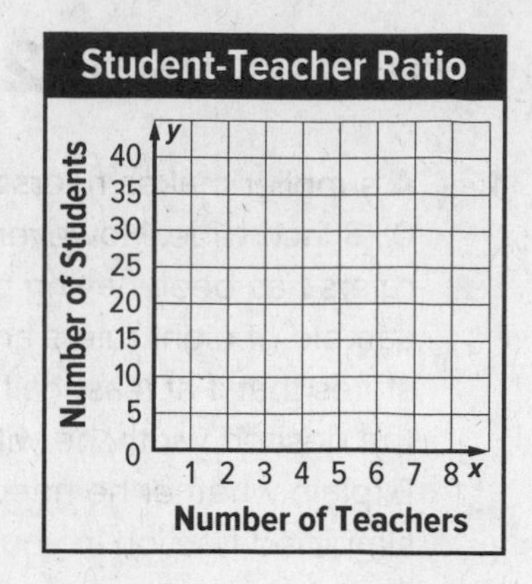

Part A: Graph a line representing this scenario.

Part B: What is the unit rate? How is it represented in the graph?

5. Veronica and Abdul are having a contest to see who can mow the greater area of lawn over the course of a week. The table shows the amount each person mowed on each day. 8.NS.1

Day	Veronica	Abdul
Monday	$\frac{1}{2}$ acre	0.65 acre
Tuesday	$\frac{1}{3}$ acre	20% of an acre
Wednesday	$\frac{6}{5}$ acres	$1\frac{1}{4}$ acres
Thursday	1 acre	100.5% of an acre
Friday	0.767 acre	$\frac{19}{25}$ acre
Saturday	33.3% of an acre	$\frac{1}{3}$ acre
Sunday	0.55 acre	$\frac{13}{25}$ acre

Part A: Sort the days into the bin of the person who mowed the greater area that day.

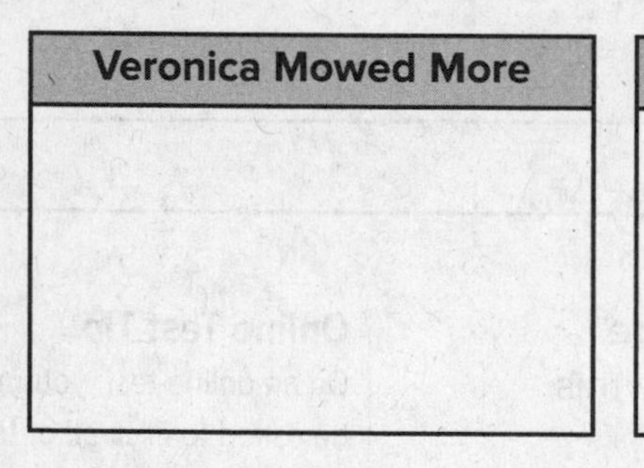

Abdul Mowed More

Online Test Tip

On an online test, you might be asked to drag the days to a bin. In this book, you will be asked to write each day in the space provided.

Part B: Who won the contest?

NAME ______________________ DATE ____________ PERIOD ________ SCORE ________

Countdown: 19 Weeks

1. A company sells only items that are in the shape of cubes. Select all of the volumes of cubes with rational number side lengths. 8.NS.1

- ☐ 8 in^3
- ☐ 33 cm^3
- ☐ 1.5 ft^3
- ☐ 9 ft^3
- ☐ 1,000 m^3
- ☐ $(4.12 \text{ yd})^3$

Online Test Tip

On an online test, you might be asked to click all of the correct answer choices. In this book, you will be asked to shade a box next to each correct answer choice.

2. Sherron is writing a computer program that solves linear equations and displays a numerical answer for the solution. 8.EE.7, 8.EE.7a

Part A: When Sherron inputs the equation $4x + 3 = 4(1 + x) + 1$, she gets an error message. Explain why.

Part B: Sherron inputs the equation $5 + 6y - 9y + 2 + 3(1 - y)$. What is the result and why?

3. A square picture frame encloses an area of 29 square inches. Its owner claims that the frame sides are between 5.25 and 5.35 inches long. Is the owner correct? Why or why not? 8.NS.2

4. A cargo ship has a stack of shipping containers. The stack is x containers wide, x containers long, and x containers tall. Circle all of the equations that could represent the total number of containers on the ship. 8.EE.2

$x^3 = 64$	$x^3 = 16$	$100 = x^3$
$x^3 = 9$	$27 = x^3$	$x^3 = 0.125$
$0.343 = x^3$	$x^3 = 8$	$216 = x^3$

5. A ball rolls in a straight line roughly 3π yards before stopping. Then someone kicks it backward 0.5π yards. 8.NS.2

Part A: On the number line, plot a point to represent the distance from the ball's initial location at 0 to its final location. Each increment on the number line represents 1 yard.

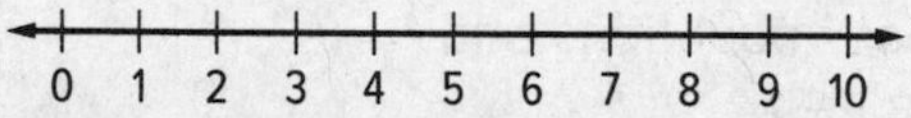

0 1 2 3 4 5 6 7 8 9 10

Part B: Explain why you cannot illustrate the distance exactly. Then give the distance rounded to the nearest hundredth.

Online Test Tip

On an online test, you might be asked to click the button to plot a point on the number line. In this book, you will be asked to draw the point on the number line.

NAME ________________ DATE ________ PERIOD ______ SCORE ______

Countdown: 18 Weeks

1. Imani is analyzing numbers. 8.NS.1, 8.NS.2

Part A: Select whether the number in each situation is rational or irrational.

	Rational	**Irrational**
A circumference of a circular picture frame is 5π, or 15.7079632..., inches.	☐	☐
A bottle contains $0.\overline{6}$ kiloliters of water.	☐	☐
The sales tax on a purchase was 6.25%.	☐	☐
The net change in Patrick's stock was –$11.	☐	☐

Part B: The diagonal of a rectangular carpet is $6\sqrt{3}$ feet long. Estimate the length of the diagonal to the nearest tenth of a foot. Then explain why you can only estimate the length, not find its exact value.

2. Enrique says that the value of $\sqrt{\frac{1}{x}}$ is a rational number for any positive, nonzero integer value of x. Select all of the values of x that could be used as counterexamples to show that Enrique's conjecture is false. 8.NS.1

☐ $x = 1$

☐ $x = 2$

☐ $x = 4$

☐ $x = 5$

☐ $x = 8$

☐ $x = 9$

3. The table shows the approximate populations of four capital cities in the United States. Write the correct city to make each statement true. 8.EE.1

City	Augusta, Maine	Cheyenne, Wyoming	Jackson, Mississippi	Montpelier, Vermont
Population (approx.)	3^9	3^{10}	3^{11}	3^8

The population of [ ] is about $\frac{1}{3}$ the population of Jackson.

The population of [ ] is about 3 times the population of Montpelier.

The population of [ ] is about 27 times the population of [ ].

Augusta
Cheyenne
Jackson
Montpelier

4. The number line shows four points labeled *A*, *B*, *C*, and *D*. Select whether each statement is true or false. 8.NS.2

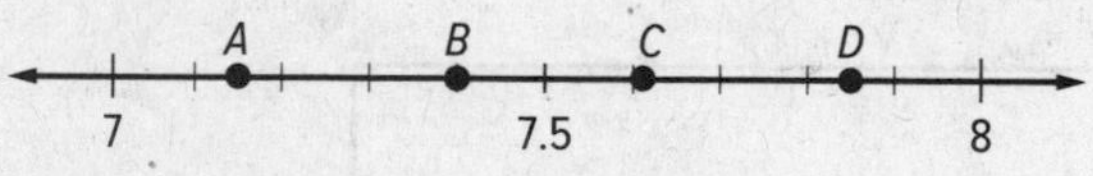

True **False**

☐ ☐ The value of $\sqrt{50}$ is between point *A* and point *B*.

☐ ☐ The coordinate of point *C* is less than $\sqrt{60}$.

☐ ☐ The coordinate of point *D* is greater than $\sqrt{63}$.

Online Test Tip

On an online test, you might be asked to click the appropriate box for each statement. In this book, you will be asked to shade in the boxes instead.

5. City Cab Company charges $3.00 per ride plus $2.00 per mile traveled. Metro Cab Company charges $1.50 per ride plus $2.50 per mile traveled. Write an equation to find *m*, the number of miles for which the total cost is the same for both taxi companies. Then solve the equation to find the number of miles when the cost is the same, and state what that cost is. 8.EE.7, 8.EE.7b

Equation: [ ]

m = [ ]

[ ] miles

Cost for that number of miles: [ ]

NAME ______________________ DATE __________ PERIOD ______ SCORE ______

Countdown: 17 Weeks

1. The diagonal of a rectangular floor is $\sqrt{40}$ feet long. 8.NS.1

Part A: Select all of the sets of numbers to which $\sqrt{40}$ belongs.

- ☐ real
- ☐ integer
- ☐ rational
- ☐ irrational
- ☐ whole
- ☐ natural

Part B: Change one digit in $\sqrt{40}$ to a different digit so that the number belongs to a different set of numbers. Explain why changing that digit changes the sets to which the number belongs.

Online Test Tip
On an online test, you might be asked to use a keypad with math symbols to enter the answer. In this book, you will be asked to write in the space provided.

2. The formula $t = \sqrt{\frac{h}{16}}$ represents the time t in seconds that it takes an object to fall from a height of h feet. A rock is dropped from a height of 80 feet. 8.NS.2

Part A: Graph on the number line a point that is an estimate of the time it takes the rock to fall to the ground.

1 1.5 2 2.5 3 3.5 4

Part B: To the nearest second, how long did it take the rock to fall?

3. The populations of five Asian capital cities are shown in the table. Order the cities from least to greatest population. 8.EE.3, 8.EE.4

City	Population in 2012
Bangkok, Thailand	8.25×10^6
Beijing, China	2.02×10^7
Manila, Philippines	1.65×10^6
Suva, Fiji	8.44×10^5
Tokyo, Japan	1.32×10^7

Bangkok Beijing Manila
Suva Tokyo

	City
Least population	
Greatest population	

Online Test Tip
On an online test, you might be asked to drag the city names into the spaces in the table. In this book, you will be asked to write in the table instead.

4. Anju purchased a storage cube that has a volume of 10 cubic feet. She wants to put it on a shelf on her wall that is 24 inches below the ceiling. Will the cube fit? Explain your reasoning. 8.EE.2

5. Angelo and Deborah are landscapers. Angelo charges $45.50 for each job plus $15 an hour. Deborah charges $20.50 for each job plus $20 an hour. Select whether each statement is true or false. 8.EE.7, 8.EE.7b

True	False	
☐	☐	For 2 hours of work, Angelo charges more.
☐	☐	For 6 hours of work, Deborah charges less.
☐	☐	The equation $45.5x + 15 = 20.5x + 20$ can be solved to find the number of hours for which the total cost is the same to hire either landscaper.
☐	☐	Both landscapers charge the same amount for a 5-hour job.

NAME ______________________ DATE __________ PERIOD ________ SCORE ________

Countdown: 16 Weeks

1. The radius of a circular fountain with area A can be approximated by solving the equation $\frac{A}{3} = r^2$. The area of the fountain is 84 square feet. 8.NS.2

Part A: Use a number line to estimate the value of the radius. Plot the square roots of the perfect squares between which the radius is located.

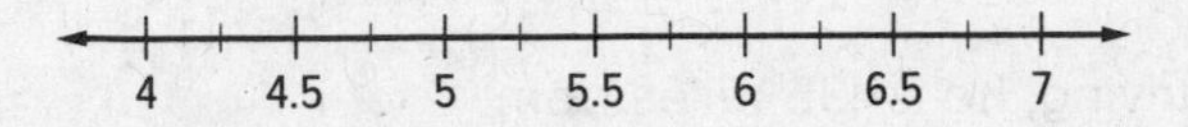

Part B: Find the estimate of the radius of the circular fountain to the nearest foot.

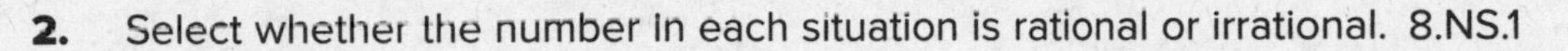

2. Select whether the number in each situation is rational or irrational. 8.NS.1

	Rational	**Irrational**
The length of a ribbon is $23.08\overline{3}$ centimeters.	☐	☐
The depth of a shark with respect to the surface of the water is –115.5 meters.	☐	☐
Amy calculates that each side of a square measures $2\sqrt{9}$ inches.	☐	☐
The circumference of a circular pie pan is 6π, or 18.8495559..., inches.	☐	☐

3. Select all of the equations that have no real solution. 8.EE.7, 8.EE.7a

- ☐ $5x - 1 - 2x = 3x - 7$
- ☐ $6x - (x - 2) = 5x - 2$
- ☐ $-3(5x + 3) = -15x - 9$
- ☐ $2 - (7x - 1) = 5x - 1$
- ☐ $10x + 4 + x = 4 + 11x - 1$

Online Test Tip
On an online test, you might be asked to click all of the correct answer choices. In this book, you will be asked to shade a box next to each correct answer choice.

4. Arturo is driving to a hotel. After 3 hours of driving, he is 135 miles from home. After 5 hours of driving, he is 225 miles from home. Arturo graphs his distance with respect to time as a line. What is the slope of the line? What does the slope tell us about Arturo's speed? 8.EE.5

Slope: ______

______

5. The table shows the number of people living in the United States and in each region of the country according to the 2010 census. Write the correct number to make each statement true. 8.EE.3, 8.EE.4

U.S. Region	Population (approx.)
Northeast	5.5×10^7
Midwest	6.7×10^7
South	1.1×10^8
West	7.2×10^7
United States (All)	3.1×10^8

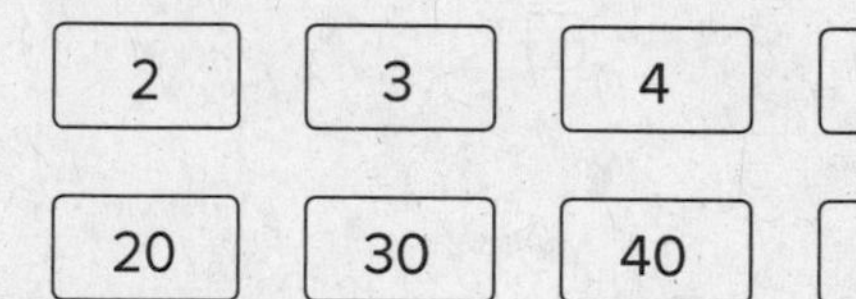

The population of the South is about ☐ times greater than the population of the Northeast.

The population of the entire United States is about ☐ times greater than the population of the South alone.

The population of the entire United States is about ☐ times greater than the population of the Midwest alone.

NAME ______________________ DATE ____________ PERIOD ________ SCORE ________

Countdown: 15 Weeks

1. Amy charges an hourly fee for each hour she babysits. The table shows how much Amy charges for different numbers of hours. 8.EE.5

Number of Hours	Charge ($)
2	12
3	18
4	24
5	30
6	36

Part A: Graph the points on the coordinate plane and connect them with a straight line.

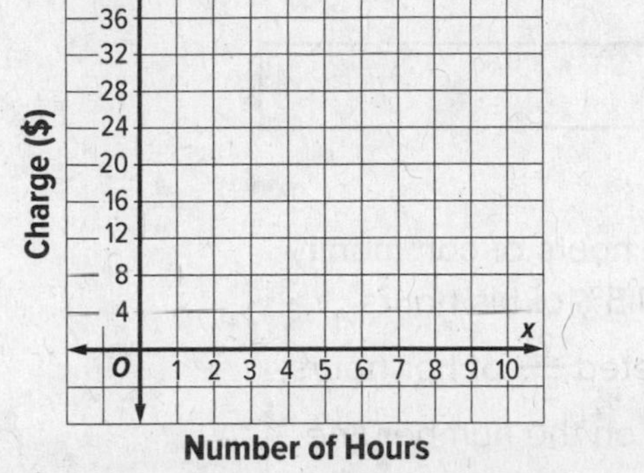

Online Test Tip

On an online test, you might be asked to click the buttons to plot points and graph a line. In this book, you will be asked to draw the points and the line on the graph.

Part B: What is the constant rate of change? What does it mean?

2. Write y-values for the empty cells in each table to make a linear function and a nonlinear function. Explain how you know your function is linear or nonlinear. 8.F.3

Linear Function

x	y
0	2
1	3
2	
3	

Nonlinear Function

x	y
1	6
2	7
3	
4	

3. The table shows the cost of buying different amounts of turkey. The total cost is a direct variation of the number of pounds purchased. Find the constant of proportionality and show how you found the answer. Then write an equation in $y = mx$ form to represent the situation. 8.F.4

Weight (lb), x	2	8	12
Cost ($), y	15	60	90

Constant of proportionality:

Equation:

4. Each member of the service club must complete 100 hours of community service during the year. So far, Kurt has completed 41.5% of his hours, Elias has completed $\sqrt{1{,}681}$ hours, Janina has completed $\frac{21}{50}$ of her hours, and Tasha has completed $\frac{3}{7}$ of her hours. Plot points on the number line to represent the number of hours of community service each club member has completed. 8.NS.1

41 41.2 41.4 41.6 41.8 42 42.2 42.4 42.6 42.8 43

5. Ariel is filling a swimming pool. Three gallons of water flow into the pool every minute. 8.F.4

Part A: Complete the table to show the number of gallons of water in the pool several minutes after Ariel begins filling it.

Time Since Filling Started (min)	Water in Pool (gal)
1	
2	
	9
4	
	15

Part B: How many gallons of water are in the pool 11 minutes after Ariel starts filling it?

NAME ______________________ DATE __________ PERIOD ________ SCORE ________

Countdown: 14 Weeks

1. Yeardley sold 3 times as many ads for the yearbook as Xavier. Xavier sold 8 fewer ads than Yeardley. The number of ads sold by each student can be represented by this system of equations: $y = 3x$ and $y = x + 8$. 8.EE.8, 8.EE.8b, 8.EE.8c

Part A: Graph the equations on the coordinate plane. Label the point of intersection.

Online Test Tip

On an online test, you might be asked to click buttons to graph lines and plot points. In this book, you will be asked to draw lines and points on a coordinate plane.

Part B: What is the solution to the system of equations? What does the solution represent?

2. The graph shows the amount in dollars left on a company's copy card after the card has been used to make different numbers of copies. Write a number or word to complete the statements. 8.F.4

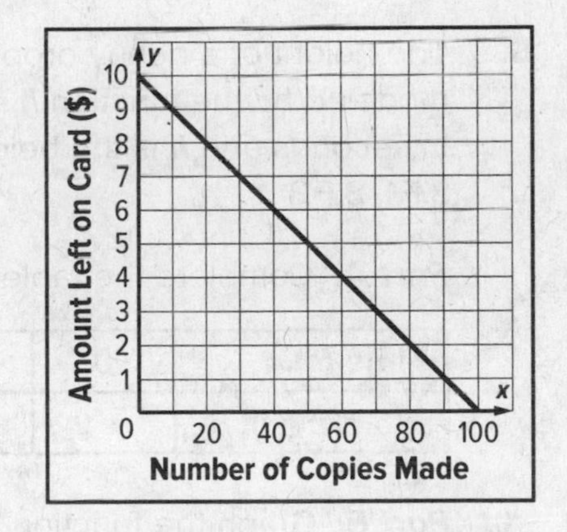

−20	0.10	−0.20
−10	0.20	−0.10
10	20	100
slope	*y*-intercept	*x*-intercept

The slope is ______. The *y*-intercept is ______.

The ______ shows the initial amount on the card in dollars.

The ______ shows that the amount on the card decreases by $ ______ each time a copy is made.

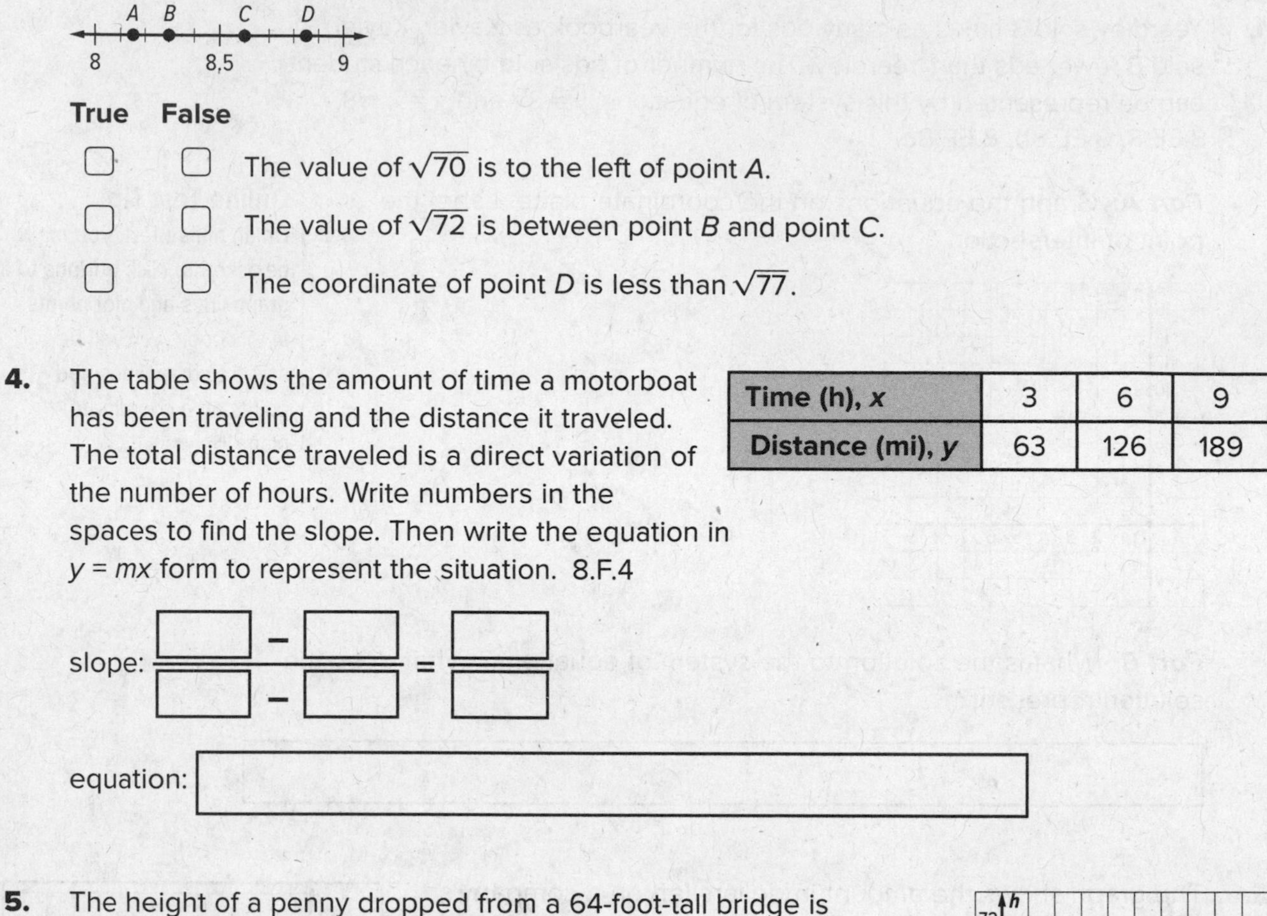

3. This number line shows four points labeled *A*, *B*, *C*, and *D*. Select whether each statement is true or false. 8.NS.2

True	False	
☐	☐	The value of $\sqrt{70}$ is to the left of point *A*.
☐	☐	The value of $\sqrt{72}$ is between point *B* and point *C*.
☐	☐	The coordinate of point *D* is less than $\sqrt{77}$.

4. The table shows the amount of time a motorboat has been traveling and the distance it traveled. The total distance traveled is a direct variation of the number of hours. Write numbers in the spaces to find the slope. Then write the equation in $y = mx$ form to represent the situation. 8.F.4

Time (h), *x*	3	6	9
Distance (mi), *y*	63	126	189

slope: $\dfrac{\square - \square}{\square - \square} = \dfrac{\square}{\square}$

equation: ☐

5. The height of a penny dropped from a 64-foot-tall bridge is modeled by the function $h = -16t^2 + 64$, where t is the time in seconds and h is the height of the penny above the lake. 8.F.1, 8.F.3

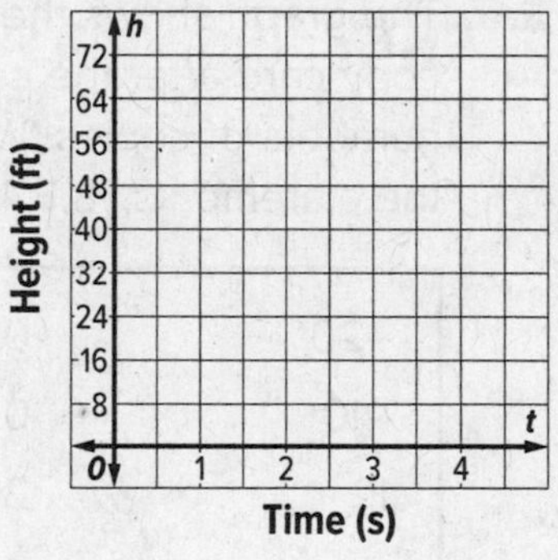

Part A: Complete the table of values below.

Time (s), *t*	0	0.5	1	1.5	2
Height (ft), *h*					

Part B: Graph the function on the coordinate plane.

Part C: How long does it take for the penny to reach the lake?

☐

Countdown: 13 Weeks

1. The cost of using a computer at an Internet café includes a flat fee plus a rate per minute of use as shown by the table. 8.F.4

Time (min), x	1	5	10	15
Total Cost ($), y	2.20	3	4	5

Select whether each statement is true or false.

Online Test Tip
On an online test, you might be asked to click the appropriate box for each statement. In this book, you will be asked to shade the boxes instead.

True	False	
☐	☐	The flat fee for Internet use is $2.00.
☐	☐	The cost increases at a rate of $0.50 for every 1 minute the computer is used.
☐	☐	The cost for using a computer for 45 minutes is $9.00.
☐	☐	The cost for using a computer for 55 minutes is $13.00.

2. The graph shows Ira's activities on his way to his grandmother's house and home again on Thursday. Write the segment that corresponds to each statement. 8.F.5

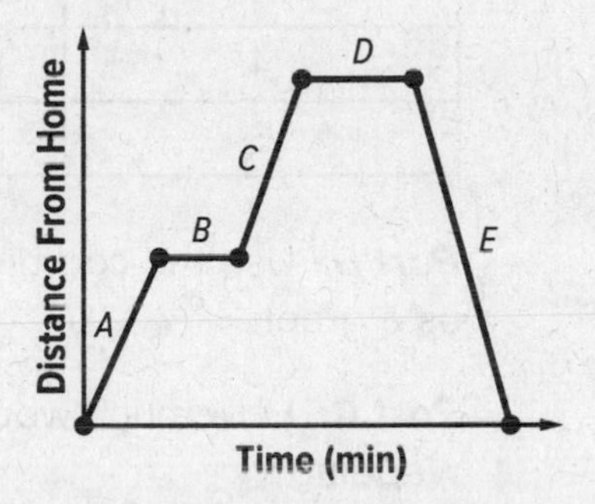

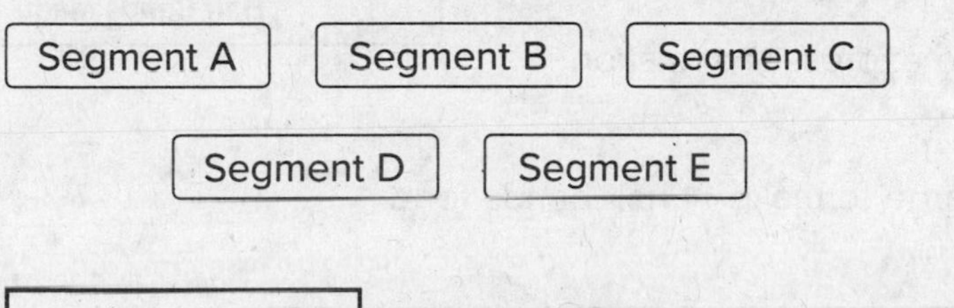

☐ Ira walks from his grandmother's house to his home.

☐ Ira visits his grandmother.

☐ Ira stops at a diner for a sandwich.

☐ Ira begins walking from his home to his grandmother's house.

☐ Ira leaves the diner and walks to his grandmother's house.

3. Mr. Okoro gave his students an assignment that was worth 100 points. Hector earned a score of 87.5%, Abby earned $\frac{87}{100}$ of the total points, Isaiah earned $\sqrt{7{,}774}$ points, and Elena earned $\frac{8}{9}$ of the total points. Plot points on the number line to represent each student's score. 8.NS.1

87 87.2 87.4 87.6 87.8 88 88.2 88.4 88.6 88.8 89

4. Jayla charges $9 for each hair band she makes. 8.F.1

Part A: Complete the table of ordered pairs to show the total amount Jayla charges for making different numbers of hair bands.

Hair Bands Made	Total Charge ($)
1	
2	
3	
4	
5	

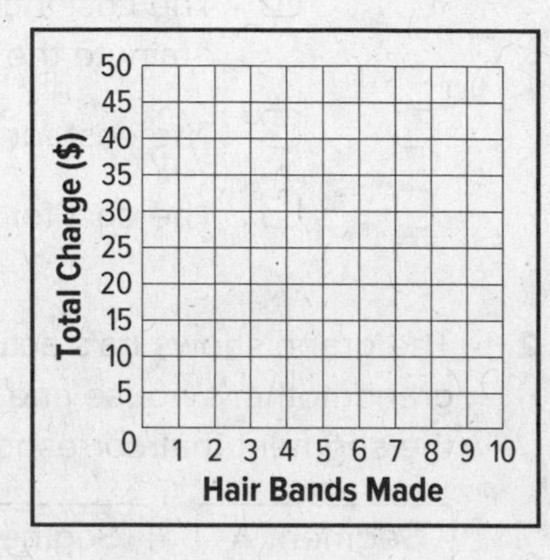

Part B: Use the coordinate plane to express the relation as a graph.

Part C: How much would Jayla charge to make 14 hair bands for a wedding?

5. An insect called a *froghopper* is 2^3 millimeters long and jumps 2^9 millimeters high. About how many times its body length did the froghopper jump? Explain your reasoning. 8.EE.1

NAME ________________ DATE ________ PERIOD ______ SCORE ______

Countdown: 12 Weeks

1. Quentin posted a video of his kitten on a Web site. The table shows the total number of "likes" his video had received by the end of each day over the course of a week. 8.F.4

Days Since Upload	1	3	5	7
Total Number of "Likes"	5,400	6,200	7,000	7,800

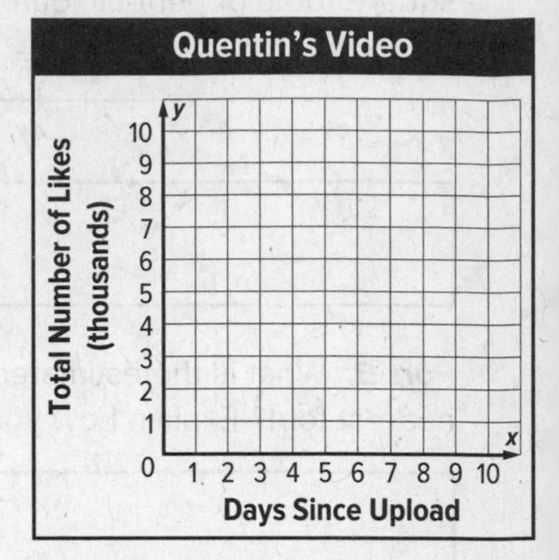

Part A: Graph the points on the coordinate plane to show the relationship.

Part B: The pattern shown in the graph continues. How many "likes" will Quentin's video have by the end of the 8th day since the upload?

2. Different types of functions have different characteristics.

Part A: Write what type of function is represented. 8.F.3

linear
nonlinear

x	y
–8	–2
–2	2.5
0	4
4	7
10	11.5

$y = -5x^2$ $y = -\frac{1}{2}x - 2$

Part B: Choose a linear function above. Describe how you could change the representation of that linear function to make it nonlinear.

3. The radius of a circle with area A can be approximated using the formula $r = \sqrt{\frac{A}{3}}$. A circular tabletop has an area of 42 ft². 8.NS.2

Part A: Use the number line to estimate the radius of the tabletop. What square root is the radius? Between which two points that represent the square roots of perfect squares is the radius located?

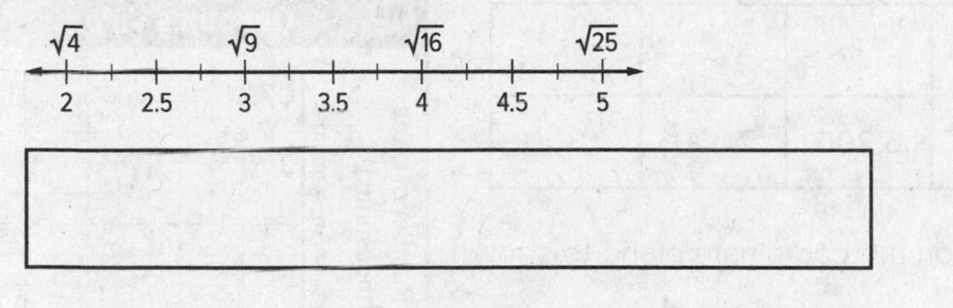

Part B: What is the estimated radius of the tabletop to the nearest foot? Explain how you found your answer.

Online Test Tip
On an online test, you might be asked to use a keypad with math symbols to enter the answer. In this book, you will be asked to write in the space provided.

4. The Caspian Sea has an area of 371,000 square kilometers. Lake Superior has an area of 8.24×10^4 square kilometers. Complete each sentence to make a true statement. 8.EE.4

The area of ______ is greater than the area of ______.

The difference in the areas of the two lakes is ______ square kilometers.

5. A fish tank full of water is being emptied so it can be cleaned. The table shows how the volume of water in the tank changes over time. Select whether each statement is true or false. 8.F.4

Time (min)	0	4	8	12
Volume (gal)	20	18	16	14

True **False**

☐ ☐ The initial amount of water in the tank was 0 gallons.

☐ ☐ The amount of water in the tank decreases at a rate of 0.5 gallon every minute.

☐ ☐ There were 19 gallons of water in the tank after 1 minute.

☐ ☐ There were 15 gallons of water in the tank after 10 minutes.

Countdown: 11 Weeks

1. Diondre goes for a bike ride. The graph represents Diondre's speed during the ride. Write the appropriate section of the graph for each description about Diondre's ride. 8.F.5

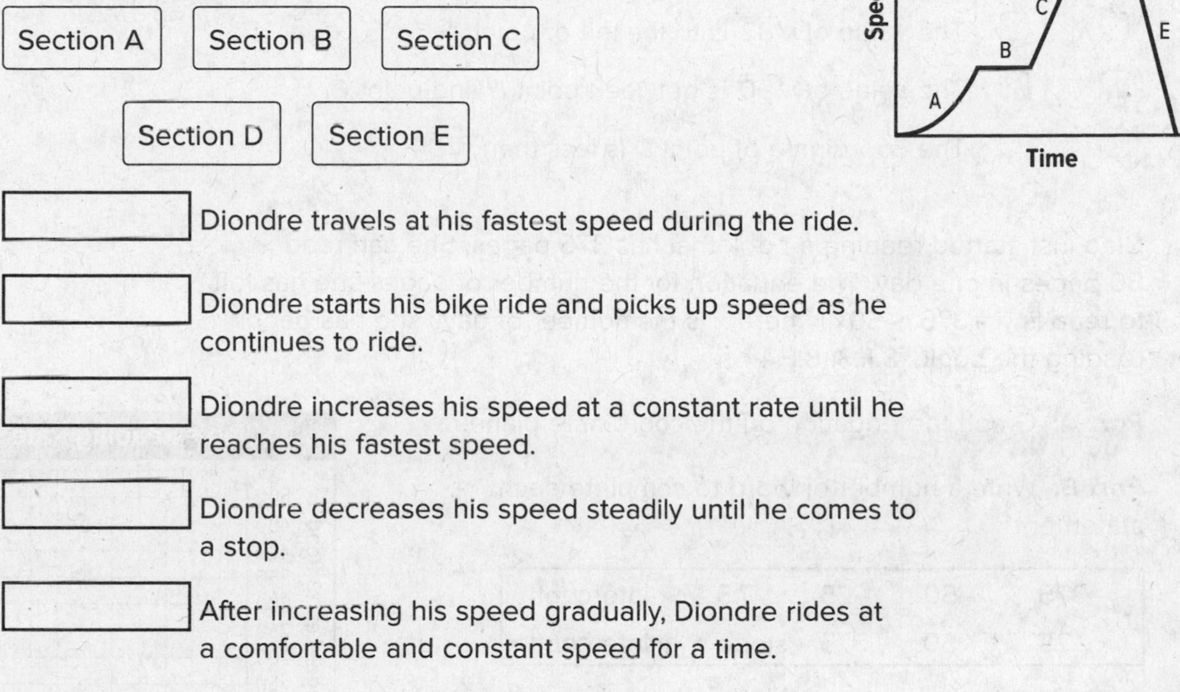

[ ] Diondre travels at his fastest speed during the ride.

[ ] Diondre starts his bike ride and picks up speed as he continues to ride.

[ ] Diondre increases his speed at a constant rate until he reaches his fastest speed.

[ ] Diondre decreases his speed steadily until he comes to a stop.

[ ] After increasing his speed gradually, Diondre rides at a comfortable and constant speed for a time.

2. A clothing store is having a 20% off sale. Renata has a coupon for $5 off. The function $f(x) = 0.8x - 5$ represents the final cost after the discount and coupon are applied of an item priced at x dollars. Complete the function machine for items A, B, C, and D. 8.F.1, 8.F.4

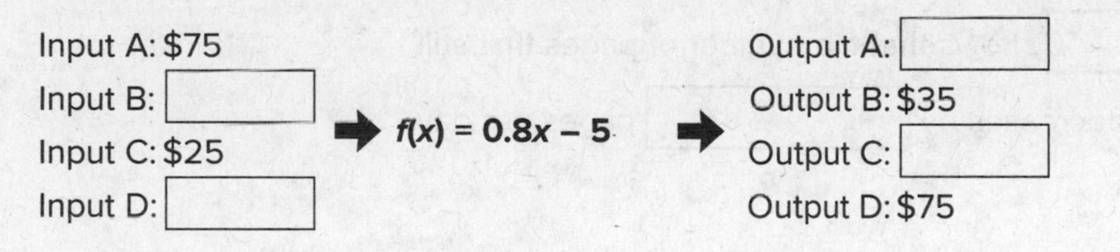

3. Kayak World charges $10 to rent a spray skirt all day plus $12.50 an hour to rent a kayak. BoatLand charges $5 to rent a spray skirt all day plus $15 an hour to rent a kayak. Write an equation to find h, the number of hours for which the total cost is the same at both rental places. Then solve the equation, and state what the cost is when it is the same. 8.EE.7, 8.EE.7b

Equation: [ ] + [ ] = [ ] + [ ]

h = [ ]

Cost for that number of hours: [ ]

4. This number line shows four points labeled *A, B, C,* and *D.* Select whether each statement is true or false. 8.NS.2

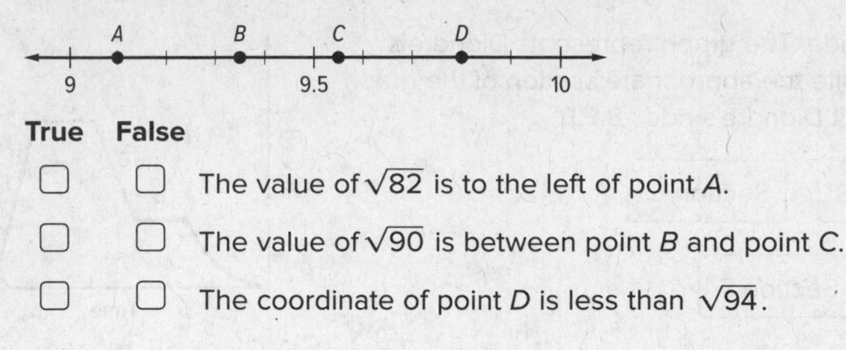

True **False**

☐ ☐ The value of $\sqrt{82}$ is to the left of point *A*.

☐ ☐ The value of $\sqrt{90}$ is between point *B* and point *C*.

☐ ☐ The coordinate of point *D* is less than $\sqrt{94}$.

Online Test Tip
On an online test, you might be asked to click the appropriate box for each statement. In this book, you will be asked to shade the boxes instead.

5. Cleo just started reading a book that has 375 pages. She can read 50 pages in one day. The equation for the number of pages she has left to read is $y = 375 - 50x$, where x is the number of days she has been reading the book. 8.F.3, 8.F.4

Part A: Graph the equation on the coordinate plane.

Cleo's Reading Rate

Pages Left to Read (y): 0, 50, 100, 150, 200, 250, 300, 350, 400, 450, 500

Number of Days (x): 0, 1, 2, 3, 4, 5, 6, 7, 8, 9, 10

Part B: Write a number or word to complete each statement.

–375	–50	–25	7.5	*x*-intercept
25	50	375	slope	*y*-intercept

The slope is ☐. The *y*-intercept is ☐.

The ☐ shows the initial number of pages to be read.

The ☐ shows that the number of pages that still need to be read decreases by ☐ pages per day.

NAME ______________________ DATE ____________ PERIOD ________ SCORE ________

Countdown: 10 Weeks

1. The path of a kicked ball can be modeled by the equation $y = 2x^2$. 8.F.3

Part A: Graph points for values of x from 0 to 3.

Part B: Is the function a linear function? Justify your answer in two ways.

2. A pet spider is kept in a shoe box and sleeps in the bottom front left corner. She strings a web from her sleeping corner and moves along it to the top back right corner. To return to her sleeping corner, she walks down the edge of the box and across the bottom to the front left corner. How much farther did she walk on her return walk? Round to the nearest tenth of an inch. 8.G.7

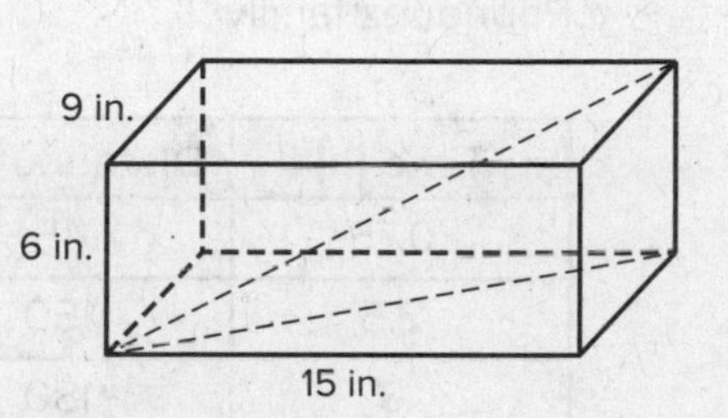

3. The diameter of Earth is 7,918 miles. A superhero can travel at the speed of light, 1.86×10^5 miles per second. Approximately how many times can the superhero circle the Earth at the equator in 1 second? Round to the nearest tenth. Justify your answer. 8.EE.3, 8.EE.4

4. Zeke and Nelly are working on a lab for their physical science class. They measure how far a car rolled after it left a ramp. Zeke measures 25 inches. Nelly says they can record $0.58\overline{3}$ yards. Is Nelly correct? Explain why or why not. 8.NS.1

5. Three families track their distance while traveling to the band competition. Each family recorded the data in a different form. Write the appropriate label to order the families by speed from fastest to slowest. 8.F.4

1: Fastest

2: Middle speed

3: Slowest

Rodriguez family

Time (h)	Distance (mi)
0.75	45
2.5	150
3	180

Martin family

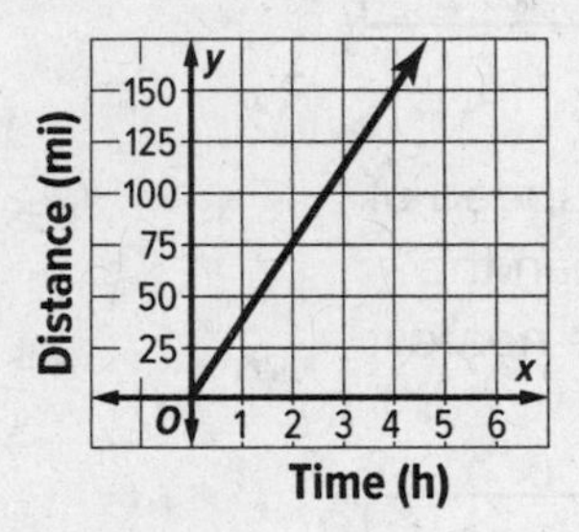

Brown family

$y = 56x$, where x is number of hours and y is distance in miles

Online Test Tip

On an online test, you might be asked to drag the expressions into the appropriate box. In this book, you will be asked to write the expressions instead.

NAME ______________________ DATE __________ PERIOD ______ SCORE ______

Countdown: 9 Weeks

1. Students build towers using marshmallows and toothpicks. They record the number of toothpicks used for the tower at different heights. 8.SP.1

Number of Toothpicks	5	15	25	30	40	45
Height (cm)	5	10	15	20	25	30

Part A: Use the data in the table to construct a scatter plot on the coordinate plane.

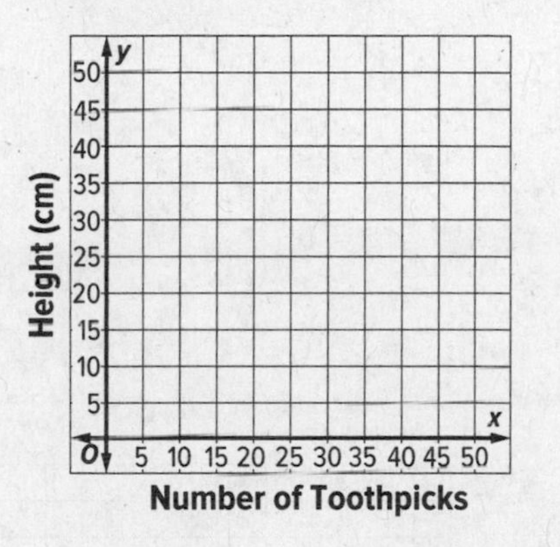

Online Test Tip
On an online test, you might be asked to click a button to plot points. In this book, you will be asked to draw the points on the coordinate plane.

Part B: Describe patterns you see in the data.

2. Elm Street and Oak Street are parallel. Avenue Z crosses each of them. The city planner needs to find the measures of the angles at each intersection. Find the measures of the labeled angles. 8.G.5

Avenue Z

$(2x + 2)°$

Elm Street

$(3x - 12)°$

Oak Street

angle between Avenue Z and Elm St.: ______

angle between Avenue Z and Oak St.: ______

3. The middle school choir had an outdoor concert to raise money for a field trip. The attendance was 350 people. A child's ticket cost \$1.50, and an adult's ticket cost \$5.00. The choir earned a total of \$917. 8.EE.8, 8.EE.8b, 8.EE.8c

Part A: Write the appropriate numbers, symbols, and variables to create a system of equations that would lead to finding the number of children and the number of adults at the concert.

a	c	1.50	5.00
350	917	+	–

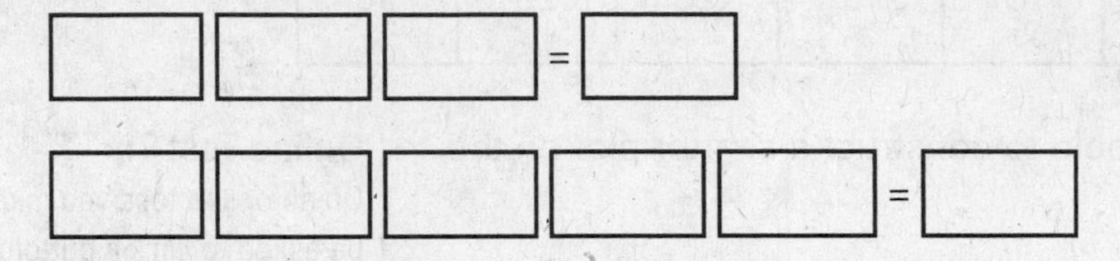

Part B: How many children and adults attended the concert?

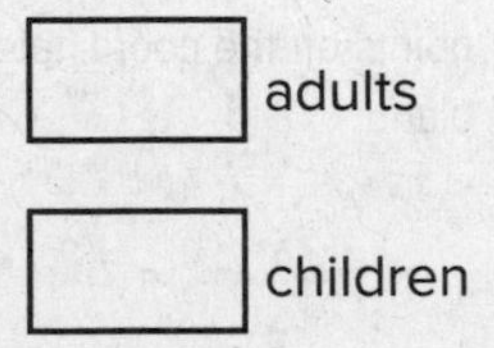

adults

children

4. Adzo says the graph is of the function $y = 2^{-1}x - \sqrt{25}$. Ben says it is $y - 5 = 0.5x$. Who is correct? Explain your answer. 8.F.2

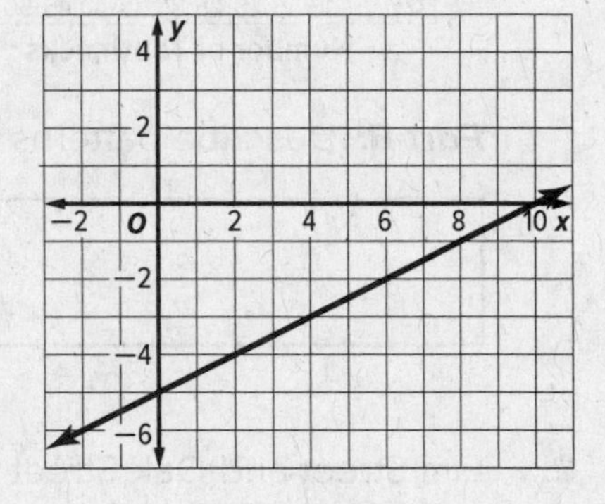

5. Graph the numbers at their approximate locations on the number line. 8.NS.2

$\sqrt{70}$	$-\sqrt{55}$	$-\sqrt{20}$	$\sqrt{32}$

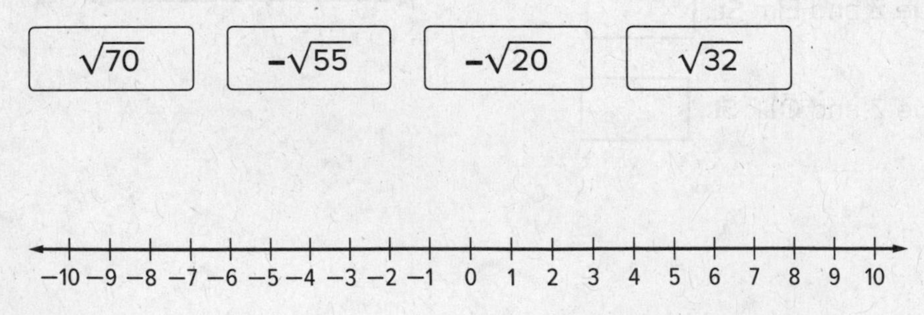

NAME ____________ DATE ________ PERIOD ________ SCORE ________

Countdown: 8 Weeks

1. Triangles *ABC* and *CDE* are slope triangles. 8.EE.6

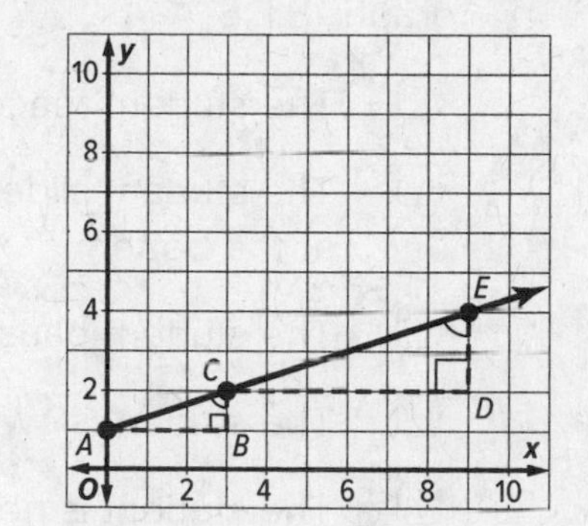

Part A: Show that the slope triangles are similar.

Part B: Compare the rise to the run for each of the triangles. Write the reason next to each step in the solution.

$$\frac{ED}{CB} = \frac{CD}{AB}$$

$$ED \cdot AB = CB \cdot CD$$

$$\frac{ED \cdot AB}{CD \cdot AB} = \frac{CB \cdot CD}{CD \cdot AB}$$

$$\frac{ED}{CD} = \frac{CB}{AB}$$

Part C: What conclusion can you draw from the work in Part B?

2. A tennis court is rectangular with a length of 120 feet and a width of 60 feet. For warm-up, a player runs along the diagonal of the court from one corner to the other. His partner runs the length and width of the court to the opposite corner. How much farther did the partner run? Explain your answer. Round to the nearest tenth. 8.G.7

3. A student climbs up the ladder of a slide and slides down. Select all of the statements that are represented by the graph. 8.F.5

- ☐ The student reaches the bottom of the slide at D.
- ☐ The student slides faster at the top of the slide than at the bottom.
- ☐ The student pauses at the top of the slide before sliding down.
- ☐ The student slows as he reaches the top of the ladder.
- ☐ The student is never more than 6 feet off the ground.

4. Every 15 minutes, the height of the water in the pool is measured and plotted. The data are shown in the table. 8.SP.2

Time (min)	15	30	45	75	90
Water Height (cm)	40	50	60	70	90

Part A: Construct a scatter plot of the data.

Part B: Would the equation $y = x + 40$ or the equation $y = 0.5x + 30$ better model the data? Explain.

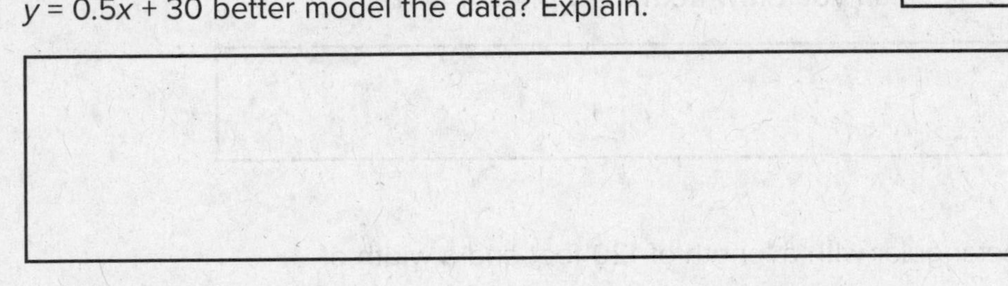

5. Roberta plots coordinates to represent the corners of her garden: $A(2.5, 1.5)$, $B(-4, 3)$, and $C(-2, -5)$. She decides to quadruple the length of each side using the origin as the center for the enlargement of her garden. Select all of the statements that are true about the new coordinates. 8.G.3

- ☐ The perimeter of the garden is 4 times the original perimeter.
- ☐ A' is located at (10, 6).
- ☐ B' is located at (–1, 0.75).
- ☐ C' is located at (–8, –20).
- ☐ The area of the garden is 8 times greater than the original.

Online Test Tip

On an online test, you might be asked to click all of the correct answer choices. In this book, you will be asked to shade a box next to each correct answer choice.

3. Kali maps two flower beds in a coordinate plane. Use transformations to show that the flower beds are congruent. 8.G.2

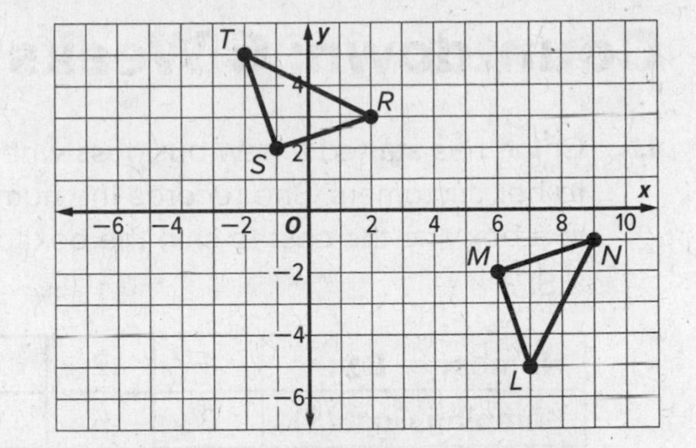

4. A town is laid out so that L Street and M Street are parallel. L Street and N Street are perpendicular, as are M Street and P Street. Select all of the statements that are true about the streets in this town. 8.G.1

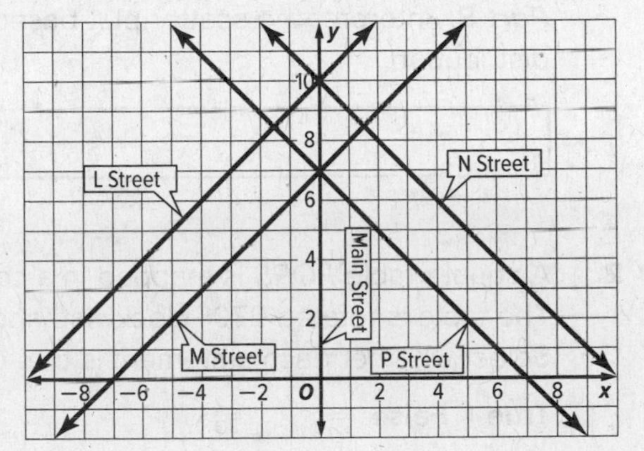

- ☐ L Street and M Street can be mapped onto N Street and P Street by a reflection across Main Street.
- ☐ N Street and P Street have the same slope as L Street and M Street.
- ☐ N Street and P Street must be parallel.

5. Juan learns to make soap and studies its density. He uses a scatter plot to map its volume and mass. He models his data with the linear equation $y = 1.25x + 1$, where x is the volume of the soap in cubic centimeters, and y is the mass of the soap in grams. 8.SP.3

Online Test Tip

On an online test, you might be asked to use a keypad with math symbols to enter the answer. In this book, you will be asked to write the answer in the space provided.

Part A: What is the slope of the line that models the data? What does it represent?

Part B: What is the y-intercept? What does it represent? Explain why the model does not work for very small volumes of soap.

NAME ______________________ DATE __________ PERIOD ________ SCORE ________

Countdown: 6 Weeks

1. Chloe has started a new business where she ships books to her customers. She records the number of books shipped in a box and the cost to ship the box for her first five orders. 8.SP.1

Number of Books	1	2	4	5	8
Shipping Cost ($)	3	5	6	8	10

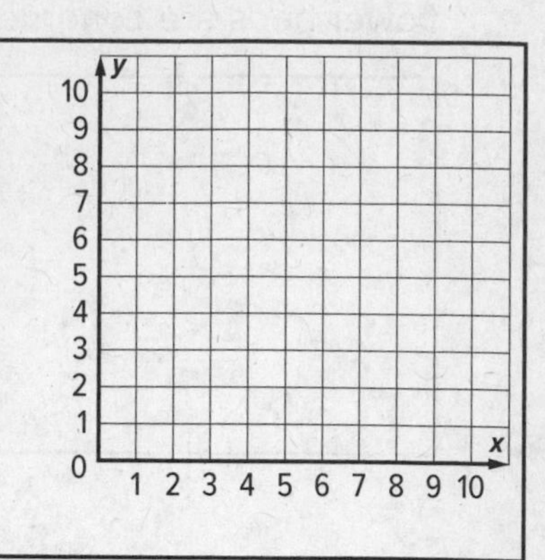

Part A: Construct a scatter plot of the data.

Part B: Interpret the scatter plot based on the shape of its distribution.

2. A square table *PQRS* is mapped in a coordinate plane. The table is rotated 270° clockwise about the origin. Select whether each statement is true or false. 8.G.3

True	False	
☐	☐	The image of point *P* is *P*′(–4, 4).
☐	☐	The image of point *Q* is *Q*′(–1, 4).
☐	☐	The image of point *R* is *R*′(–4, 1).
☐	☐	Square *PQRS* can also be mapped onto *P*′*Q*′*R*′*S*′ by translating it 5 units left.
☐	☐	*PQRS* and its image are congruent polygons.

NAME ______________________ DATE ____________ PERIOD ________ SCORE ________

Countdown: 5 Weeks

1. Abby is collecting data for her science fair project about nutrition. She gathers data about the number of grams of fat and the number of calories in a serving of fruit. 8.SP.1

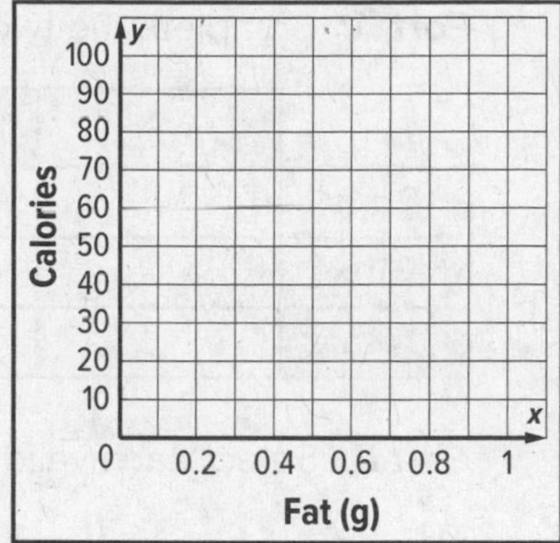

Fruit	Apple	Banana	Kiwi	Orange	Pear	Strawberry
Fat (g)	0.1	0.3	0.5	0.3	0.7	0.9
Calories	48	95	49	62	98	28

Part A: Make a scatter plot of the data.

Part B: Describe any patterns in the data.

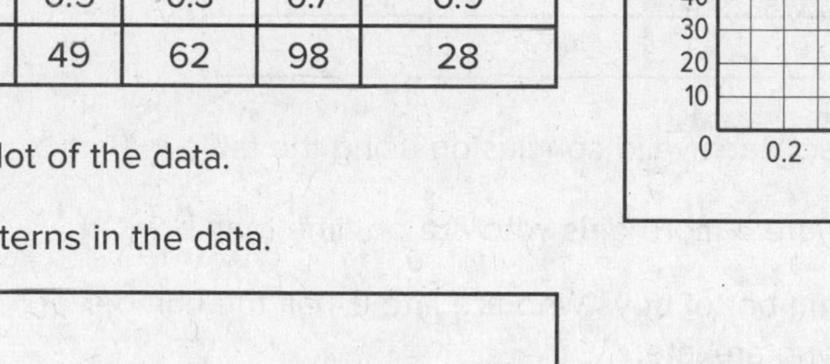

2. $\overline{AB}$ and $\overline{CD}$ are plotted on a coordinate plane. Select whether each statement is true or false. 8.G.1, 8.G.1a

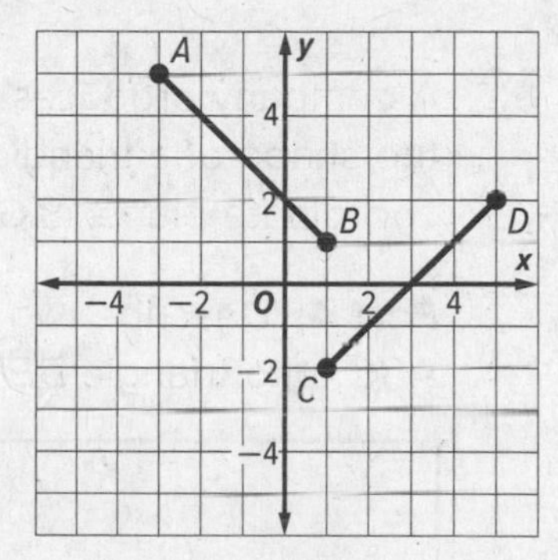

True	False	
☐	☐	$AB = CD$
☐	☐	The image of point A reflected across the y-axis is $D(5, 2)$.
☐	☐	$\overline{AB}$ can be mapped onto $\overline{CD}$ by a reflection and a translation.
☐	☐	$\overline{AB}$ can be mapped onto $\overline{CD}$ by a rotation about the origin.

3. Michael maps two triangular courtyards on a coordinate plane. Write numbers to describe the effects of the translation of $\triangle ABC$ onto $\triangle DEF$. What can you conclude about these triangles? Explain. 8.G.3

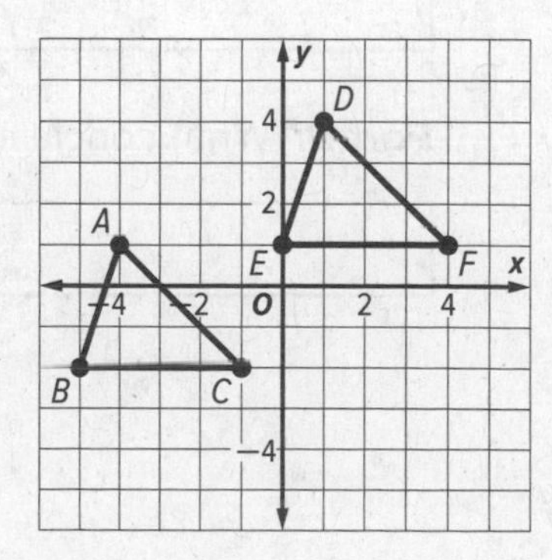

$(x, y) \rightarrow (x + \square, y + \square)$

4. Lucia invites 48 friends, including 20 boys, to a party. There are a total of 32 who were on time, and of those, 18 are girls. 8.SP.4

Part A: Complete the two-way table to summarize the data.

	On Time	Late	Total
Boys			
Girls			
Total			

Part B: Select each valid conclusion using the table in Part A.

- ☐ There are 4 more girls who are on time than boys.
- ☐ The number of boys who are late is half the number of girls who are late.
- ☐ There are 6 guests who are boys and are late.
- ☐ To find the total number of late guests, subtract 32 from 48.

Online Test Tip

On an online test, you might be asked to click all of the correct answer choices. In this book, you will be asked to shade a box next to each correct answer choice.

5. A company produces a new key pocket that is in the shape of a triangle. They plot the shapes on a coordinate plane. 8.G.4

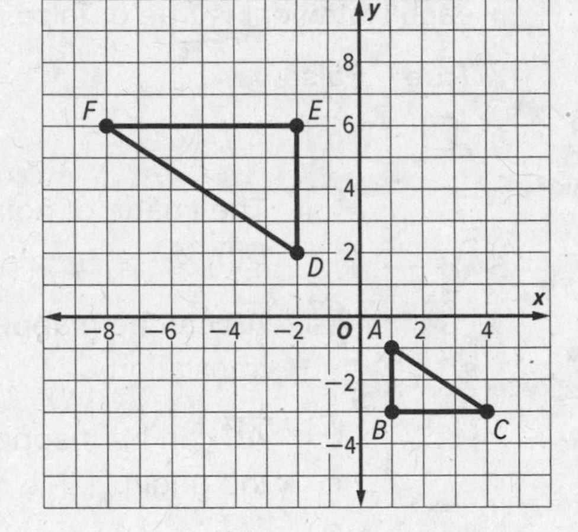

Part A: Describe two sequences that could map triangle *ABC* onto triangle *DEF*.

Part B: What conclusion can you draw about the triangles?

NAME ______________________ DATE ____________ PERIOD ________ SCORE ________

Countdown: 4 Weeks

1. Bento surveys some of his friends. He records the number of hours that they studied for a Spanish test and their score on the test. 8.SP.1

Time (h)	4	2.5	3	1	0	1.5
Score	100	80	90	90	70	75

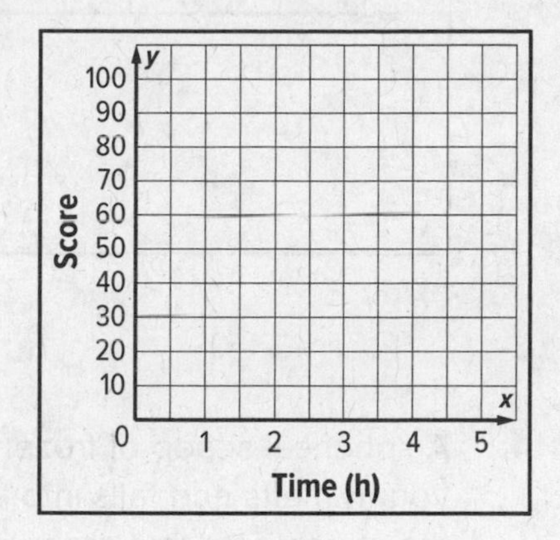

Part A: Construct a scatter plot of the data.

Part B: Describe any patterns in the data.

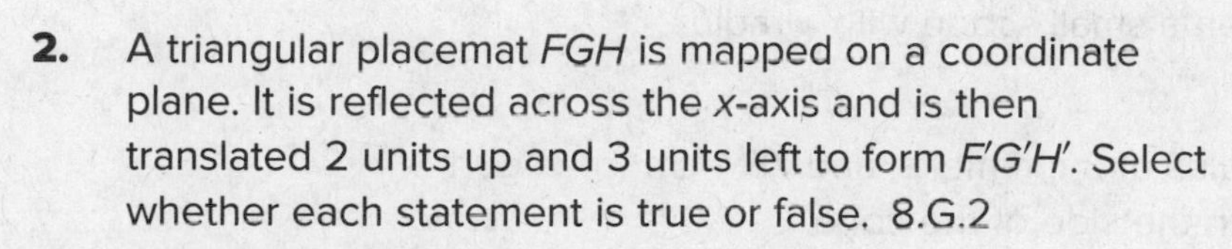

2. A triangular placemat FGH is mapped on a coordinate plane. It is reflected across the x-axis and is then translated 2 units up and 3 units left to form $F'G'H'$. Select whether each statement is true or false. 8.G.2

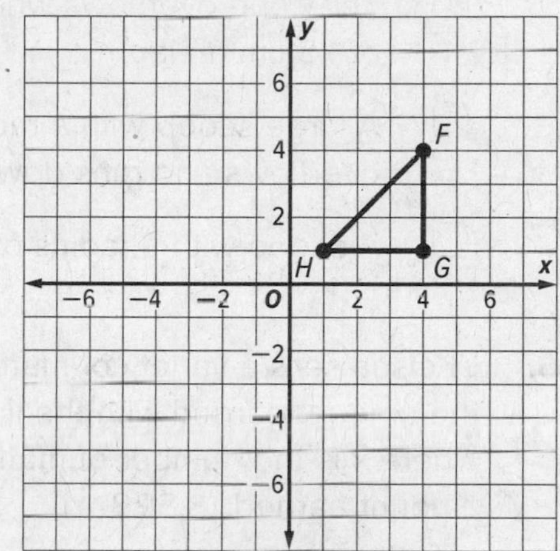

True	False	
☐	☐	The image of point F is $F'(0, -4)$.
☐	☐	The image of point G is $G'(1, 1)$.
☐	☐	The image of point H is $H'(1, -1)$.
☐	☐	The image of point H is $H'(-2, 1)$.
☐	☐	Triangle FGH is congruent to triangle $F'G'H'$.
☐	☐	A 90° rotation can be applied to triangle $F'G'H'$ to get a congruent triangle $F''G''H''$.

Online Test Tip

On an online test, you might be asked to click the appropriate box for each statement. In this book, you will be asked to shade in the boxes instead.

3. The diagram shows how a post broke during strong winds. How tall was the post originally? Explain your answer. 8.G.7

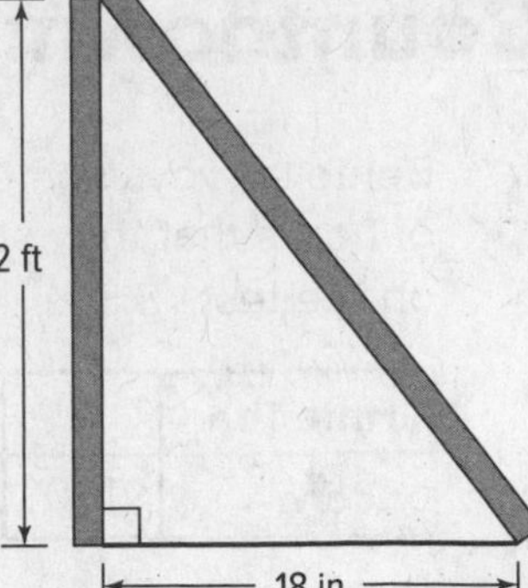

4. A spherical scoop of frozen yogurt is put on top of a cone. Assume the yogurt melts and falls into the cone until the cone is full. Select all of the statements that are true about the frozen snack. Round all answers to the nearest tenth. 8.G.9

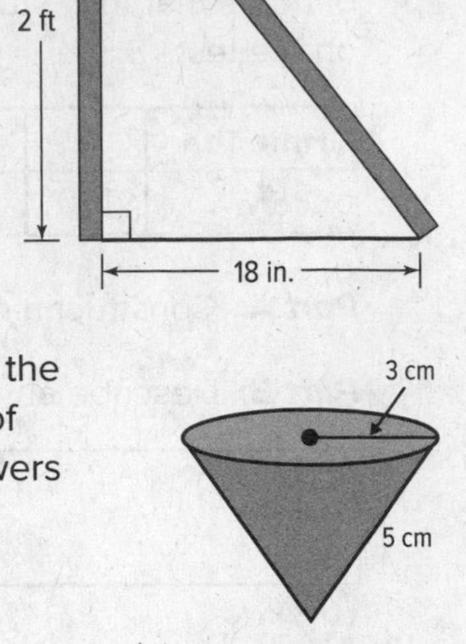

- ☐ The height of the cone is 4 cm.
- ☐ The cone overflows when a small scoop with a radius of 1.5 cm melts.
- ☐ A large scoop with a radius of 3 cm melts, and 75.4 cm^3 of yogurt overflows and runs down the side of the cone.
- ☐ A scoop with a radius of 2.8 cm has the same volume as the cone.

5. L'Keisha sells a variety of muffins each morning. She models the amount earned with the linear equation $y = 3x - 10$, where x is the number of muffins she sells and y is the amount earned. 8.SP.3

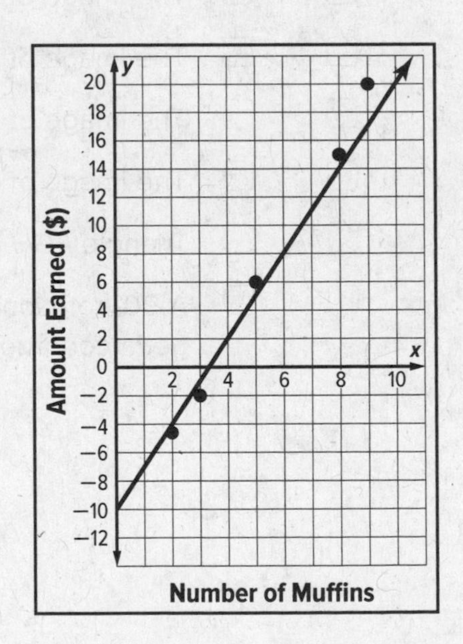

Part A: What is the slope of the line modeling L'Keisha's profits? What does it represent?

Part B: What is the y-intercept? What does it represent?

4. A road divides the neighborhood park into two parts. Calvin plots one part in a coordinate plane. The part of the park shown is a reflection over the x-axis of the other part. 8.G.3

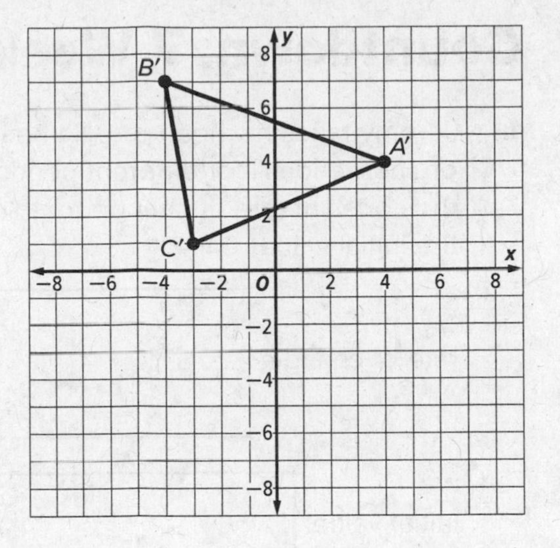

Part A: Draw the other part of the park.

Part B: Write the coordinates of the vertices of the part that you drew. Then describe the effects of a reflection across the x-axis on the coordinates.

5. The choir started selling CDs of their concerts as a fundraiser in 2008. The table shows the number of CDs sold each year. 8.SP.2

Years Since 2008	1	2	3	4	5	6
Number of CDs Sold	460	380	370	310	225	175

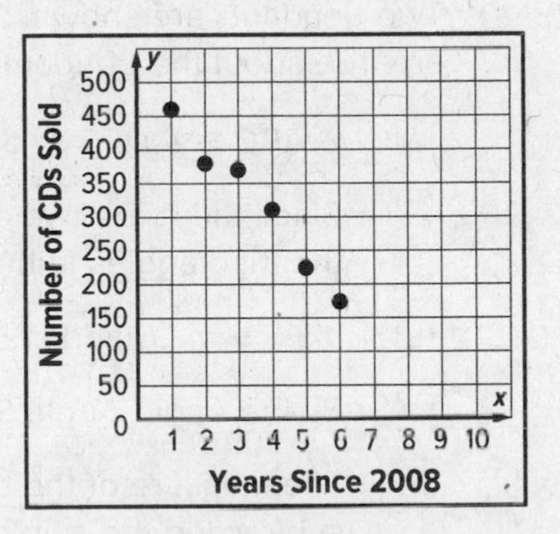

Part A: Draw a line of best fit.

Part B: Write the equation of the line of best fit. According to the model, how many CDs were sold in 2008? Predict how many CDs will be sold in 2016. Justify your answer.

Online Test Tip

On an online test, you might be asked to click a button to graph a line. In this book, you will be asked to draw the line in the coordinate plane.

NAME ______ DATE ______ PERIOD ______ SCORE ______

Countdown: 7 Weeks

1. Jeremy takes his heart rate (in beats per minute) after running on the treadmill for different periods of time. Find and describe the constant rate of change for this function. Find and describe the initial value. 8.F.4

Time (min)	Heart Rate (bpm)
4	84
10	108

rate of change:

initial value:

2. Carrie creates triangular pendants to be worn as necklaces. Two pendants are shown. Select all of the statements that are true about the pendants. 8.G.4

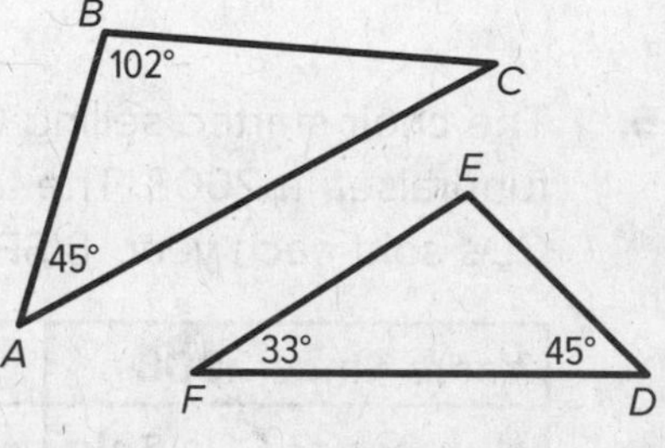

- ☐ $\triangle ABC \cong \triangle DEF$ by the SAS Similarity Theorem.
- ☐ Since there are two corresponding congruent angles, the third angles in the triangles must also be congruent.
- ☐ $m\angle E \cong m\angle B$ and $m\angle C \cong m\angle F$
- ☐ By the Angle-Angle Similarity, $\triangle ABC \sim \triangle DEF$.
- ☐ The measure of the third angle in each triangle can be found by subtracting the sum of the given angles from 360°.

3. Members of a book club pay lower prices for individual books and a flat shipping rate. One member graphs how much she spends and draws a line of best fit. Write an equation for the line of best fit. What does the slope represent? What does the y-intercept represent? 8.SP.3

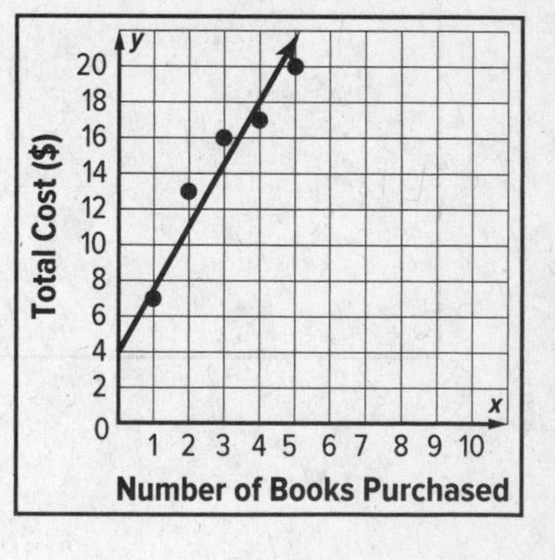

NAME ______________________ DATE ____________ PERIOD ________ SCORE ________

Countdown: 3 Weeks

1. Bruce records how his car depreciated over time. 8.SP.1

Years Since Purchase	0	1	4	5	8
Value (Thousands of $)	20	13	9	8	7

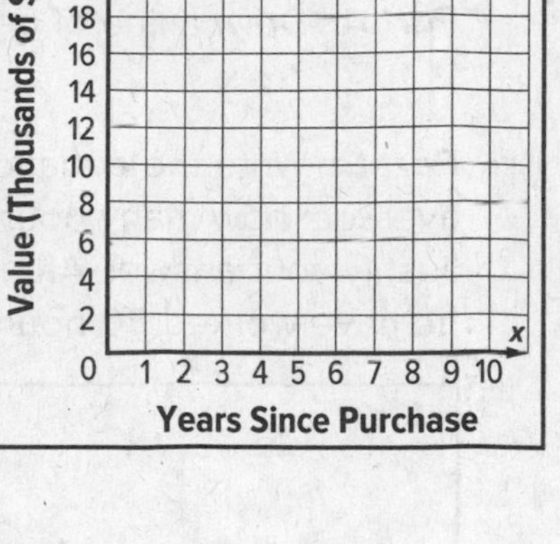

Part A: Construct a scatter plot of the data.

Part B: Describe the association. Then write a statement that is supported by the data.

2. George conducts a science investigation for which he rolls a toy car down a ramp. He graphs his results. 8.SP.3

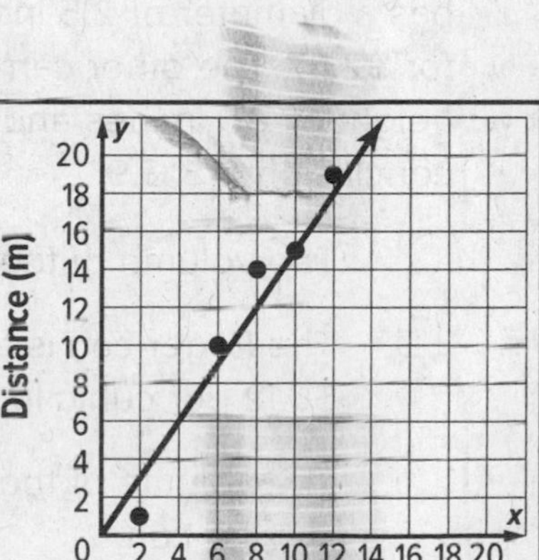

Part A: What is the slope of the line that models the data? What does it represent?

Part B: What is the y-intercept? What does it represent?

3. A waiter tracks the number of hours he is asked to work each week since he started his job. The scatter plot shows the number of hours he worked. 8.SP.2

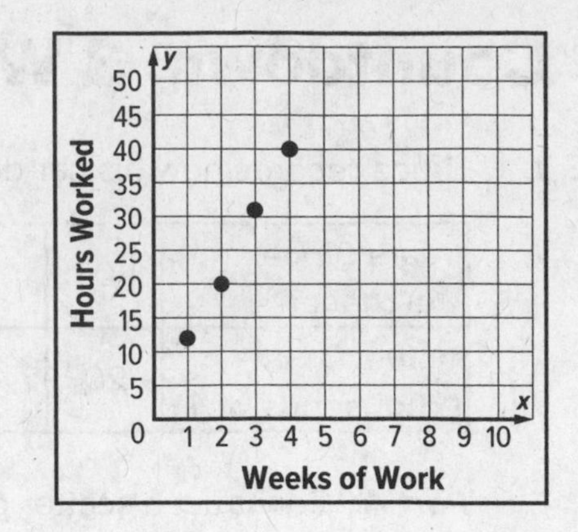

Part A: Draw a line of best fit.

Part B: Write the equation of your line of best fit. On average, how many hours does he work each week? Justify your answer. After how many weeks will he have worked 80 hours? Explain your answer.

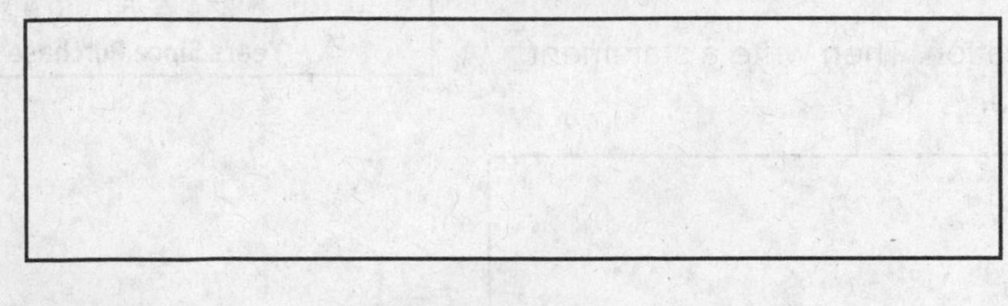

4. Baked beans are available in two different-sized cans. One can has a diameter of 2.5 inches and a height of 4.5 inches and sells for $2.87. The other can has a diameter of 4.5 inches and a height of 2.5 inches and sells for $5.95. Select all of the correct conclusions. 8.G.9

- ☐ The volume of the smaller can is about 22.1 cubic inches.
- ☐ The larger can is the better buy because it costs about $0.12 per cubic inch.
- ☐ The volume of the larger can is about 1.8 times the volume of the smaller can.
- ☐ The smaller can costs about $0.13 per cubic inch.

Online Test Tip
On an online test, you might be asked to click all of the correct answer choices. In this book, you will be asked to shade a box next to each correct answer choice.

5. Leanna tears off the corners of a triangle and aligns them as shown. Select whether each statement is true or false. 8.G.5

True	False	
☐	☐	This diagram shows that the sum of the measures of the angles of a triangle is 180°.
☐	☐	The three angles of a triangle can be arranged to form a straight angle.
☐	☐	This experiment would have different results with a right triangle.

NAME _______________ DATE ________ PERIOD ______ SCORE ______

Countdown: 2 Weeks

1. Yasmin records the number of miles driven and the number of gallons of gas used on her road trip. 8.SP.1

Distance (mi)	50	90	140	180	200
Gas Used (gal)	2	3	6	8	9

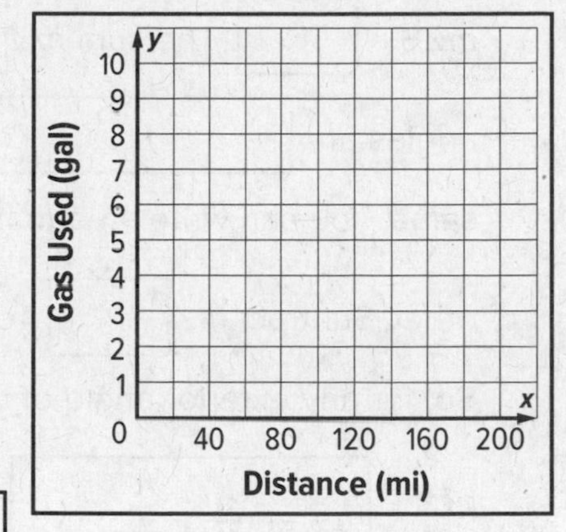

Part A: Construct a scatter plot of the data.

Part B: What patterns do you see in the data? What conclusion can you draw?

2. A map is shown on a coordinate plane, where each square represents one square mile. The school is located at (–3, –5). The bus barn is located at (2, 1). Select whether each statement is true or false. 8.G.8

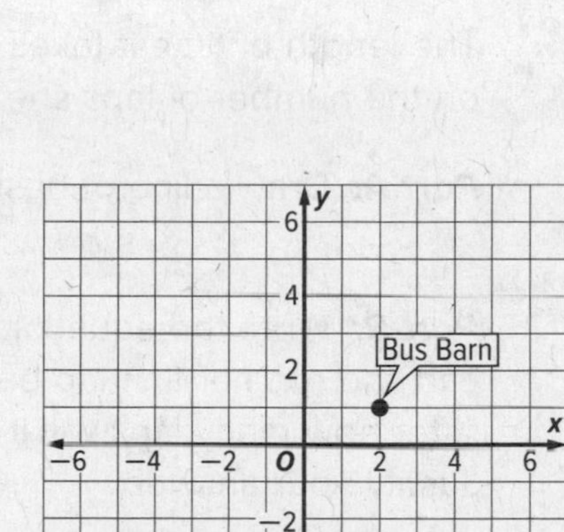

True	False	
☐	☐	You can make a right triangle by adding a point at (2, –5) or (–3, 1).
☐	☐	The school is approximately 7.8 miles from the bus barn.
☐	☐	The buses can travel only along the grid lines. The distance that the bus must travel from the school to the bus barn is almost twice the distance that the school is from the barn along a straight line.
☐	☐	The exact distance between the school and the bus barn is $\sqrt{51}$ miles.

Online Test Tip

On an online test, you might be asked to click the appropriate box for each statement. In this book, you will be asked to shade in the boxes instead.

3. Complete the sentences. 8.G.5

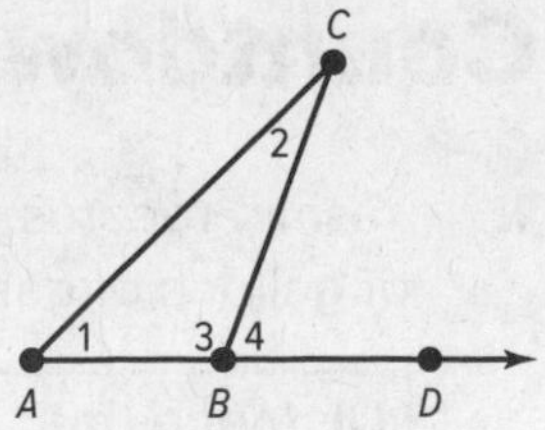

The sum of the angles in a triangle is always the same: $m\angle1 + m\angle2 + m\angle3 =$ ______. The sum $m\angle$ ______ $+ m\angle3 = 180°$ because these angles are ______. Because the angle sums are the same, you can write an equation with these expressions equal to each other. Subtract $m\angle$ ______ from each side to get $m\angle1 + m\angle2 = m\angle$ ______.

So, for any exterior angle of a triangle, its measure is equal to the sum of the ______ interior angles.

4. The length of time it takes Carlita to run a lap depends on the number of laps she has already completed. 8.SP.2

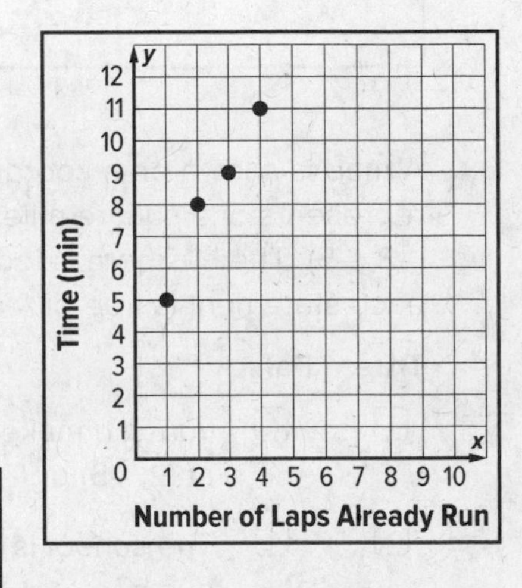

Part A: Draw a line of best fit on the scatter plot.

Part B: Write the equation of your line of best fit. How fast can she run her first lap before she runs any other laps? After how many laps will it take her 14 minutes to run a lap? Justify your answer.

5. Two basketball teams play a total of 44 games. No game can end in a tie. The Lions won 13 games. There were a total of 15 losses, and the Tigers won twice as many games as they lost. 8.SP.4

	Lions	Tigers	Total
Wins	13		
Losses			15
Total			

Part A: Complete the two-way table.

Part B: Select all of the conclusions that are valid about the data.

- ☐ The Tigers played 4 more games than the Lions.
- ☐ The relative frequency of winning in the Lions' column is 0.45.
- ☐ The relative frequency of the Tigers losing by row is 0.20 greater than the relative frequency of their losing by column.
- ☐ The Tigers played about 55% of the total number of games.

NAME ______________________ DATE __________ PERIOD ______ SCORE ______

Countdown: 1 Week

1. Juaquim planted wildflower seeds. He compared the number of seeds he planted in each bed to the number of plants that grew. 8.SP.1

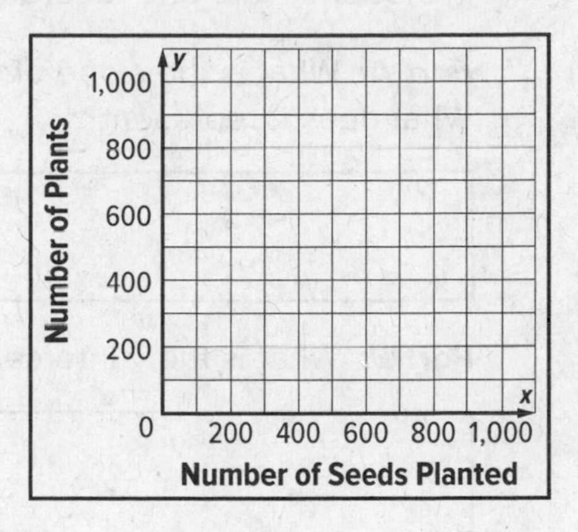

Seeds Planted	100	300	500	800	900
Plants	50	200	400	650	800

Part A: Construct a scatter plot of the data.

Part B: What pattern do you see in the data?

2. The dance team started going to competitions in 2008. The graph shows the number of trophies they have won every year. 8.SP.2

Online Test Tip

On an online test, you might be asked to click buttons to plot the line of best fit. In this book, you will be asked to draw the line on the coordinate plane.

Part A: Draw a line of best fit on the scatter plot.

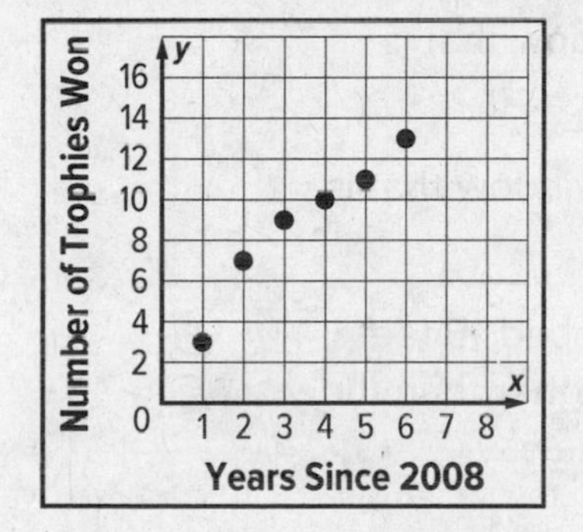

Part B: Write an equation of the line of best fit. How many trophies were won in 2008? Predict how many trophies will be won in 2016. Justify your answer.

3. Abay is calculating the work required to move an object in a science lab. She records her data in a graph. 8.SP.3

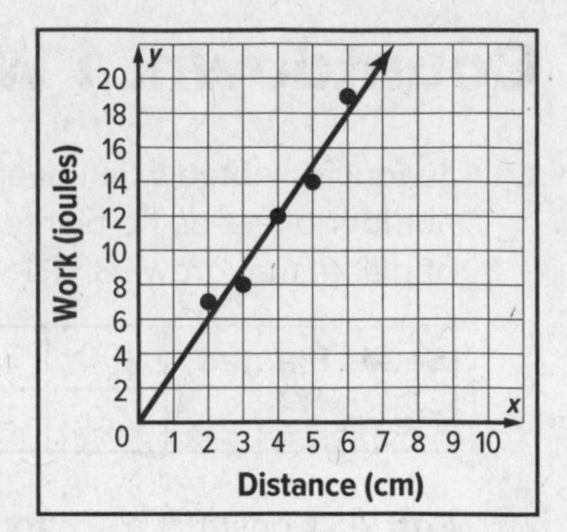

Part A: What is the slope of the line that models the data? What does it represent?

Part B: What is the *y*-intercept? What does it represent?

4. The base of a 25-foot ladder is positioned 10 feet from the bottom of the building it leans against. An extension can be pulled out to make it a 30-foot ladder. Select whether each statement is true or false. Round answers to the nearest foot. 8.G.7

True	False	
☐	☐	With the extension, the ladder can reach a window that is 28 feet above the ground.
☐	☐	Without the extension, the ladder will reach a window that is 24 feet above the ground.
☐	☐	The base of the ladder with the extension is placed 15 feet from the base of the building. It will reach no higher than the original ladder, without the extension at 10 feet away.

5. There are 100 students at a science fair competition; 44 are middle school students. Of the 36 students who win an award, 25 are in high school. 8.SP.4

Part A: Complete the two-way table.

	Middle School	High School	Total
Award			36
No award			
Total	44		

Part B: Select each conclusion that is valid for the data.

☐ 64% of the students do not win in the competition.

☐ Half of the high school students win an award.

☐ One-third of the middle school students win an award.

☐ There were fewer high school students who did not win than middle school students who did not win.

NAME ______________________ DATE ____________ PERIOD ________ SCORE ________

Chapter 1 Test

1. Arnaldo is analyzing numbers. 8.NS.1, 8.NS.2

Part A: Select whether the number in each situation is rational or irrational.

	Rational	Irrational
A bottle contains $0.\overline{6}$ kiloliters of water.	☐	☐
The area of the floor covered by a circular rug is 8π, or 25.1327412..., square feet.	☐	☐
Each side of a square measures $\sqrt{9}$ centimeters.	☐	☐

Part B: The diagonal of rectangular tile A is $3\sqrt{2}$ inches long. The diagonal of rectangular tile B is $2\sqrt{3}$ inches long. Which tile has a longer diagonal? Explain how you got your answer.

2. The table shows the approximate populations of four countries. Write the correct country to make each statement true. 8.EE.1

Country	Austria	Lesotho	Netherlands	Surinam
Population	2^{23}	2^{21}	2^{24}	2^{19}

Austria
Lesotho
the Netherlands
Surinam

The population of ________ is about $\frac{1}{2}$ that of the Netherlands.

The population of ________ is about $\frac{1}{4}$ that of Lesotho.

The population of ________ is about 8 times the population of ________.

3. Sort the expressions into the appropriate bins based on their values compared to 9. 8.EE.1

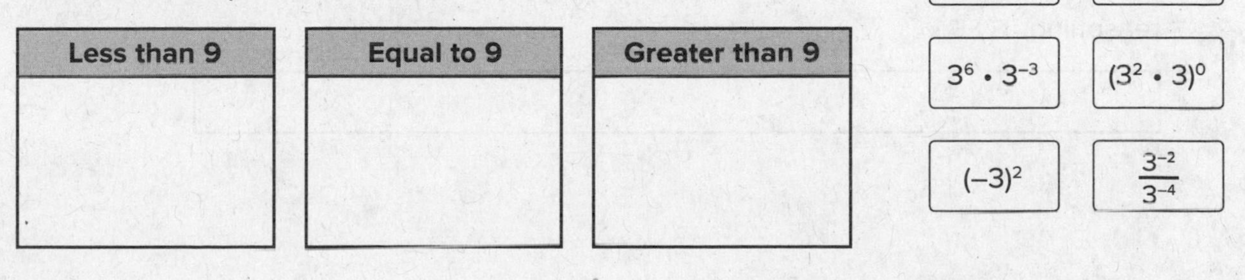

4. The table shows the diameters, in kilometers, of the five planets in the solar system that are farther from the sun than Earth. Write the five planets in order from largest to smallest planet by diameter. 8.EE.3

Planet	Diameter (km)
Jupiter	1.43×10^5
Mars	6.79×10^3
Neptune	4.95×10^4
Saturn	1.21×10^5
Uranus	5.11×10^4

	Planet	Diameter (km)
Largest		
Smallest		

5. The metric system uses prefixes to describe different lengths. 8.EE.1

10^0	10^1	10^2
10^3	10^4	10^5
10^6	10^7	10^{-1}
10^{-2}	10^{-3}	10^{-5}
10^{-4}	10^{-6}	10^{-7}

Part A: Complete the table by writing the correct power of 10.

Metric Unit	Number of Meters	
	Standard Form	Power of 10
megameter	1,000,000	
kilometer	1,000	
meter	1	
millimeter	0.001	
micrometer	0.000001	

Part B: In the table, look for a pattern in the powers of 10. Describe the relationship between the exponents and place value.

6. A jumping spider that is 3^{-4} meters long jumps 3^{-1} meters high. About how many times its body length did the spider jump? Explain your reasoning. 8.EE.1

7. Keisha is writing a report on state capitals. She notes that in 2010, Frankfurt, Kentucky, had a population of about 26,000, while Montgomery, Alabama, had a population of about 2.3×10^5. Write in the spaces provided to make each statement true. 8.EE.4

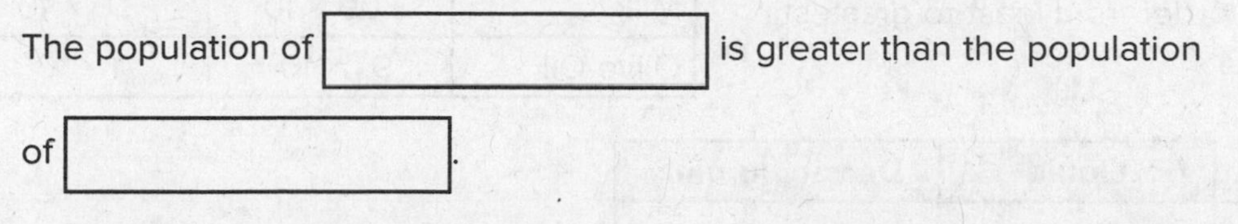

The population of ______ is greater than the population of ______.

In scientific notation, the difference in the number of people living in the two capitals is ______.

8. Oceanographers divide the oceans into layers, as shown in the table. Depths below sea level are represented as negative integers. Select whether each statement is true or false. 8.EE.4

Ocean Zones

Zone	Depth
Sunlight Zone	0 ft to –660 ft
Twilight Zone	–660 ft to –3,300 ft
Midnight Zone	–3,300 ft to –13,000 ft
Abyssal Zone	–13,000 ft and below

True	False	
☐	☐	A whale swimming at a depth of -5.9×10^2 feet is in the sunlight zone.
☐	☐	A jellyfish swimming at a depth of -3.4×10^3 feet is in the midnight zone.
☐	☐	A crab swimming at a depth of -6.4×10^2 feet is in the twilight zone.
☐	☐	A squid swimming at a depth of -1.8×10^4 feet is in the abyssal zone.

9. Ling is finding the volume of a cube with an edge length of $5ab^3$. Her work is shown. 8.EE.1

Part A: Circle the step(s) that show an error.

Part B: Find the correct volume for the cube.

Part C: Describe Ling's error(s) and how she should correct her work.

Part A:

Step 1 $V = (5ab^3)^3$

Step 2 $V = 5^3(a)^3(b^3)^3$

Step 3 $V = 15a^3b^6$

Part B: $V =$

10. Density is a measure of how compact a substance is. To calculate density, divide mass by volume. Calculate the density of each liquid shown in the table. Write the four liquids in order from least to greatest density. 8.EE.4

Liquids	Mass (g)	Volume (cm^3)
Honey	1.19×10^3	8.5×10^2
Mercury	6.8×10^{-1}	5×10^{-2}
Milk	3.09×10^3	3.0×10^3
Olive Oil	9.1×10^2	1×10^3

	Liquid	Density (g/cm^3)
Least		
Greatest		

11. Golden Gate Park in San Francisco, California, is rectangular in shape and measures approximately 1.6×10^4 feet by 2.7×10^3 feet. One acre is equal to 4.356×10^4 feet. About how many acres does Golden Gate Park cover? Round to the nearest hundredth. Explain your answer. 8.EE.4

12. Dayshawn has a storage cube with a volume of 7 cubic feet. What is the shortest space in feet in which the cube will fit? Explain. 8.EE.2

13. The table shows the land areas of the five continents that are not islands. Write the continents in order from least to greatest land area. 8.EE.3

Continent	Land Area (mi^2)
Africa	1.16×10^7
Asia	1.72×10^7
Europe	3.84×10^6
North America	9.37×10^6
South America	6.88×10^6

	Continent
Least Land Area	
Greatest Land Area	

14. The diagonal of a rectangular quilt is $\sqrt{324}$ feet long. 8.NS.1

Part A: Select all of the sets of numbers to which $\sqrt{324}$ belongs.

real	rational	whole
integer	irrational	natural

Part B: Change one digit in $\sqrt{324}$ to a different digit. Explain how and why changing that digit changes the set of numbers to which it belongs.

15. The table shows several planets and their distances from the sun. Write the correct number to make each statement true. 8.EE.3, 8.EE.4

Planet	Distance from Sun (km)
Mercury	5.8×10^7
Venus	1.1×10^8
Saturn	1.43×10^9
Neptune	4.5×10^9

2	3	4	5
20	25	40	250

Neptune is about ☐ times farther from the sun than Saturn.

Neptune is about ☐ times farther from the sun than Venus.

Saturn is about ☐ times farther from the sun than Mercury.

Venus is about ☐ times farther from the sun than Mercury.

16. Lori found this information while doing research on stars. Select whether the answer to each question is yes or no. 8.EE.3, 8.EE.4

- The sun is approximately 1.4×10^6 kilometers across.
- A low-mass star can be approximately 700 thousand kilometers across.
- A red giant star can be approximately 1×10^8 kilometers across.

Yes	No	
☐	☐	Is a red giant star about 700 times larger than the sun?
☐	☐	Is the sun about 20 times larger than a low-mass star?
☐	☐	Is a red giant star about 143 times larger than a low-mass star?
☐	☐	Is a low-mass star about half the size of the sun?

17. The area of each small square in the figures is 64 square units. 8.EE.2

Part A: Write the perimeter of each figure.

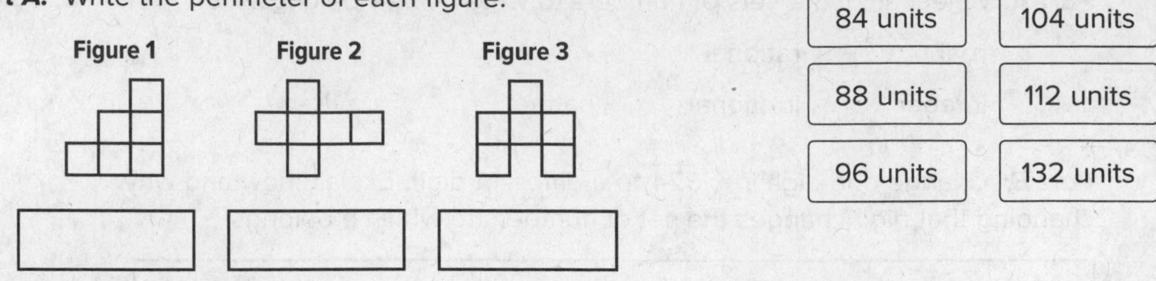

Part B: Do any of the figures have the same perimeter? If so, identify the figures and explain why.

18. The number line shows four points labeled *A*, *B*, *C*, and *D*. Select whether each statement is true or false. 8.NS.2, 8.EE.2

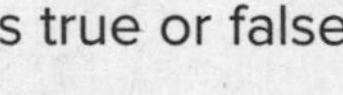

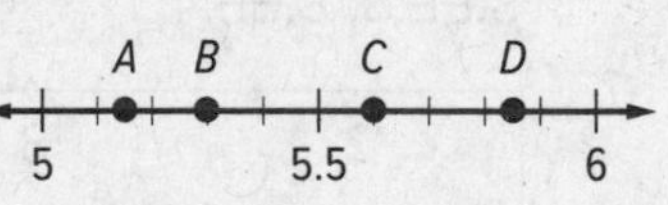

True **False**

☐ ☐ The value of $\sqrt{28}$ is to the left of point *A*.

☐ ☐ The value of $\sqrt{30}$ is between point *B* and point *C*.

☐ ☐ The coordinate of point *D* is less than $\sqrt{32}$.

19. The table shows the masses of the particles in an atom. The numbers are from a calculator. Write the particles in order from least to greatest mass. 8.EE.3, 8.EE.4

Subatomic Particles	Mass (g)
Proton	1.673 E–24
Electron	9.109 E–28
Neutron	1.674 E–24

Least Mass **Greatest Mass**

20. Ms. Diaz gave her students a project that was worth 100 points. Jacey earned a 92%, Omar earned $\sqrt{8,649}$ points, Keiko earned $\frac{182}{200}$ of the total points, and Matt earned $\frac{11}{12}$ of the total points. Plot points on the number line to represent each student's score. 8.NS.1

91 91.2 91.4 91.6 91.8 92 92.2 92.4 92.6 92.8 93

NAME ______________________ DATE ____________ PERIOD ________ SCORE ________

Chapter 2 Test

1. Sort the equations into the bin that correctly describes its solution. 8.EE.7, 8.EE.7a

$0.25n + 4 = 0.4(n + 4)$	$-3(6n - 1) = -18n + 3$	$8n - 28 - n = 7(n - 4)$
$5(2z + 4) = 7z + 8$	$17 - 3(2n - 5) = 30 - 6n$	$-2(8x + 2) = -16x + 2$

No Solution	One Solution	Infinitely Many Solutions

2. Yuriko ran 3 more than twice as many miles as Paul did yesterday. Yuriko ran 7 miles yesterday. Let x represent the number of miles Paul ran. 8.EE.7, 8.EE.7b

Part A: Draw algebra tiles on the equation mat to model this situation.

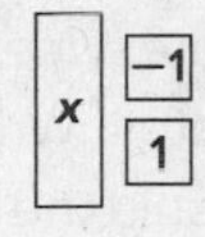

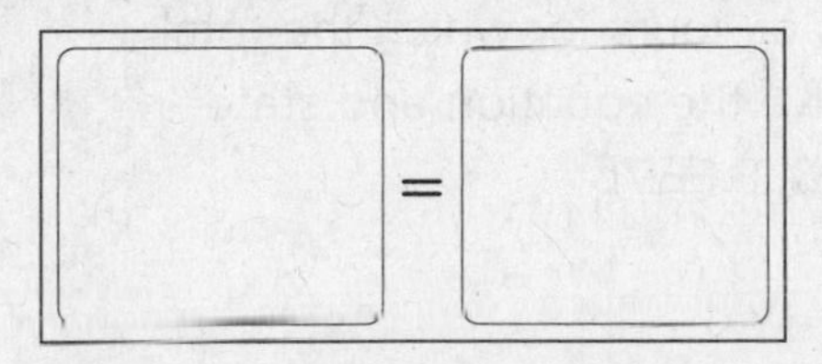

Part B: Solve to find x. How many miles did Paul run?

3. Jorge buys two magnets. Each magnet is shaped like an equilateral polygon, and they have the same perimeter. Select whether each statement is true or false. 8.EE.7, 8.EE.7b

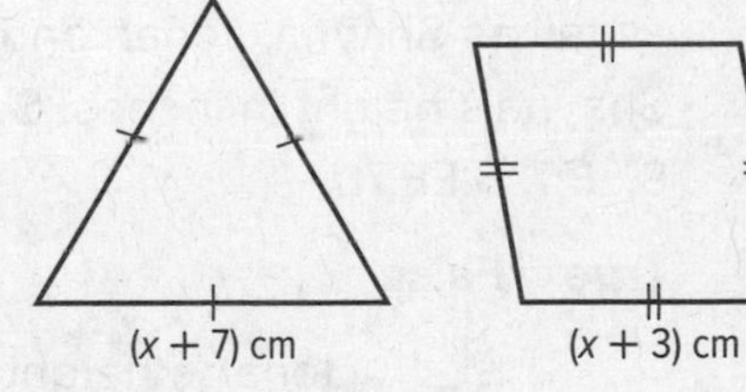

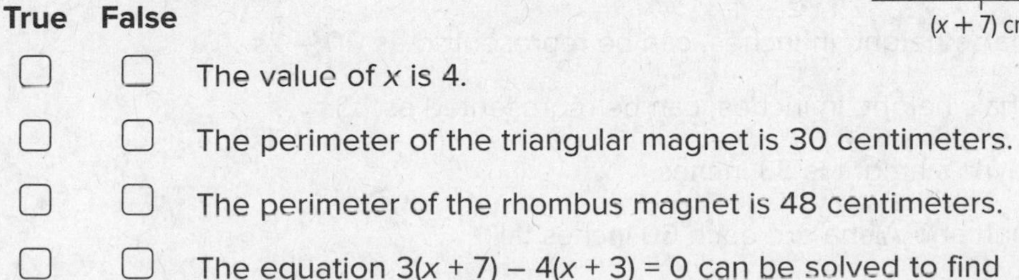

True	False	
☐	☐	The value of x is 4.
☐	☐	The perimeter of the triangular magnet is 30 centimeters.
☐	☐	The perimeter of the rhombus magnet is 48 centimeters.
☐	☐	The equation $3(x + 7) - 4(x + 3) = 0$ can be solved to find the value of x.

4. Write a number in each box to make an equation that has exactly one real solution. 8.EE.7, 8.EE.7a

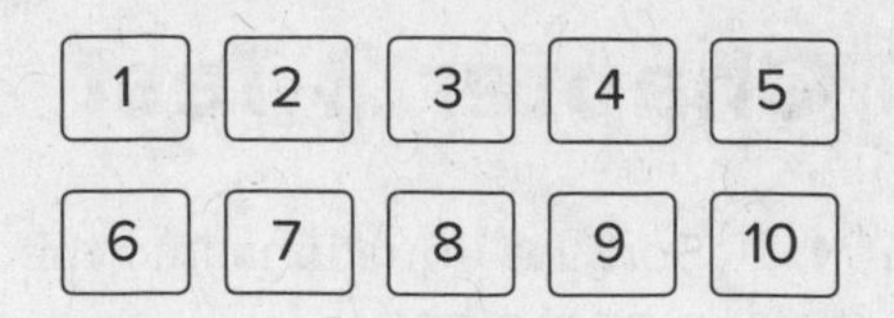

$3(2a + 1) - a = \square a + \square$

5. In one physical education class, $\frac{5}{8}$ of the students were playing basketball. After 3 more students joined, 18 students were playing basketball. How many students are in the class? Circle all the equations that could represent this situation. Then find the answer. 8.EE.7, 8.EE.7b

$\frac{5}{8}x = 18 + 3x$	$\frac{5}{8}(x + 3) = 18$	$\frac{5}{8}x = 18 - 3$
$18 = \frac{5}{8}x - 3$	$\frac{5}{8}x + 3 = 18$	$\frac{5}{8}x + 3x = 18$

There are ☐ students in the class.

6. SkateWorld charges $10.00 for admission plus $2.50 per hour to rent ice skates. IceLand charges $7.00 for admission plus $4.00 per hour to rent ice skates. Write an equation to find *h*, the number of hours for which the total cost is the same at both skating rinks. Then solve the equation and state what the cost is for that number of hours. 8.EE.7, 8.EE.7b

Equation: ☐ = ☐

$h =$ ☐

Cost for that number of hours: ☐

7. Jonah is 20 inches shorter than 2 times Shayna's height. Aisha is 1.5 times as tall as Shayna. Jonah and Aisha are the same height. Let *s* represent Shayna's height in inches. Select whether each statement is true or false. 8.EE.7, 8.EE.7b

True	False	
☐	☐	Jonah's height, in inches, can be represented as $20 - 2s$.
☐	☐	Aisha's height, in inches, can be represented as $1.5s$.
☐	☐	Shayna's height is 33 inches.
☐	☐	Jonah and Aisha are each 60 inches tall.

8. Select all of the equations that have infinitely many solutions. 8.EE.7, 8.EE.7a

- ☐ $6x + 7 - 2x = 4x - 7$
- ☐ $9x - (2x + 5) = 7x - 5$
- ☐ $-5(2x + 3) = -10x + 15$
- ☐ $5 - (3x - 2) = 2x + 2$
- ☐ $12x + 3 + x = 4 + 13x - 1$

9. Write a number in each box to make an equation with a solution of 5. 8.EE.7, 8.EE.7a, 8.EE.7b

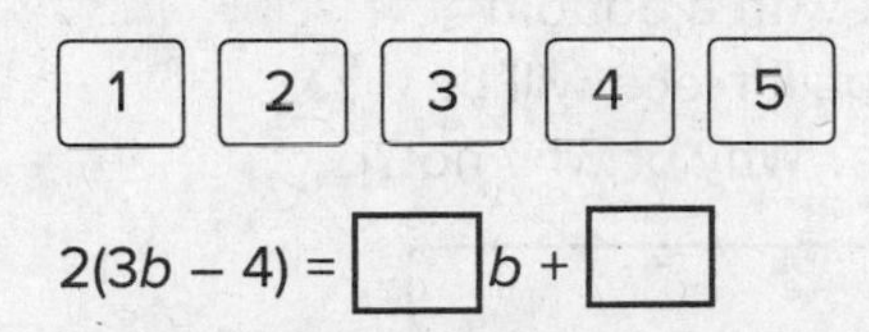

$2(3b - 4) = \square b + \square$

10. The table shows expressions to represent the number of eighth-grade students enrolled in different world language classes. The number of students enrolled in French and German is equal to the number of students enrolled in Chinese and Spanish. 8.EE.7, 8.EE.7b

Class	Number of Students
Chinese	$2n$
French	$7n + 6$
German	$4n - 2$
Spanish	$2(4n + 6)$

Part A: Model the situation with an equation. Write the appropriate expression in each box.

$2n$ $7n + 6$ $4n - 2$ $2(4n + 6)$

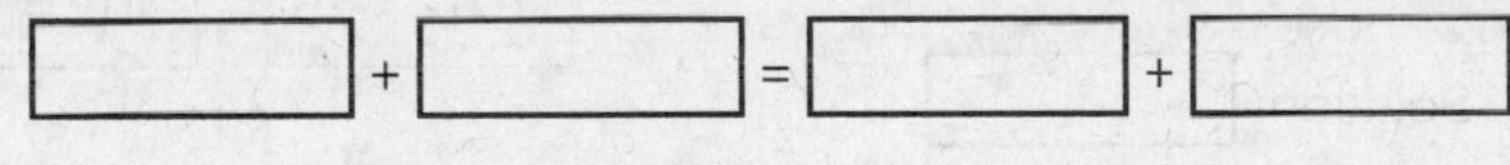

$\square + \square = \square + \square$

Part B: Solve the equation. Then identify the number of students enrolled in each language class.

$n = \square$

Chinese: ☐ students   German: ☐ students

French: ☐ students   Spanish: ☐ students

11. Complete the equation so that it has an infinite number of solutions. Write one number in each box. 8.EE.7, 8.EE.7a

$2(4k - 2) - 2k = \square k - \square$

12. Pearl is making a quilt. One quilt piece is shaped like the trapezoid shown. The fabric to make the quilt piece has an area of 22.5 square inches. The formula for the area of a trapezoid is $A = \frac{1}{2}h(b_1 + b_2)$. 8.EE.7, 8.EE.7b

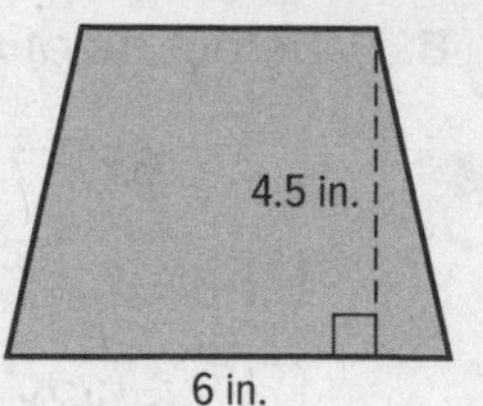

Part A: Write an equation you can use to find the length of the top base in the quilt piece. Then find the base length.

Equation:

Base length:

Part B: Steve wants to make a quilt piece like Pearl's but with a bottom base that is twice as long. He claims that the area of his quilt piece will be double the area of Pearl's piece. Is Steve's claim accurate? Why or why not?

13. Select the correct equation for each situation. Then solve each problem. 8.EE.7, 8.EE.7b

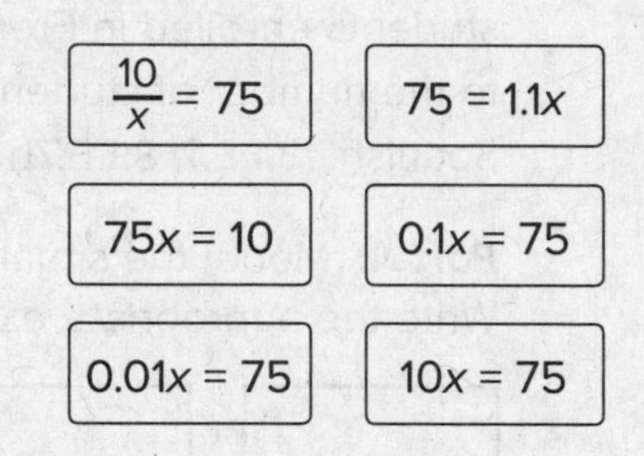

Part A: Dorian deposits $75 in his bank account. It is 10% of the total amount of money he earned last month working part-time. How much money did Dorian earn last month?

Equation: Solution:

Part B: A rope is 75 feet long. It is 10 times the length Carmen needs for her jump rope. How many feet of rope does Carmen need?

Equation: Solution:

14. Angles A and B are supplementary. The measure of angle B is 5 less than 4 times the measure of angle A. Write an equation to represent this situation and define the variable you choose. Then find the measures of the angles. 8.EE.7, 8.EE.7b

15. Jacob is solving an equation. His work is shown. 8.EE.7, 8.EE.7b

Equation: $-0.5(20x - 10) - 2 = 13$

Step 1: $-10x - 5 - 2 = 13$

Step 2: $-10x - 7 = 13$

Step 3:
$$\begin{array}{r} -10x - 7 = 13 \\ +7 \quad +7 \\ \hline -10x = 20 \end{array}$$

Step 4:
$$\frac{-10x}{-10} = \frac{20}{-10}$$
$$x = -2$$

Part A: Circle the first step in which Jacob's work shows an error.

Part B: Describe Jacob's error(s) and how he should correct his work.

Part C: Find the correct value of x.

$x =$ ☐

16. Sylvia and Raul are computer technicians who make house calls. Sylvia charges a flat fee of \$35.50 plus \$16 per hour. Raul charges a \$15.50 flat fee plus \$20 per hour. Select whether each statement is true or false. 8.EE.7, 8.EE.7b

True	False	
☐	☐	For 2 hours of work, Sylvia charges more than Raul.
☐	☐	For 6 hours of work, Raul charges less than Sylvia.
☐	☐	The equation $35.5x + 16 = 15.5x + 20$ can be solved to find the number of hours for which the total cost is the same to hire either technician.
☐	☐	Both technicians charge the same amount for a 5-hour job.

17. The table shows the total distance Mr. Wilder drove each day last week. The total distance Mr. Wilder drove last week is two thirds of the distance he drove this week. Write and solve an equation to show how far Mr. Wilder drove this week. 8.EE.7, 8.EE.7b

Day	Sunday	Monday	Tuesday	Wednesday	Thursday	Friday	Saturday
Miles	9.5	12.5	5.5	7.8	5.5	3.2	10.0

Equation: ☐

Miles this week: ☐

18. Write a number in each box to make an equation that has no real solution. 8.EE.7, 8.EE.7a

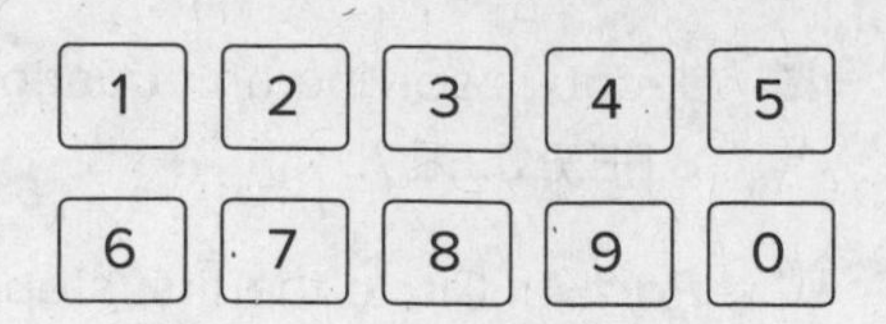

$4(a - 2) + a =$ ☐ $a -$ ☐

19. The perimeter of a rectangular carpet is 44 feet. The length of the carpet is $(3n + 3)$ feet and the width is $(2n - 1)$ feet. Select whether each statement is true or false. 8.EE.7, 8.EE.7b

True	False	
☐	☐	The equation $3n + 3 + 2n - 1 = 44$ can be solved to find the value of n.
☐	☐	The width of the carpet is 4 feet.
☐	☐	The length of the carpet is 15 feet.
☐	☐	The carpet is a square.
☐	☐	The equation $44 - 2(2n - 1) = 2(3n + 3)$ can be solved to find the dimensions of the carpet.

20. An online shopping company uses boxes like the one shown to ship purchases to customers. 8.EE.7, 8.EE.7b

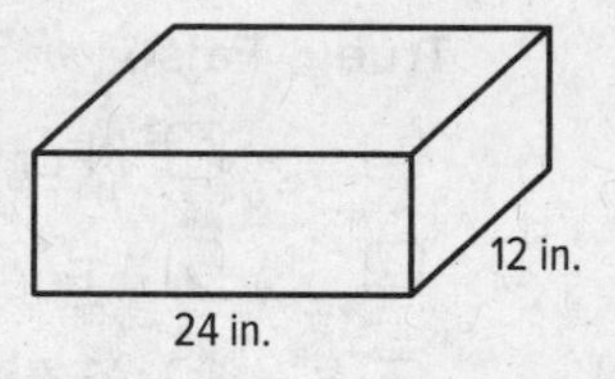

Part A: The shipping box needs 1,224 square inches of cardboard to make its six sides, without overlap. What is the height of the box? Use the formula for surface area of a prism $S.A. = 2wh + 2\ell w + 2\ell h$ to write an equation. Then find the box height.

Equation: ☐

Height of box: ☐

Part B: Would packing material with volume 2500 cubic inches fit into this shipping box? Explain.

☐

NAME ______________________ DATE __________ PERIOD ________ SCORE ________

Chapter 3 Test

1. The table shows the total number of miles Marcus has biked. 8.EE.5

Part A: Graph the points on the coordinate plane and connect them with a straight line.

Number of Weeks	Total Distance (mi)
1	75
2	150
3	225
4	300
5	375
6	450

Total Distance (mi)

500, 450, 400, 350, 300, 250, 200, 150, 100, 50

O 1 2 3 4 5 6 7 8 9 10

Number of Weeks

Part B: What is the rate of change, and what does it represent?

2. Luisa makes and sells necklaces. The total amount she charges is a direct variation of the number of necklaces bought. Write numbers in the spaces and find the slope. Then write an equation in $y = mx$ form to represent the situation. 8.F.4

Number of Necklaces, x	3	5	8
Total Charge ($), y	$39	$65	$104

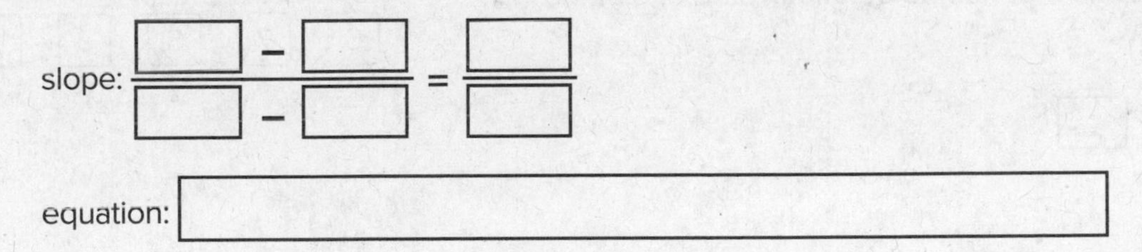

slope:

equation:

3. The cost y in dollars to park in a garage is found by the equation $y = 2.50 + 0.75x$, where x is the number of hours parked. Select whether each statement is true or false. 8.F.3, 8.F.4

True	False	
☐	☐	The graph of $y = 2.50 + 0.75x$ passes through (0, 0).
☐	☐	The graph of $y = 2.50 + 0.75x$ is a straight line.
☐	☐	The y-intercept represents the flat fee for parking, which is $2.50.
☐	☐	The slope represents the total cost of one hour of parking, which is $0.75.

4. Write the equation that is represented by each graph. 8.EE.8, 8.EE.8c, 8.F.5

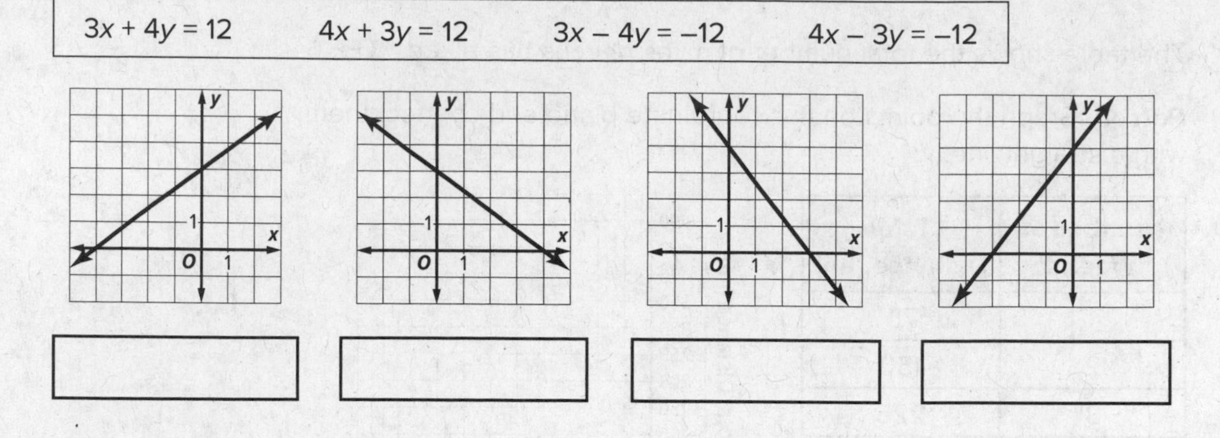

5. Carlos saves the same amount each week. After 2 weeks, Carlos has saved $12.50. After 4 weeks, he has saved $25. After 6 weeks, he has saved $37.50. 8.EE.5

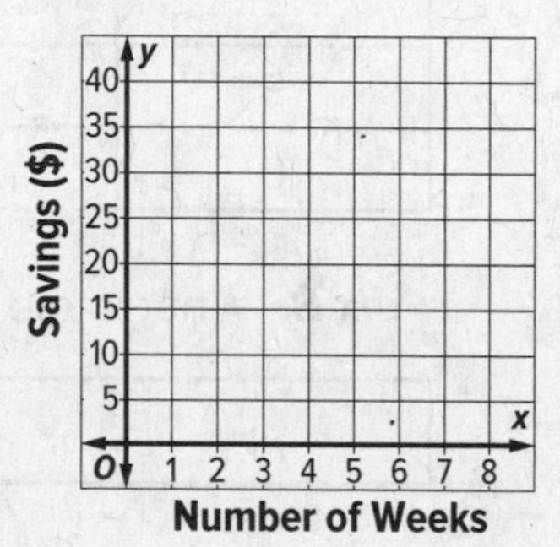

Part A: Graph the information as points on the coordinate plane and connect them with a straight line.

Part B: What is the slope, and how does it relate to the unit rate?

6. Write numbers in the spaces to create a system of linear equations that has no solution. 8.EE.8, 8.EE.8b

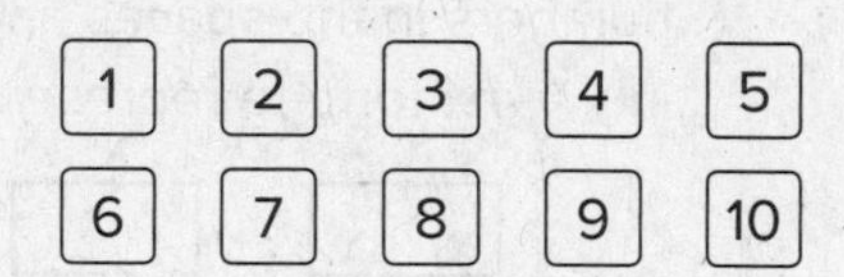

$y = 2(4x + 3)$

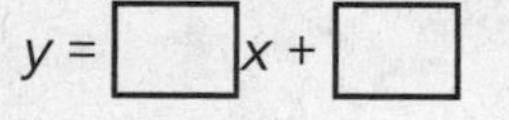

7. Ethan is typing a 500-word essay for school. He can type 25 words in one minute. The equation for the number of words he has left to type is $y = 500 - 25x$, where x is the number of minutes he has been typing. Write a number or word to complete the statements. 8.F.3, 8.F.4

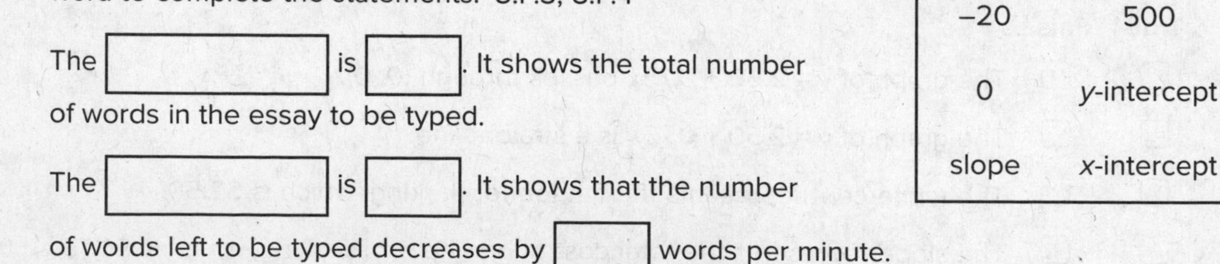

The is . It shows the total number of words in the essay to be typed.
The is . It shows that the number of words left to be typed decreases by words per minute.
–500
20
–25
25
–20
500
0
y-intercept
slope
x-intercept

8. The distance y in miles traveled by a striped marlin in x hours is shown on the graph. Each ocean creature's distance in miles is a direct variation of the time it travels in hours. Select whether each ocean creature travels faster than the striped marlin. 8.EE.5, 8.F.2

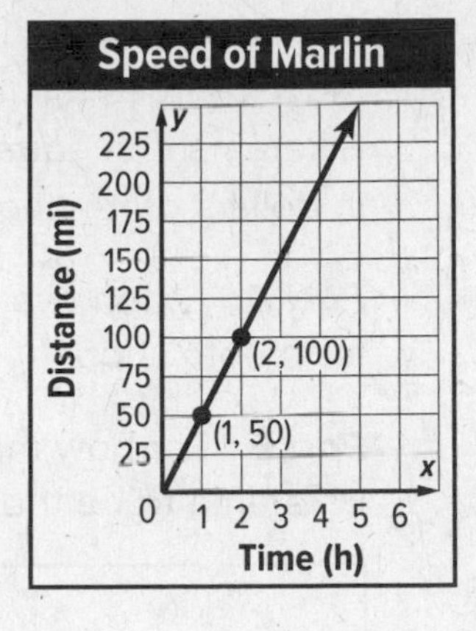

Yes	No	
☐	☐	a tuna that travels at a speed of 43.5 miles per hour
☐	☐	a swordfish whose distance y in miles is represented by the equation $y = 60x$, where x is the number of hours
☐	☐	a wahoo fish that travels 144 miles in 3 hours and 192 miles in 4 hours
☐	☐	a mako shark whose distance y in miles is represented by the equation $y = 31x$, where x is the number of hours

9. The table shows how Ms. Mwanda's earnings as a realtor change depending on her house sales. 8.EE.6, 8.F.4

Sales (thousands), *x*	$200	$400	$600
Total Earnings, *y*	$20,000	$30,000	$40,000

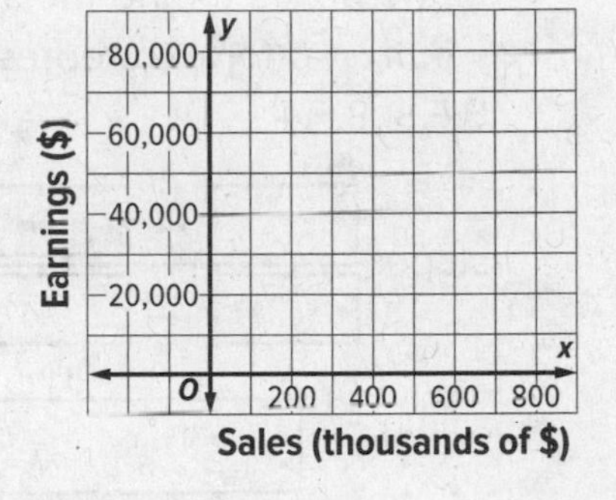

Part A: Graph the points on the coordinate plane and connect them with a straight line.

Part B: Write an equation in slope-intercept form to represent the relationship

10. Anoki draws two lines on the same coordinate plane. Line AB passes through (–2, 9) and has a slope of –5. Line CD passes through (–1, 12) and (1, 4). 8EE.8, 8.EE.8a, 8.EE.8c

Part A: Write an equation in point-slope form for each line.

$\overleftrightarrow{AB}$:

$\overleftrightarrow{CD}$:

Part B: The lines Anoki drew do not intersect on his graph. He says they will never intersect. Is Anoki correct? Explain.

11. Zack considers renting a bicycle from two different shops. The Rider charges a flat rate of \$72 to rent a bike for a day. At Bikerama, the equation $y = 12x$ is used to determine the cost y in dollars of renting a bike for x hours. 8.EE.8, 8.EE.8a, 8.EE.8b

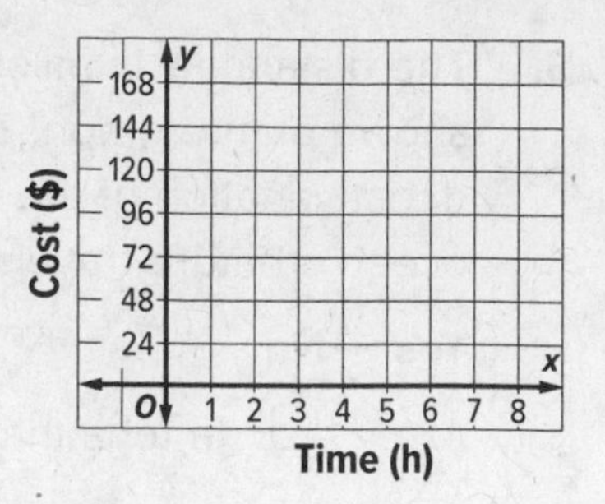

Part A: Graph two lines to represent the costs of renting bikes from both shops.

Part B: For how many hours would Zack need to rent a bike for Bikerama to be the better deal?

12. An elevator on the top floor starts to descend at a constant rate, as shown by the graph. Write numbers in the boxes to find the slope. Write an equation in $y = mx + b$ form to represent the situation. 8.EE.6, 8.F.3, 8.F.4

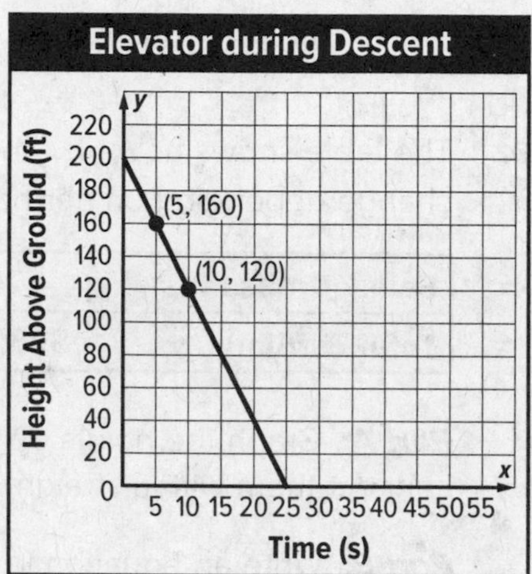

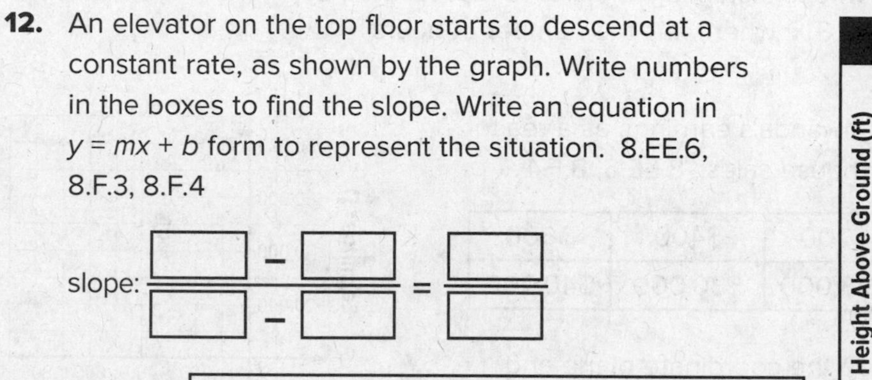

slope: $\dfrac{\square - \square}{\square - \square} = \dfrac{\square}{\square}$

equation:

13. Latoya increases the number of kilometers she runs each week. She plotted the number of kilometers she ran each week and then drew this line through the points. Select whether each statement is true or false. 8.EE.5, 8.F.5

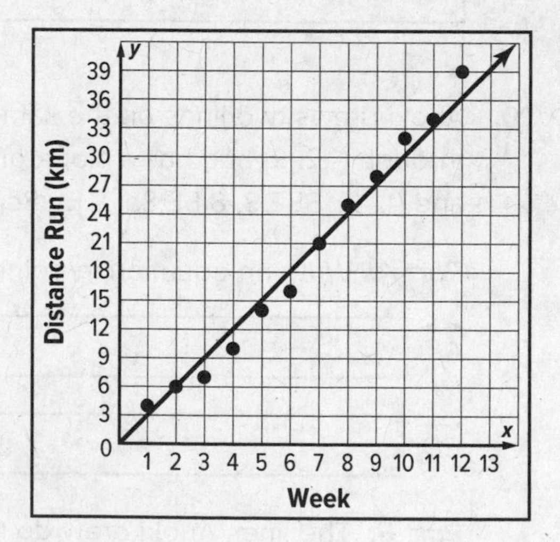

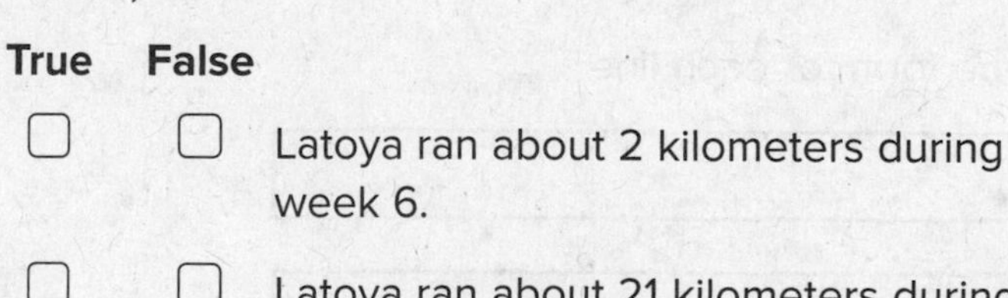

True	False	
☐	☐	Latoya ran about 2 kilometers during week 6.
☐	☐	Latoya ran about 21 kilometers during week 7.
☐	☐	The slope of the line is $\frac{1}{3}$.
☐	☐	Latoya runs at a constant rate of 3 kilometers per week.
☐	☐	Latoya runs about 3 more kilometers each week than she did the previous week.

14. There are 5 times as many girls as boys taking French this year. Sixty students are taking French this year. Let g represent the number of girls and b represent the number of boys. 8.EE.8, 8.EE.8b, 8.EE.8c

b
g
boys
girls
60

Part A: Write labels into the bar diagram to model the situation.

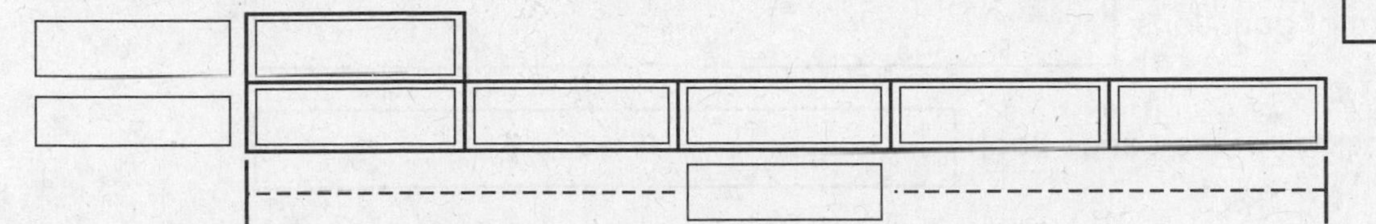

Part B: Use the bar diagram to write and solve a system of equations. How many boys and girls are taking French this year?

System of equations:

Solution:

15. Sort the systems of equations into the appropriate bins that describe their solutions. 8.EE.8, 8.EE.8b

$y = 2(x + 3)$ $y = 2x + 6$	$y = 4x + 4$ $y = 4x + 1$	$y = -x$ $y = x - 1$

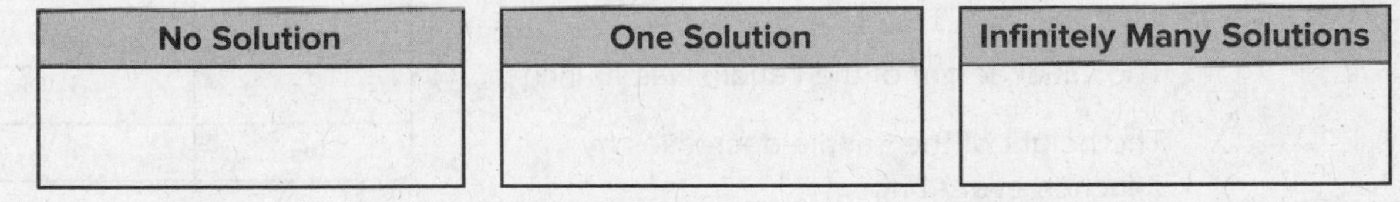

16. Line m has a slope of $\frac{3}{2}$ and passes through (0, –1). Luz and Demetrius each point to (0, –1). Luz then moves her finger 6 units to the right. From there, how many units up is line m? Demetrius moves his finger 6 units down. From there, how many units left is line m? 8.EE.6

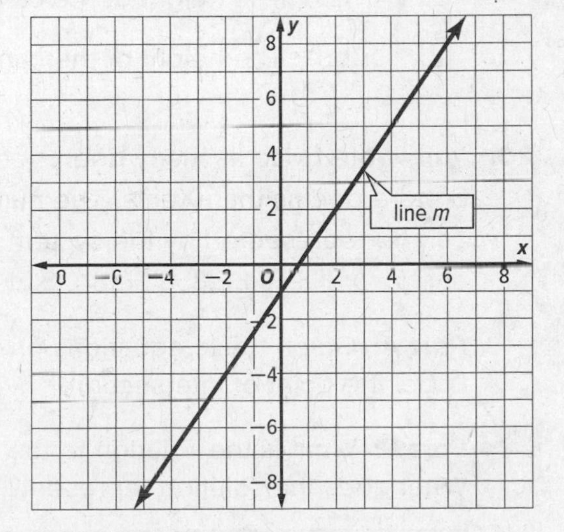

Luz:

Demetrius:

17. The width of a rectangular dance floor is 5 meters less than the length. The perimeter of the floor is 38 meters. Set up a system of equations to represent the length ℓ and the width w. Then solve the system of equations to find the dimensions of the dance floor. 8.EE.8, 8.EE.8b, 8.EE.8c

System of equations:

Dimensions of the dance floor:

18. The total cost in dollars y of buying peanuts at a health food store varies directly with x, the number of pounds purchased. Macadamia nuts cost 4 times as much as peanuts at the store. Write an equation to represent the cost y of buying x pounds of macadamia nuts. 8.EE.5

Peanuts (lb), x	2	4	6	8
Cost ($), y	9	18	27	36

19. The table shows how the height of a candle y changes x hours after it has been lit. Select whether each statement is true or false. 8.F.4

Time (h), x	Candle Height (in.), y
0	16
2	12
4	8
6	4

True	False	
☐	☐	The initial height of the candle was 16 inches.
☐	☐	The height of the candle decreases by 2 inches every 1 hour.
☐	☐	The height of the candle after 3 hours is 6 inches.
☐	☐	The height of the candle after 7 hours is 2 inches.

20. Yuri wrote twice as many poems as Xenia. Yuri wrote 3 more poems than Xenia. The number of poems written can be represented by the system of equations: $y = 2x$ and $y = x + 3$. 8.EE.8, 8.EE.8b, 8.EE.8c

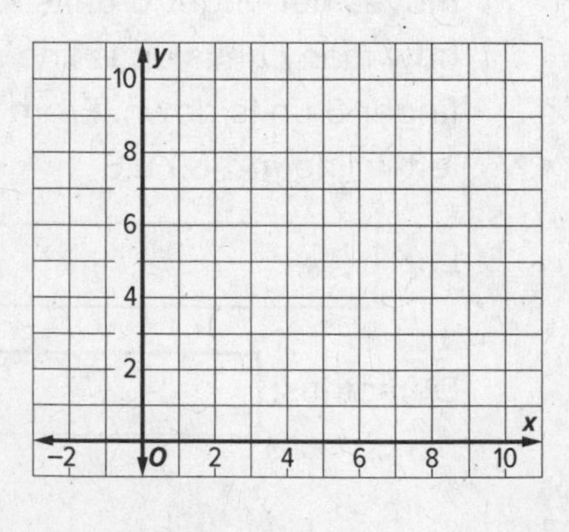

Part A: Graph these equations on the coordinate plane. Label the point of intersection.

Part B: What is the solution to the system of equations? What does the solution represent?

NAME ________________ DATE ________ PERIOD ________ SCORE ________

Chapter 4 Test

1. The table shows the number of students enrolled in a community college over the course of several years. 8.F.4

Semester	1	3	5	7
Enrollment	1,800	1,950	2,100	2,250

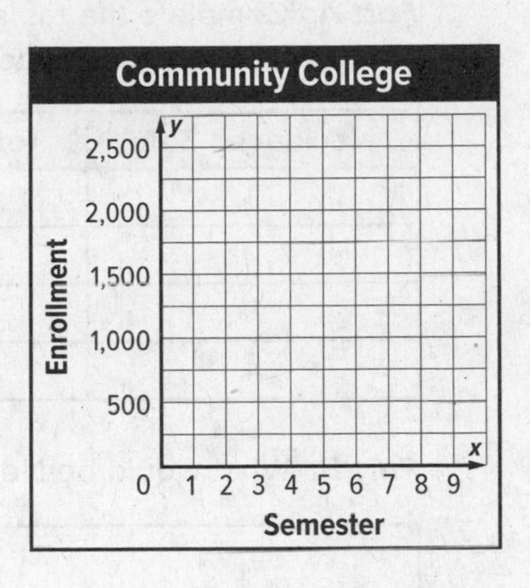

Part A: Graph the relationship on the coordinate plane.

Part B: The pattern shown in the graph continues. How many students will be enrolled in the school by the eighth semester?

2. An electronics store is having a 10% off sale. Dante has a coupon for $20 off. The function $f(x) = 0.9x - 20$ represents the final cost after the discount and coupon are applied for an item priced at x dollars. Complete the function machine for items A, B, C, and D. 8.F.1, 8.F.4

$18	$65
$25	$70
$27	$80
$40	$90

Input A: $50
Input B: ______
Input C: $100
Input D: ______

➡ $f(x) = 0.9x - 20$ ➡

Output A: ______
Output B: $43
Output C: ______
Output D: $52

3. Members of the softball team order custom sweatshirts. They must pay a $45 design fee for the entire order plus $18.50 per shirt. Complete the table to show the cost of buying n shirts. 8.F.1, 8.F.4

Number of Sweatshirts, n	1	3	6	9	10
Total Cost ($), $c(n)$					

4. The bookstore sells used books for $2 each and bookmarks for $1 each. Gabriela has $7 to spend. The function $y = 7 - 2x$ represents the number of used books x and the number of bookmarks y she can buy. Select whether each statement is true or false. 8.F.3, 8.F.4

True **False**

☐ ☐ She can buy 0 bookmarks and 7 used books.

☐ ☐ She can buy 2 used books and 3 bookmarks.

☐ ☐ She can buy 4 used books and 1 bookmark.

5. Neveah earns a profit of $6 for each necklace she sells. 8.F.1

Part A: Complete the table of ordered pairs to show her total profits for making several necklaces.

Necklaces Sold	Total Profits ($)
1	
2	
3	
4	

Part B: What would be Neveah's total profit after selling 13 necklaces?

6. Antoine has some money saved. He plans to start saving a certain amount each week to add to his savings, as shown in the graph. Find the slope and y-intercept. Then describe what the y-intercept and slope represent. 8.F.4

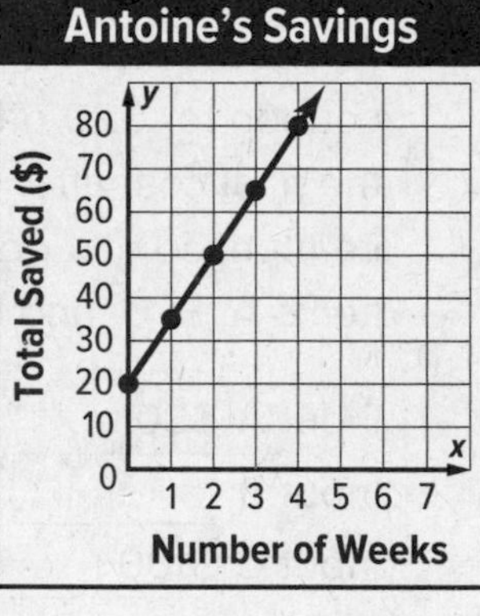

y-intercept: ______ slope: ______

7. The graph shows Ella's activities on her way home from camp one summer day. Write the segment that corresponds with each statement. 8.F.5

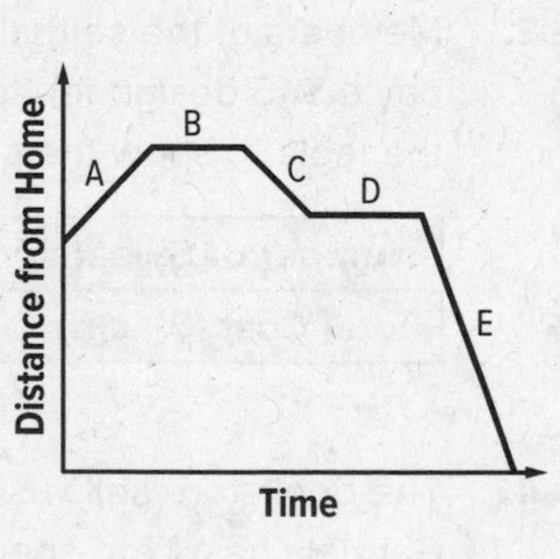

Segment A | Segment B | Segment C | Segment D | Segment E

______ Ella walks from camp to the library.

______ Ella gets a ride home from Maria's house.

______ Ella spends time at the library.

______ Ella spends time at Maria's house.

______ Ella goes from the library to Maria's house.

8. The function $h = 0.078d^2$ represents the distance d in kilometers an observer can see from a height of h meters above the ground. 8.F.3, 8.F.5

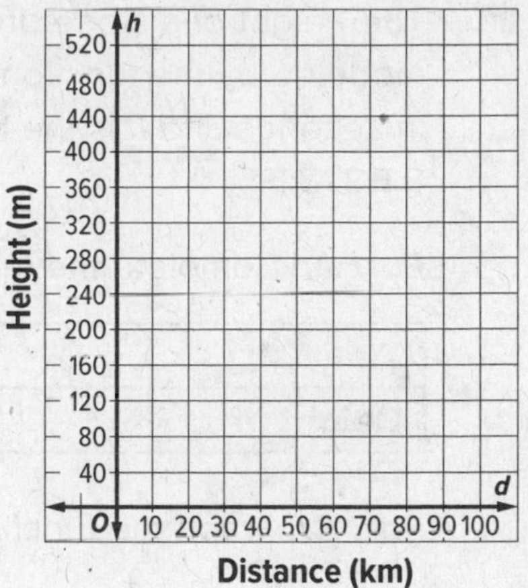

Part A: Complete the table of values to represent the function.

Distance (km), d	0	20	40	60	80
Height (m), h					

Part B: Graph the function on the coordinate plane.

Part C: Use the graph to estimate how far a tourist can see from the observation deck of the Empire State Building, which is 380 meters above ground level.

9. Zoo members pay \$3.50 per ticket for entrance to a special gorilla exhibit. The price of a ticket for non-members is represented in the table. 8.F.2

Number of Tickets	1	2	3	4	5
Total Price ($)	7.50	15.00	22.50	30.00	37.50

Part A: Graph both functions on the coordinate plane.

Part B: Compare the rates of change and y-intercepts of the linear functions. Explain what each represents.

10. Adam ran a 15-kilometer race. He completed the race in 1.6 hours. Adam's speed for the first kilometer can be represented by the function $d = 9.2h$, where d is distance in kilometers and h is time in hours. Was Adam's average speed for the first kilometer of the race faster or slower than his average speed for the entire race? Justify your answer. 8.F.2

11. The height of a stone dropped from a 256-foot-tall bridge is modeled by the function $h = -16t^2 + 256$, where t is the time in seconds and h is the height of the stone above the lake. 8.F.3, 8.F.5

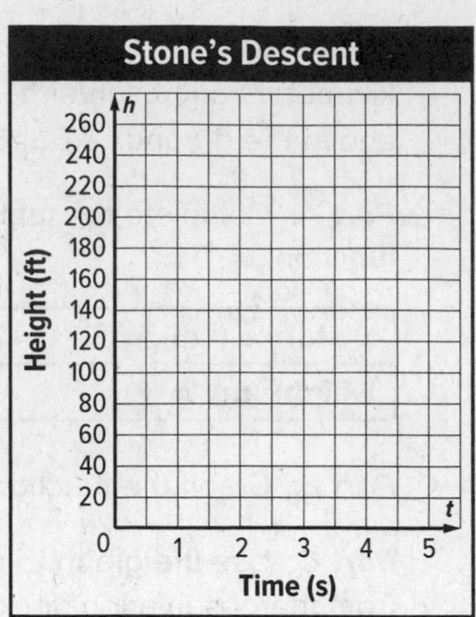

Part A: Complete the table of values.

Time (s), *t*	0	1	2	3	4
Height (ft), *h*					

Part B: Graph the function on the coordinate plane.

Part C: How long does it take for the stone to reach the lake?

12. Different types of functions have different characteristics.

Part A: Write what type of function is represented. 8.F.3

linear

nonlinear

x	*y*
−2	1
0	5
1	4
3	−4
4	−11

$y = 0.5x^2 - 1$

$y = 4x - \frac{1}{2}$

Part B: Choose a nonlinear function above. Describe how you could change the representation of that nonlinear function to make it linear.

13. Max and his dad are racing electric karts. The junior kart Max is racing produces speeds of 20 miles per hour. The adult kart Max's dad is racing produces speeds represented by the function $d = 45h$, where d is the distance in miles after h hours. How much farther could Max's dad travel than Max in 0.75 hour? 8.F.2, 8.F.4

14. A dog is running at a constant speed. It then sees a squirrel and races after it, picking up speed as it runs. Which graph best displays this relationship? Explain your reasoning. 8.F.5

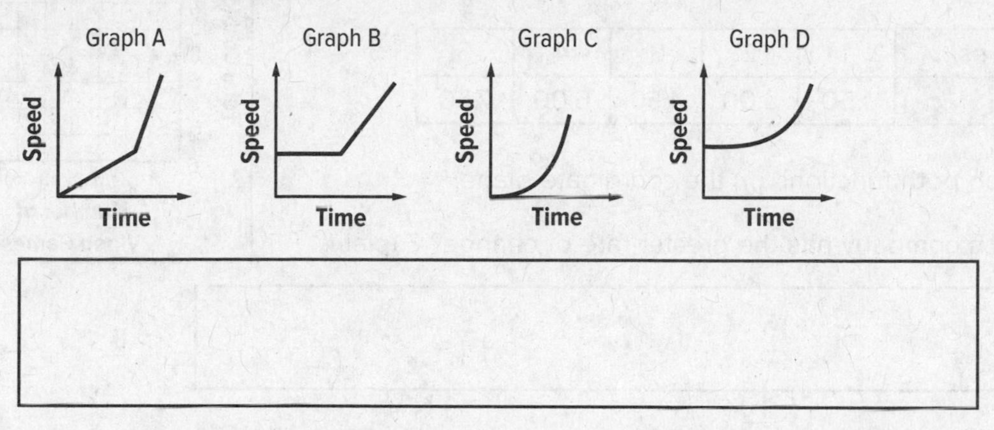

15. A cable company charges a fee to install a cable modem plus a monthly fee for Internet service. The table shows this linear relationship. Select whether each statement is true or false. 8.F.4

Number of Months	0	2	4	6
Total Cost ($)	50	90	130	170

True	False	
☐	☐	The initial fee for installation is $50.
☐	☐	The total cost increases by $20 each month.
☐	☐	The total cost for a year of service would be $340.

16. Humberto has a $30 gift card for online games. The cost of 1 game is $2.95. Complete the table to show the balance remaining on Humberto's gift card after buying n games. 8.F.1, 8.F.4

Games Purchased, n	2	4	5	7	10
Balance Remaining ($), $g(n)$					

17. Write appropriate y-values in each table to make a linear function and a nonlinear function.

Linear Function

x	y
0	3
1	5
2	
3	

Nonlinear Function

x	y
0	3
1	5
2	
3	

18. The cost c to rent v video games from an online game rental Company A is represented by the function $c = 2.5v$. The cost to rent video games from Company B is shown in the table. 8.F.2

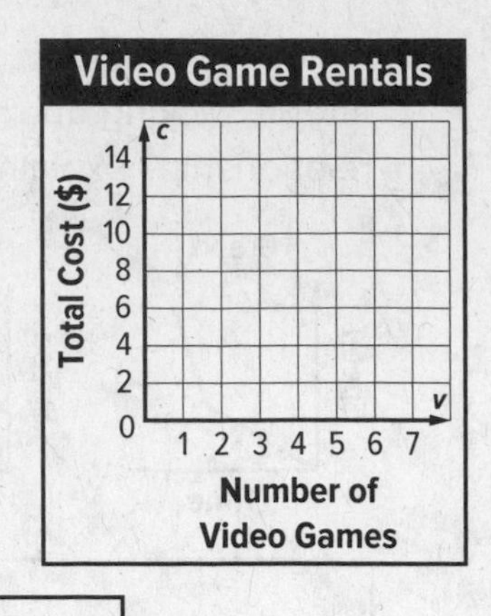

Video Games, v	1	2	3	4	5
Total Cost ($), c	1.50	3.00	4.50	6.00	7.50

Part A: Graph both functions on the coordinate plane.

Part B: Which company has the greater rate of change? Explain.

Part C: Naquana pays $7.50 to rent several video games from one of the companies. How many games could she rent?

☐ games from Company A OR ☐ games from Company B

19. Ernesto wants to buy a new $400 bike. He earns $12.50 per hour working at a store and saves all his money. The function $f(x) = -12.50x + 400$ represents the amount he still needs to save after working x hours. Complete the function machine for hours and savings A, B, and C. 8.F.1, 8.F.4

20	88
30	125
65	150
75	275

Input A: 10 h
Input B: ☐ h
Input C: 26 h

➡ $f(x) = -12.5x + 400$ ➡

Output A: $ ☐
Output B: $25
Output C: $ ☐

20. Anna makes this conjecture: "The graph of any parabola (U-shaped curve) represents a nonlinear function." Which graph provides a counterexample to Anna's conjecture? Explain your reasoning. 8.F.1, 8.F.3

Graph A

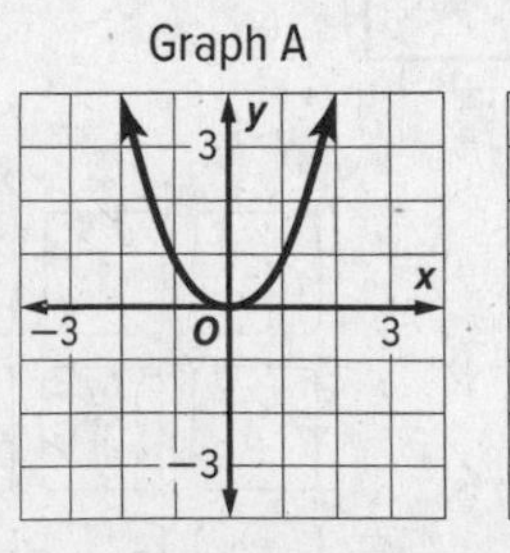

Graph B

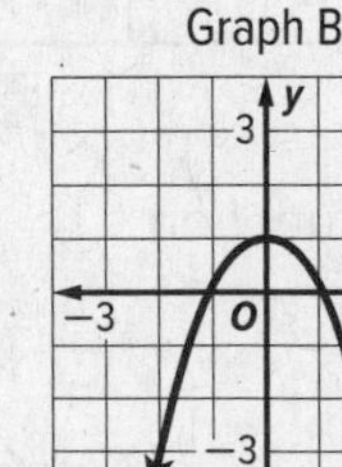

Graph C

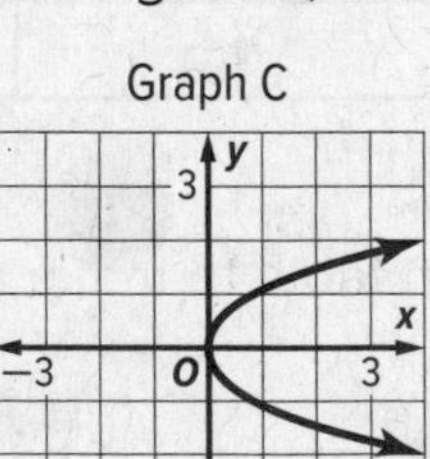

NAME ______________________ DATE __________ PERIOD ________ SCORE ________

Chapter 5 Test

1. Lines a and b are parallel and cut by the transversal c. Find the value of x. Explain how you found your answer. Then label the degree measures of the six unlabeled angles on the diagram. 8.G.5

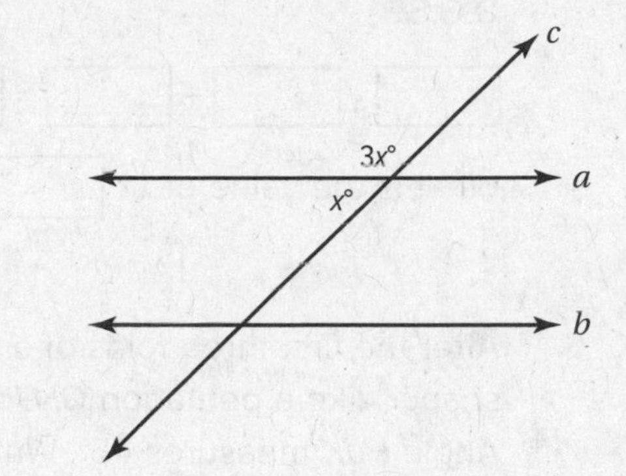

[ ]

2. A 41-foot ladder is leaning against a building. The bottom of the ladder is 8 feet from the base of the building. Write an equation that could be used to find x, the height in feet the ladder reaches on the building. To the nearest foot, how high does the ladder reach on the building? 8.G.7, 8.EE.2

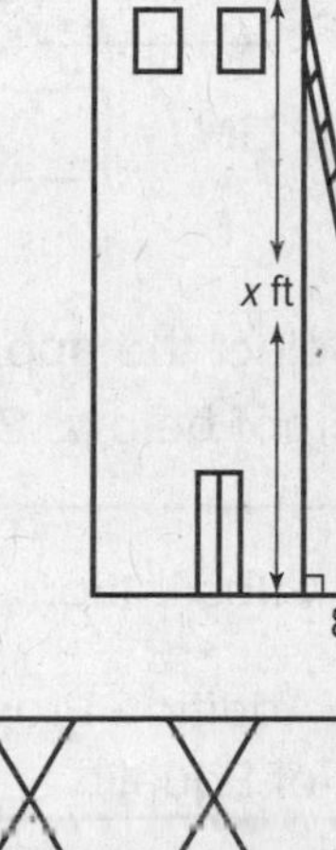

Equation: [ ] + [ ] = [ ]

Height: [ ]

3. Kaylee is using two different shapes of tiles to cover her kitchen floor, as shown. 8.G.5

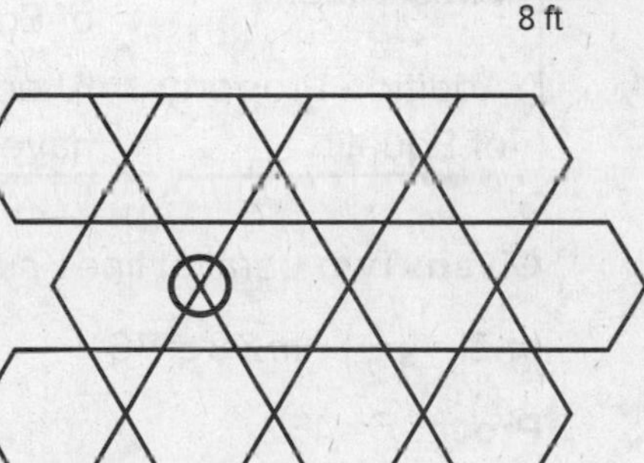

Part A: Write the correct values to complete the equations to find x and z, the degree measures of the interior angles of the two kinds of tiles.

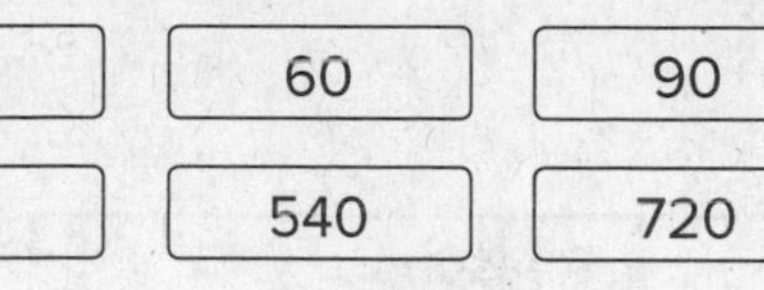

3	6	60	90
120	180	540	720

Equilateral Triangle:

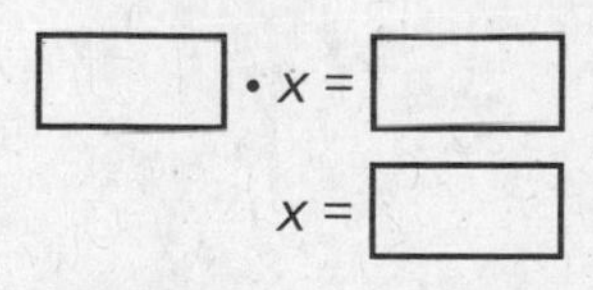

[ ] • x = [ ]

x = [ ]

Regular Hexagon:

[ ] • z = [ ]

z = [ ]

Part B: What is the sum of the degree measures of the angles at the circled vertex? Explain how you know.

[ ]

4. A triangular flower bed has the angle measures shown. Write values to complete the equation to find the value of x. 8.G.5

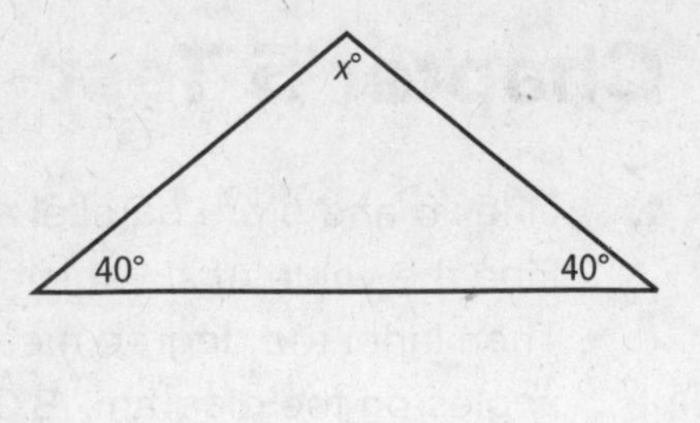

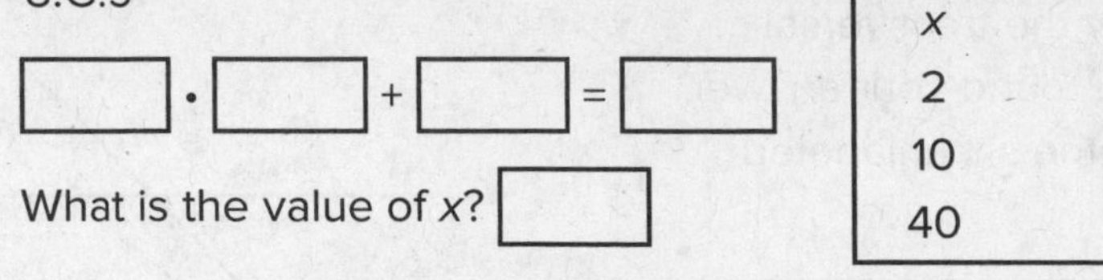

What is the value of x? ☐

5. After the first three folds of a paper airplane design, the paper is shaped like a pentagon $GHJKL$. Angles GHJ and LKJ are congruent. Angle HJK measures 45°. Write the correct measures to complete the equation to find x, the measure of angle GHJ. 8.G.5

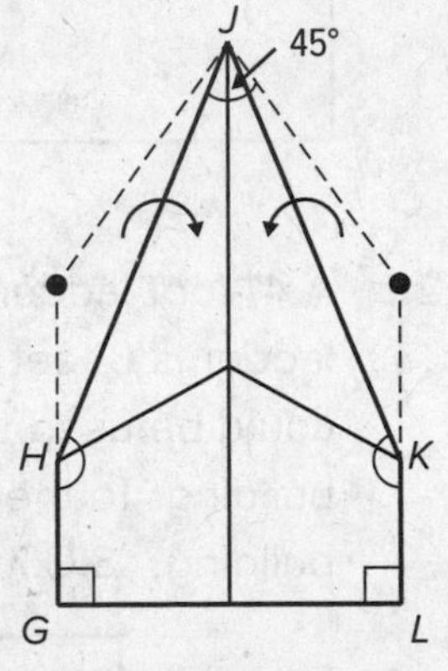

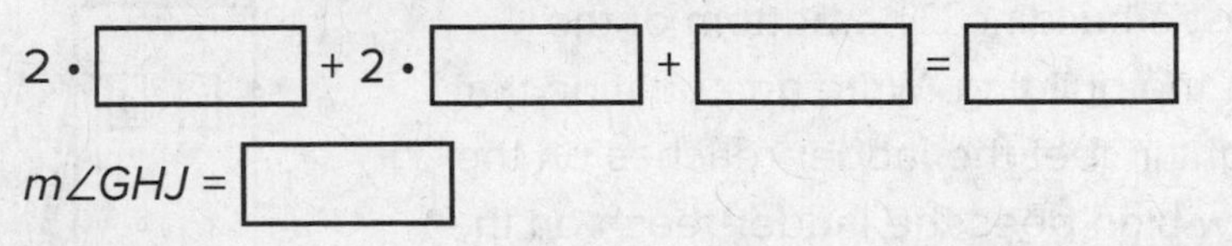

$m\angle GHJ =$ ☐

6. Select the appropriate reason for each statement of the geometric proof below. 8.G.5, 8.G.6

Substitution	Multiplication Property of Equality	Alternate exterior angles have equal measures.
Addition Property of Equality	Alternate interior angles have equal measures.	Vertical angles have equal measures.

Given: Two parallel lines cut by a transversal,
$m\angle 1 = \left(\frac{x}{2}\right)^{\circ}$, $m\angle 8 = 76°$

Prove: $x = 152$

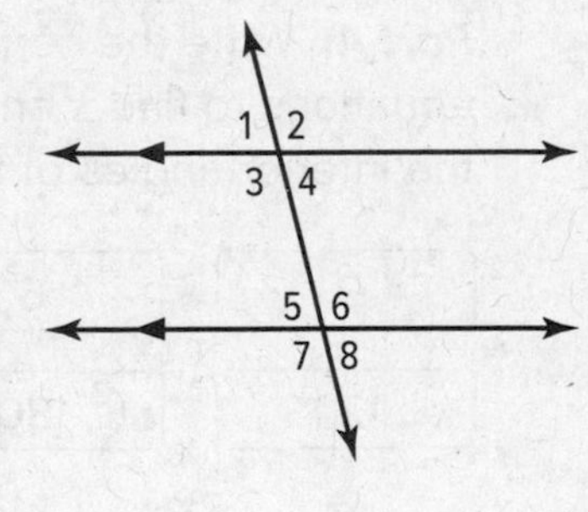

Proof:

Statements	Reasons
1. $m\angle 1 = \left(\frac{x}{2}\right)^{\circ}$, $m\angle 8 = 76°$	Given
2. $m\angle 1 = m\angle 8$	
3. $\frac{x}{2} = 76$	
4. $x = 152$	

7. Aliyah drew a right triangle with sides *a*, *b*, and *c*, as shown. She then drew squares on grid paper, cut them out, and placed them beside the legs of the triangle. Write words or numbers to describe the figure she should draw and place beside the hypotenuse in order to demonstrate the Pythagorean Theorem. 8.G.6

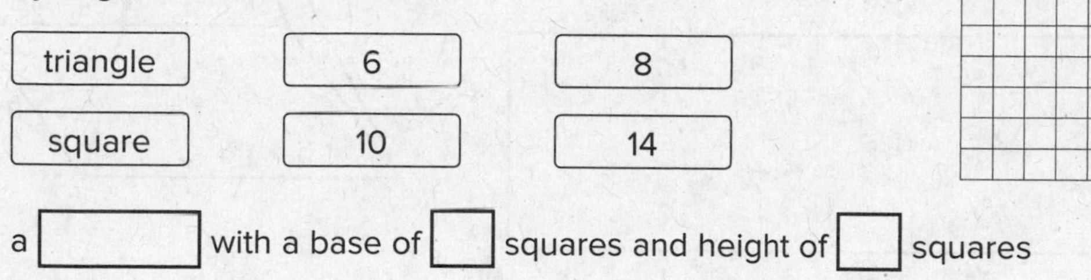

a ☐ with a base of ☐ squares and height of ☐ squares

8. Select whether each line segment has a length of 25 units. 8.G.8

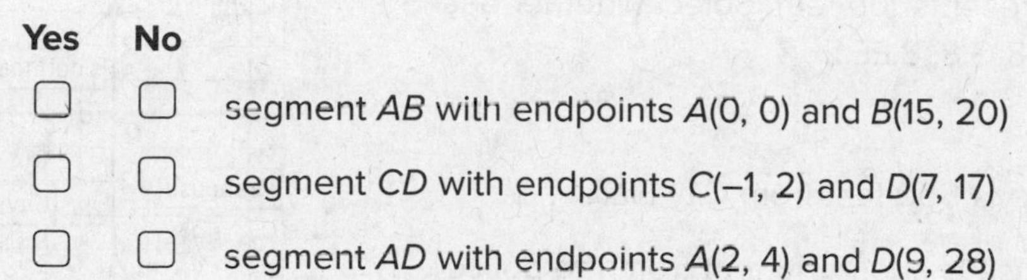

Yes	No	
☐	☐	segment *AB* with endpoints *A*(0, 0) and *B*(15, 20)
☐	☐	segment *CD* with endpoints *C*(–1, 2) and *D*(7, 17)
☐	☐	segment *AD* with endpoints *A*(2, 4) and *D*(9, 28)

9. The shape of Colorado is almost a rectangle. Estimate the land area in square miles. Explain your answer. 8.G.7

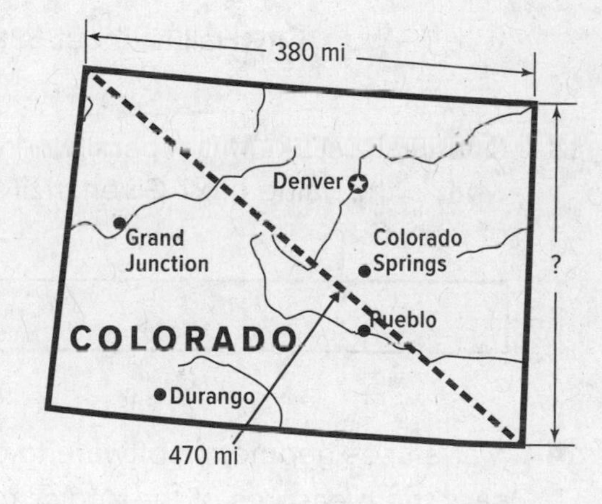

10. Nadia draws a right triangle with two side lengths measuring 3 centimeters and 4 centimeters. She says that there is only one right triangle that can be drawn with these conditions. Is she correct? Justify your response with specific examples. 8.G.7

11. Abdul built a pyramid for a world history project. The height of the pyramid is 9 inches. The distance from the center of its base to vertex *F* is 6 inches. What is the length of segment *AF*? Round your answer to the nearest tenth of an inch. Explain how you found your answer. 8.G.7, 8.EE.2

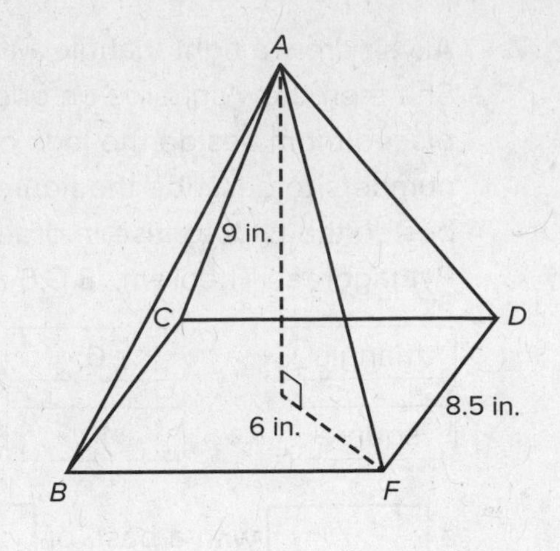

12. The points on the coordinate plane show different locations in a town center. Each unit represents 100 feet. Select whether each statement is true or false. 8.G.8, 8.EE.2

Police Station
Courthouse
Firehouse
City Hall

True	False	
☐	☐	The firehouse is 500 feet from City Hall.
☐	☐	The courthouse is about 316 feet from the police station.
☐	☐	City Hall is about 538 feet from the police station.

13. Quadrilateral *JKLM* is a parallelogram. Given $m\angle JML = (x - 20)°$, what is the value of *x*? Given $m\angle NKL = 4y°$, what is the value of *y*? 8.G.5

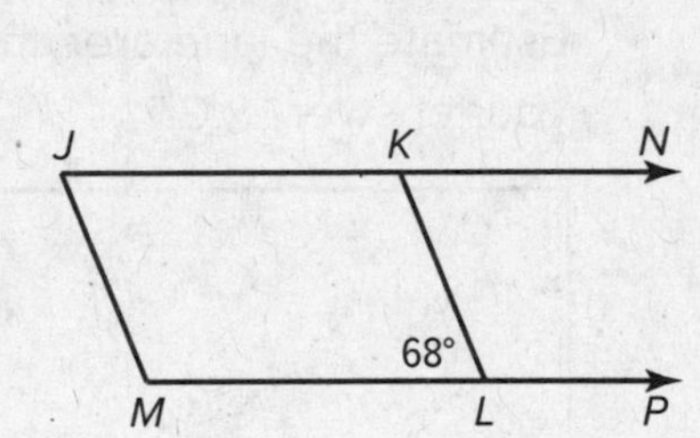

14. Marta uses geometry software to draw a triangle. She says the measures of the angles of her triangle are in the ratio 2:3:4. What are the measures of the angles? Explain how you found your answer. 8.G.5

15. Cole found *BC*. His work is shown. 8.G.7

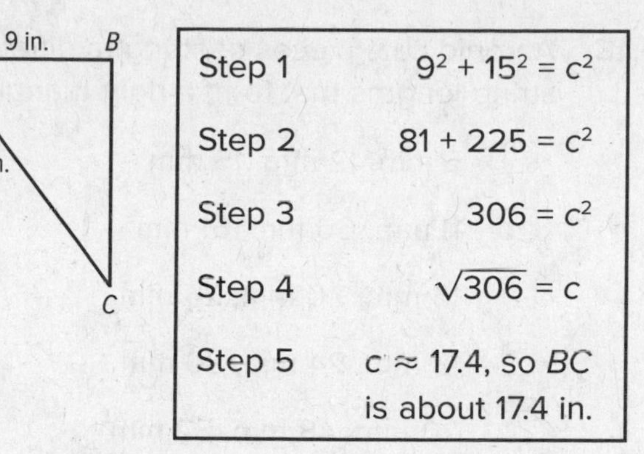

Step 1	$9^2 + 15^2 = c^2$
Step 2	$81 + 225 = c^2$
Step 3	$306 = c^2$
Step 4	$\sqrt{306} = c$
Step 5	$c \approx 17.4$, so *BC* is about 17.4 in.

Part A: Circle the first step in which his work shows an error.

Part B: Find the correct length of side *BC*.

BC = 

Part C: Describe Cole's error(s) and how he should correct his work.

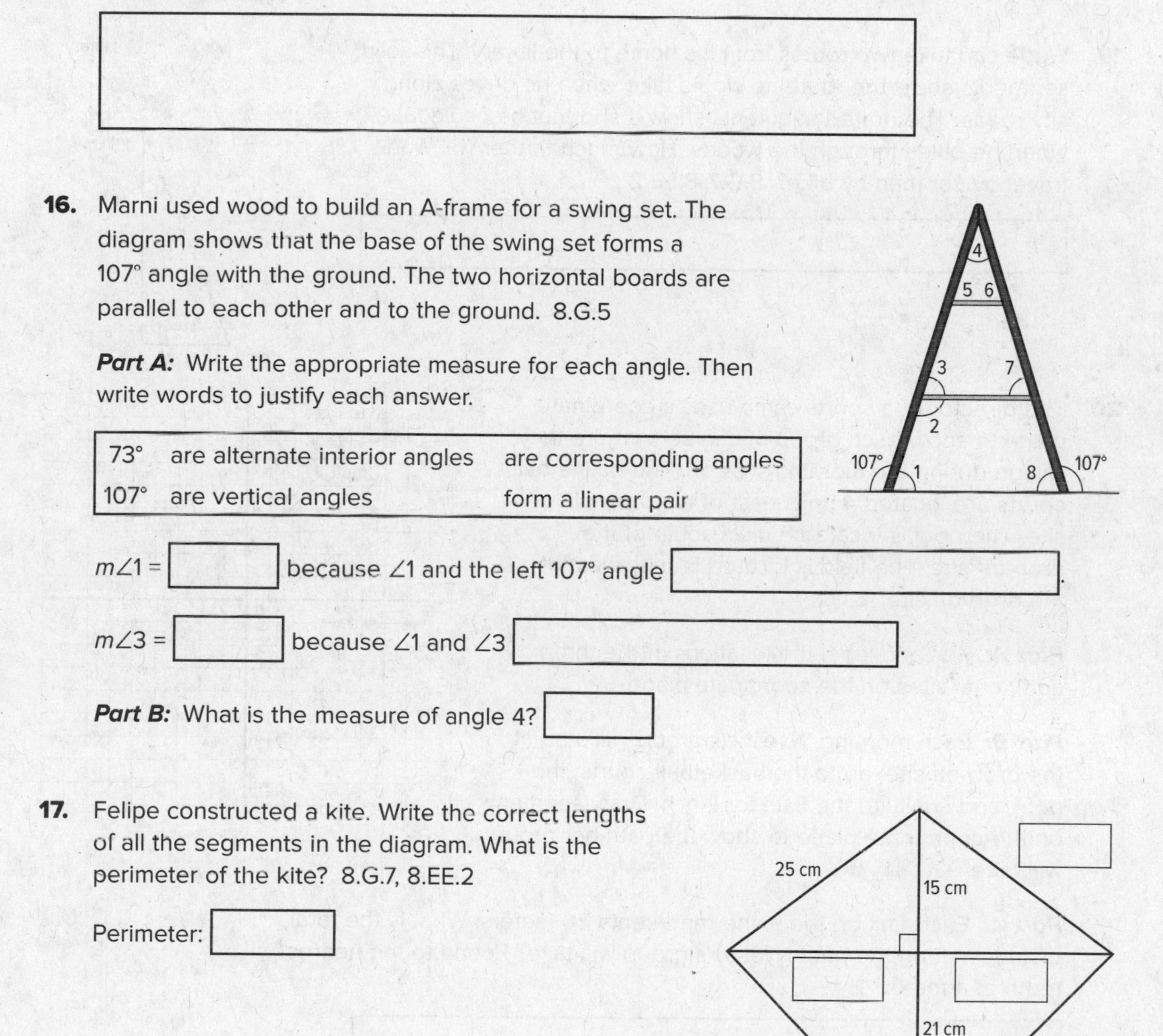

16. Marni used wood to build an A-frame for a swing set. The diagram shows that the base of the swing set forms a 107° angle with the ground. The two horizontal boards are parallel to each other and to the ground. 8.G.5

Part A: Write the appropriate measure for each angle. Then write words to justify each answer.

73°	are alternate interior angles	are corresponding angles
107°	are vertical angles	form a linear pair

$m\angle 1 =$ ☐ because ∠1 and the left 107° angle ☐.

$m\angle 3 =$ ☐ because ∠1 and ∠3 ☐.

Part B: What is the measure of angle 4? ☐

17. Felipe constructed a kite. Write the correct lengths of all the segments in the diagram. What is the perimeter of the kite? 8.G.7, 8.EE.2

Perimeter: ☐

18. Antonio cuts pieces of string to different lengths. Select all of the sets of string lengths that form a right triangle. 8.G.6, 8.G.7

- ☐ 5 mm, 12 mm, 15 mm
- ☐ 11 mm, 60 mm, 61 mm
- ☐ 15 mm, 20 mm, 24 mm
- ☐ 18 mm, 24 mm, 30 mm
- ☐ 20 mm, 48 mm, 52 mm

19. Wade can take two routes from his home to the library. The solid segments show the route he would take when he drives along city roads. The dotted segments show a shortcut he could take when he bikes through the woods. How much farther will Wade travel by car than by bike? 8.G.7, 8.EE.2

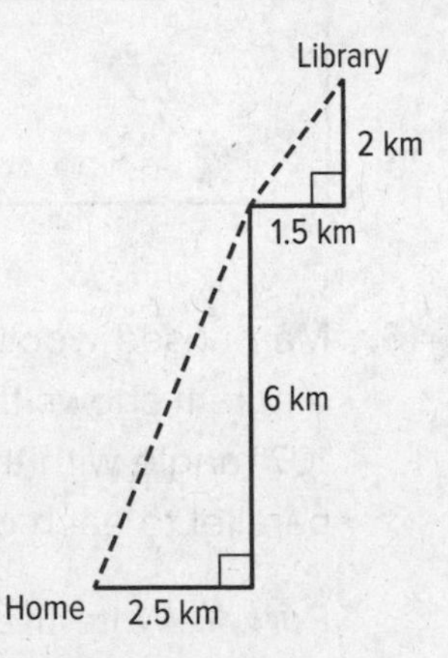

20. The director of a sports camp uses a coordinate plane to show each group of campers where they will go during the morning session. The basketball courts are located 4 units east of the drop-off site. The pool is located 8 units south of the drop-off site. The field is located 5 units west of the drop-off site. 8.G.8

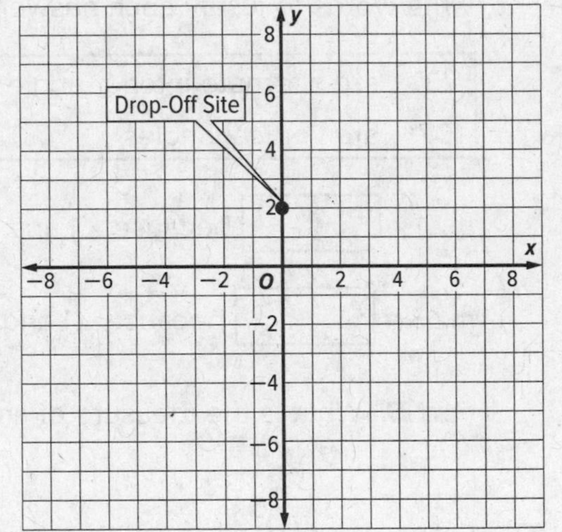

Part A: Plot and label the locations of the three additional sites on the coordinate plane.

Part B: Each morning, Nyesha's group will start at the drop-off site, go to the basketball courts, the pool, and finally to the field for lunch. Draw segments on the coordinate plane to show the path her group will take.

Part C: Each unit on the plane represents 20 meters. What is the total distance along the path Nyesha's group will take? Round to the nearest tenth of a meter.

NAME ______________________ DATE __________ PERIOD ________ SCORE ________

Chapter 6 Test

1. Write the appropriate transformation for each picture. 8.G.1, 8.G.3

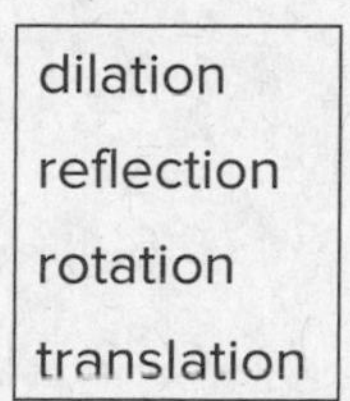

2. Triangle JKL has vertices $J(-1, -1)$, $K(4, 1)$, and $L(5, -4)$. The triangle represents the original location of where an architect drew a playground. 8.G.3

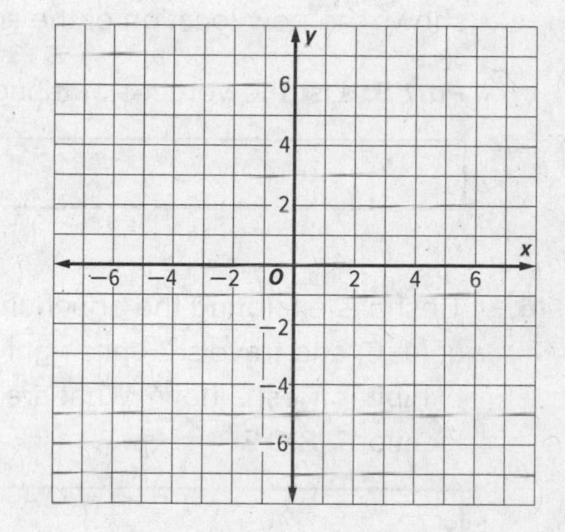

Part A: Graph triangle JKL. Then graph the image of the triangle after it is translated 5 units left and 4 units up to show the new location of the playground.

Part B: List the vertices of triangle $J'K'L'$.

3. Triangle ABC represents the location of a planter in Malcolm's garden. Malcolm translates this triangle 5 units left and 2 units down to show the location of a second planter. The image is triangle $A'B'C'$. Write the word or number to make each statement true. 8.G.1, 8.G.1a, 8.G.1b

acute	obtuse	right
2	3	5

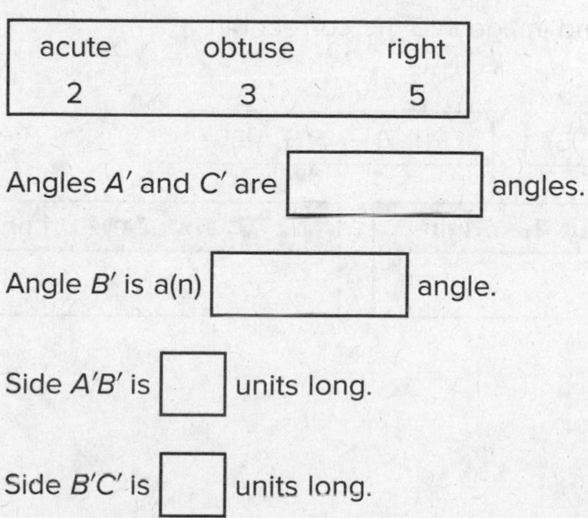

Angles A' and C' are ______ angles.

Angle B' is a(n) ______ angle.

Side $A'B'$ is ______ units long.

Side $B'C'$ is ______ units long.

4. The coordinates of a point and its image after a reflection are given. Select the correct line of reflection for each. 8.G.3

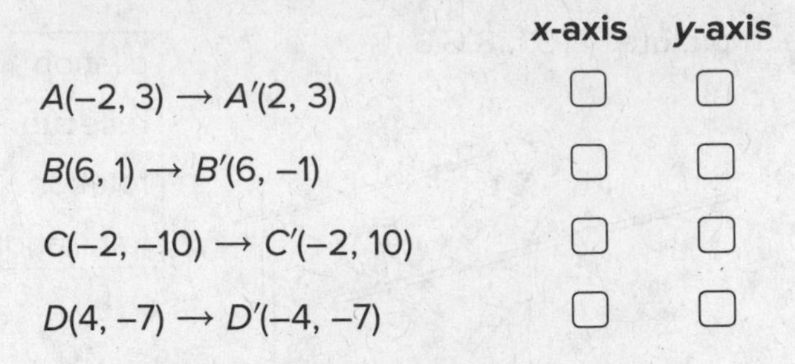

	x-axis	*y*-axis
$A(-2, 3) \rightarrow A'(2, 3)$	☐	☐
$B(6, 1) \rightarrow B'(6, -1)$	☐	☐
$C(-2, -10) \rightarrow C'(-2, 10)$	☐	☐
$D(4, -7) \rightarrow D'(-4, -7)$	☐	☐

5. Ms. Summer drew triangle *ABC* to show the current location of a roped-off sculpture at a museum. 8.G.3

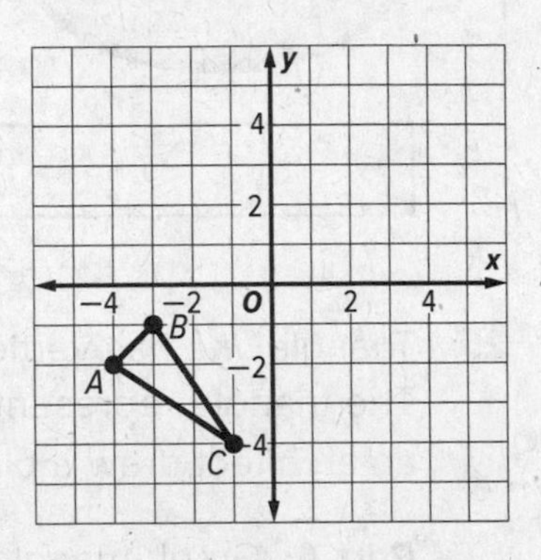

Part A: Reflect the triangle over the *x*-axis and then translate it 3 units to the right and 1 unit up to form triangle $A''B''C''$. This shows the new location of the sculpture.

Part B: List the vertices of triangle $A''B''C''$.

6. Tiesha is exploring the aquarium. She is at the jellyfish exhibit at (4, 6) and travels 2 units right and 4 units down. At what exhibit is Tiesha now? What are the coordinates of Tiesha's new location? 8.G.3

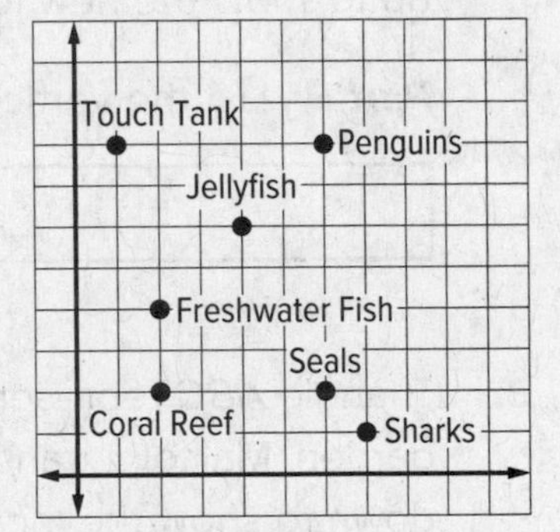

7. The coordinates of a point and its image after a single clockwise rotation about the origin are given. Sort each point and image into the correct bin to show the degree of rotation. 8.G.3

$P(-3, 2) \rightarrow P'(-2, -3)$ | $Q(-4, -5) \rightarrow Q'(4, 5)$ | $R(1, 7) \rightarrow R'(7, -1)$

90° about the origin	180° about the origin	270° about the origin

8. Aaron is experimenting with geometry software. He dilates triangle *DEF* so that the image of point *F* is *F*′(10, 5). 8.G.3

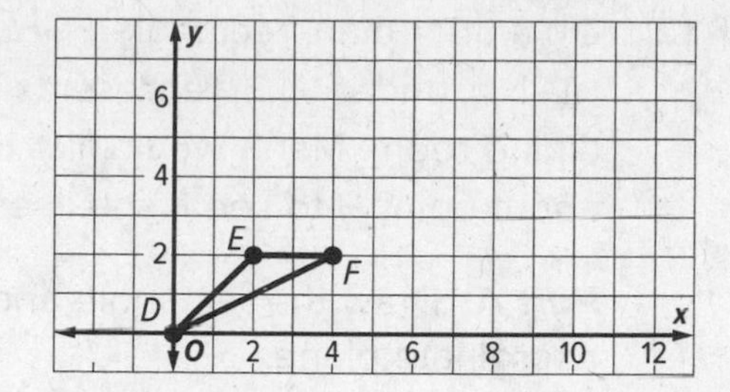

Part A: Draw the image, triangle *D*′*E*′*F*′.

Part B: What is the scale factor of the dilation? Is the dilation a reduction or an enlargement?

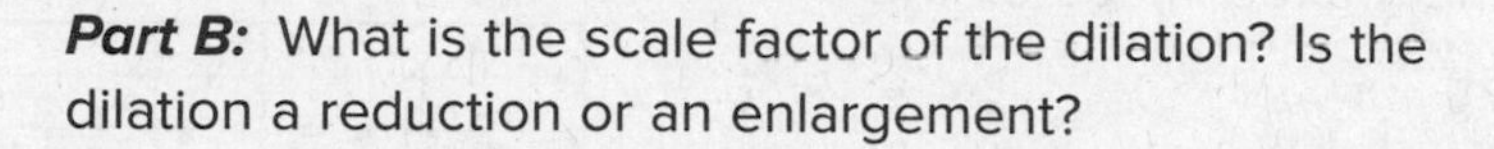

9. Triangle *R*′*S*′*T*′ is the image of triangle *RST* after one or more transformations. Select whether each transformation or sequence of transformations produces triangle *R*′*S*′*T*′. 8.G.3

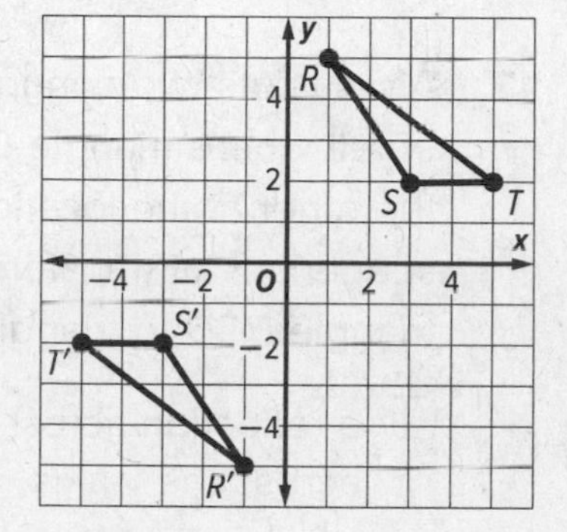

Yes	No	
☐	☐	Triangle *RST* is rotated 180° about the origin.
☐	☐	Triangle *RST* is reflected across the *y*-axis and then reflected across the *x*-axis.
☐	☐	Triangle *RST* is reflected across the *y*-axis and then translated 4 units down.

10. Julissa drew a partial cloverleaf with point *C* at (2, 2) on the coordinate plane. She then rotated this figure 90°, 180°, and 270° clockwise about the origin to complete the design. Plot and label the locations of points *C*′, *C*″, and *C*‴. 8.G.3

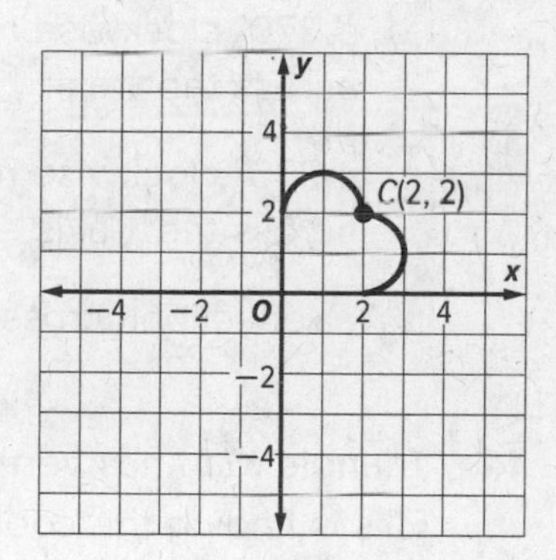

11. Darren draws triangle *XYZ* with vertices *X*(−4, −4), *Y*(−2, 6), and *Z*(10, 2). He then translates it by (*x* + 8, *y* − 12) to form triangle *X*′*Y*′*Z*′. Write symbols and numbers to show how Darren could translate triangle *X*′*Y*′*Z*′ so it completely covers the original triangle *XYZ*. 8.G.3

translation: (*x* ☐☐, *y* ☐☐)

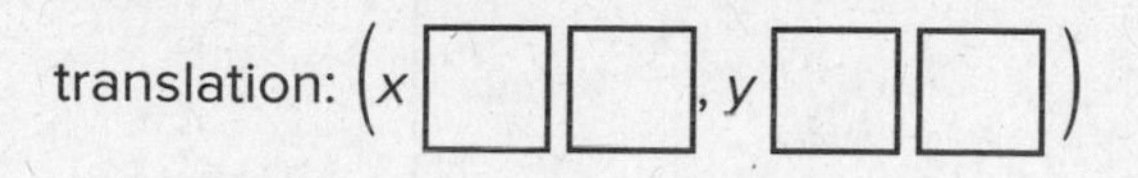

12. On a floor plan, rectangle $FGHJ$ with vertices $F(-5, 3)$, $G(-5, 1)$, $H(-1, 1)$, and $J(-1, 3)$ represents the location of a table in Marta's dining room. Marta would like to rotate the table 90° clockwise about point H to see if she likes the new placement. 8.G.1, 8.G.3

Part A: Draw the rectangle and the rotated image on the coordinate plane.

Part B: List the vertices of the corners of the rotated table.

13. Alyssa cuts two congruent pieces of felt. She glues one piece of felt where triangle BCD is located. She moves and glues the other at the location of triangle $B'C'D'$. Select all of the sequences of transformations that Alyssa could use to move triangle BCD to triangle $B'C'D'$. 8.G.3

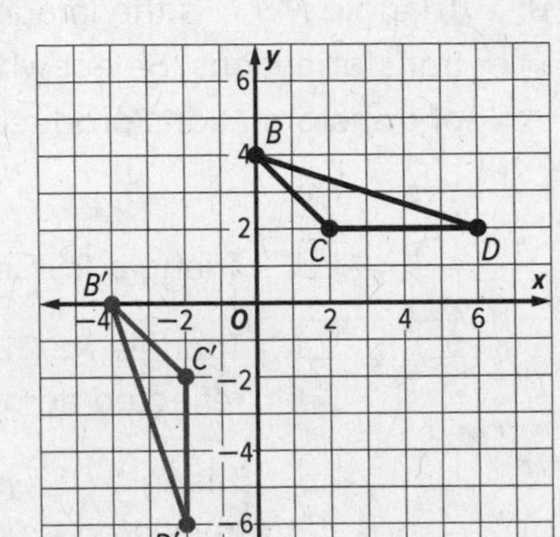

- ☐ a reflection across the x-axis followed by a reflection across the y-axis
- ☐ a 90° clockwise rotation about the origin followed by a reflection across the y-axis
- ☐ a 270° clockwise rotation about the origin followed by a reflection across the y-axis
- ☐ a 270° clockwise rotation about the origin followed by a reflection across the x-axis
- ☐ a reflection across the y-axis followed by a translation of 2 units down

14. Triangle KLM has vertices $K(4, 3)$, $L(6, -1)$, and $M(-1, 0)$. Ellis is finding the coordinates of the image of triangle KLM after a reflection across the x-axis. His answers are shown. Circle the part(s) of his answer that contain errors. Then describe and correct the error(s). 8.G.3

$K(4, 3) \rightarrow K'(4, -3)$

$L(6, -1) \rightarrow L'(6, 1)$

$M(-1, 0) \rightarrow M'(1, 0)$

15. Parallelogram *FGHJ* shows the location of several parking spaces that were painted in a parking lot. Bernardo translates this parallelogram 3 units to the right and 4 units up to show where several other parking spaces will be painted. Select whether each statement about the new parallelogram is true or false. 8.G.1, 8.G.1a, 8.G.1c

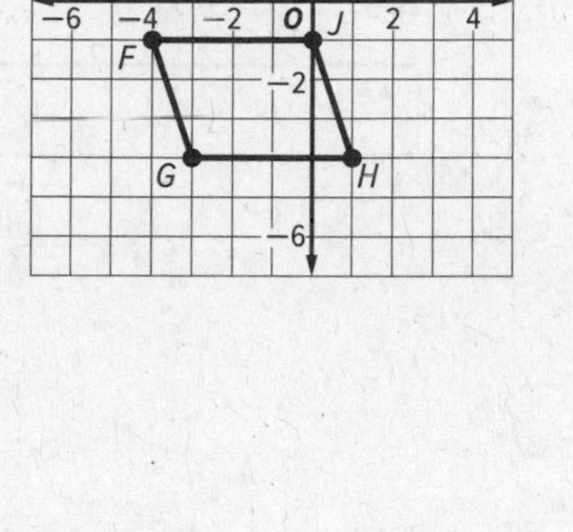

True	False	
☐	☐	Side $F'J'$ is longer than side FJ.
☐	☐	Side $G'H'$ has the same length as side FJ.
☐	☐	Lines $F'G'$ and $H'J'$ are parallel.
☐	☐	Lines $F'J'$ and $G'H'$ are parallel.

16. Triangle *PQR* shows a pennant Brittany designed and placed on her wall in support of her school's baseball team. She wants to enlarge the pennant by a scale factor of 2, with (0, 0) as the center of dilation, and then move it 7 units higher on her wall. 8.G.3

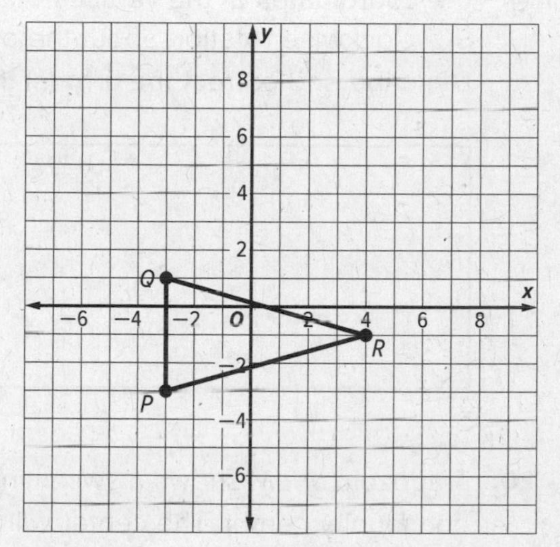

Part A: Graph triangle $P''Q''R''$ to show the new size and location of the pennant.

Part B: List the coordinates of the vertices of the image.

17. Nick will move a storage bin from its current location to the new location shown on the coordinate plane. Describe how Nick could do this, using transformations. 8.G.3

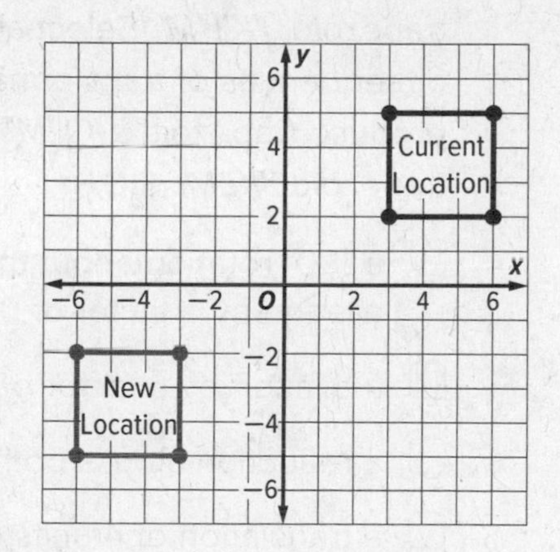

Using One or More Translations	
Using One or More Reflections	
Using One or More Rotations	

18. Cami drew part of a jet on the coordinate plane and then reflected what she had drawn over the y-axis to complete the drawing. Identify the coordinates of the images of points A, B, and C. 8.G.3

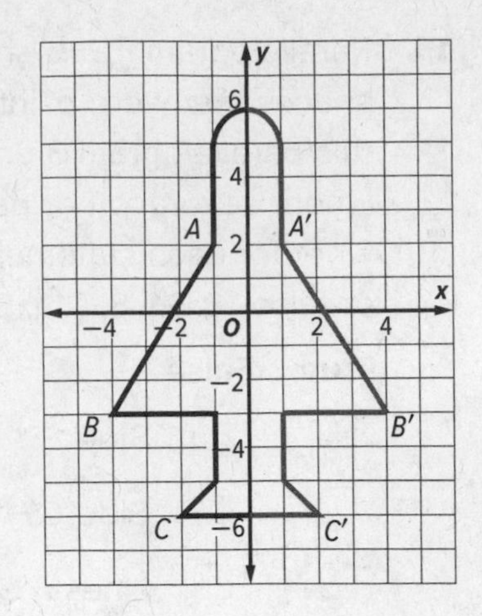

19. Triangle STV has vertices $S(-2, 5)$, $T(2, -4)$, and $V(7, 3)$. Mia found the coordinates of the vertices of the image of triangle STV after a 90° clockwise rotation about the origin. Her answers are shown. Describe and correct the error(s) that Mia made. 8.G.3

$S(2, 5) \rightarrow S'(-5, 2)$

$T(2, -4) \rightarrow T'(4, 2)$

$V(7, 3) \rightarrow V'(-3, 7)$

20. Trapezoid $JKLM$ shows a swimming pool at a community center. The center will build a second children's swimming pool, represented by trapezoid $J'K'L'M'$. Select all of the transformations or sequences of transformations that would produce trapezoid $J'K'L'M'$ when applied to trapezoid $JKLM$. 8.G.3

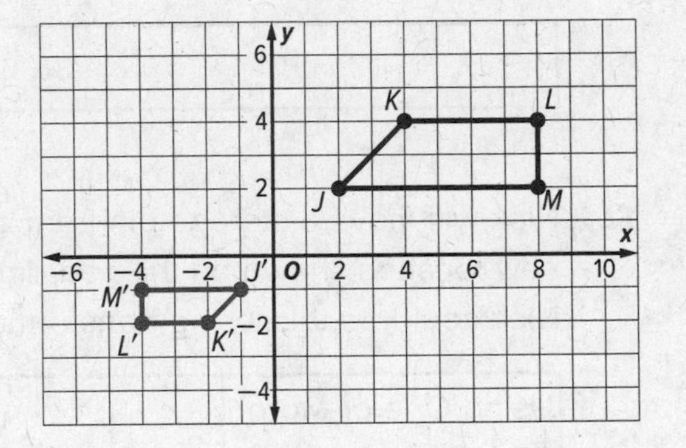

- ☐ a 180° rotation about the origin followed by a dilation by a factor of 0.5
- ☐ a dilation by a factor of 0.5 followed by a 180° rotation about the origin
- ☐ a reflection across both axes followed by a dilation by a factor of 2
- ☐ a translation of 4 units down and 6 units to the left followed by a dilation by a factor of 2
- ☐ a dilation by a factor of −0.5

NAME ______________________ DATE ____________ PERIOD ________ SCORE ________

Chapter 7 Test

1. Agustín is using pattern blocks to create a design. Trapezoids *A* and *B* are congruent, and trapezoid *A* is the preimage of trapezoid *B*. Describe possible transformations he could have used. 8.G.1, 8.G.2

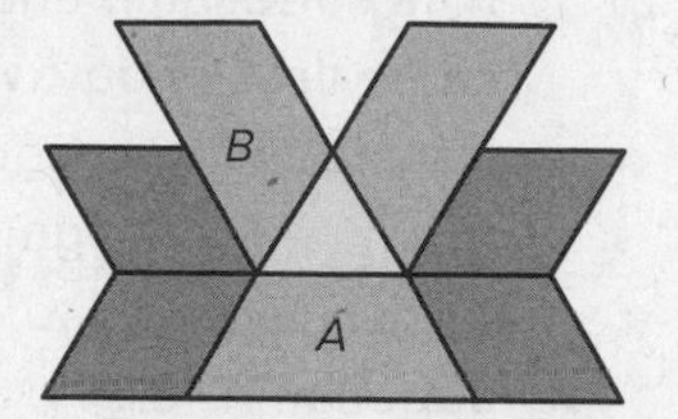

2. Po-ning uses computer software to reflect the right triangle *JKL* across line *KL*. Select all of the statements that must be true of Po-ning's figures. 8.G.1, 8.G.1a, 8.G.2

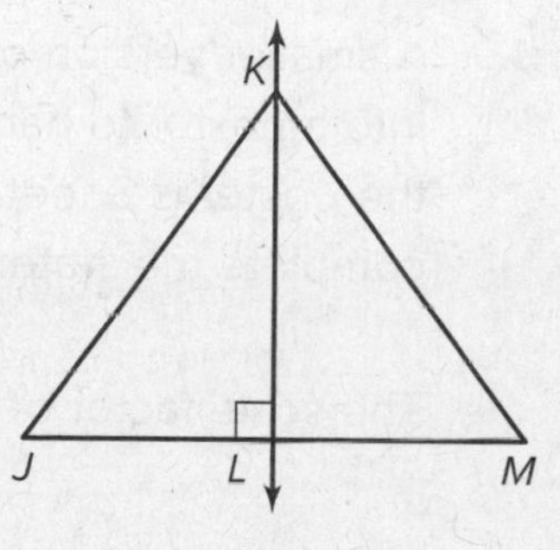

- ☐ $\Delta JKL \cong \Delta MKL$
- ☐ $\overline{JL} \cong \overline{ML}$
- ☐ $\overline{KL} \cong \overline{KM}$
- ☐ Triangle *JKM* is an isosceles triangle.

3. Sofia sews 3 rectangular tablecloths. The first measures 70 inches by 90 inches. She enlarges these dimensions by a scale factor of 1.2 to make a second tablecloth. Then she enlarges the dimensions of the second tablecloth by a scale factor of 1.5 to make the third tablecloth. What are the dimensions of the third tablecloth? Are all of the tablecloths similar rectangles? Explain. 8.G.4

4. Quadrilateral *ABCD* is transformed to create a similar quadrilateral *JKLM*. Select whether each statement is true or false. 8.G.4

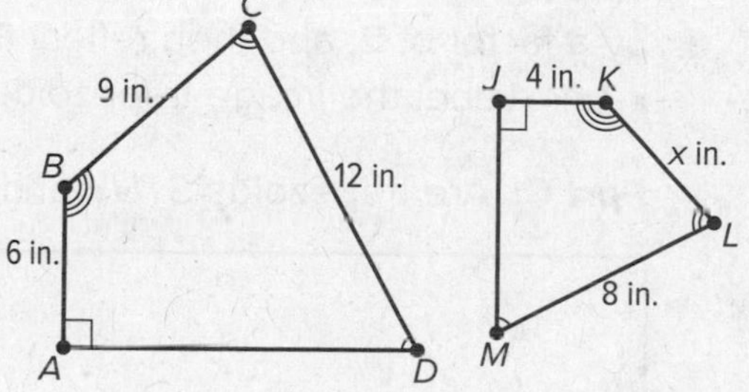

True	False	
☐	☐	Quadrilateral *ABCD* is dilated by a scale factor of $\frac{1}{3}$ to form quadrilateral *JKLM*.
☐	☐	The value of *x* is 6.
☐	☐	Quadrilateral *ABCD* was rotated, translated, and dilated to form quadrilateral *JKLM*.

5. The triangle formed by a 4-foot-tall mailbox and its 6-foot shadow is similar to the triangle formed by a streetlamp and its 21-foot shadow at the same time of day. What scale factor is used to transform the image of the streetlamp triangle from the preimage of the mailbox triangle? Use this scale factor to determine the height h of the streetlamp. 8.G.4

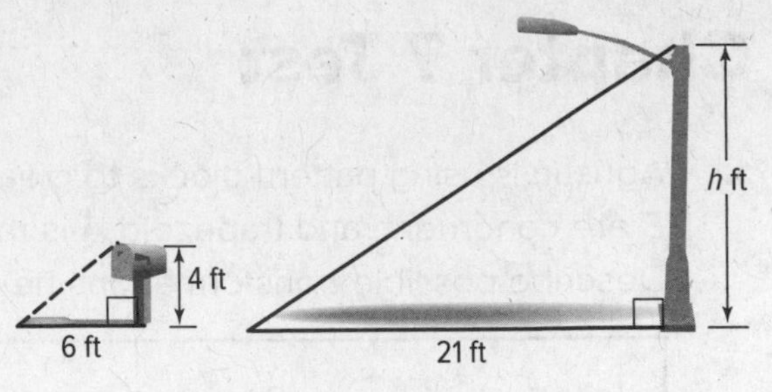

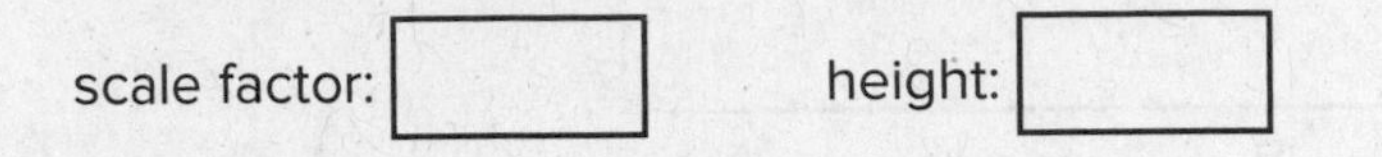

6. A smaller version of the school banner shown is made into a poster to hang during Spirit Week. The perimeter of the poster is 3 feet. Write the appropriate numbers to complete the statements. 8.G.4

$\frac{1}{36}$	$\frac{1}{6}$
$\frac{1}{3}$	$\frac{1}{2}$

The scale factor of the reduction is ☐.

The area of the poster is ☐ square foot.

7. Deion states that trapezoid $NPQR$ must be similar to trapezoid $STUV$ because $\frac{PQ}{TU} = \frac{NR}{SV} = \frac{1}{2}$. 8.G.4

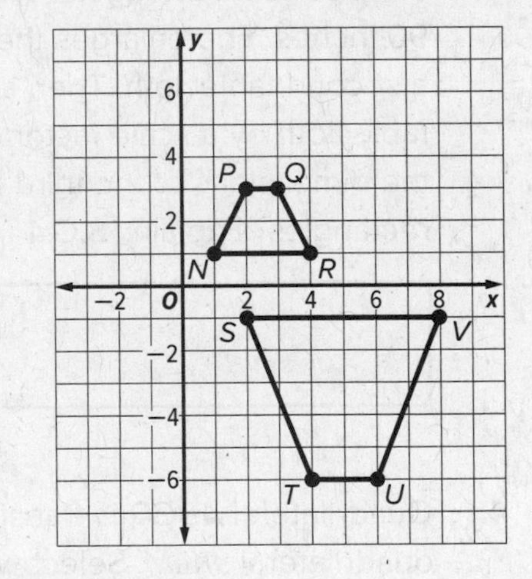

Part A: Explain the flaw in Deion's reasoning.

Part B: On the coordinate plane, dilate trapezoid $NPQR$ by a factor of 2, and then reflect the image across the x-axis. Label the image trapezoid $N'P'Q'R'$.

Part C: Are trapezoids $STUV$ and $N'P'Q'R'$ similar? Explain.

8. The plans for a boat ramp are shown. Find the slope of side $\overline{MN}$ using ΔMNP. Compare the slope of $\overline{MN}$ to the slope of $\overline{MS}$ using ΔMST. How will the slope between any two points on $\overline{MN}$ compare? Explain why. 8.EE.6

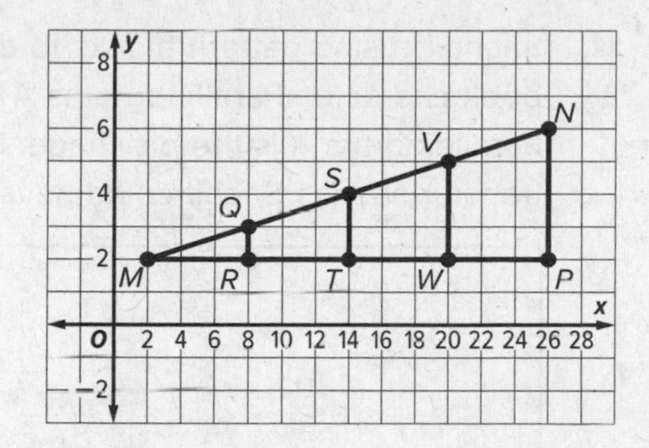

slope of $\overline{MN}$:

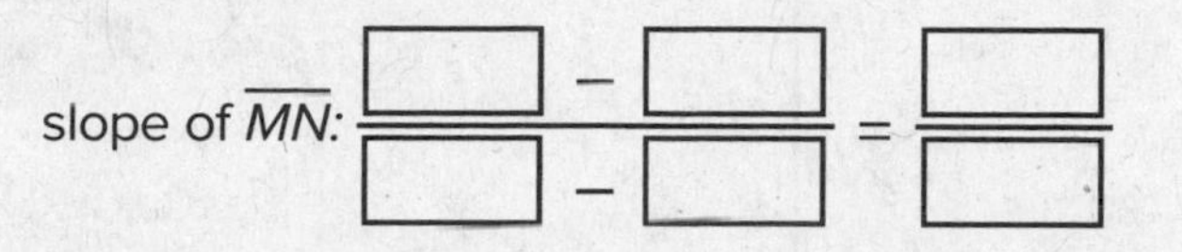

9. Triangle ABC is congruent to triangle DEF. 8.G.1, 8.G.1b, 8.G.2

Part A: Describe possible transformations that could be used to prove $\Delta ABC \cong \Delta DEF$.

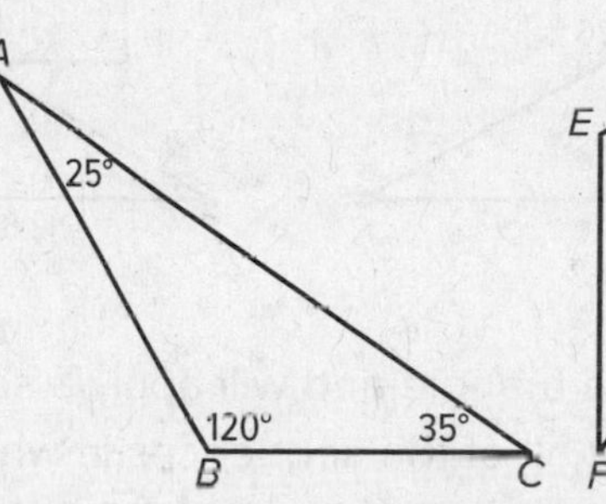

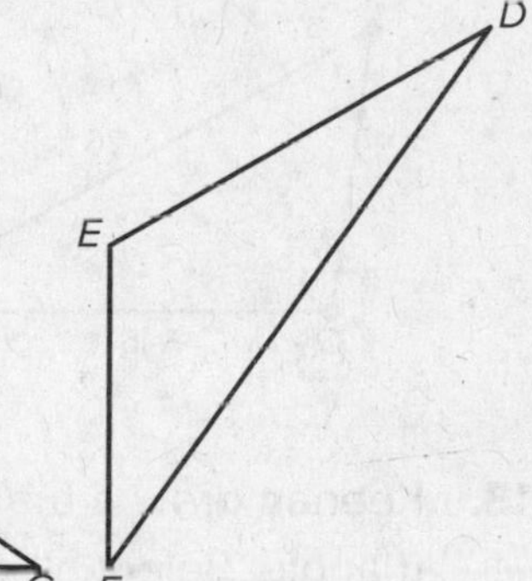

Part B: Write the value of each variable.

$m\angle D = x°$, so $x =$ ☐.

$m\angle E = 2y°$, so $y =$ ☐.

$m\angle F = (z + 15)°$, so $z =$ ☐.

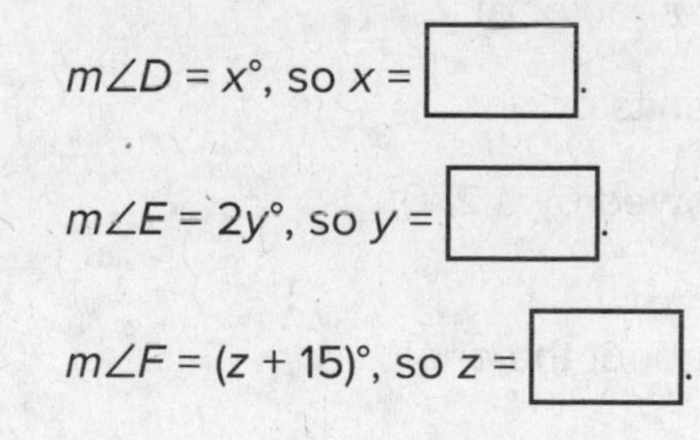

10	25	60	120
20	35	70	240

10. The rectangular sandbox in a city playground has an area of 45 square feet. Mr. Lopez builds a new sandbox for the playground so its dimensions are each $\frac{2}{3}$ those of the original sandbox. What is the area of the new sandbox? 8.G.4

11. Sachit is using pattern blocks to draw a crown for a comic book character. Parallelograms *A* and *B* are congruent. Parallelogram *A* is the preimage. Describe possible transformations Sachit could have used. 8.G.1, 8.G.2

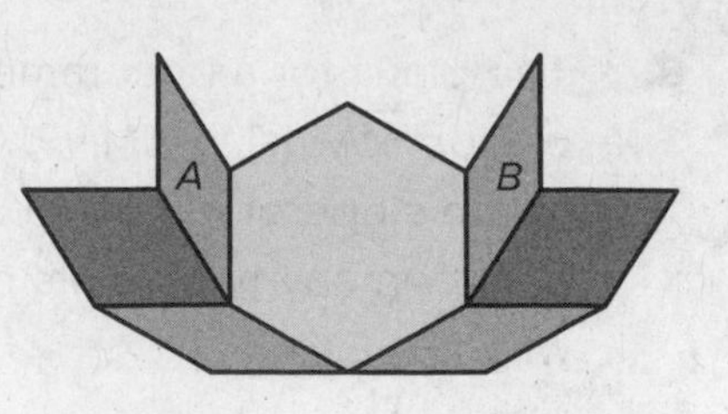

12. Triangle *PQR* is similar to triangle *XYZ*. Write the correct values to label the missing side lengths of triangle *XYZ*. 8.G.4

$7\frac{1}{2}$ ft	$15\frac{1}{2}$ ft	$13\frac{1}{3}$ ft
$26\frac{2}{3}$ ft	15 ft	27 ft

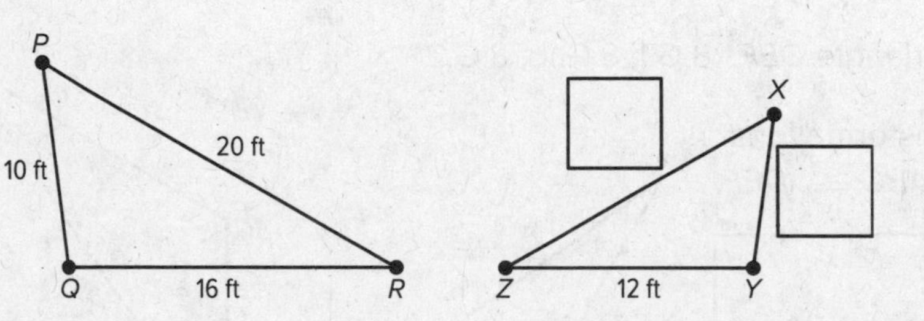

13. Keenan drew a triangle and will apply a sequence of transformations to the triangle. Select all of the sequences in which the image has a perimeter greater than the original triangle. 8.G.2, 8.G.4

- ☐ reflection across the *y*-axis followed by a dilation by a factor of 2
- ☐ dilation by a factor of $\frac{5}{2}$ followed by a translation 3 units down
- ☐ translation 5 units down and 2 units to the right followed by a 270° clockwise rotation about the origin
- ☐ dilation by a factor of $\frac{2}{5}$ followed by a 180° rotation about the origin

14. A land surveyor draws a diagram of a lake. The two triangles are similar. What scale factor is used to produce the triangle crossing the lake from the triangle on the bank? Use the scale factor to determine *x*, the distance across the lake. 8.G.4

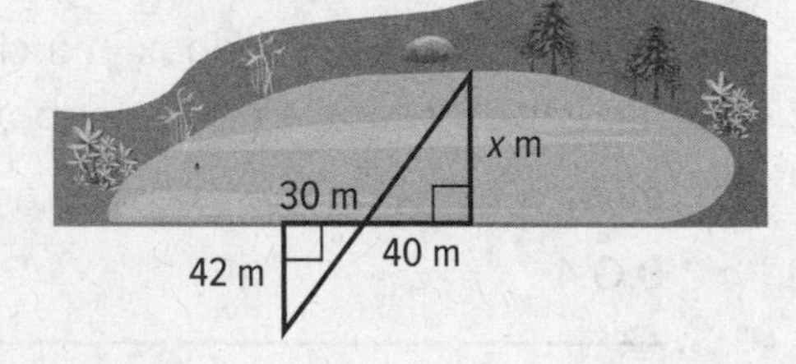

scale factor: ☐ distance: ☐

15. Right triangle ABC has vertices $A(0, 0)$, $B(2, 0)$, and $C(2, 1)$. Any triangle that is similar to ΔABC and has its hypotenuse on line AC is a slope triangle with ΔABC. Select whether each triangle is a slope triangle with ΔABC. 8.EE.6

Yes	No	
☐	☐	triangle ADF with vertices $A(0, 0)$, $D(4, 0)$, and $F(4, 2)$
☐	☐	triangle BGH with vertices $B(2, 0)$, $G(6, 0)$, and $H(6, 4)$
☐	☐	triangle JKL with vertices $J(6, 3)$, $K(12, 3)$, and $H(12, 6)$
☐	☐	triangle MNP with vertices $M(0, 4)$, $N(4, 4)$, and $P(4, 6)$

16. Lines m and p are cut by the transversal n. Determine the value of x. Write the measures of the six angles. 8.G.5

x = ☐

17. Liam and Minya make conjectures about equilateral triangles.

Liam states, "All equilateral triangles are congruent."
Minya states, "All equilateral triangles are similar."

Who is correct—Liam, Minya, neither, or both? Explain why each conjecture is correct or incorrect. 8.G.2, 8.G.4, 8.G.5

18. Triangle *ABC* was dilated, with point *A* as the center of dilation, to form triangle *ADE* as shown. Maddie writes and solves a proportion to find *x*, the length of side *BC*. 8.G.4

Step 1: $\Delta ABC \sim \Delta ADE$

Step 2: $\frac{BC}{DE} = \frac{AB}{BD}$, so $\frac{x}{20} = \frac{6}{9}$.

Step 3: $9 \cdot x = 6 \cdot 20$

Step 4: $9x = 120$

Step 5: $x = \frac{120}{9} = 13\frac{1}{3}$

Part A: Circle the first step in which her work shows an error.

Part B: Find the correct length of side *BC*.

BC = [ ]

Part C: Describe Maddie's error(s) and how she should correct her work.

19. Triangle *EFG* has vertices *E*(–4, 7), *F*(–4, 4), and *G*(0, 4). Triangle *GHJ* has vertices *G*(0, 4), *H*(0, –2), and *J*(8, –2). 8.EE.6

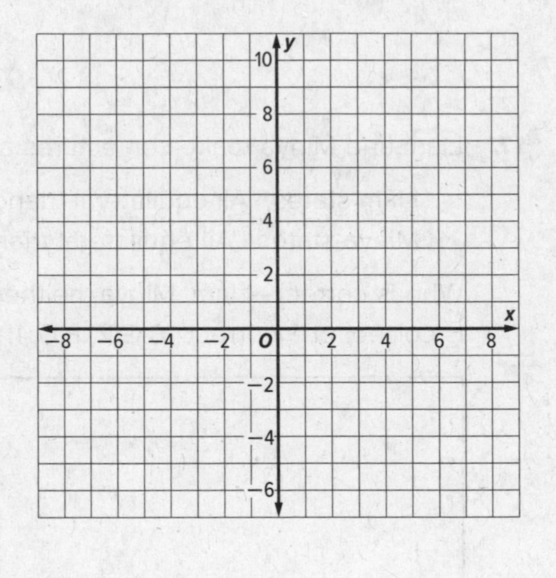

Part A: Draw the triangles and the line that runs through their hypotenuses.

Part B: Find the slope of the line. Then describe the relationship between the slope triangles and the slope of the line.

20. A square photograph has 12-inch-long sides. Martin has the photograph enlarged so its new perimeter is 192 inches. Write the correct numbers to complete each statement. 8.G.4

The perimeter of the enlargement is [ ] times the perimeter of the original.

The area of the enlargement is [ ] times the area of the original.

The area of the enlargement is [ ] square inches.

NAME _______________ DATE _______ PERIOD _______ SCORE _______

Chapter 8 Test

1. Mykelti has two containers—one shaped like a cone and the other shaped like a cylinder. Mykelti fills the cone to the top with 392π cubic inches of water. 8.G.9

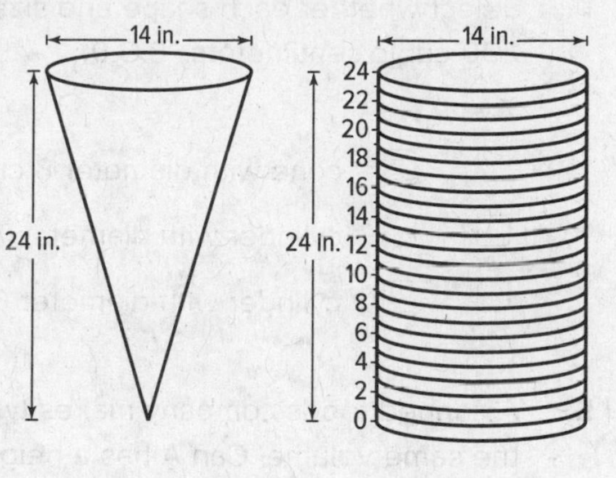

Part A: Mykelti pours all the water from the cone into the cylinder. Shade the cylinder to show the volume of water now in the cylinder.

Part B: Complete each statement.

The water height of the cylinder is ☐ the height of the cone.

The base area of the cylinder is ☐ the base area of the cone.

2. The volume of a playground ball is approximately $523\frac{1}{3}$ cubic centimeters. Write the appropriate numbers or variables to complete the volume formula. Then use the formula to calculate the radius of the ball to the nearest centimeter. 8.G.9

2	5
3	125
4	r
$392\frac{1}{2}$	$523\frac{1}{3}$

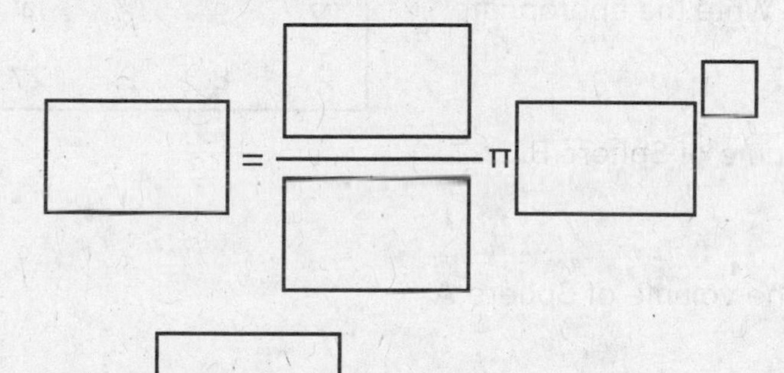

radius: ☐ cm

3. Four cones have heights and radii as shown. Complete the table to order the cones from least to greatest volume. Round to the nearest tenth. 8.G.9

	Cone	Volume (m³)
Least		
Greatest		

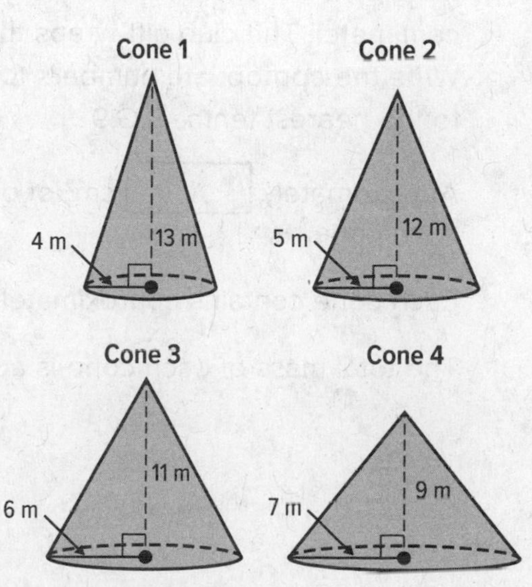

4. Alejandro is buying paper cups in the shapes of cylinders and cones. Select whether each shape and size of cup has a volume of at least 200 cubic centimeters. 8.G.9

Yes	No	
☐	☐	cone with diameter 8 cm, height 8 cm
☐	☐	cylinder with diameter 7 cm, height 6 cm
☐	☐	cylinder with diameter 6 cm, height 7 cm

5. A canned foods company makes two different cylindrical cans, each with the same volume. Can A has a height of 9 centimeters and a radius of 4 centimeters. Can B has a radius of 6 centimeters. What is the height of Can B? Explain how you found your answer. 8.G.9

6. Sphere A has a radius of r feet. Sphere B has a radius of $2r$ feet. Sphere C has a radius of $3r$ feet. Write the appropriate values to complete the statements. 8.G.9

$\frac{1}{27}$	$\frac{1}{9}$	$\frac{1}{8}$	$\frac{1}{4}$
2	8	9	27

The volume of Sphere A is ☐ the volume of Sphere B.

The volume of Sphere C is ☐ times the volume of Sphere A.

7. The environmental club is selling cones of birdseed that can be hung outside. The birdseed weighs about 3.5 grams per cubic centimeter. The club gift-wraps the cones in paper and sells them. Write the appropriate numbers to complete the statements. Round to the nearest tenth. 8.G.9

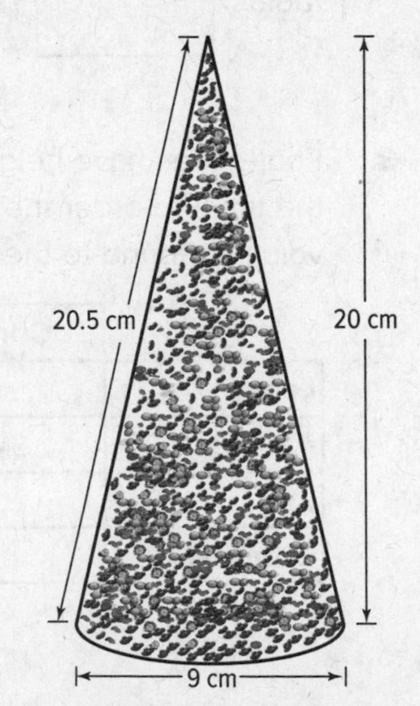

Approximately ☐ cm^2 of paper are needed to cover each cone.

Each cone contains approximately ☐ cm^3 of birdseed.

The total mass of each cone is approximately ☐ kg.

8. Hiro's soccer coach used two cones of different sizes during practice. 8.G.9

Cone 1 | Cone 2

6 in. 3 in. | 6 in. 3 in.

Part A: Hiro says that the two cones have the same volume. Without doing any calculations, do you think he is correct? Explain your reasoning.

Part B: Verify your answer for Part A by calculating the volumes of the cones. Round to the nearest tenth.

volume of Cone 1: ______ volume of Cone 2: ______

9. Louie calculates how many cubic feet of oil the cylindrical drum shown can hold. His work contains an error. 8.G.9

2 ft

3.5 ft

Step 1: $V = \pi(2)^2(3.5)$

Step 2: $V = \pi(4)(3.5)$

Step 3: $V = 14\pi \approx 44.0$

Part A: Circle the first step in which his work shows an error.

Part B: Find the correct volume of the cylinder. Round to the nearest tenth.

Part C: Describe Louie's error(s) and how he should correct his work.

10. Frozen yogurt completely fills the cone and the hemisphere above the cone. Select whether each statement is true or false. 8.G.9

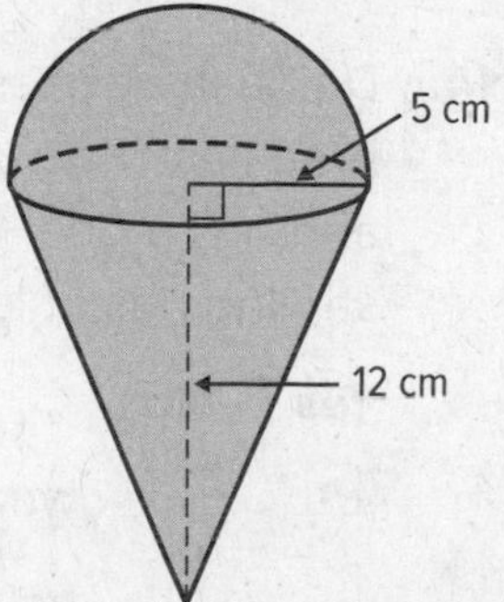

True	False	
☐	☐	The slant height of the cone is 13 cm.
☐	☐	The lateral area of the cone is approximately 188.5 cm².
☐	☐	The volume of frozen yogurt is approximately 576.0 cm³.

11. This net folds into a cylindrical pencil holder with a base diameter of 5 inches and a height of 6 inches. Write the dimensions on the net. Then find the surface area of the cylinder. Round to the nearest tenth. 8.G.9

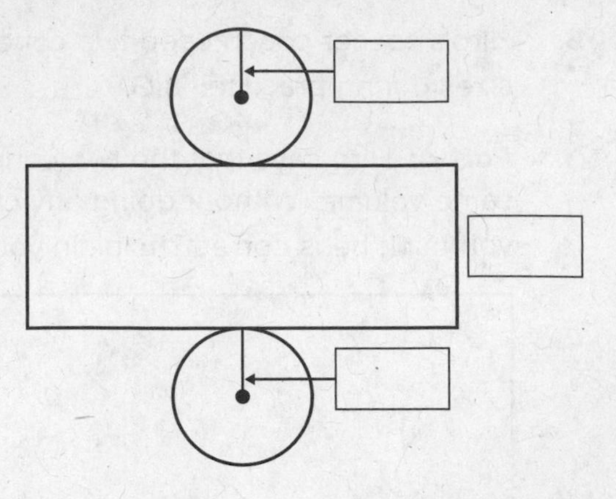

12. Catalina has a cylindrical aquarium. To clean the tank, she removes the fish and rocks. She also removes some water, leaving only 216π cubic inches of water in the tank. 8.G.9

Part A: Shade the aquarium to approximate the volume of water left in the tank.

Part B: After she cleans the tank, Catalina fills it to the top with water. How many cubic inches of water does she add to the tank? Round to the nearest tenth.

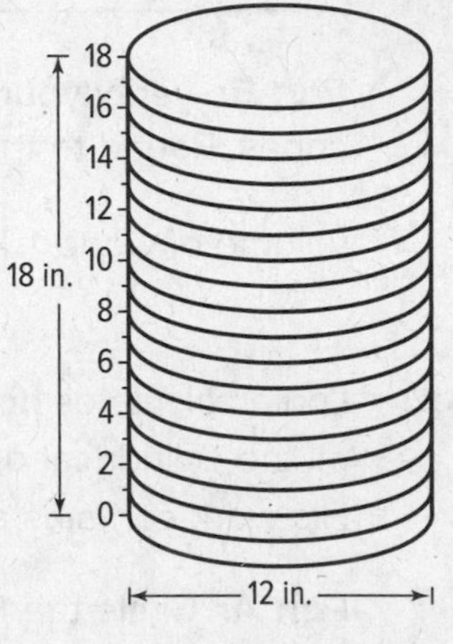

13. Four cylinders have the dimensions shown. Complete the table to order the cylinders from least to greatest volume. Round to the nearest tenth. 8.G.9

	Cylinder	Volume (m³)
Least		
Greatest		

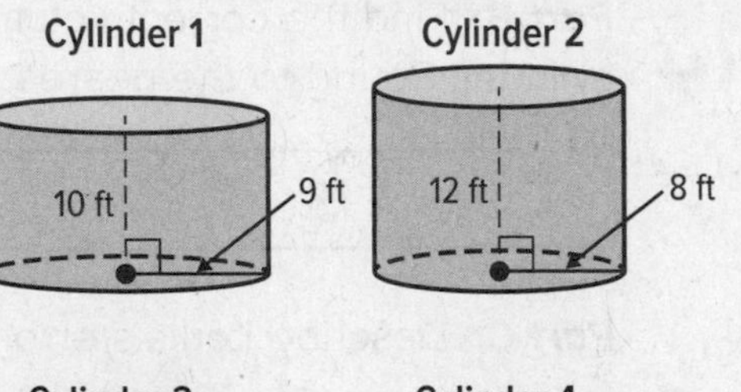

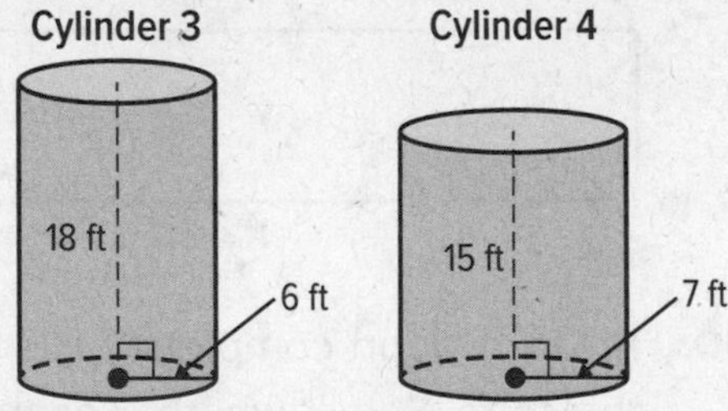

14. Dr. Bach advises his patients to eat grapefruit for breakfast. Each grapefruit is shaped like a sphere and has a peel 1 centimeter thick. Select whether each serving has at least 500 cubic centimeters of fruit. 8.G.9

Yes **No**

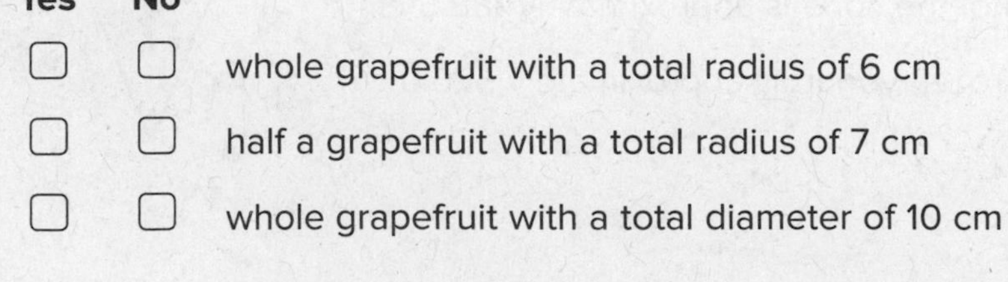

whole grapefruit with a total radius of 6 cm
half a grapefruit with a total radius of 7 cm
whole grapefruit with a total diameter of 10 cm

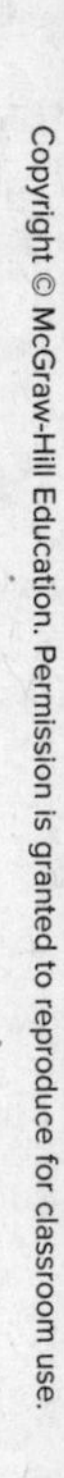

15. A lead pipe has a height of 40 centimeters, a total diameter of 10 centimeters, and an internal diameter of 8 centimeters, as shown. How much lead is contained in one pipe? Round to the nearest tenth. 8.G.9

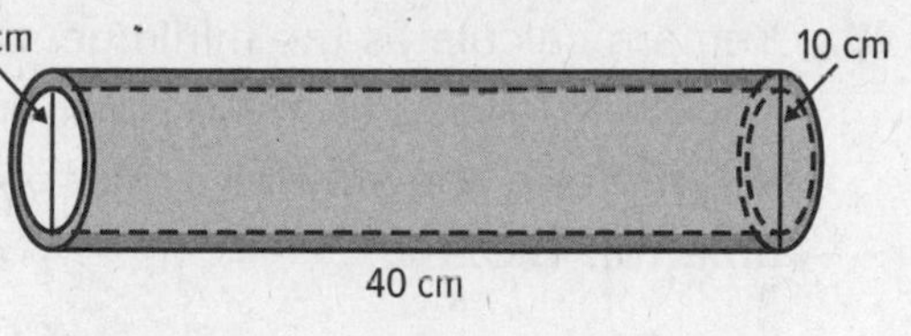

16. A company sells pineapple juice in two sizes—a small individual size and a large family size. Both cans are similar in shape. Write the values to complete the statements. 8.G.9

$\frac{1}{64}$	$\frac{1}{27}$	$\frac{1}{16}$	$\frac{1}{4}$
4	16	27	64

Family Size
32 cm
24 cm
Individual Size
8 cm
6 cm

The height of the large can is ☐ times the height of the small can.

The surface area of the small can is ☐ times the surface area of the large can.

The volume of the large can is ☐ times the volume of the small can.

17. Dominique knows that the volume of a hemisphere is equal to half the volume of a sphere with the same radius. Based on that, she states, "A hemisphere with radius *r* has the same volume as a sphere with a radius one-half as long." Is Dominique's conjecture true or false? Use examples or a counterexample to justify your response. 8.G.9

18. Kamara calculates the minimum amount of paper needed to make a paper cone like the one shown. Her work contains an error. 8.G.9

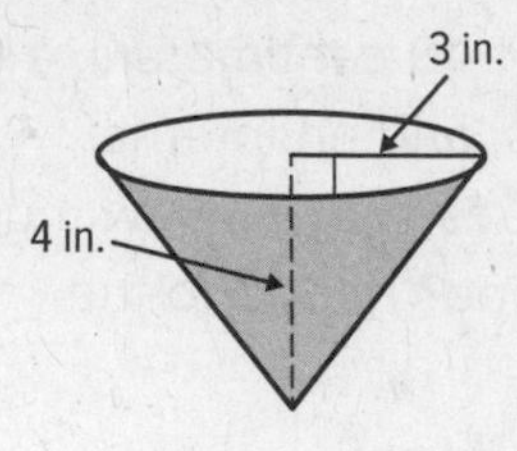

Step 1: $L.A. = \pi r\ell$

Step 2: $L.A. = \pi(3)(4)$

Step 3: $L.A. = 12\pi \approx 37.7$

Part A: Circle the first step in which her work shows an error.

Part B: Find the correct lateral area of the cone. Round to the nearest tenth.

Part C: Describe Kamara's error(s) and how she should correct her work.

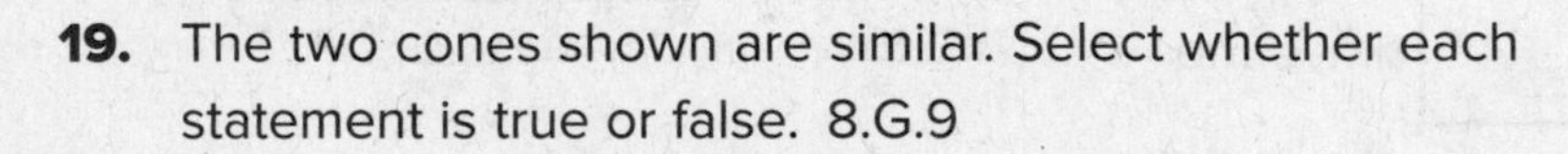

19. The two cones shown are similar. Select whether each statement is true or false. 8.G.9

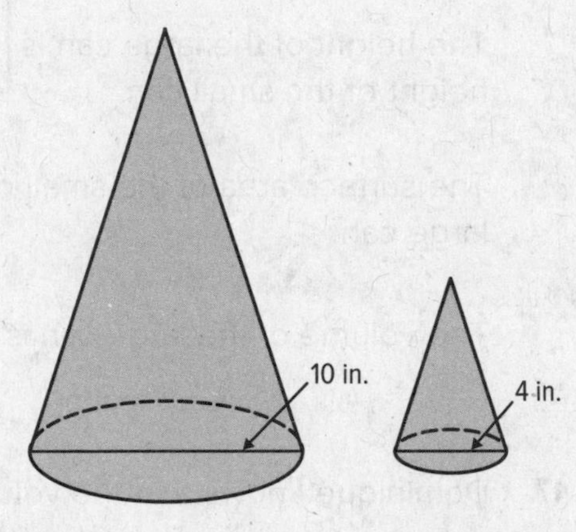

True	False	
☐	☐	The scale factor from the small cone to the large cone is $\frac{5}{2}$.
☐	☐	The surface area of the large cone is $\frac{25}{4}$ times the surface area of the small cone.
☐	☐	The volume of the large cone is $\frac{25}{4}$ the volume of the small cone.

20. A pet store sells a spherical exercise ball for hamsters. The ball fits in the cube-shaped box, touching the top, bottom, and sides of the box. Write values to complete each statement. Round to the nearest tenth. 8.G.9

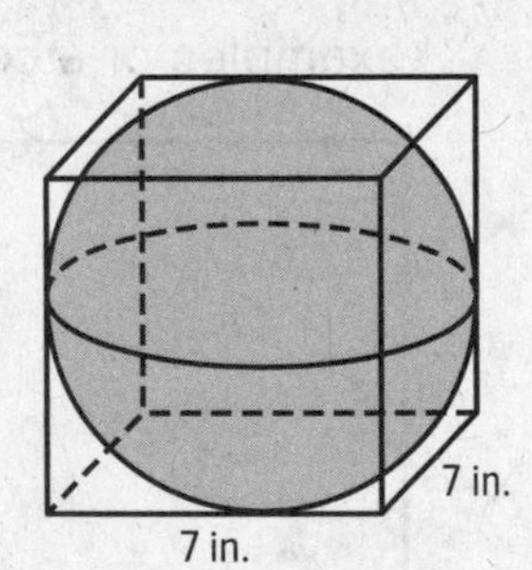

The volume of the box is ☐ in^3.

The volume of the exercise ball is approximately ☐ in^3.

The volume of the empty space in the box is approximately ☐ in^3.

NAME ______________________ DATE ____________ PERIOD ________ SCORE ________

Chapter 9 Test

1. The table shows cost per t-shirt of different-sized t-shirt orders. 8.SP.1

T-Shirts Ordered	100	200	300	400	500
Cost per Shirt ($)	18	17	14	12	8

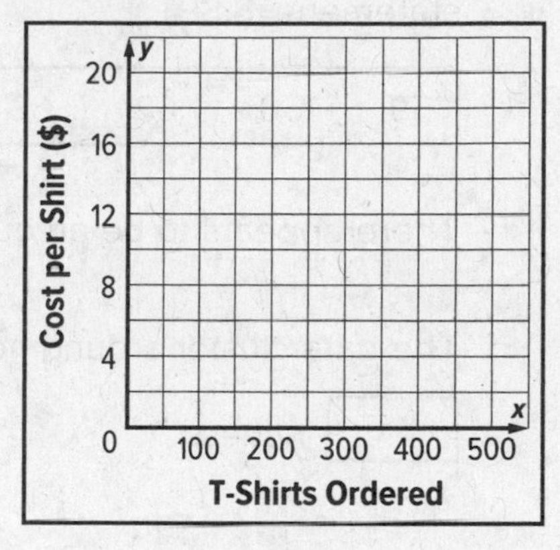

Part A: Construct a scatter plot of the data.

Part B: Describe any patterns in the data.

2. A regional model United Nations was created in 2001. Maggie creates a scatter plot to show the number of students participating in the program from 2001 to 2014. She drew a line of best fit to show the trend. 8.SP.2, 8.SP.3

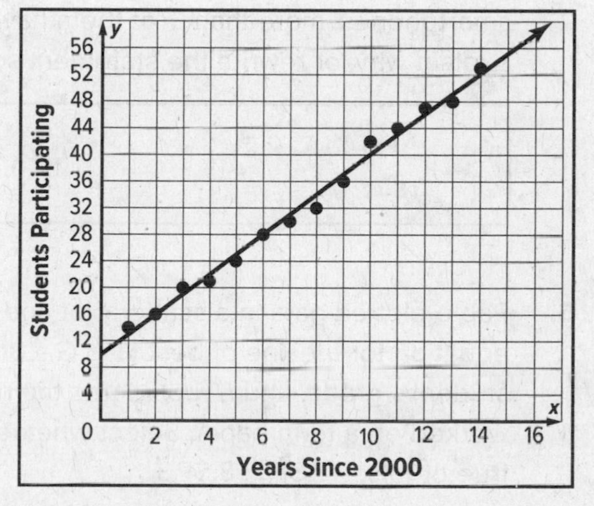

Part A: Write the numbers that best represent the equation of the line of best fit.

0.3	3	8	10	0.4	4	9	15

$y =$ ______ $x +$ ______

Part B: Use the equation to make a conjecture about the number of students participating in the model U.N. in 2018.

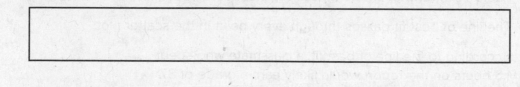

3. Yoruba surveyed seventh and eighth graders at a school assembly. He found that 39 seventh graders agree with a plan to install larger lockers while 8 do not. Of the 43 eighth graders surveyed, 18 agree with the plan. Complete the two-way table based on this information. 8.SP.4

	Agree	Disagree	Total
Seventh Graders			
Eighth Graders			
Total			

4. The scatter plot shows the heights of mothers and their adult daughters. Write values to complete each statement. 8.SP.1

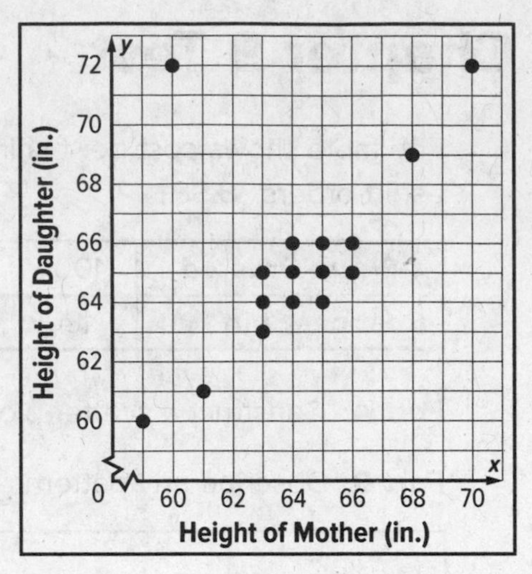

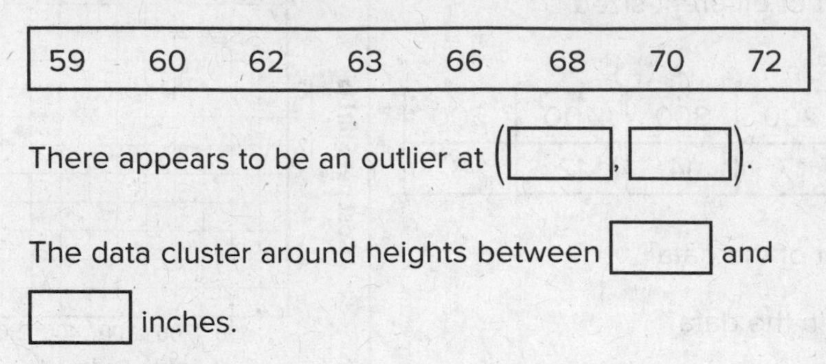

There appears to be an outlier at (☐ , ☐).

The data cluster around heights between ☐ and ☐ inches.

5. Out of 100 students who have a curfew, 76 of them also have a smartphone. Thandeka says, "Of the students in my school who have smartphones, more than $\frac{3}{4}$ of them have a curfew." Is her statement correct? Explain why, or rewrite the statement so it is correct. 8.SP.4

6. Pablo plotted data in a scatter plot and drew a line of best fit. The equation for the line of best fit is $G = 8h + 50$, where G represents a student's grade, and h represents the number of hours the student worked on a term paper. Select whether each statement is true or false. 8.SP.2, 8.SP.3

True	False	
☐	☐	Pablo's scatter plot shows a positive, linear association.
☐	☐	The line of best fit passes through every point in the scatter plot.
☐	☐	According to the line of best fit, a classmate who spent 1.5 hours on the report would likely earn a grade of 87.

7. Graph eight points on each coordinate plane to create a scatter plot that matches the given association. 8.SP.1

Positive, Linear Association

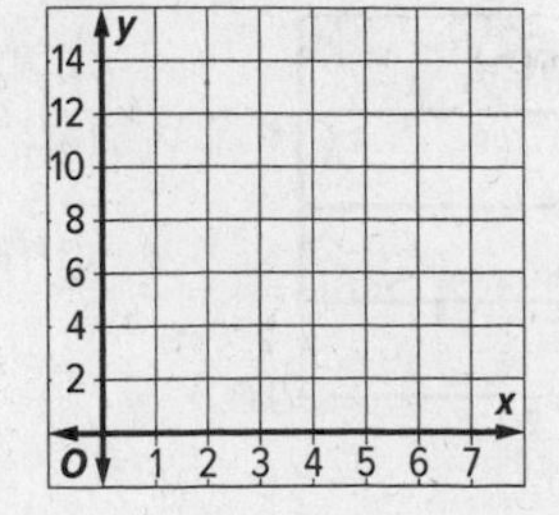

Positive, Nonlinear Association

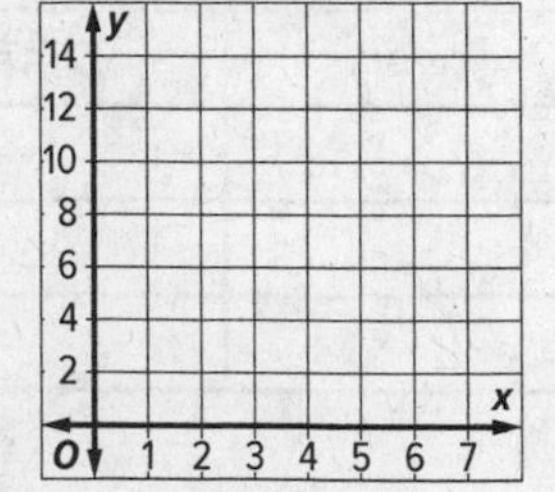

8. Seventh-grade students were surveyed to find out which language they would enjoy studying. Complete the two-way table based on the Venn diagram. Then find the relative frequency of students who chose neither Spanish nor French to the total number of students. Round to the nearest hundredth. 8.SP.4

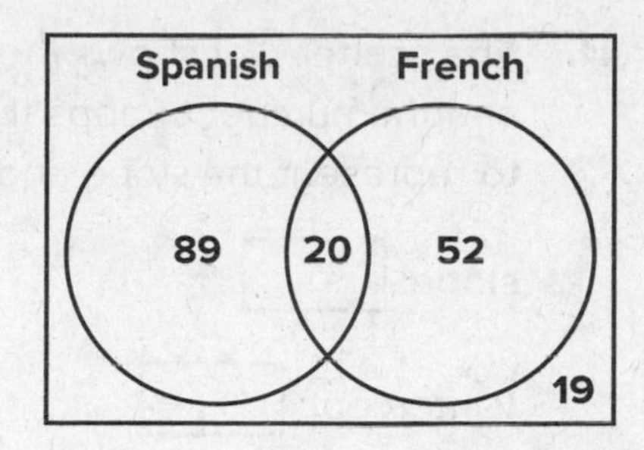

	Spanish	Not Spanish	Total
French			
Not French			
Total			

Relative frequency (not Spanish, not French): ☐

9. The table shows the number of e-mails sent out to advertise a play. The number of people who attended that play is also shown. 8.SP.1, 8.SP.2

E-mails Sent	100	200	300	400	500	600	700	800
Attendance	20	25	40	45	55	60	70	75

Part A: Construct a scatter plot of the data. Then draw a line of best fit.

Part B: Does the line of best fit have a positive or negative slope? Explain what this represents.

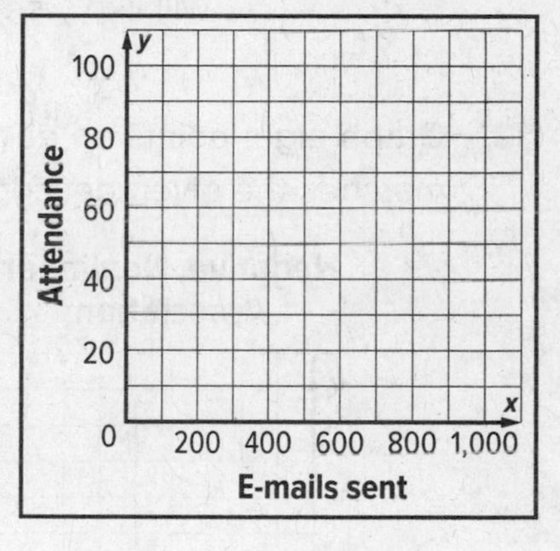

10. Jean-Marc records his running times and distances in a table. 8.SP.1

Time (min)	25	30	45	60	70
Distance Run (km)	4	6	8	10	12

Part A: Construct a scatter plot of the data.

Part B: Write a statement that is supported by the scatter plot.

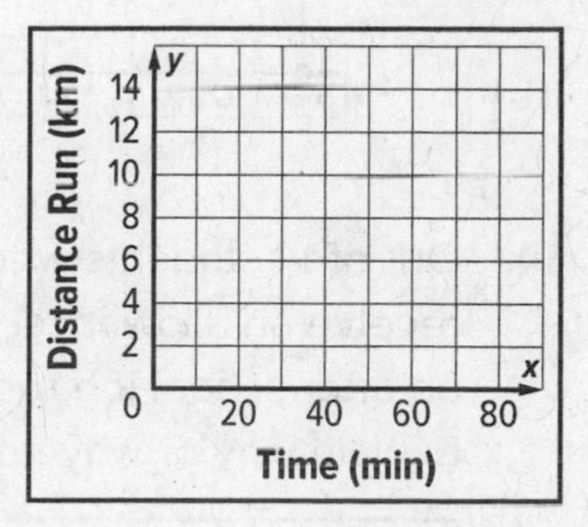

11. The scatter plot shows the ages of several customers and the number of apps they purchased. Write numbers to represent the slope and the y-intercept. 8.SP.3

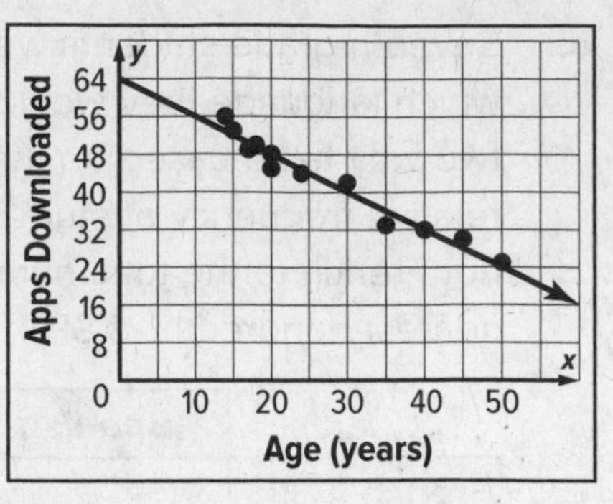

slope: ☐

y-intercept: ☐

12. Ms. Okafor works at a car dealership. She plotted the data in a scatter plot and drew a line of best fit. The equation for the line is $P = -2{,}500a + 20{,}000$, where P represents the selling price and a represents the age of the car in years. Select whether each statement is true or false. 8.SP.2, 8.SP.3

True	False	
☐	☐	The scatter plot shows a nonlinear association.
☐	☐	The slope is negative because the selling price decreases as the age of the car increases.
☐	☐	According to the line of best fit, a sedan that is 7 years old will likely sell for about $2,500.

13. Graph eight points on each coordinate plane to create a scatter plot that matches the given description. 8.SP.1

Negative, Nonlinear Association

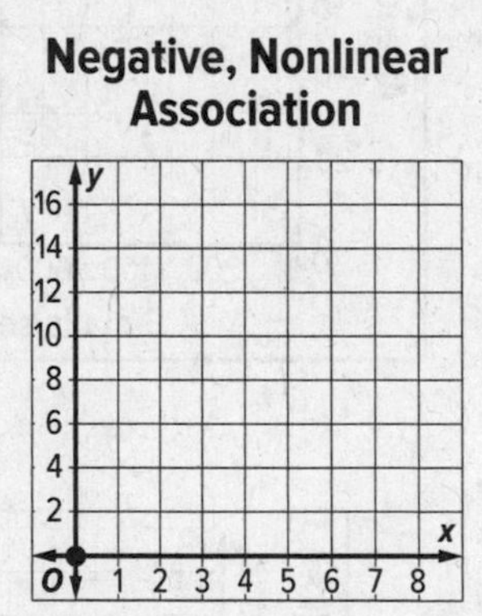

No Association

y
16
14
12
10
8
6
4
2
O
1 2 3 4 5 6 7 8
x

14. Out of 14 students who have an after-school job, 8 of them also receive an allowance. Carmen says, "Less than half of the students with an after-school job receive an allowance." Is her statement correct? Explain why or why not. 8.SP.4

15. Arturo recorded the number of years of experience and the hourly wages of store employees in the scatter plot. He then used all the points to draw the line shown. 8.SP.1, 8.SP.2

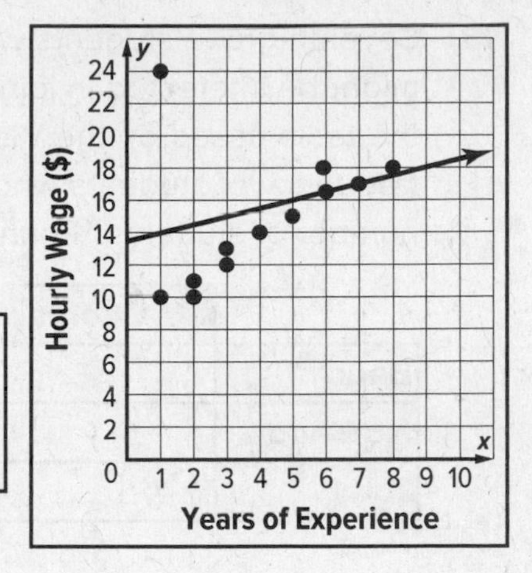

Part A: Explain why Arturo's line is not a good fit for the data and what error he may have made.

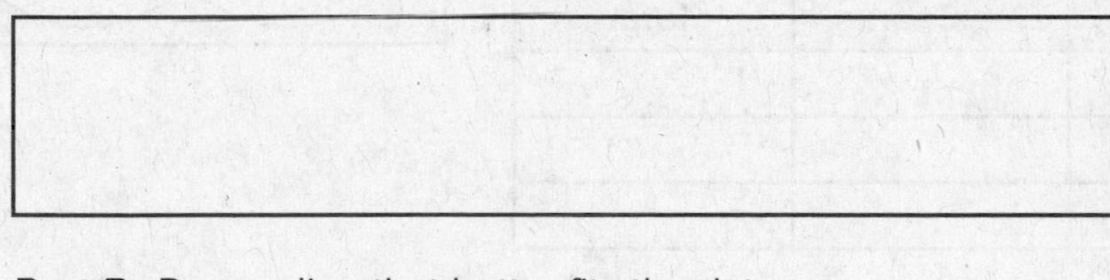

Part B: Draw a line that better fits the data.

16. The two-way table shows the number of eighth-grade students who participate in school sports and clubs. Complete the table to find the relative frequencies of students in the survey by columns. Round to the nearest hundredth. Then interpret the relative frequencies. 8.SP.4

	Sport	No Sport	Total
Club	52;	35;	87
No Club	16;	37;	53
Total	68	72	140

17. Fatima lit a quick-burning candle and recorded its height every 10 minutes as it burned. She created a scatter plot of the data and drew a line of best fit to show the trend. Select whether each statement is true or false.
8.SP.2, 8.SP.3

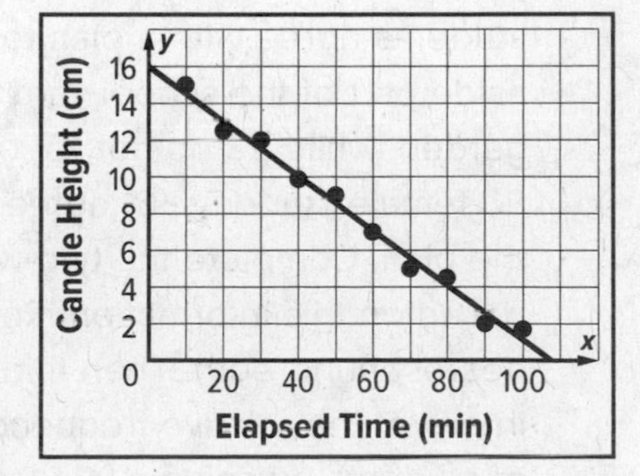

True	False	
☐	☐	The y-intercept of the line of best fit is about 16.
☐	☐	The candle's height decreases by approximately 0.15 centimeter for each minute the candle burns.
☐	☐	After 90 minutes, the height of the candle is approximately 1 centimeter.

18. Seventh-grade students were surveyed to find out if they might be interested in joining the band or chorus. Complete the table based on the Venn diagram. What is the relative frequency of students who chose only chorus to the total number of students? Round to the nearest hundredth. 8.SP.4

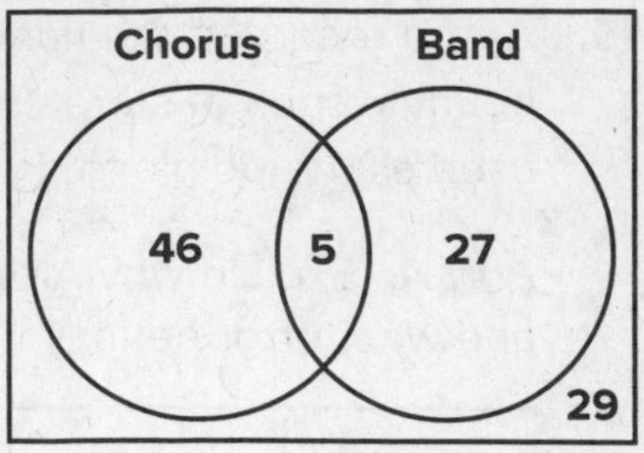

Chorus
Band
46
5
27
29

	Chorus	No Chorus	Total
Band			
No Band			
Total			

Relative frequency (only chorus):

19. The scatter plot shows the number of hot pretzels and the number of drinks sold each day at a snack stand during baseball games. 8.SP.2, 8.SP.3

Part A: Graph a line of best fit for these data.

Part B: Use your line of best fit to find the number of drinks that will be sold when 90 pretzels are sold.

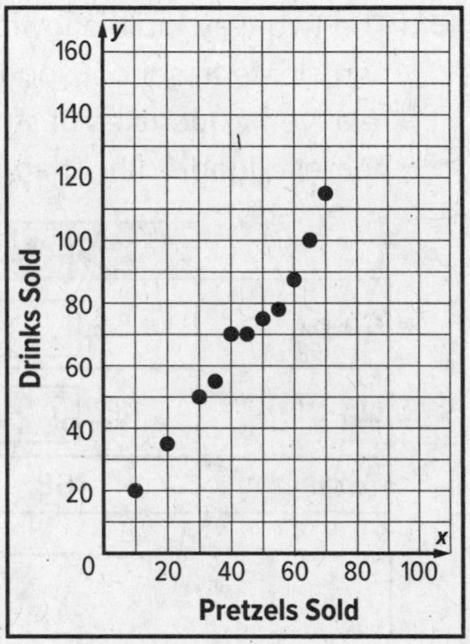

y
160
140
120
100
80
60
40
20
0
Drinks Sold
x
20 40 60 80 100
Pretzels Sold

20. Julieta surveyed eighth-grade students. She found that 35 male students agree with a plan to set aside part of the school yard for a garden, while 23 do not. Of the 83 female students, 61 agree with the plan. Complete the two-way table based on this information. Round to the nearest hundredth. Then find and interpret the relative frequencies of students by column. 8.SP.4

	Agree	Disagree	Total
Male	35; 0.36		
Female			
Total			

NAME ______________________ DATE ____________ PERIOD ________ SCORE ________

Chapter 1 Performance Task

Designing a Newspaper

Students who work on their school newspapers are invited to a presentation about publishing and layout in a large auditorium. The speaker, Ms. Marx, is a journalist from Great Britain.

Write your answers on another piece of paper. Show all your work to receive full credit.

Part A

The auditorium contains 196 seats. These seats are divided into 4 congruent square sections. Write an equation to determine the number of rows r of seats in each square section. How many rows of seats are in each section? How many seats are in each row?

Part B

Ms. Marx explains that newspapers try to avoid empty space on a page. She shows a chart of the sizes of paper in the A-series, which she uses in Europe.

Paper Size	Length and Width (approx.)
A3	420 mm × 297 mm
A4	297 mm × 210 mm
A5	210 mm × 148.5 mm

Find the area of each paper size in the table. Compare the area of A5 to A3 and the area of A5 to A4. Describe the relationships of the areas in both fraction form and by using integer exponents. How does each paper size area compare to the next larger or next smaller size area?

Part C

Assume all papers in the A-series continue the relationship discovered in Part B. What is the area of paper that is size A1? Size A7? Use integer exponents and their equivalents to support your work.

Part D

Ms. Marx explains that the aspect ratio of an image is the proportional relationship between its length and width. The aspect ratio for the pages in the A-series is $\sqrt{2}$. Is the aspect ratio rational or irrational? Explain. Then estimate the aspect ratio to the nearest hundredth. Does your estimate make sense given the dimensions for A3, A4, and A5 pages shown in the table?

Part E

Some common U.S. paper sizes are noted in the table. When the aspect ratios of paper sizes are the same, they can fit together in a newspaper without any empty space on each page. Can these two paper sizes be used together easily for a newspaper? Is the aspect ratio for each U.S. paper size a rational or irrational number? Explain.

Paper Size	Length and Width (approx.)
Letter	11 in. × 8.5 in.
Legal	14 in. × 8.5 in.

Part F

Ms. Marx explains that while it is important to think about the layout of your publication, you must also note how many copies you sell. This table shows the circulation figures (or approximate number of copies sold) for several newspapers in the United Kingdom for a recent month.

Newspaper	Circulation
The Sun	2.1×10^6
Daily Mirror	9.7×10^5
Daily Telegraph	5.2×10^5
Financial Times	2.2×10^5
The Independent	6.3×10^4

About how many times greater is the circulation of *The Sun* than the circulation of the *Daily Telegraph*? How many more issues of the *Daily Mirror* were sold than the *Financial Times*?

NAME _______________ DATE _______ PERIOD _______ SCORE _______

Chapter 2 Performance Task

A Plan to Plant a School Garden

Ms. Denton is working with students to plan a school garden. The school principal tells her that she can use 144 square yards of a school field for the garden.

Write your answers on another piece of paper. Show all your work to receive full credit.

Part A

To save money on fencing, Ms. Denton decides to select a patch of land for the garden that has the shortest perimeter. Should she choose a square patch of land or a rectangular patch that is not a square? Explain your reasoning.

Part B

For the vegetables, Ms. Denton wants two rectangular planter beds that are each 6 feet longer than they are wide. Corinna draws up plans and represents the width of each planter bed as w feet. She identifies the perimeter of each planter bed as $(4w + 6)$ feet. Is Corinna's expression accurate? Explain.

Part C

Jayson wants to know the exact width, w, and length of these vegetable planter beds so he can start sawing wood to make the structures. Tyler tells Jayson that the perimeter of each bed is $(3w + 14)$ feet. Lourdes says that the perimeter of each bed is $(4w + 12)$ feet. Both students are correct. Find the width and length, in feet, of each planter bed.

Ms. Denton hopes the school will make its own compost in the future. Currently she must buy compost for the garden and have it delivered. Company A sells compost for $12.50 per bag plus a $50 delivery fee. Company B sells compost for $11 per bag plus a $95 delivery fee.

Part D

How many bags of compost must Ms. Denton buy and have delivered to pay the same total amount to each company? What is the cost for that number of bags? Write an equation and let *b* represent the number of bags.

Part E

Jayson also builds triangular flower beds for the 4 corners of the garden. Each flower bed needs 52 feet of fencing to surround it. Ms. Denton wants to put compost in each flower bed. What is the total area of the corner flower beds?

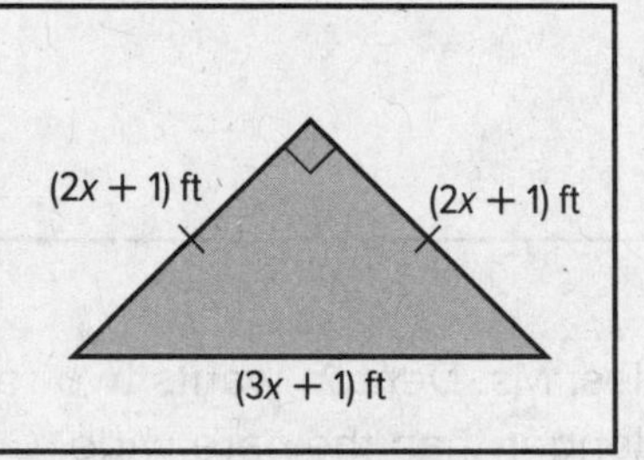

Part F

Kanti knows that it costs $304 to cover the 4 corner flower beds with compost from Company B. How many bags of compost would each flower bed need? Would it be more or less expensive to buy the compost for all the flower beds from Company A? Justify your answer.

NAME ______________________ DATE ____________ PERIOD ________ SCORE ________

Chapter 3 Performance Task

Managing a Team

Francine and José are the managers of their school's basketball teams. One of their jobs is collecting data about the players during practices and games.

Write your answers on another piece of paper. Show all your work to receive full credit.

Part A

José keeps track of each player's training runs. The table shows a record of Damon's training run. Damon felt that he ran faster at the beginning of his run than during the last 10 minutes of his run. Graph the data and write an equation in slope-intercept form to represent Damon's run. Use your graph and equation to explain whether Damon's feelings are accurate.

Time (min), x	Distance (m), y
0	0
5	900
10	1,800
15	2,700
20	3,600
25	4,500

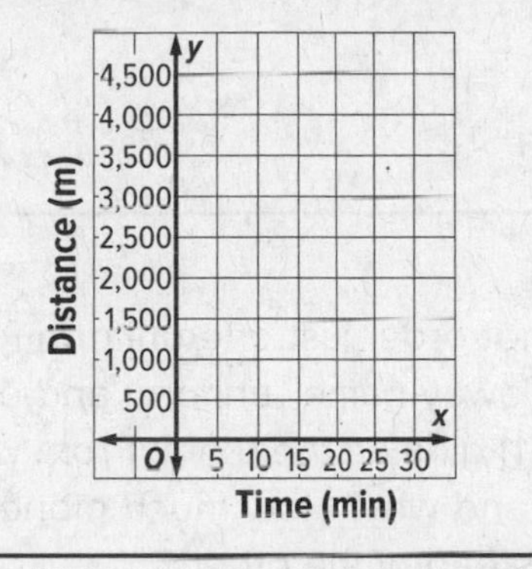

Part B

Francine keeps track of how many minutes players play each game and how many points they score. Her data for Talia are shown on the graph.

The line drawn passes through (8, 2) and (20, 5) to show the trend of the data. What is the slope of the line? Explain what the slope represents in this situation.

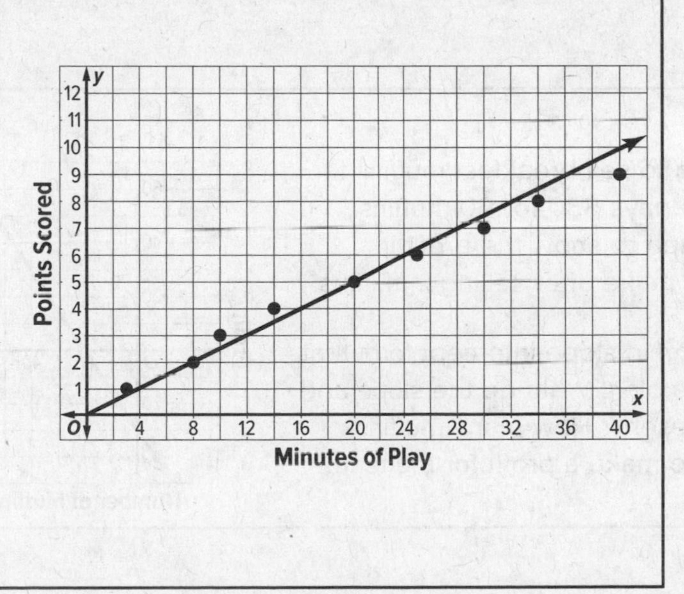

Both the girls' and boys' teams are heading to the regional championships. Francine and José want to raise funds to help the teams get there in style.

Part C

Francine wants to raise enough money to buy new uniforms for the 11 members of the girls' team. The Uni-Forme Company charges \$22 per uniform plus a flat fee for shipping of \$100. The Sports Shoppe charges \$30 per uniform and offers free shipping. Write a system of equations to represent the situation. Then graph the system and use it to estimate which company offers the better price for 11 uniforms. Solve the system algebraically to verify that your estimate is correct.

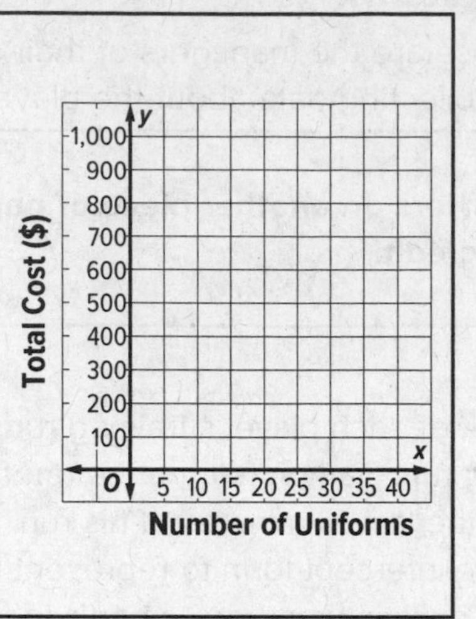

Part D

Francine realizes that she cannot order just one uniform for each team member. She needs one blue "away game" uniform and one white "home game" uniform for each of the 11 girls on the team. From which company should she order the uniforms and why? How much money will Francine save by using one company instead of the other?

Part E

José is planning to sell breakfast muffins for a fundraiser. He pays \$30 for 60 muffins. He makes a graph to show the profit in dollars y he will make after selling x muffins.

Write an equation in slope-intercept form that describes José's plan. What do the slope and y-intercept represent? How many muffins must José sell to make a profit for the team?

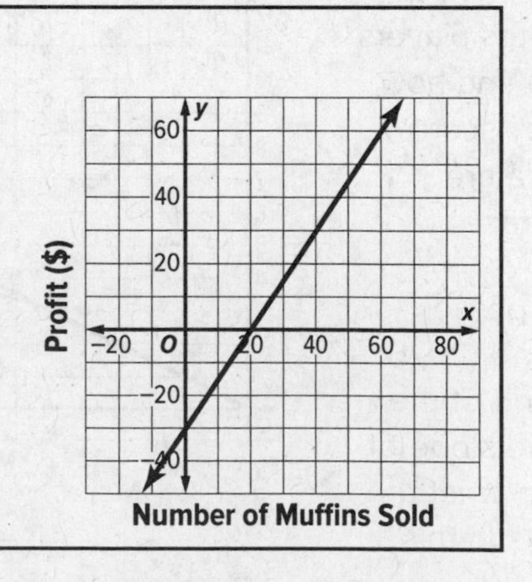

NAME _______________ DATE _______ PERIOD _____ SCORE _____

Chapter 4 Performance Task

Saving for College

Mr. and Mrs. Sanchez plan for a college education when their baby is born. They have already saved \$500 and want to invest that money in a savings account at a local bank until their child is 18 years old. One account that the bank offers provides 4% interest to parents for college tuition.

Write your answers on another piece of paper. Show all your work to receive full credit.

Part A

The bank offers two accounts. One account has a 4% simple interest rate. Simple interest I can be found with $I = prt$, using the principal p, the decimal rate r, and the time t in years. The equation $y = 500 + 500(0.04)x$ represents investing \$500 in this account, where y is the total amount in the account and x is the number of years invested. Explain the equation. Does the equation represent a function? Is it linear?

Part B

The bank also has an account offering 4% monthly compound interest, which means that the interest will be applied to both the original principal and any interest accumulated each month. The table and graph show how the total amount in the account y will change over x years.

Compound Interest	
***x* (years)**	***y* (total \$)**
0	500
1	520.37
3	563.64
6	635.37
9	716.24
12	807.39
18	1,025.99

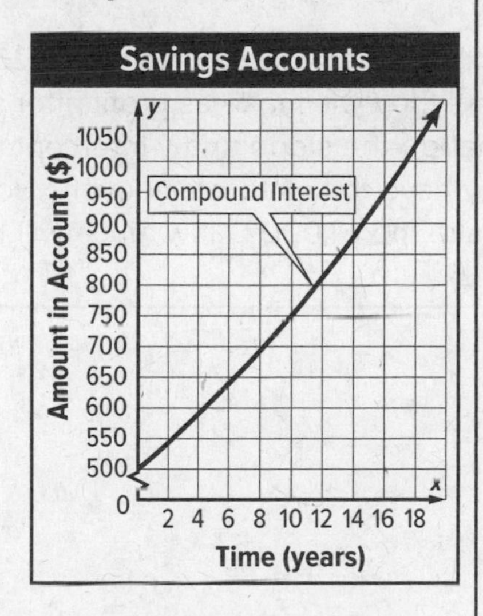

Make a table of values for the simple interest equation from Part A. Graph the equation on the same graph. Compare and contrast the two types of interest. Include a discussion about the rates of change.

The amount in the savings account is not the only way to save money. The Sanchez family wants to raise at least $1,000 more. So they decide to make and sell bracelets in addition to their regular jobs.

Part C

After work one day, Mrs. Sanchez plans to stop at the crafts store and at the bank. The crafts store is about halfway from her work to her home. The bank is right around the corner from her home. She estimates that it will take her longer at the crafts store to buy jewelry components than it will at the bank. Sketch a qualitative graph to represent Mrs. Sanchez's drive home, where the y-axis indicates the distance from the home. Number each segment, and provide a key to show what each segment represents.

Part D

The Sanchez family creates the equation $y = 2.25x - 200$ to show the amount y in dollars they will make as profit after selling x bracelets. Graph the equation. What do the slope and y-intercept represent? How many bracelets will they have to sell to break even? How many bracelets will they have to sell to make the $1,000? How much will they make after selling 1,000 bracelets?

NAME _______________ DATE _______ PERIOD _____ SCORE _____

Chapter 5 Performance Task

Park Redesign

People come to Wild Lake Park for many activities, but it can be difficult to get around the park in a vehicle. Mr. Miller, an architect, has been hired to redesign the roads. Currently two parallel roads exist: Wild Way and Shore Street. They are intersected by Lake Lane. Mr. Miller suggests building Right Road and Boat Boulevard.

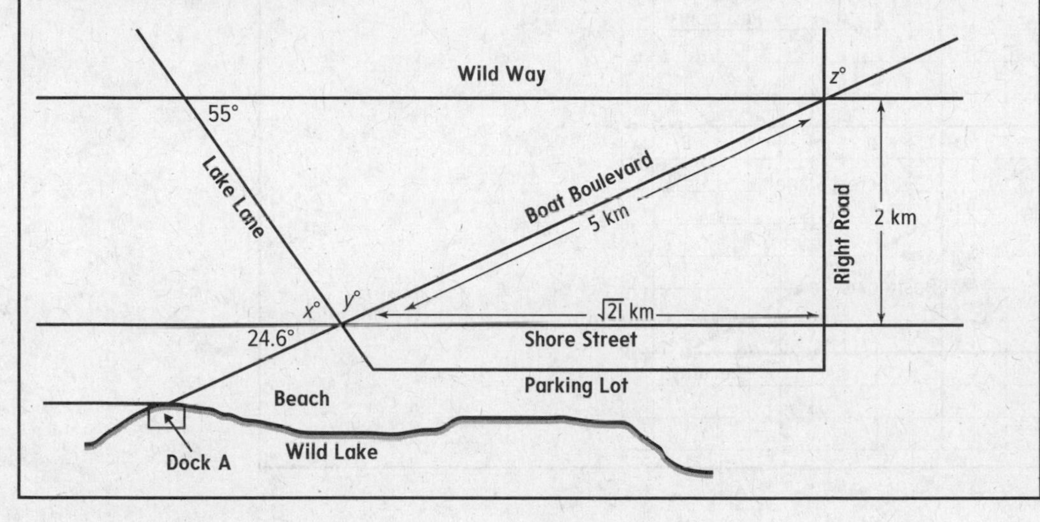

Write your answers on another piece of paper. Show all your work to receive full credit.

Part A

The map shows that Wild Way intersects Lake Lane at a 55° angle. Find the values of x and y, the measures of the angles formed when Boat Boulevard intersects Shore Street and Lake Lane. Explain how you found your answers.

Part B

Mr. Miller named one of the new roads Right Road because it forms a right angle when it intersects Shore Street. His business partner wants to ensure that the road is perpendicular before naming it. Use the converse of the Pythagorean Theorem to determine whether Right Road was designed correctly. Explain your reasoning.

Part C

At the intersection of Right Road and Boat Boulevard, what is the measure of angle labeled $z°$? Justify your response.

To help pay for the renovations, a music festival will be held to benefit Wild Lake Park. The festival director, Valeria, maps out the event locations. On the festival map, each unit is equal to 0.2 mile.

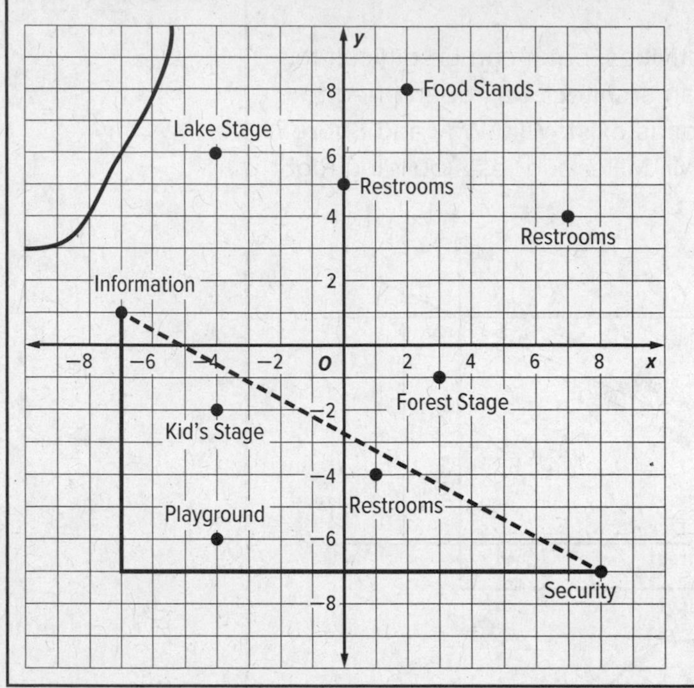

Part D

Local regulations for outdoor festivals require that restrooms be available within 0.5 mile of food stands. Does the current setup fit this criterion? Explain.

Part E

Valeria will need to travel from Information to Security frequently.

- She can ride a golf cart along the solid lines from one to the other at 12 miles per hour.
- She can walk along the dashed line at 4 miles per hour.

She wants to use the faster method. How should she travel? Explain.

Part F

Valeria wants to place the first aid station so that it is exactly 1 mile from each of the stages. In what location should the first aid station be placed? Prove that your location is the correct distance from all three stages.

NAME ________________ DATE ________ PERIOD ______ SCORE ______

Chapter 6 Performance Task

Geometry at the Gym

Kazakov's Gym is a gymnastics center. Coach Kasakov, the gym's owner, says that an understanding of geometry and spatial relationships is key to being a strong gymnast. He also uses geometry to rearrange his gym equipment.

Write your answers on another piece of paper. Show all your work to receive full credit.

Part A

Coach Kazakov hangs posters to inspire his gymnasts. Use what you know about transformations to describe the gymnasts' movements in each poster.

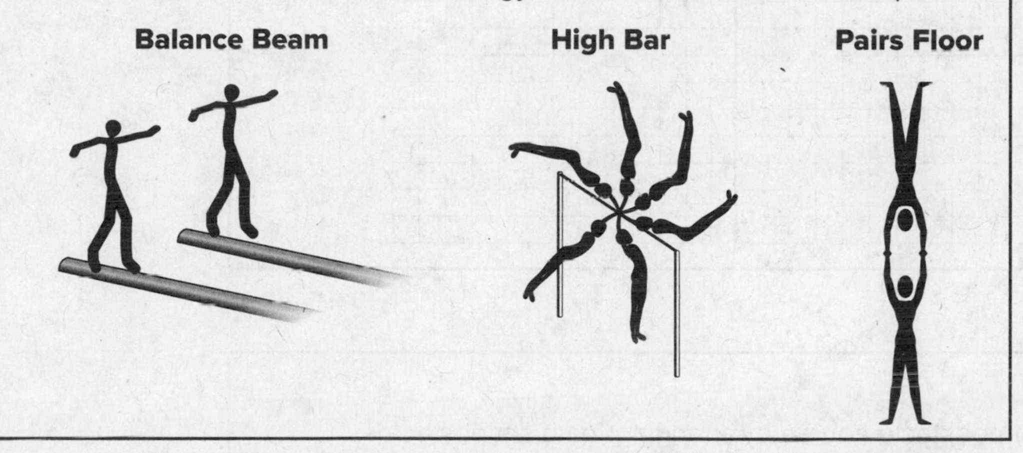

Part B

Coach Kasakov uses computer software to rearrange the gym for the boys' team practice. He draws a segment with endpoints $A(1, 5)$ and $B(1, 1)$ and a second segment with endpoints $C(1.5, 5)$ and $D(1.5, 1)$ to represent the parallel bars. On a coordinate plane, draw segments AB and CD. Then translate them 2 units to the right and 6 units down to show where the coach will move the parallel bars. What does the diagram show about the bars now? Are they still parallel? Are they longer, shorter, or the same length as the original bars? Explain how you know.

Part C

A rectangle with vertices $F(-5, -2)$, $G(-5, -1)$, $H(-3, -1)$, and $J(-3, -2)$ represents the current location of the pommel horse. Coach Kasakov rotates the rectangle 90° clockwise about the origin to show where he wants to move the horse. Identify the coordinates of the vertices of the image. Compare the shape and size of the original rectangle with the size and shape of its image. Explain your reasoning.

Anita is an assistant coach at the gym. She uses Coach Kasakov's software to plan how she will set up for a children's birthday party. Here is what she has drawn so far.

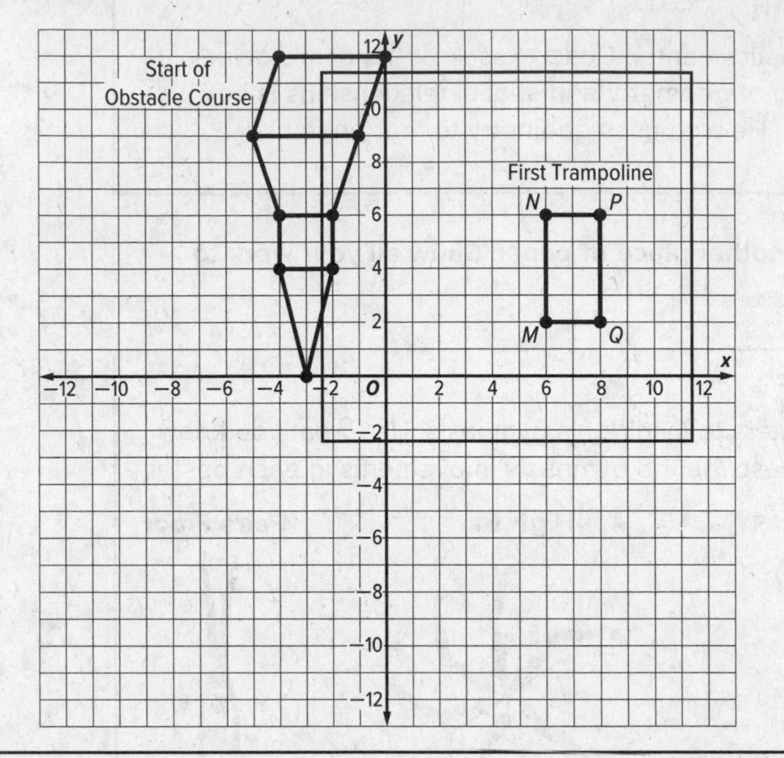

Part D

Anita will make an obstacle course by arranging foam shapes across the room. The sequence of shapes in Quadrant II shows the first part of the course. She reflects each shape across the *x*-axis to show the rest of the course. Draw the rest of the course.

Part E

Rectangle *MNPQ* shows the location of the first trampoline Anita will use for the party. She uses one or more transformations, including a dilation, to draw rectangle *M'N'P'Q'*, which shows the location of the second trampoline. The image includes point *M'*(−9, −3) and point *N'*(−9, −9). Determine the coordinates of vertices *P'* and *Q'*. Then describe one or more transformations Anita could have used to draw the second trampoline. What is the scale factor? Is the image an enlargement or a reduction? What does this indicate about the second trampoline?

NAME ______________ DATE ________ PERIOD ______ SCORE ______

Chapter 7 Performance Task

A Party for Isabella

Reynaldo and his daughter Rosie are hosting a birthday party for Rosie's grandmother Isabella. Reynaldo built horseshoe pits in his yard for the party. The object is to throw a horseshoe from one end of the pit around a wooden stake at the other end. Rectangles *ABCD* and *FGHJ* show the raised horseshoe pits. Points $S_1(3.5, 3)$ and $S_2(43.5, 3)$ show the locations of the wooden stakes. Each unit on the grid represents 1 foot.

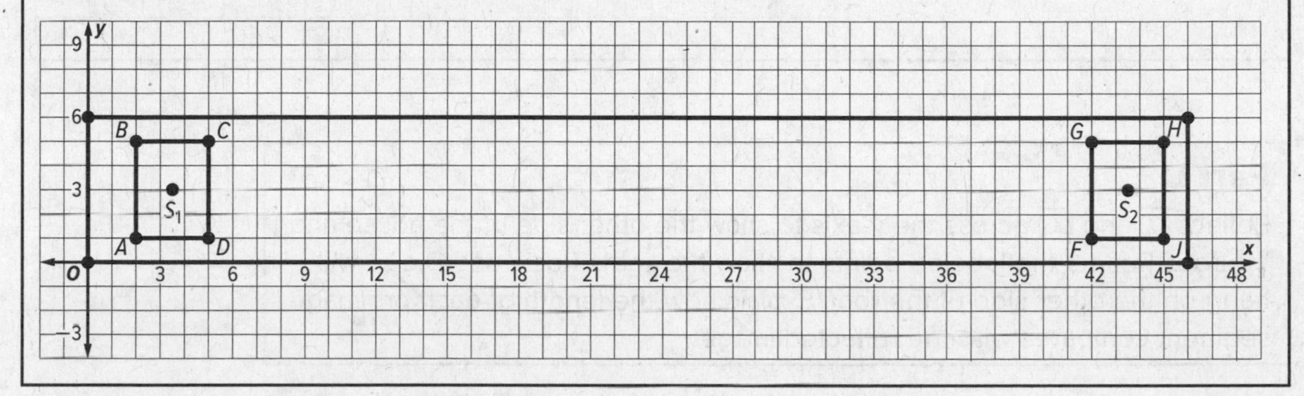

Write your answers on another piece of paper. Show all your work to receive full credit.

Part A

Diego wants to know how far apart the stakes are, so he transforms point S_1 to point S_2. Describe the transformation and give the distance.

Part B

Diego realizes his own yard isn't long enough for the horseshoe pit. Uncle Reynaldo says that in a similar game called *quoits*, the stakes are only 21 feet apart. Describe a translation that could be used to move point S_2 and rectangle *FGHJ* so that the new location of the stake, point S_3, is 21 units from S_1. Identify the coordinates of the vertices of quadrilateral *F'G'H'J'* and point S_3. Compare the size and shape of the new quadrilateral *F'G'H'J'* with the preimage.

Part C

Rosie hangs a piñata from a tree branch while Isabella watches. The tree and Isabella cast shadows as shown. How tall is the tree? Explain how you used similar triangles.

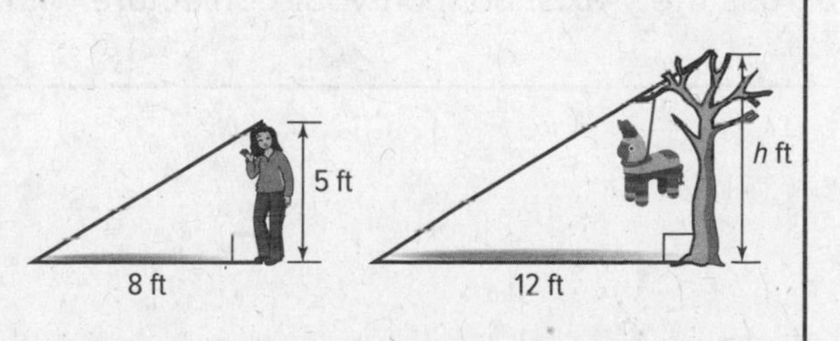

Rosie and Diego decorate the house. Half of the house's roof and a side of the house are represented on the coordinate plane. Rosie and Diego attach lights to one side of the house's roof, as shown by points L, M, N, P, and Q.

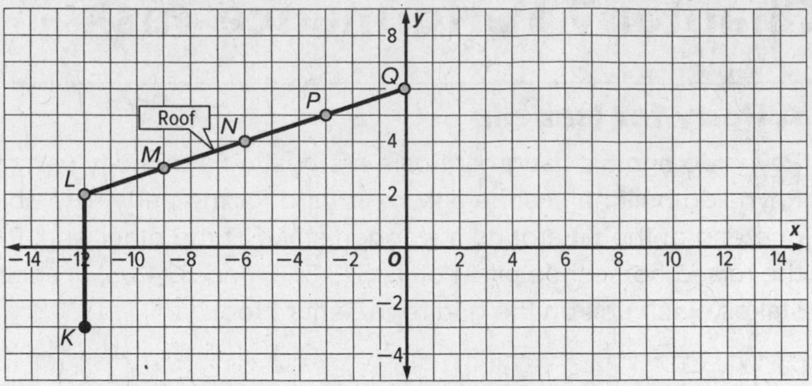

Part D

Reflect $\overline{KL}$ and $\overline{LQ}$ across the y-axis to show the other side of the house and the roof. Reflect the labeled points to show the lights Rosie and Diego will hang on the other side of the roof. Explain how the length of each preimage segment compares with the reflected image.

Part E

The *pitch* of a roof refers to the slope of the roof. Find the pitch of the left side of the roof. Then verify the slope by using a different set of points. Does it matter which points you choose? Explain.

Part F

Calculate the slope of $\overline{L'Q'}$. How does the slope of $\overline{LQ}$ compare to the slope of its image $\overline{L'Q'}$? Make a conjecture about the slope of a line and the slope of its reflection across the y-axis. Support your conjecture with a separate example.

NAME ______________________ DATE ____________ PERIOD ________ SCORE ________

Chapter 8 Performance Task

Good Sports Company

The Okeke family owns and operates a sporting goods company called Good Sports. To create a trustworthy product, they must be precise during the manufacturing process.

Hakeem oversees the making of baseballs. Baseballs have three main parts, as shown. Each part must be made precisely to conform to league standards.

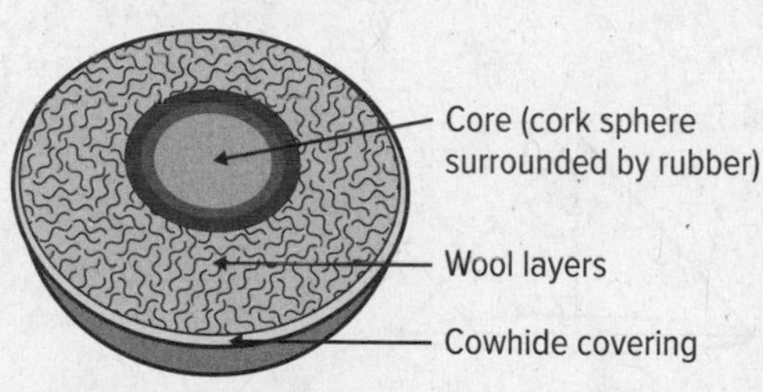

Write your answers on another piece of paper. Show all your work to receive full credit.

Part A

The diameter of the spherical core of the baseball measures approximately 1.31 inches. What is the volume of the core of the baseball? Round to the nearest hundredth.

Part B

Layers of wool are wound tightly around each core, resulting in a sphere with a radius of approximately 1.41 inches. What is the volume of the wool? Round to the nearest hundredth.

Part C

After the cowhide covering is sewn on, each baseball has a total diameter between 2.86 inches and 2.94 inches. What are the possible circumferences of a baseball? What are the possible volumes of a baseball? Write your answers as ranges, and round to the nearest hundredth.

Part D

Baseballs are not the only products made by the company. Good Sports also produces plastic cones with a 3.5-inch diameter and an 8-inch slant height.

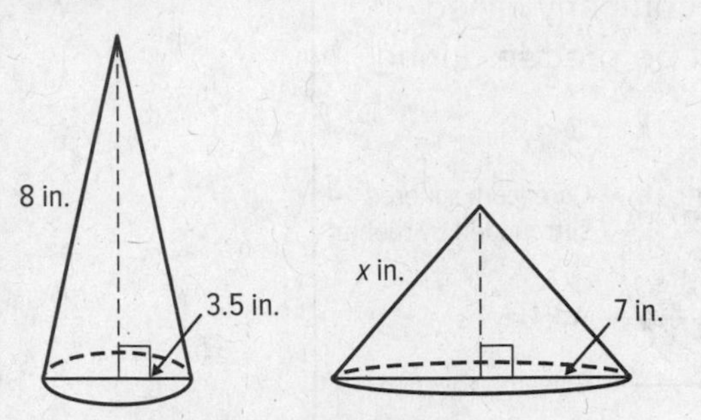

Amma is in charge of new product development. She thinks the company should also produce cones with a diameter of 7 inches. She wants to use the same amount of plastic to produce each cone. What is x, the slant height of the cone that Amma wants to build? Assume both cones are open on the bottom.

Part E

To conform to tennis standards, each tennis ball the company manufactures must measure between 2.575 inches and 2.70 inches in diameter.

Kahlil is in charge of packaging and distribution. He packages 3 maximum-sized tennis balls in one cylindrical can. He wants to fit the tennis balls snugly so that each ball touches the next one and the sides of the can. What are the diameter d and the height h of each can?

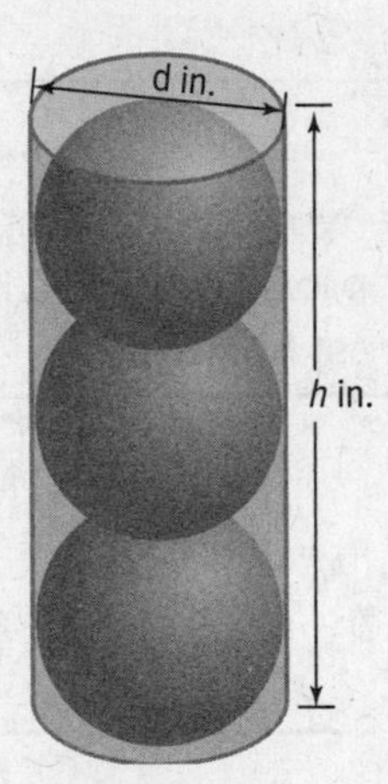

Approximately what percentage of the container will be filled by the tennis balls? Round to the nearest tenth of a percent. Approximately how many cubic inches of empty space remain in the container? Round to the nearest hundredth.

NAME ______________________ DATE ____________ PERIOD ________ SCORE ________

Chapter 9 Performance Task

For this Performance Task, your teacher will ask you to conduct a survey and do research to provide the data for your analysis and data displays.

Make a Run for It

Running is great exercise. Some runners enter races and join track teams, while others run to condition themselves for other sports or just to stay fit. Some of the greatest runners in the world compete in the Olympics.

For this task, survey 32 students and ask them if they run for exercise or participate in an organized sport. Then do research to find Olympic gold medalist times in the men's 100-meter dash from 1900 to the present.

Write your answers on another piece of paper. Show all your work to receive full credit.

Part A

Create a two-way table to show the results of your survey. Label the columns "Runs" and "Does Not Run" and the rows "Sport" and "No Sport." Find the relative frequencies for the values in the table related to all the students surveyed. Round the relative frequencies to the nearest hundredth. Use this information to describe the students in your survey.

Part B

Find the relative frequencies from your table by column, rounded to the nearest hundredth. Are students who run likely to play sports? Are students who do not run likely to play sports? Explain.

Part C

Find the relative frequencies from your table by row, rounded to the nearest hundredth. Are students who play sports more likely to run? Are students who do not play sports likely to run? Explain.

In the Summer Olympics, male and female athletes participate in a variety of track and field events. These events involving running, jumping, and throwing. One track-and-field running event is the men's 100-meter dash.

Part D

Make a scatter plot of the data you collected about the Olympic men's 100-meter dash. Record the years since 1900 on the *x*-axis and the gold medalists' times on the *y*-axis. Then draw a line of best fit. Describe the association shown by the scatter plot.

Part E

Calculate the slope and *y*-intercept of your line of best fit. Then write an equation for your line of best fit. Use the equation to predict the times for the gold medalists in the men's 100-meter dash at the Olympics in 2020 and in 2056. Compare the results to the 2012 results.

NAME ______________________ DATE ____________ PERIOD ________ SCORE ________

Benchmark Test, Chapters 1–3

1. Emmett is analyzing different types of numbers.

Part A: Select whether the number in each situation is rational or irrational.

	Rational	Irrational
A carpenter uses a $\frac{3}{16}$-inch drill bit.	☐	☐
The diagonal of a square potholder measures $\sqrt{225}$ centimeters.	☐	☐
A checking account has a balance of –$125.50.	☐	☐
The area of a plate that Desiree made in pottery class is 7π, or 21.9911485..., square feet.	☐	☐

Part B: The edge length of a cube-shaped box is $2\sqrt{5}$ inches long. Estimate the length of the edge to the nearest tenth of an inch. Then explain why you can only estimate this length, not find its exact value. 8.NS.1, 8.NS.2

2. Sort the equations into the bin that correctly describes the solutions. 8.EE.7, 8.EE.7a

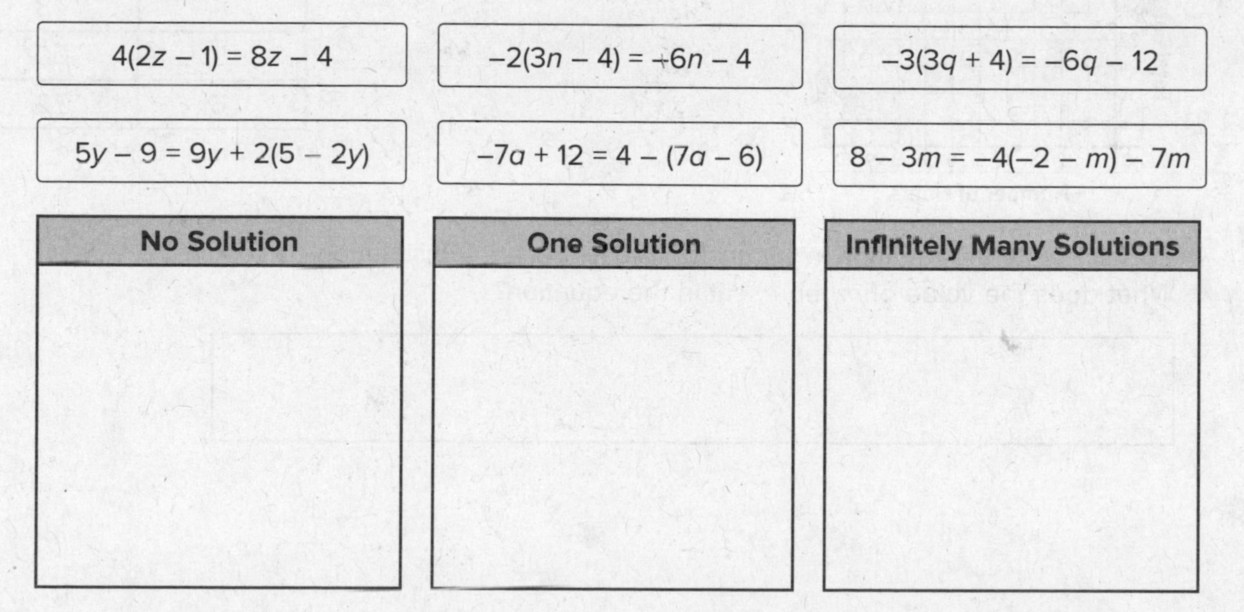

3. The graph shows the distance in meters that a lion can run over several seconds.

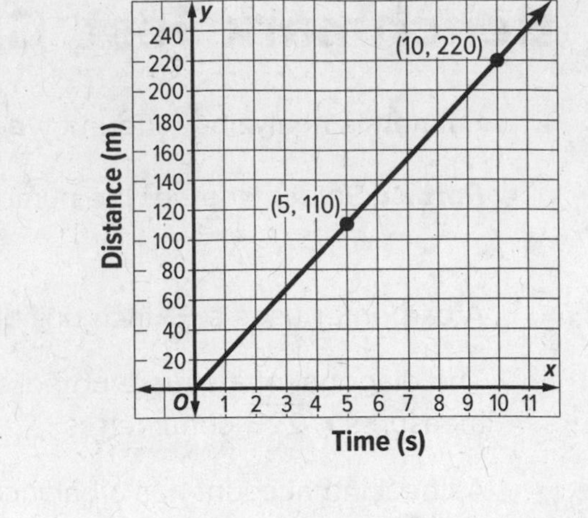

For each animal described, the distance traveled in meters is a direct variation of the time in seconds. Select whether each animal described travels faster than the lion. 8.EE.5, 8.F.2

Yes	No	
☐	☐	A springbok runs 73.2 meters in 3 seconds and 97.6 meters in 4 seconds.
☐	☐	A zebra is traveling at a rate of 17.78 meters per second.
☐	☐	The equation $y = 22.36x$ shows the number of meters, y, a wildebeest runs in x seconds.
☐	☐	A Thomson's gazelle runs 38 meters in 2 seconds and 114 meters in 6 seconds.

4. The table shows the amount of money Liana earns per hour working as a hostess at a restaurant. 8.EE.5, 8.EE.6

Number of Hours	Total Earnings ($)
1	12
2	24
3	36
4	48
5	60
6	72

Part A: Graph the points on the coordinate plane and connect them with a straight line.

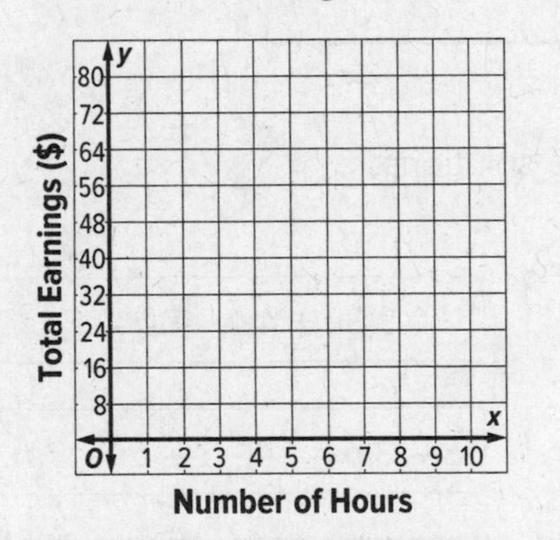

Part B: Write an equation in $y = mx$ form to represent the situation. What does the value of m represent in the equation?

5. The table shows the total distance Jayden biked each day last week.

Day	Sunday	Monday	Tuesday	Wednesday	Thursday	Friday	Saturday
Distance Biked (km)	11.5	8.7	6.3	9.2	4.5	6.0	13.8

The total distance Jayden biked last week is 1.25 times the distance he biked this week. Write and solve an equation to show how far Jayden biked this week. 8.EE.7, 8.EE.7b

Equation: ____________

Distance biked this week: ____________

6. Match each equation to the appropriate graph. 8.EE.8, 8.EE.8c, 8.F.5

$2x - 4y = 8$	$2x + 4y = -8$
$4x - 2y = 8$	$4x + 2y = -8$

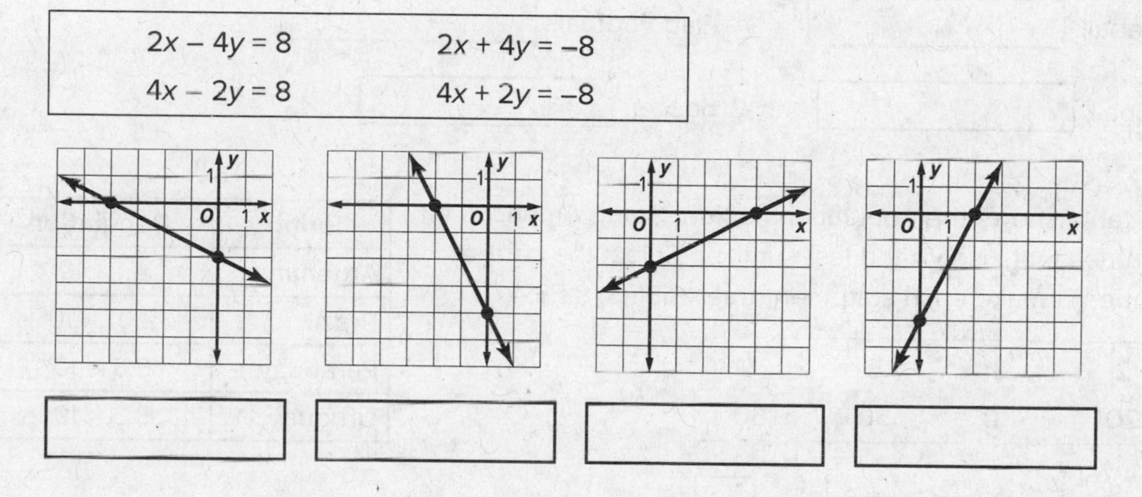

7. Manuel purchased a storage cube that has a volume of 9 cubic feet. He wants to put it on a shelf on his wall that is 24 inches below the ceiling. Will the cube fit? Explain your reasoning. 8.EE.2

8. The expressions represent the number of middle school students who signed up for 4 different spring intramural sports. The number of students signed up for baseball and kickball is equal to the number of students signed up for flag football and soccer. 8.EE.7, 8.EE.7b

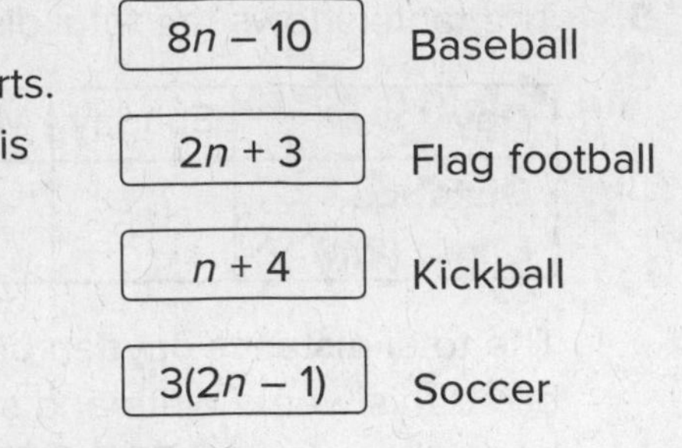

Part A: Model the situation with an equation by writing the correct expression in each space.

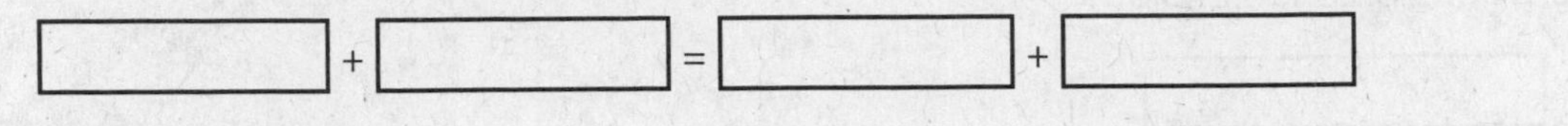

Part B: Solve the equation. Then identify the number of students signed up for each sport.

$n =$ ______

Baseball: ______ Flag Football: ______

Kickball: ______ Soccer: ______

9. The table shows the populations of four South American countries that Lisa visited last summer. Select the correct number to make each statement true. 8.EE.3, 8.EE.4

Country	Population
Argentina	4.1×10^7
Brazil	2.01×10^8
Paraguay	6.8×10^6
Uruguay	3.3×10^6

2	3	5	6
20	30	50	60

The population of Brazil is about ☐ times greater than the population of Uruguay.

The population of Argentina is about ☐ times greater than the population of Paraguay.

The population of Brazil is about ☐ times greater than the population of Argentina.

The population of Paraguay is about ☐ times greater than the population of Uruguay.

10. Select all of the equations that have infinitely many solutions. 8.EE.7, 8.EE.7a

- ☐ $-6(2x + 3) = -12x - 18$
- ☐ $-7(2x - 2) = -14x - 14$
- ☐ $9 - (8x - 3) = 8x + 12$
- ☐ $4x + 5 + x = 7 + 5x - 2$
- ☐ $12x - (3x - 4) = 9x + 4$

11. A bucket is filled with 3,000 milliliters of water. A hole in the bucket causes water to leak from the bucket as shown by the graph. 8.F.3, 8.F.4

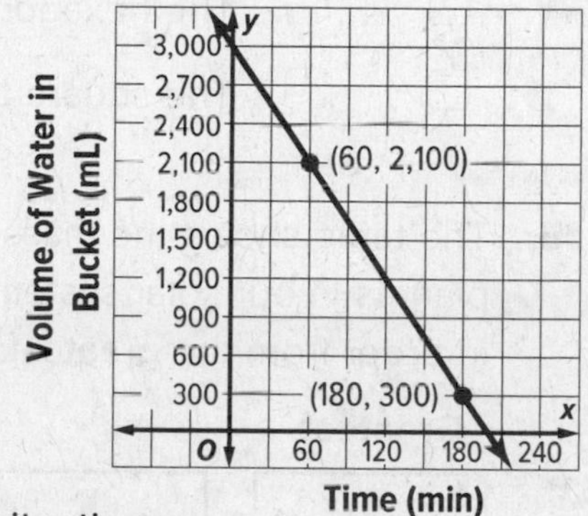

Part A: Write numbers in the boxes to find the slope.

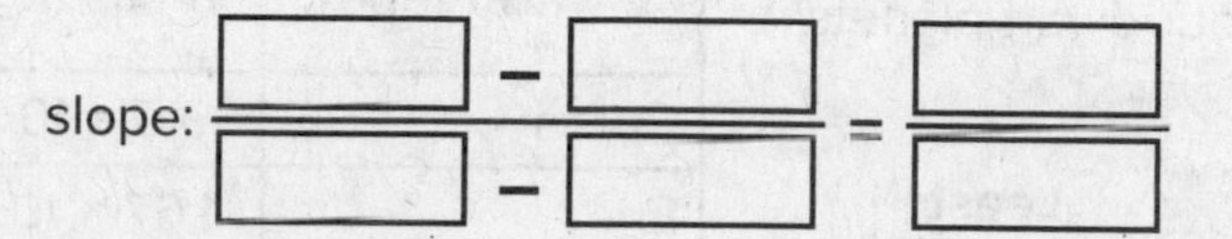

Part B: Write an equation in $y = mx + b$ form to represent the situation.

12. Celinda scored 2 more than 3 times as many strikes as Teresa did while they were bowling. Celinda scored 8 strikes. Let x represent the number of strikes Teresa scored. 8.EE.7, 8.EE.7b

Part A: Draw algebra tiles on the equation mat to model this situation.

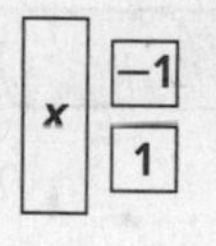

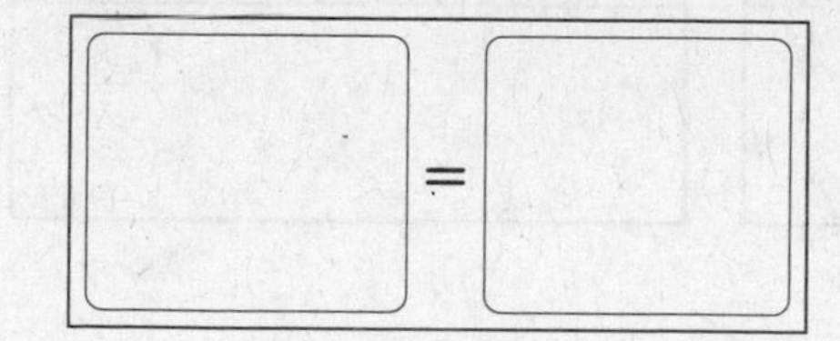

Part B: Solve to find x. How many strikes did Teresa score?

13. A scientist has an insect collection. She has a feather-winged beetle that is 2^{-5} centimeters long and a long-horned beetle that is 2^{4} centimeters long. About how many times longer is the long-horned beetle than the feather-winged beetle? Explain your reasoning. 8.EE.1

14. Debbie is going to tile her kitchen floor using one of the tiles shown. Both tiles are regular polygons and have the same perimeter. Select whether each statement is true or false. 8.EE.7, 8.EE.7b

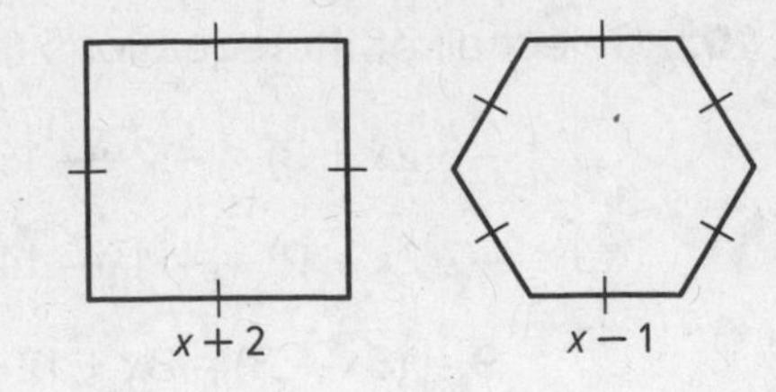

True	False	
☐	☐	The equation $4x + 2 = 6x - 1$ can be used to find the side lengths.
☐	☐	The value of x is 7.
☐	☐	The hexagonal tile has sides 8 units long.
☐	☐	The square tile has sides 9 units long.

15. The table shows the masses, in kilograms, of four dwarf planets in our solar system. Write these four dwarf planets in order from the greatest to least mass. 8.EE.4

Dwarf Planet	Mass (kg)
Ceres	9.5×10^{20}
Eris	1.67×10^{22}
Haumea	4.01×10^{21}
Pluto	1.3×10^{22}

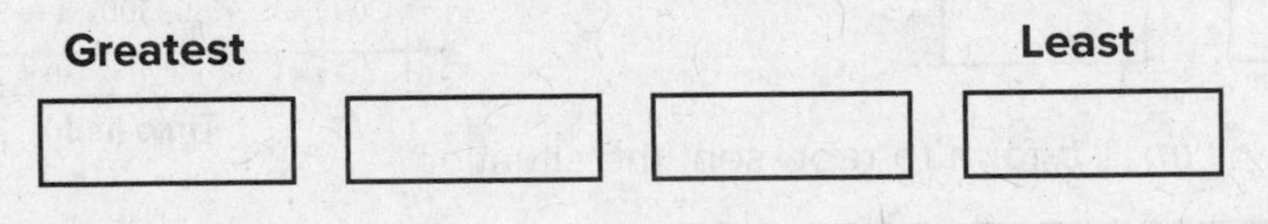

16. Sort the systems of equations into the appropriate bins that describe their solutions. 8.EE.8, 8.EE.8b

$y = -3x$
$y = 3x - 3$

$y = 6(x - 3)$
$y = 6x - 18$

$y = 5(x - 6)$
$y = 5x - 6$

No Solution	One Solution	Infinitely Many Solutions

17. The South China Sea has an area of 895,000 square miles, and the Mediterranean Sea has an area of 1.14×10^6 square miles. Write the name of a sea or a number to make each statement true. 8.EE.4

The ☐ Sea has a greater area than the ☐ Sea.

The difference in the areas of the two seas is approximately ☐ square miles.

18. Carter buys a bus card. The table shows the amount in dollars left on the card after it had been used for several rides. The relationship is graphed on a coordinate plane. Write a number or word to complete the statements. 8.F.4

Number of Rides Taken	0	2	4
Balance on Bus Card ($)	20	15	10

The slope is [ ]. The y-intercept is [ ].

The [ ] shows the initial amount on the card in dollars.

The [ ] shows that the amount on the card decreases by $[ ] each time a ride is taken.

−20	0.40
−5	2.50
−2.5	5
−0.4	20
slope	y-intercept

19. Retta won 4 times as many ribbons at the county fair as Ximena did. Ximena won 6 fewer ribbons than Retta. The number of ribbons won by each friend can be represented by this system of equations. 8.EE.8, 8.EE.8b, 8.EE.8c

$y = 4x$
$y = x + 6$

Part A: Graph these equations on the coordinate plane. Plot the point of intersection.

y
12
10
8
6
4
2
−2 O 2 4 6 8 10 12 x
−2

Part B: What is the solution of the system of equations? What does the solution represent?

20. The formula $t = \sqrt{\frac{h}{16}}$ represents the time in seconds t that it takes an object to fall from a height of h feet. 8.NS.2

Part A: Estimate, to the nearest integer, the time it takes each stone to fall when dropped from the given height.

Stone A: $h = 160$ feet [ ]

Stone B: $h = 544$ feet [ ]

Part B: Show on the number line how you estimated each time.

Stone A:

1 1.5 2 2.5 3 3.5 4

Stone B:

3 3.5 4 4.5 5 5.5 6

NAME ______________________ DATE ____________ PERIOD ________ SCORE ________

Benchmark Test Performance Task, Chapters 1–3

For this Performance Task, research and record the population and land area for New York City, Los Angeles, Chicago, Houston, and Philadelphia, as well as each city's distance from your school.

Moving to the City

Going to college, getting a job, or pursuing a dream can sometimes mean moving to a new city. You can compare data about various cities.

Write your answers on another piece of paper. Show all your work to receive full credit.

Part A

Write the populations in scientific notation with 2 digits and the land areas to the nearest tenth of a square mile. Are the numbers rational or irrational? Why might it be useful to have population data in scientific notation?

Part B

To find population density, divide the population of a region by the area in square miles. Choose 3 cities and write them in order from least to greatest population. Then order the cities by population density. Are the orders the same? Discuss why this does or does not occur.

Part C

Choose one city. You plan to travel at a constant speed of 50 miles per hour. Make a graph to show the distance in miles y you travel in x hours. Use your graph to estimate how many hours it would take to drive from your school to the city. Write and solve an equation to check.

Part D

Your car gets 30 miles per gallon of gas. Gas costs $3.90 per gallon. You spend $125 per day on meals and lodging. Write an equation in slope-intercept form for the total cost in dollars y of a one-way trip over x days. You plan to drive 10 hours per day. How much will your trip cost?

Part E

Choose a different city. Create an equation to show the total cost y for x days. Explain differences between the equations you wrote in Parts D and E. Solve the system of equations. Which trip would be more expensive? Why?

NAME ______________________ DATE __________ PERIOD ________ SCORE ________

Benchmark Test, Chapters 4–6

1. Daiki's first album is released. The table shows the number of his albums that were sold in the first few days. 8.F.4

Day	1	2	4	7
Albums Sold	36,000	40,000	48,000	60,000

Part A: Graph the relationship on the coordinate plane.

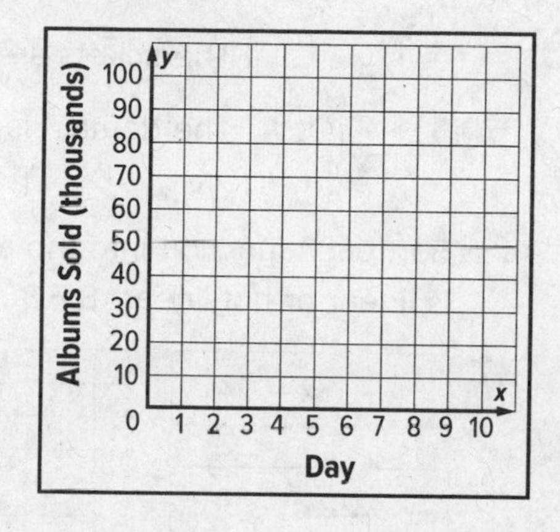

Part B: The pattern of Daiki's album sales continues. How many people will buy the album on the tenth day?

2. Layla bought t-shirts to sell. She spent \$100. She earns a \$5 profit on each t-shirt she sells. The function $f(x) = 5x - 100$ represents her total profit from selling x t-shirts. Write values to complete the function machine for the number of t-shirts sold and the total profits, in dollars, for days A, B, C, and D. 8.F.1, 8.F.4

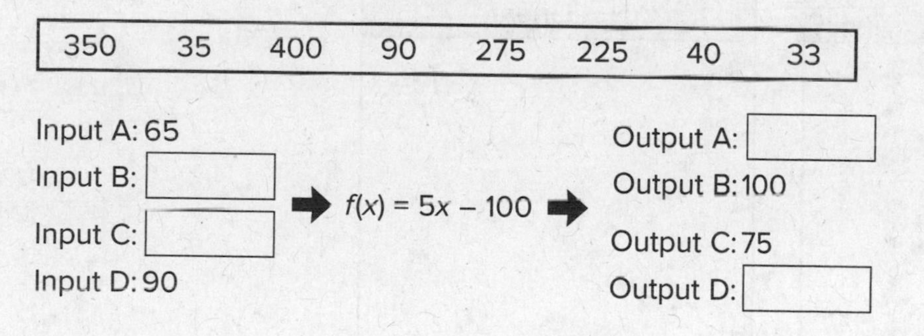

3. The local theater offers a package where an individual pays $75 a year for membership and a reduced rate for all tickets. Benjamin is a member, goes to 3 plays one year, and pays a total of $180. Select whether each statement is true or false. 8.F.4

True	False	
☐	☐	The function $y = 25x + 75$ gives the price y of going to x plays.
☐	☐	The domain represents the total cost.
☐	☐	The tickets are $35 each.
☐	☐	The domain is discrete because you cannot buy a fraction of a ticket.

4. Sort each function into the appropriate bin based on whether it is linear or not linear. 8.F.3

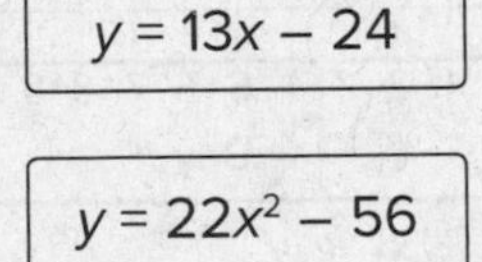

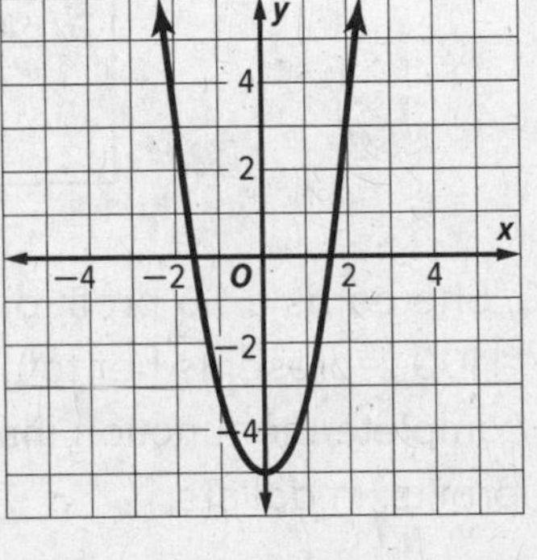

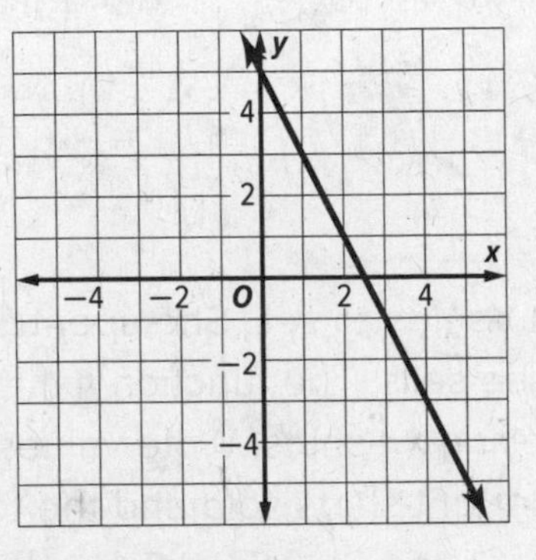

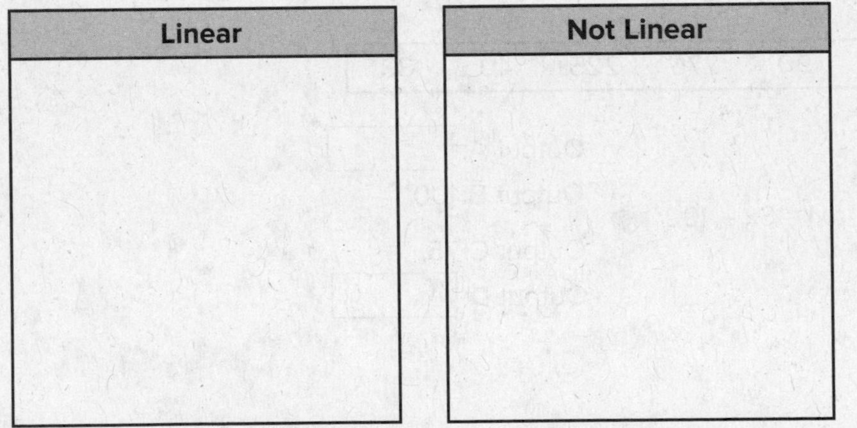

5. The function $y = 27x$ represents the miles y that Miguel's car travels in the city using x gallons of gas. On the highway, the car will go 236 miles on 8 gallons of gas. Is the average number of miles per gallon (mpg) greater in the city or on the highway? Justify your answer. 8.F.2

6. Bao estimates the temperature throughout her camping trip by listening to crickets. The table shows the number of chirps and her estimates. 8.F.4

Number of Chirps	76	100	120
Temperature (°F)	59	65	70

Part A: Select the correct values to model the situation with a linear function.

40	76	6	50	65	0.25
1	32	4	59	100	24

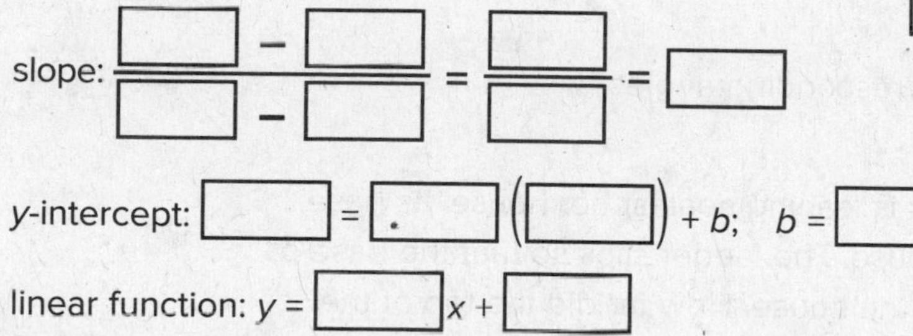

Part B: What do the slope and the y-intercept represent?

7. Teetonka is selling tickets to a fundraiser for his school's garden. He thinks he can make more money by reducing the price and selling more tickets. The total amount he will make y by selling tickets at price x can be modeled by the equation $y = 240x - 20x^2$ and the graph. 8.F.5

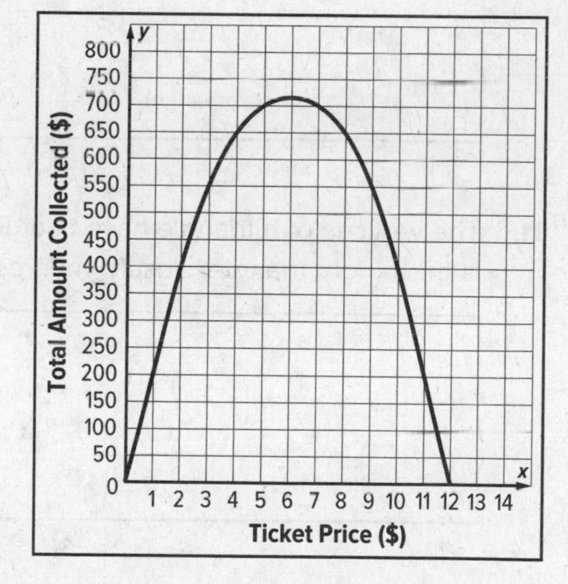

Part A: At what high price will nobody buy tickets? Justify your answer.

Part B: At what price will Teetonka make the most money? How much? How many tickets will he sell at this price? Explain how you found the answers.

8. Lines m and n are parallel and cut by the transversal q. Identify each statement as true or false. 8.G.5

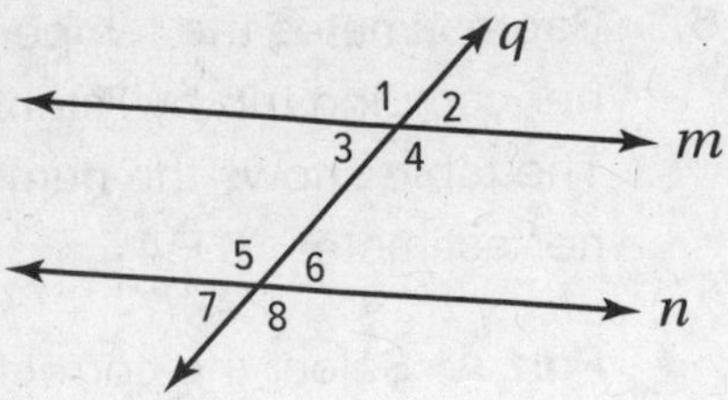

True	False	
☐	☐	$\angle 1 \cong \angle 8$
☐	☐	$m\angle 4 = 110°$, so $m\angle 5 = 70°$.
☐	☐	$m\angle 7 = m\angle 3$
☐	☐	$\angle 3$ and $\angle 8$ are corresponding angles.

q
1 2
3 4
m
5 6
7 8
n

9. Tiana is on a 25-foot ladder that is leaning against her house. Its base is 7 feet from the base of the house. The ladder slips so that the base of the ladder is 8 feet farther from the house. How far did the top of the ladder move down the wall? 8.G.7

10. A pencil box in the shape of a rectangular prism measures 3 inches by 4 inches by 12 inches. What is the length of the longest pencil that can fit in the box? Explain your answer. 8.G.7

11. The vertices of a triangle have coordinates $A(3, 4)$, $B(-2, -1)$, and $C(-7, 6)$. Is this a right triangle? Justify your response. 8.G.7, 8.G.8

12. Nascha's sons set up a tent for a campout in the backyard. The tent's instruction manual identifies the measures of the angles when the tent is set up correctly. 8.G.5

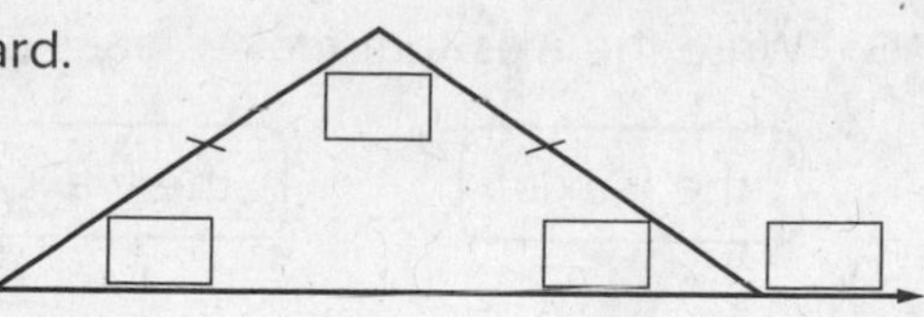

Part A: Write the appropriate angle measures in the spaces.

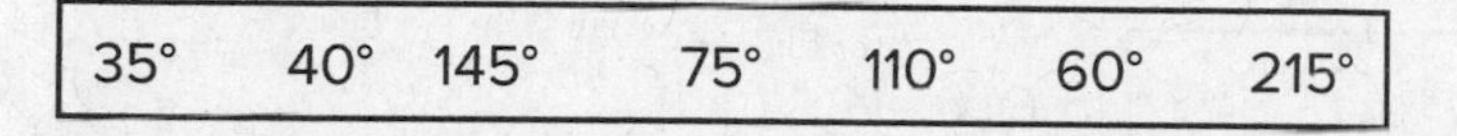

Part B: Justify each measure that you wrote in the triangle.

13. Aarav designs a pentagonal greenhouse. Her brother Inesh helps with the construction. He tells her, "Just make sure that your design has 5 sides and the sum of the interior angles is 360°." Did Inesh give his sister correct advice? Explain your answer. 8.G.5

14. Kevin is shown this figure. He says, "The sum of the measures of the exterior angles of this figure is 360°. The sum of the measures of the exterior angles of a hexagon is 360°. So, this figure is a hexagon." 8.G.5

Part A: What type of reasoning is being used, inductive or deductive? Explain your answer.

Part B: What is the error in Kevin's reasoning?

15. Write the axis that makes each statement true. 8.G.3

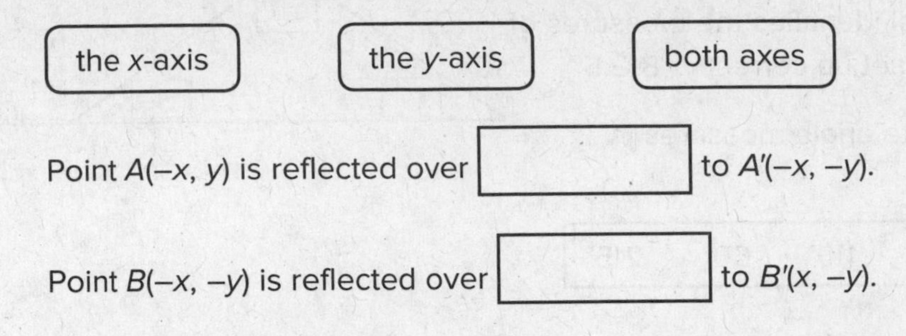

the x-axis | the y-axis | both axes

Point $A(-x, y)$ is reflected over ______ to $A'(-x, -y)$.

Point $B(-x, -y)$ is reflected over ______ to $B'(x, -y)$.

16. Jorge plots the floor plan of his room on a coordinate plane. The rectangle with vertices $A(2, 3)$, $B(2, -4)$, $C(-7, -4)$, and $D(-7, 3)$ represents his bed. It is translated 3 units up and 4 units to the left. Select all of the points that would be vertices of the translated figure. 8.G.3

- ☐ $A'(5, -1)$
- ☐ $B'(-2, -1)$
- ☐ $C'(-3, -7)$
- ☐ $D'(-11, 6)$

17. Triangle XYZ is translated 2 units right and 1 unit down. What are the vertices of triangle $X'Y'Z'$? 8.G.3

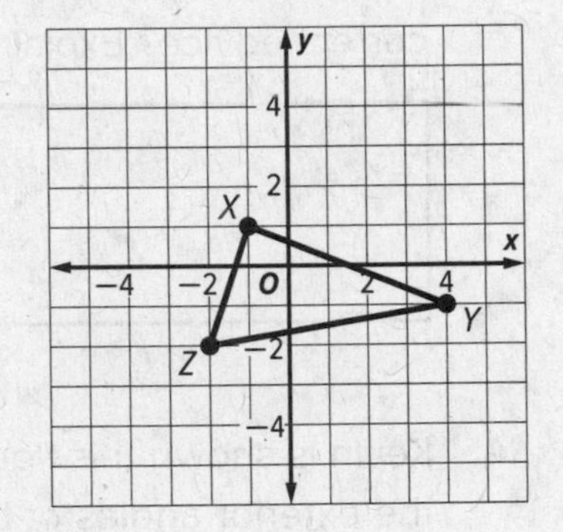

18. A company logo contains a triangle with vertices $F(3, 9)$, $G(0, 6)$, and $H(-3, -3)$. After a dilation, the image of F is $F'(4, 12)$. 8.G.3

Part A: What is the scale factor of the dilation?

Part B: What are the images of vertices G and H after the dilation?

Part C: Is this dilation an enlargement or a reduction? Explain your answer.

19. D'Andrea draws plans for a park on a coordinate plane. She includes a community table *ABCDE*. She changes the location of the table by reflecting it over the *x*-axis. Graph the reflection. 8.G.3

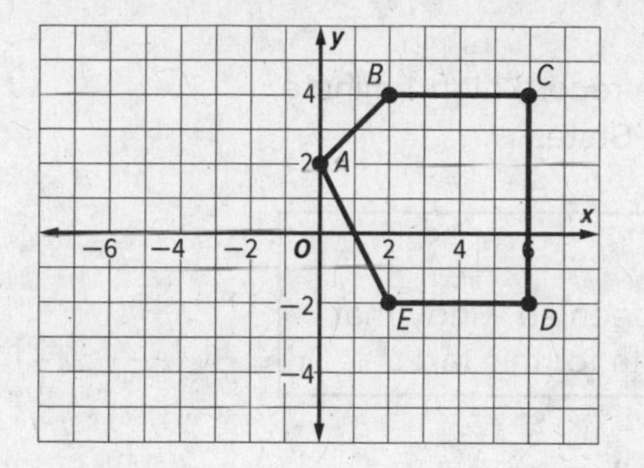

20. The position of a lab table shaped like a parallelogram is shown on the coordinate plane. The table is then rotated 270° clockwise about the origin. Select whether each point is a vertex of the rotated image. 8.G.3

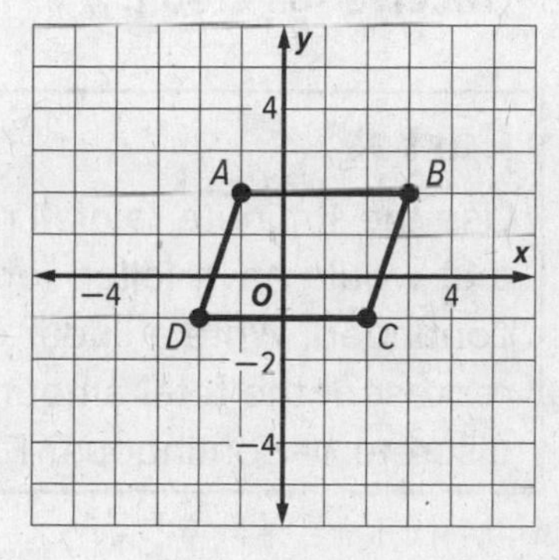

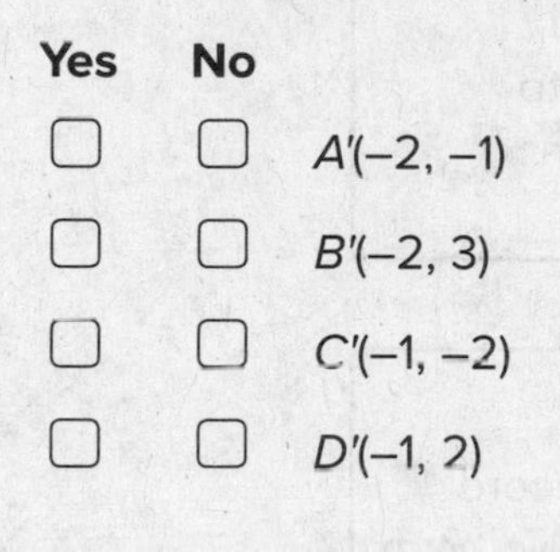

Yes	No	
☐	☐	$A'(-2, -1)$
☐	☐	$B'(-2, 3)$
☐	☐	$C'(-1, -2)$
☐	☐	$D'(-1, 2)$

NAME ______________ DATE ________ PERIOD ______ SCORE ______

Benchmark Test, Performance Task, Chapters 4–6

For this Performance Task, research and write down the record high 1-minute rainfall and the record high 1-hour rainfall for the United States.

Soaking Up a Storm

Have you ever gotten drenched in the rain? Has it ever been so windy that the rain seems to fall sideways? Use your researched data for this task.

Write your answers on another piece of paper. Show all your work to receive full credit.

Part A

Use the 1-minute rainfall record. Make a table to show the amount of rain that would have fallen for 2, 3, and 4 minutes, assuming this rate had continued. Write a linear equation and make a graph of the function to represent the total amount of rainfall *r* after *m* minutes. Is the function discrete or continuous? Explain your answer.

Part B

Use the 1-hour rainfall record. How long would it take to reach the record high 1-hour rainfall at the 1-minute rate? How many inches of rain would have fallen in an hour at that rate? Use the function from Part A to find the values.

Part C

The graph shows the wind speed over a period of time during a rainstorm. Describe each section of the qualitative graph.

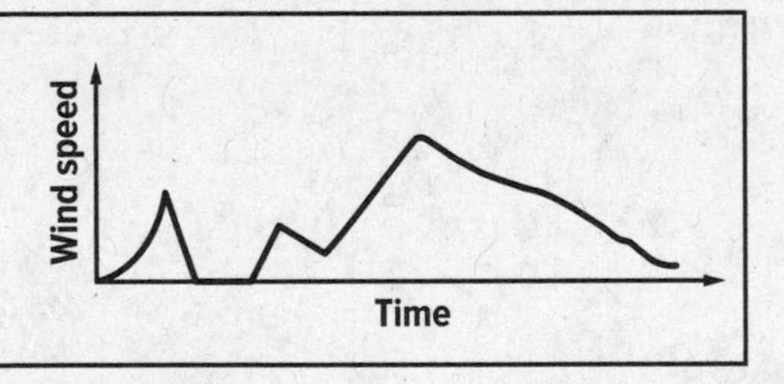

Part D

Sometimes during rain events, a tree or branch will fall. The treetop shown fell in a straight line from the top of the tree to its current location. How far did point *A* on the tree travel to reach Point *B* on the ground? Before the tree broke, what kind of symmetry did it display? Explain.

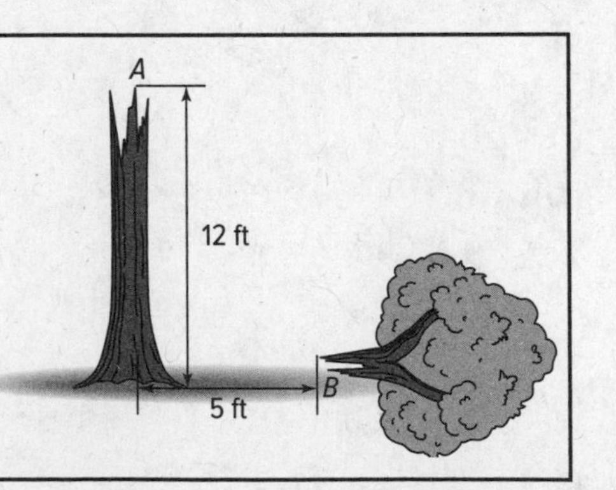

NAME ______________________ DATE ____________ PERIOD ________ SCORE ________

Benchmark Test A, Chapters 1–9

1. Luis is creating a solar system with a star called Shine. Luis made a table to show the size of this solar system. Express your answers in scientific notation whenever possible. 8.EE.3, 8.EE.4

Luis' Solar System		
Planets	**Distance from Shine (mi)**	**Diameter (ft)**
Abba	3.525×10^{16}	3.525×10^{7}
Berta	7.008×10^{18}	4.748×10^{8}
Canni	2.263×10^{19}	7.003×10^{9}

How many more miles is Canni from Shine than Abba is? [ ]

Approximately how many times bigger is the diameter of Canni than the diameter of Abba? [ ]

How many more miles is Canni from Shine than Berta is? [ ]

2. Box A has a length of 8 inches and its width and height are equal. Its volume is 1,656 cubic inches. Estimate the height of Box A. Write the volume formula to find the height. Then locate the height between two perfect squares. Finally estimate the height to the nearest whole number and explain why. 8.NS.2, 8.EE.2

Volume formula: [ ]

Height between perfect squares: $\sqrt{\square} < \sqrt{\square} < \sqrt{\square}$.

Height estimate: [ ]

3. Select whether each statement is true or false. 8.NS.1, 8.EE.1

True	False	
☐	☐	The number $\sqrt{5}$ is an irrational number because its decimal expansion does not repeat.
☐	☐	The number $6.\overline{6}$ is a rational number because its decimal expansion repeats.
☐	☐	The number 1,785.2 is a rational integer.
☐	☐	$2^3 \cdot \sqrt{2} = 2^3 \cdot 2^{-2} = 2$
☐	☐	$\frac{4^5}{4^2} \cdot \frac{4^{-1}}{4^{-3}} = 4^5 \cdot 4^3 \cdot 4^{-1} \cdot 4^{-2} = 4^8 \cdot 4^{-3} = 4^5$

4. Jackson bought an equal number of notebooks and binders. The notebooks cost \$1.25 each, and the binders cost \$3.50 each. He spent a total of \$28.50. 8.EE.7, 8.EE.7b

Deanna's solution:

Let x be the number of notebooks.

$$1.25x + 3.5x = 28.50$$
$$4.75x = 28.50$$
$$x = 6$$

Jackson purchased 6 notebooks.

Part A: Select whether each statement is true or false.

True	False	
☐	☐	Deanna correctly used x to represent the number of notebooks Jackson bought.
☐	☐	Deanna added the coefficients correctly.
☐	☐	Deanna computed $28.50 \div 4.75$ accurately.
☐	☐	Deanna is correct that Jackson purchased 6 notebooks.

Part B: How many binders did Jackson buy? What was their cost?

☐

5. Sort the equations into the bin that correctly describes the solution. 8.EE.7, 8.EE.7a

$6a + 19 = 2(3a + 5) + 9$	$0.3(a - 8) = 0.2(a + 4)$	$0.25(24 - 12a) = -3a + 6$
$2(5a + 4) = 4a + 8$	$3(2a + 1) - a = 6 + 5a$	$2(a - 2) = 2(a - 3) - 2$

No Solution	One Solution	Infinitely Many Solutions

6. A cell phone company has two price plans for their service. Select whether each statement is true or false. 8.EE.7, 8.EE.7b

	Monthly Charge	Minute Limit	Over Limit Price per Minute
Plan A	\$26	1,000	\$0.20
Plan B	\$12	500	\$0.48

True	False	
☐	☐	The plans cost the same when the over-limit minutes are 50.
☐	☐	Plan B costs more than Plan A when over-limit minutes are less than 50.
☐	☐	A customer would choose Plan B over Plan A when he or she plans on using under 500 minutes a month.

7. ***Part A:*** Complete the table to order the equations by the steepness of the slopes of their graphs from greatest to least. 8.EE.5, 8.EE.6

$y = 3x + 2$ $\qquad y = \frac{2}{5}x - 7$

$y = -\frac{1}{6}x + 5$ $\qquad y = -4x - 3$

Steepest slope	
Flattest slope	

Part B: Select whether each statement is true or false.

True	False	
☐	☐	The graph of $y = 3x + 2$ is a line that intersects the vertical axis at 2.
☐	☐	The points (0, –7) and (2, –2) lie on the graph of $y = \frac{2}{5}x - 7$.
☐	☐	The graph of $y = -\frac{1}{6}x + 5$ is a line with a vertical change of –1 when the horizontal change is 6.
☐	☐	The graph of $y = -4x - 3$ is a line that intersects the vertical axis at –4.
☐	☐	The graph of $y = \frac{2}{5}x - 7$ has a run that moves to the right 5 units when the rise moves up 2 units.

8. Write an equation to represent each situation. Then solve the system of equations to answer the question. 8.EE.8, 8.EE.8b, 8.EE.8c, 8.F.4

Jake pays a monthly rate of $42 for cell service and $0.28 for each minute over 300 minutes.

Carlos pays a flat rate of $80 per month for unlimited minutes.

For how many minutes in one month will Jake and Carlos pay the same amount?

9. One equation in a system of equations is $y = 2x + 3$. The other equation is $y = -3x + 8$. 8.EE.8, 8.EE.8a, 8.EE.8c

Part A: Graph the system of equations on the coordinate plane provided.

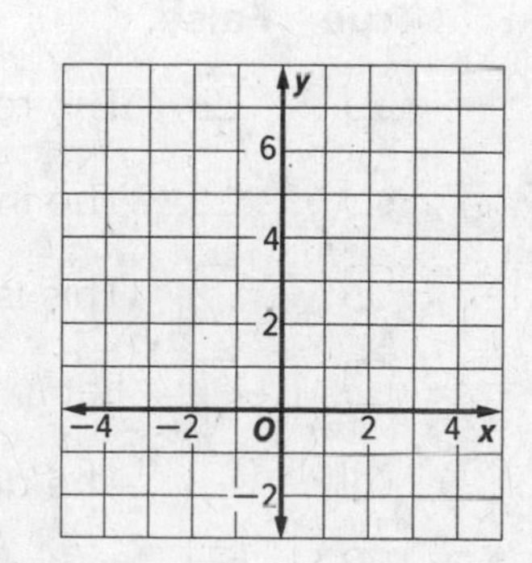

Part B: What is the solution of the system? Describe the graph of the system and how it relates to the number of solutions.

10. ***Part A:*** Sort the systems of equations into the appropriate bins by the type of solution. 8.EE.8, 8.EE.8a, 8.EE.8b

$y = x + 4$ and $y = x - 3$	$3x + 2y = 5$ and $-3x - 2y = -5$
$y = 0.5x + 0.2$ and $y = 0.4x - 0.3$	$y = 7x + 1$ and $y = 7x - 1$

$y = 102x + 6$ and $y = 78x - 9$

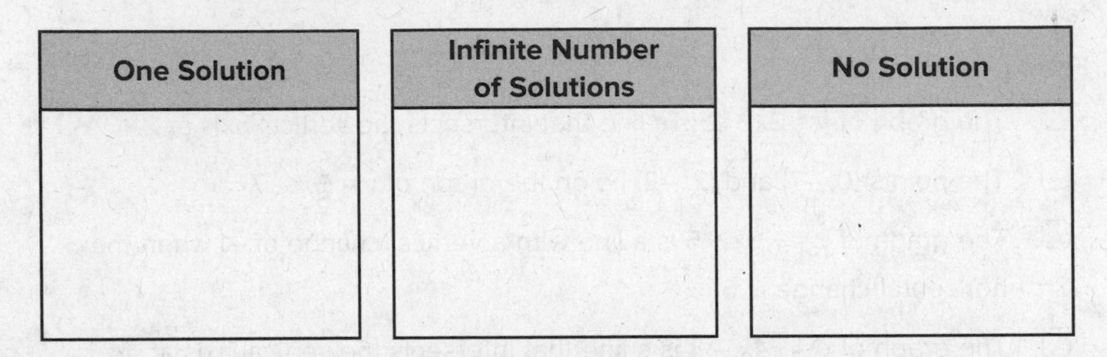

One Solution	Infinite Number of Solutions	No Solution

Part B: Solve the system of linear equations $y = x + 4$ and $y = x - 3$ algebraically. Then describe the type of graph of this system.

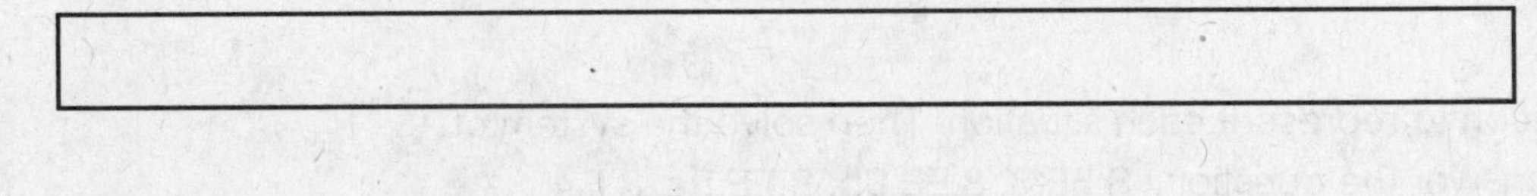

11. Ayani is selling candy bars for his school fundraiser. For every 5 bars of candy sold, he gets a prize. 8.F.1

Part A: Graph the relation between number of candy bars sold and total number of prizes earned on the coordinate plane. Label the *x*- and *y*-axes, and assign numbers to the grid lines on the axes.

Part B: Select whether each statement is true or false.

True	False	
☐	☐	The relation is a function because it assigns to each input exactly one output.
☐	☐	The independent variable is the number of candy bars sold.
☐	☐	This is a continuous function.
☐	☐	Let $f(x) = y$. Then $f(x) = \frac{1}{5}x$.
☐	☐	The domain is the set of positive multiples of 5.
☐	☐	The point (10, 50) is an ordered pair in the set of this relation.

12. Zweena rides her bike 10 miles per hour on a biking trail. She starts at mile marker 2 and heads in the direction of mile marker 3. Each marker indicates a distance of 1 mile. 8.F.2, 8.F.4

Time Riding (min)	Mile Marker

Part A: Complete the table with five data points that map the relation between the location of Zweena on the bike trail and time riding.

Part B: Juanita rides her bike on the same biking trail. The equation $y = 12x$ represents the relation between the location of Juanita on the bike trail and time riding. Select whether each statement is true or false.

True	False	
☐	☐	Both relations are linear functions.
☐	☐	Juanita's constant rate of change is greater than Zweena's.
☐	☐	Zweena has ridden 1 mile farther than Juanita after each has biked for 30 minutes.
☐	☐	Juanita started at mile marker 0.
☐	☐	Juanita's linear function has an initial value greater than Zweena's.
☐	☐	Zweena and Juanita will be at the same mile marker after riding for an hour.

13. Pedro is building sheds for a housing development. The area of the shed depends on the size of the plot on which it is built. The dimensions of the shed are $(x - 1)$ meters by $(2x - 4)$ meters. 8.F.3, 8.F.5

Part A: Graph the relation between the value of x and the area of the shed on the coordinate plane. Label axes and assign numbers to the grid lines on the axes.

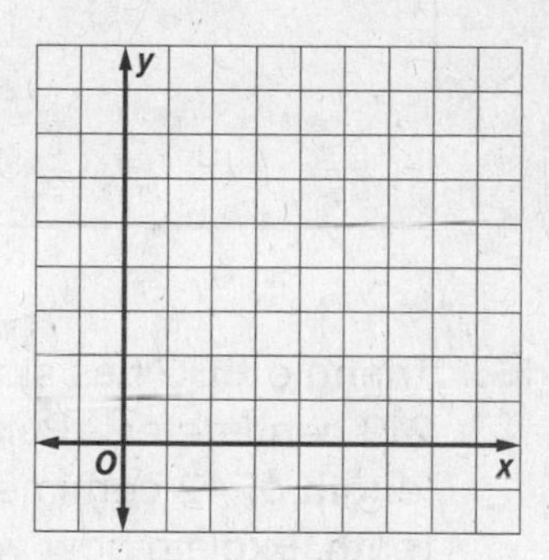

Part B: Select whether each statement is true or false.

True	False	
☐	☐	This relation is a continuous function.
☐	☐	The function decreases for $x \leq 1$.
☐	☐	The function is linear.
☐	☐	The function increases for $x \geq 2$.
☐	☐	The function has a constant rate of change.
☐	☐	When $x = 3$, the shed is 2 m wide by 2 m long, and the area is 4 m^2.

14. A bowler rolls a ball down the lane. After it passes the pins, the ball gets swept to the side into a chute for a short period of time. The chute then brings the ball back to the bowler. 8.F.5

Part A: Sketch a qualitative graph to represent the ball's distance from the bowler at any given time.

Part B: Describe any patterns you see in your graph.

15. The figure is a regular hexagon. Lines k, m, and n are parallel. Line p intersects lines k, m, and n. The measure of $\angle 1$ is 120°. Find the measure of $\angle 13$. Justify your response. You can use any angles on the figure in your response. 8.G.5

16. Triangle ABC has sides $\overline{AB}$, $\overline{BC}$, and $\overline{AC}$. AB is 108 centimeters and BC is 210 centimeters. Point D is on $\overline{AC}$. $\overline{BD}$ is perpendicular to $\overline{AC}$ and has a length of 42 centimeters. What is the length of $\overline{AC}$? Round to the nearest tenth. Explain how you solved the problem. 8.G.7

17. Select whether the statements describe similar figures. 8.G.4, 8.EE.6

Yes	No	
☐	☐	A square has an area of 16 ft^2 and another square has an area of 81 ft^2.
☐	☐	The slope of a right triangle's hypotenuse is 3 and the slope of another right triangle's hypotenuse is –3.
☐	☐	The perimeter of a hexagon is 30 in. and the perimeter of another hexagon is 60 in.
☐	☐	A pentagon is reflected over the y-axis and then dilated by a scale factor of 0.4.
☐	☐	The slope of a right triangle's hypotenuse is 4 and the slope of another right triangle's hypotenuse is 0.25.

18. The beads on a loom line up in an array of rows and columns just like on a coordinate plane. You can make a pattern by performing a transformation of the shaded box with vertices at (2, 0), (4, 0), (2, 2), and (4, 2). 8.G.1, 8.G.3

Part A: Perform $(x, y) \rightarrow (x + 2, y + 2)$ and shade in the result. Then perform $(x', y') \rightarrow (x' - 2, y' + 2)$ and shade in the result.

Part B: What type of transformations did you perform? Explain.

19. Triangle ABC with vertices $A(0, 0)$, $B(0, -5)$, and $C(-4, -5)$ is transformed 3 separate times. Starting with triangle ABC each time, complete the table with a description of the three transformations on triangle ABC. 8.G.1, 8.G.3

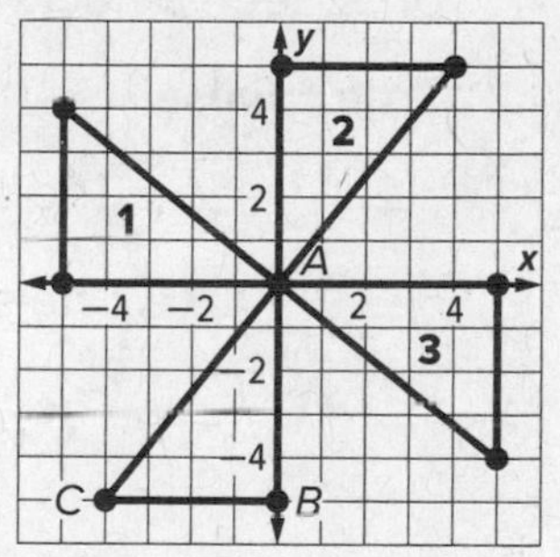

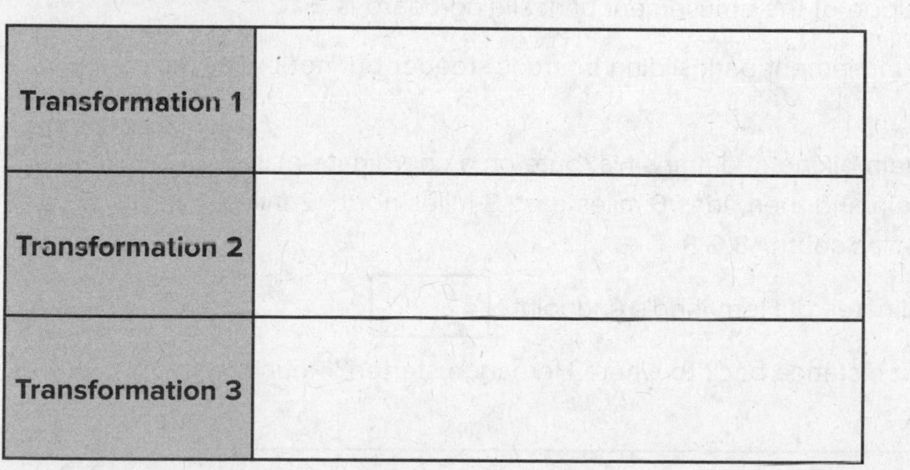

Transformation 1	
Transformation 2	
Transformation 3	

20. A trapezoid *ABCD* has vertices *A*(0, 0), *B*(8, 0), *C*(6, 4), and *D*(2, 4). 8.G.3

Part A: The trapezoid is dilated by a scale factor of 0.5 and then translated 6 units right and 8 units up. Find the coordinates of trapezoid *A″B″C″D″*.

Part B: The translation is performed first and then the dilation. Will you get the same set of coordinates as in Part A? Explain.

21. Ana is 5.5 feet tall. Her shadow is 2.4 feet long. The hot-air balloon on the ground next to her is casting a 26.4-foot-long shadow. A nearby flagpole is 42 feet tall. Find each measure to the nearest tenth. 8.G.4, 8.G.7

height of the hot-air balloon:

length of the shadow of the flagpole:

22. The sliding board at a pool has a height of 14 feet and a horizontal length from ladder to bottom of slide of 12 feet. The amusement park sliding board has a height of 40 feet and a horizontal length from ladder to bottom of slide of 32 feet. Select whether each statement is true or false. 8.G.7, 8.EE.6

True	False	
☐	☐	The slope of the pool sliding board is $\frac{7}{6}$ ft.
☐	☐	The slope of the amusement park sliding board is $\frac{4}{5}$ ft.
☐	☐	The amusement park sliding board is steeper but not by much.

23. Hernando is mountain biking and maps his route on a coordinate plane. He starts at the origin and then rides 6 miles east, 3 miles north, 2 miles east again, and 8 miles south. 8.G.8

What are the coordinates of Hernando's endpoint?

What is the shortest distance back to where Hernando started? Round to the nearest tenth.

24. A pump fills exercise balls with air at a rate of 300 cubic inches per minute. The table shows how long it takes to inflate different balls. Complete the table with the radius of each exercise ball. Round to the nearest tenth. 8.G.9

Time to Fill with Air (min)	5	10	15	20	25
Radius (in.)					

25. A company makes posts to prevent cars from traveling in pedestrian areas. The post is a cone 40 inches in height and 10 inches in diameter at the base. The tip of the cone is filled with a plastic plug and then filled with concrete. What is the volume of concrete needed to make one post? 8.G.9

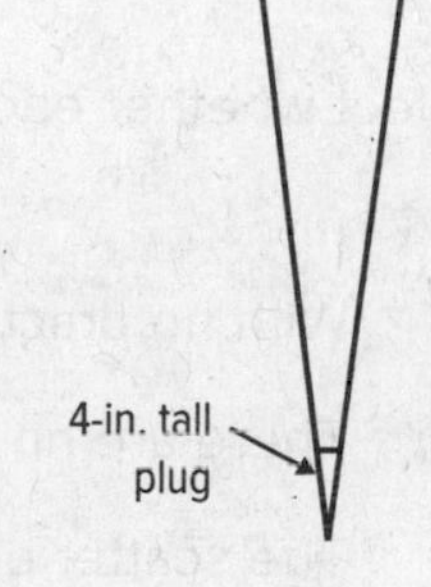

[ ]

26. A right triangle has a base of 4 units and a height of 8 units. Select whether each sequence of transformations produces a congruent triangle. 8.G.4

Yes	No	
☐	☐	a dilation by a scale factor of 2 and then a reflection over the *x*-axis
☐	☐	a rotation of 90° and then a translation of 10 units right
☐	☐	a reflection over the *y*-axis and then a rotation of –45°
☐	☐	a vertical translation of –3 and then a dilation by a scale factor of 0.5

27. The two-way table shows the number of students who prefer to bring or buy their lunch at school. Complete the table. Find the relative frequencies of the students by row. Round to the nearest hundredth. 8.SP.4

	Buy Lunch	Bring Lunch	Totals
Females	222	261	
Males	256	200	
Totals			

28. A survey of 450 people showed that 265 people live near a mountain. A total of 288 people ride a bike and 206 of them live near a mountain. Complete the two-way table. 8.SP.4

	Bike	No Bike	Totals
Live Near a Mountain	206		265
Not Near a Mountain			
Totals	288		450

29. On a TV game show, a large cylinder of water fills a beach ball while a contestant performs a task. When the beach ball is full, the contestant must stop. The cylinder has a diameter of 6 feet and is 8 feet tall. The beach ball has a diameter of 6.4 feet. When the beach ball is full, how much water is left in the cylinder? Round your answer to the nearest hundredth. 8.G.9

30. The scatter plot shows the relationship between the number of times per week a golfer practices and her average 18-hole score. 8.SP.2, 8.SP.3

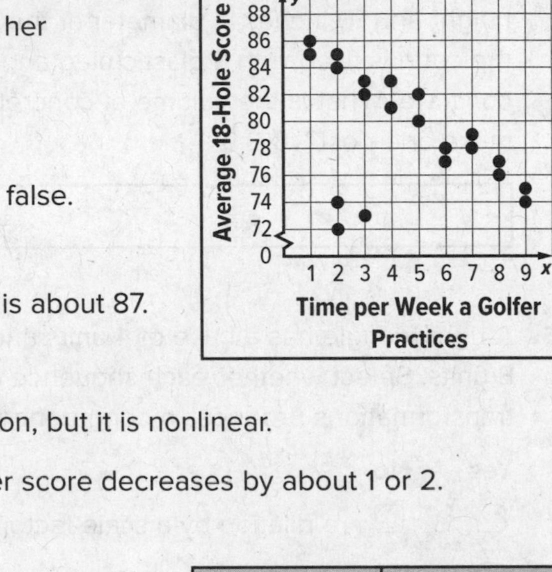

Part A: Draw a line of best fit for the data.

Part B: Select whether each statement is true or false.

True	False	
☐	☐	With no practice, the golfer's score is about 87.
☐	☐	There are no outliers or clusters.
☐	☐	The scatter plot shows an association, but it is nonlinear.
☐	☐	For each time a golfer practices, her score decreases by about 1 or 2.

31. Geoff asked 10 employees how long it takes them to get to work and how far their homes are from work. Their responses are in the table. 8.SP.1, 8.SP.2

	Time (min)	Distance (mi)
Allie	15	5
Johnson	20	15
Cayla	25	15
Sylvia	25	10
Omar	30	20
Carter	30	10
Phil	35	25
Jess	35	10
Terry	45	35
Jameel	45	15

Part A: Plot the data to make a scatter plot.

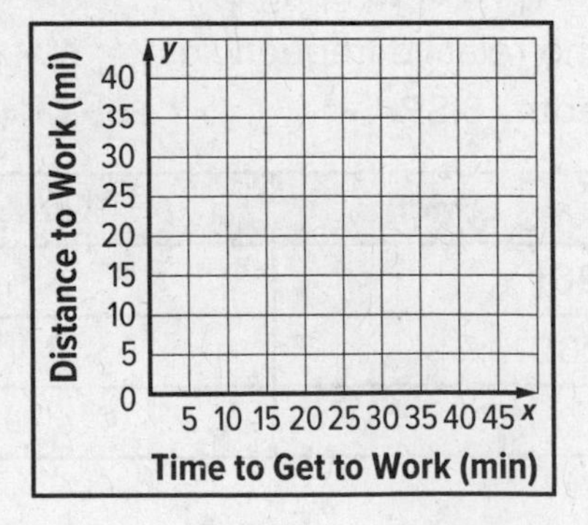

Part B: Interpret the scatter plot of the data.

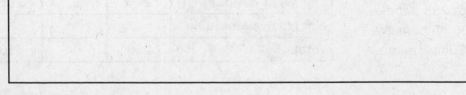

NAME ______________________ DATE ____________ PERIOD ________ SCORE ________

Benchmark Test A, Performance Task, Chapters 1–9

It's All Downhill From Here!

Sisay and Mika are collecting data at their local ski resorts. They are interpreting and analyzing the data from different ski runs, also called ski slopes.

Write your answers on another piece of paper. Show all your work to receive full credit.

Part A

Sisay's average speed skiing down beginner ski runs is shown in the table. Mika's average speed skiing down beginner ski runs is represented by the graph. Which girl skied faster? Justify your response.

Sisay's Average Speed	
Time Skiing (s)	**Distance Traveled (m)**
0	0
1	4.2
2	8.4
3	12.6
4	16.8
5	21.0

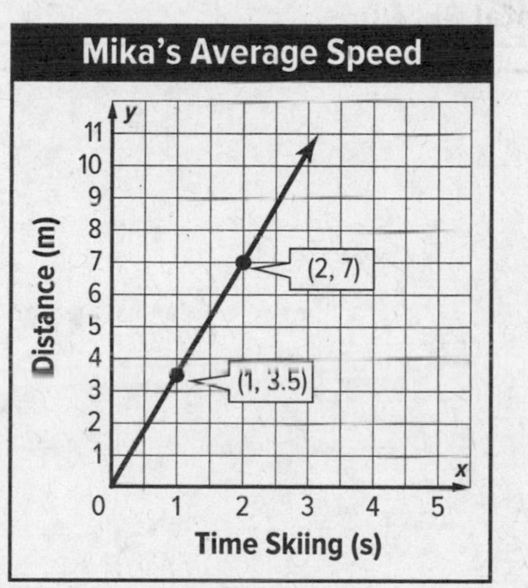

Part B

The ski resort Powder Fresh charges \$62 to ski for the day and \$48 an hour for a ski guide who also gives lessons. The ski resort Got Snow charges \$70 to ski for the day and \$43 an hour for a ski guide who also gives lessons. Write a function that represents the total cost to ski for the day and receive services from a ski guide for each resort. Algebraically find when these functions are equal and explain what that means in the context of this situation.

Mika and Sisay collected data on 46 ski runs at the local ski resorts. In addition to the skiing costs, they found data about the measurements of the ski runs. By looking at the ski runs as right triangles, the data can be analyzed and compared.

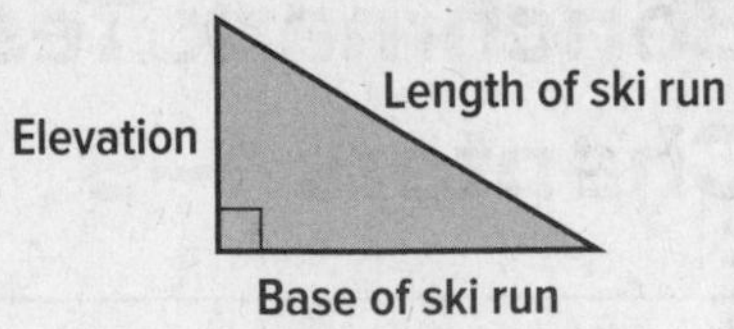

Elevation

Length of ski run

Base of ski run

Part C

The two-way table shows the elevation at the top of the 46 ski runs and the length of the ski runs. Find and interpret the relative frequencies of the ski runs by row. Round to the nearest hundredth.

	Length of Ski Run: 400 m	Length of Ski Run: 550 m	Total Ski Runs
Elevation: 150 m	22	3	25
Elevation: 300 m	2	19	21
Total Ski Runs	24	22	46

Part D

The *grade* of a ski run is measured as a percent when the elevation of the ski run is divided by the base length of the ski run. Find the grades of the four different ski runs listed in the two-way table, and compare the steepness of the ski runs.

NAME ______________________ DATE ____________ PERIOD ________ SCORE ________

Benchmark Test B, Chapters 1–9

1. Angus encounters many different kinds of numbers. 8.NS.1, 8.NS.2

Part A: Select whether the number in each situation is rational or irrational.

Rational	Irrational	
☐	☐	A pan holds 144π, or 452.38934. . ., cubic inches.
☐	☐	A hex nut is labeled "$\frac{7}{16}$ inch."
☐	☐	The temperature inside a freezer is –10.1°F.
☐	☐	The interest rate on a loan is 4.15%.

Part B: The diagonal of a square fabric swatch is $2\sqrt{2}$ inches long. Estimate the length of the diagonal to the nearest tenth of an inch.

[ ]

2. The table shows the approximate populations of four African countries. Write the correct number from the numbers listed to make each statement true. 8.EE.3, 8.EE.4

Country	Population
Eritrea	5×10^6
Ethiopia	1×10^8
Nigeria	2×10^8
Uganda	4×10^7

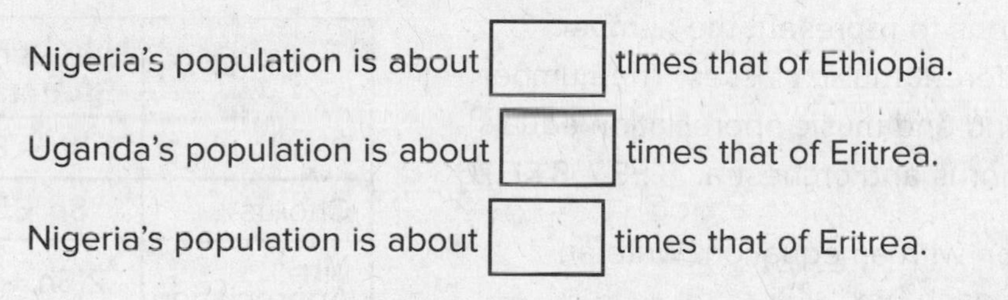

Nigeria's population is about [ ] times that of Ethiopia.

Uganda's population is about [ ] times that of Eritrea.

Nigeria's population is about [ ] times that of Eritrea.

2	3	8	35
40	70	200	350

3. A tree frog that is 2^{-7} meters long jumps about 2^{-2} meters high. About how many times higher than its body length does the frog jump? Explain your reasoning. 8.EE.1

[ ]

4. Sort each equation into the appropriate bin that correctly describes its solution. 8.EE.7, 8.EE.7a

$2(4p + 5) = 6p + 5$ $-3(5x - 3) = -15x + 9$ $-(x + 4) = -x + 4$

No Solution	One Solution	Infinitely Many Solutions

5. Joachin purchased a speaker in the shape of a cube that has a volume of 11 cubic feet. He wants to put it on a shelf on his wall that is 24 inches below the ceiling. Will the cube fit? Explain your reasoning. 8.EE.2

6. Tanisha is using two tiles on her bathroom. Both tiles are regular polygons and have the same perimeter. Select whether each statement is true or false. 8.EE.7, 8.EE.7b

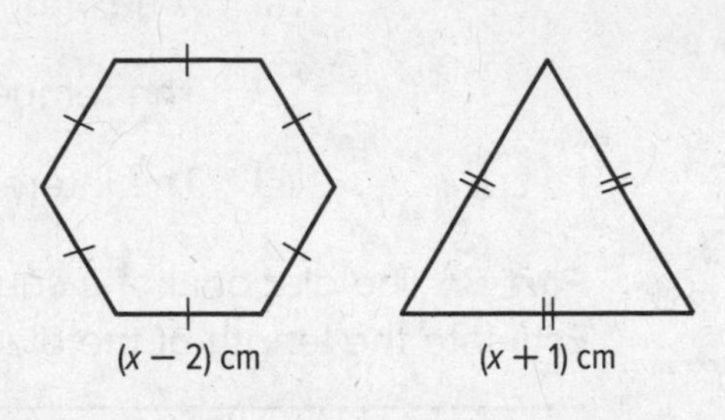

True	False	
☐	☐	The equation $6x - 2 = 3x + 1$ can be used to find the side lengths.
☐	☐	The value of x is 5.
☐	☐	The hexagonal tile has sides 3 cm long.
☐	☐	The triangular tile has a perimeter of 6 cm.

7. The table shows expressions to represent the number of students enrolled in different music classes. The number of students enrolled in band and music appreciation equals the number enrolled in chorus and orchestra. 8.EE.7, 8.EE.7b

Class	Number of Students
Band	$3n - 8$
Chorus	$8n + 5$
Music Appreciation	$2(5n + 3)$
Orchestra	$4n$

Part A: Model the situation with an equation. Write an appropriate expression in each box.

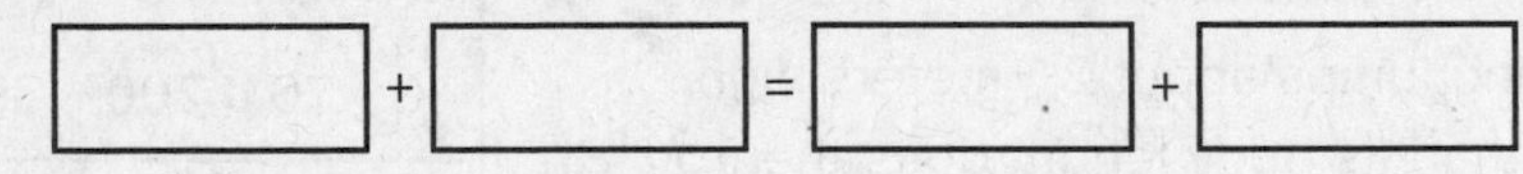

$3n - 8$ | $8n + 5$ | $2(5n + 3)$ | $4n$

Part B: Solve the equation and identify the number of students enrolled in each music class.

Band: ☐ students

Chorus: ☐ students

Music Appreciation: ☐ students

Orchestra: ☐ students

8. The table shows the amount of money Tyler earns per hour working as a locksmith. 8.EE.5, 8.EE.6

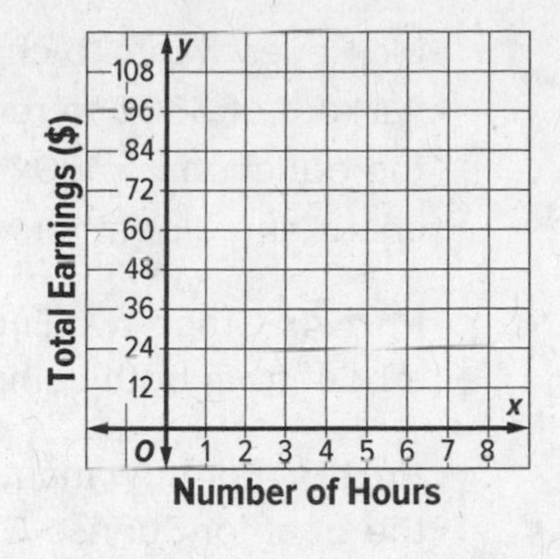

Number of Hours	Total Earnings ($)
2	36
3	54
4	72
5	90
6	108

Part A: Graph the points on the coordinate plane and connect them with a straight line.

Part B: Write an equation in $y = mx$ form to represent the situation. What does the value of m represent in the equation?

9. Sort the systems of equations into the appropriate bins to describe the solutions. 8.EE.8, 8.EE.8b

$y = 4(x - 7)$ $y = 4x - 28$	$y = 2x$ $y = -2x + 2$	$y = -3(x - 4)$ $y = -3x - 12$

No Solution	One Solution	Infinitely Many Solutions

10. A pail is filled with 2,000 milliliters of water. A hole in the bucket causes water to leak from the bucket, as shown by the graph. Write numbers to find the slope of the line. Then write an equation in $y = mx + b$ form to represent the situation. 8.F.3, 8.F.4

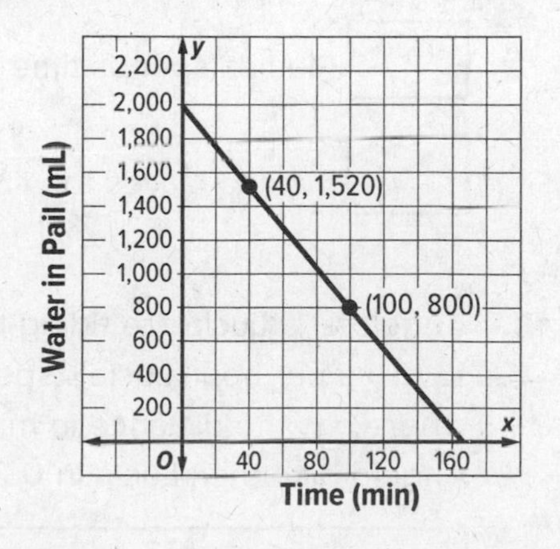

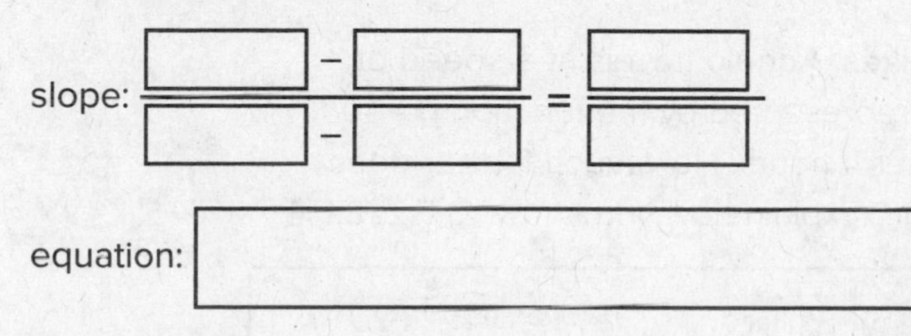

slope: $\frac{\square - \square}{\square - \square} = \frac{\square}{\square}$

equation:

11. Mr. Reyes wants to charter a boat. Captain's Charters charges a flat rate of $600 to rent a boat for a day. At Sunrise Charters, the equation $y = 150x$ shows the cost y in dollars, of chartering a boat for x hours. 8.EE.8, 8.EE.8a, 8.EE.8c

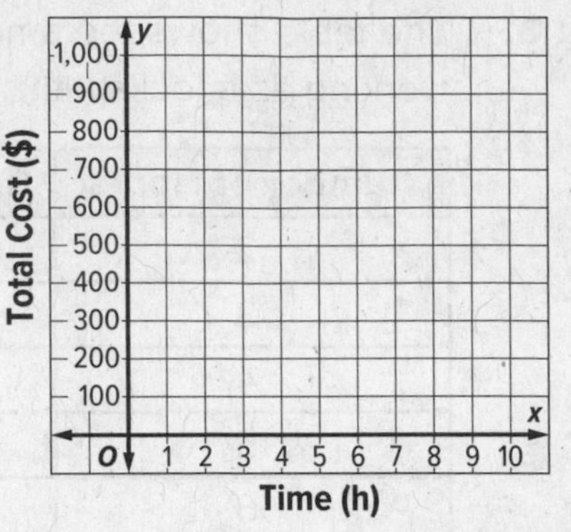

Part A: Graph two lines to represent the costs of chartering a boat from both companies.

Part B: For how many hours would Mr. Reyes need to charter the boat for Sunrise Charters to be less expensive?

12. The graph represents Matilda's speed while driving from her home to the library and then to the store. Write the letter of the section of the graph that matches each statement. 8.F.5

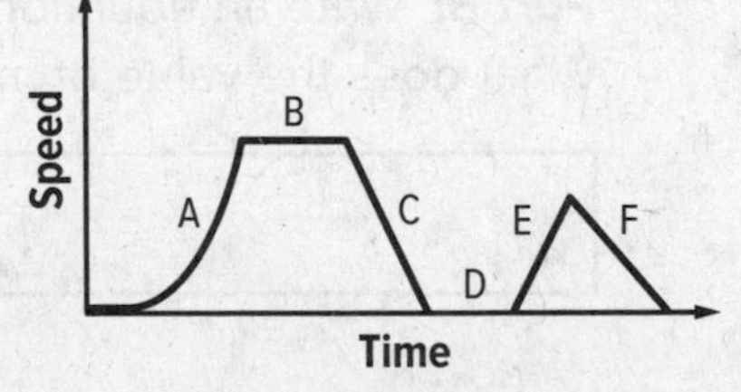

A B C D E F

After increasing her speed, Matilda drives at a constant speed.

Matilda decreases her speed steadily until she arrives at the store and stops.

Matilda begins to drive, and her car picks up speed as she drives.

Matilda decreases her speed steadily until she arrives at the library.

Matilda spends time at the library.

Matilda leaves the library and steadily increases her speed.

13. Angelo and Lucia are riding their bikes. Angelo travels at a speed of 12 miles per hour. Lucia's speed is represented by the function $d = 10h$, where d is the distance in miles after h hours. How much farther does Angelo bike than Lucia in 0.25 hour? Explain how you know. 8.F.2, 8.F.4

14. A shoe store is having a 30% off sale, and Fernanda has a coupon for \$5 off her total purchase. The function $f(x) = 0.7x - 5$ represents the final cost of an x-dollar item after the discount and coupon are applied. Complete the function machine for original prices and final costs of items A, B, C, and D. 8.F.1, 8.F.4

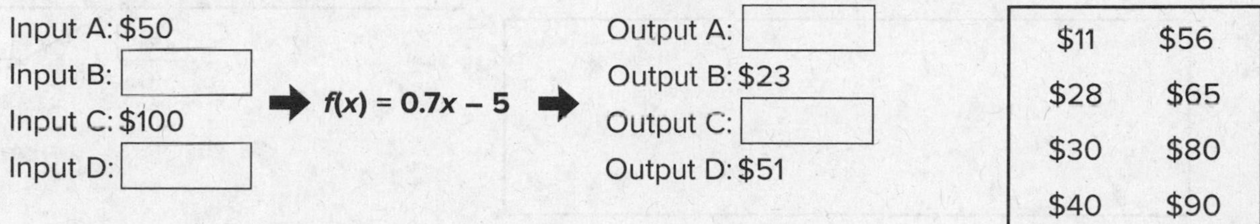

15. Jocelyn constructed a kite. Write the correct measurements in the diagram. Find the perimeter of the kite. 8.G.7, 8.EE.2

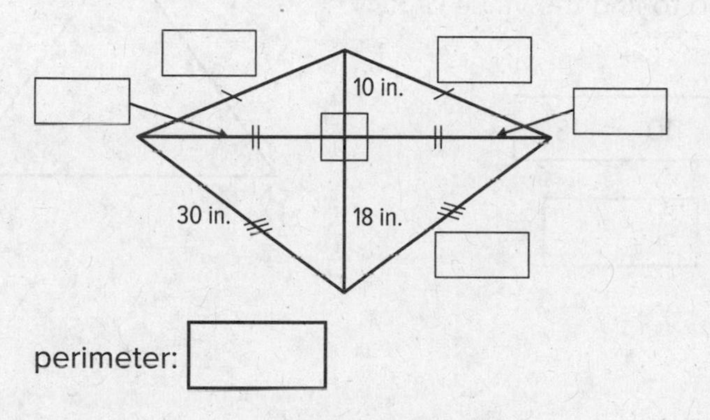

perimeter:

16. Quasia is using a coordinate plane to design part of a pairs race for field day. Runner 1 for each pair begins at the cone, and Runner 2 stands at a point 9 units west of the cone. Runner 1 runs 4 units north of the cone to retrieve a baton and then runs directly to Runner 2 and passes the baton. Runner 2 then runs to a bucket that is 6 units south of the cone and drops the baton in the bucket. 8.G.8, 8.EE.2

Part A: Plot the locations of the runners, the baton, and the bucket. Then draw the path of the entire relay race.

Part B: Each unit represents 20 meters. What is the length of the entire relay race course? Round to the nearest meter, if necessary.

17. Lines a and b are parallel and cut by the transversal c. Find the value of x. Explain how you found your answer. Then label the degree measures of the six unlabeled angles on the diagram. 8.G.5

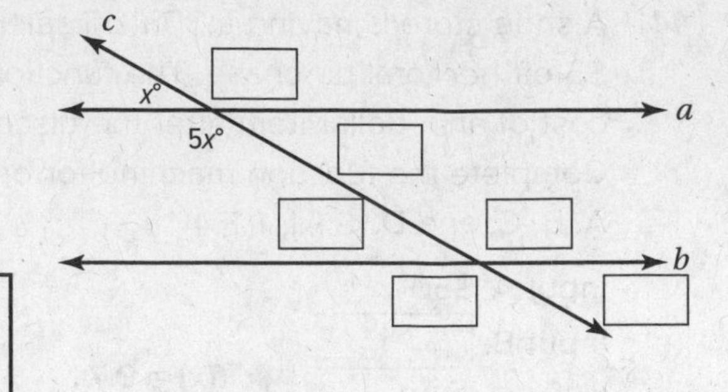

18. A triangle has the angle measurements shown. Write values to complete an equation that could be used to find the value of x. Then find x. 8.G.5

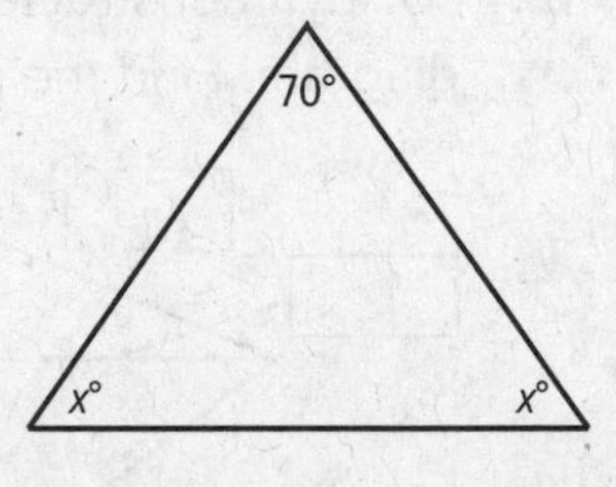

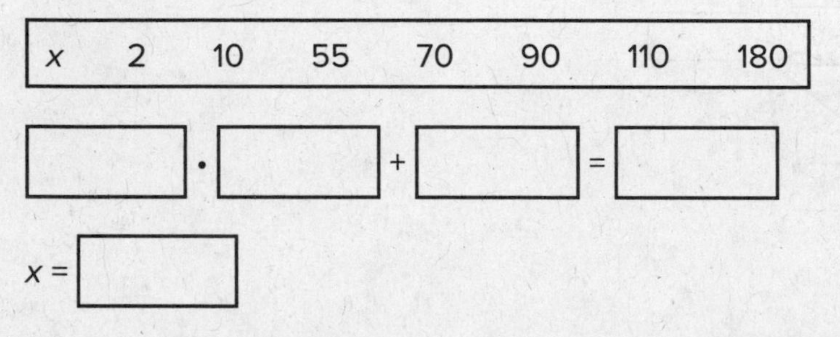

☐ · ☐ + ☐ = ☐

x = ☐

19. Trapezoid $M'N'P'Q'$ is the image of trapezoid $MNPQ$ after one or more transformations. Select each transformation or sequence of transformations that produces trapezoid $M'N'P'Q'$. 8.G.3

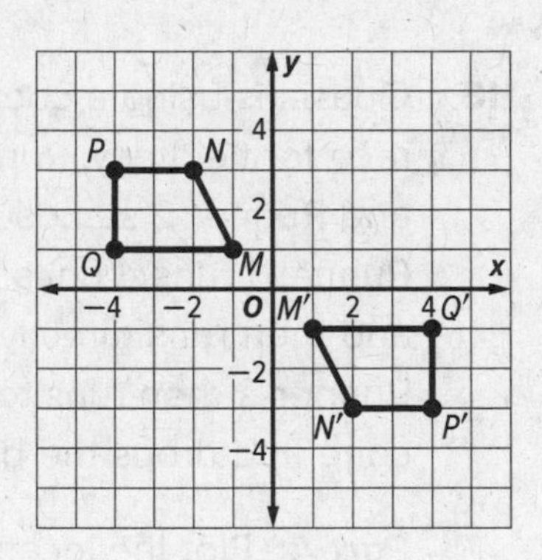

- ☐ a rotation 180° about the origin
- ☐ a rotation 90° about the origin and then a rotation 90° about the origin again in the same direction
- ☐ a reflection across the y-axis and then a rotation 90° clockwise about the origin
- ☐ a reflection across the x-axis, then a translation 8 units to the right
- ☐ a reflection across the x-axis, then a reflection across the y-axis

20. Parallelogram *BCDF* shows the location of a raised flowerbed in Kelly's yard. Kelly translates the parallelogram 2 units to the right and 6 units down to show where she will move the flowerbed. Select whether each statement is true or false. 8.G.1, 8.G.1a, 8.G.1c

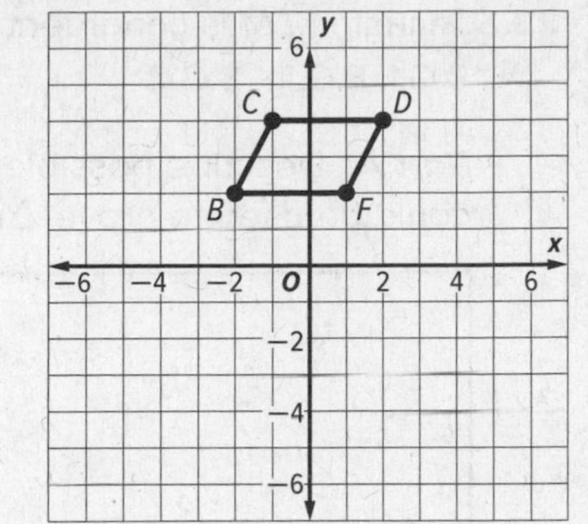

True	False	
☐	☐	Side $B'C'$ is the same length as side BC.
☐	☐	Side $C'D'$ is longer than side CD.
☐	☐	Lines $C'D'$ and $B'F'$ are parallel.
☐	☐	Lines $B'C'$ and $F'D'$ are parallel.

21. Triangle *ABC* is dilated so that the image of point *B* is $B'(4, 8)$. 8.G.3

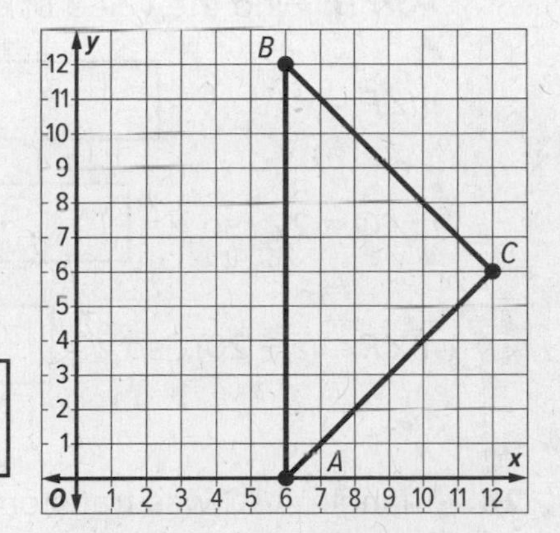

Part A: Draw the image, triangle $A'B'C'$.

Part B: What is the scale factor of the dilation? Is the dilation a reduction or an enlargement?

22. Dean is using pattern blocks to draw a jewel for an art project. Parallelograms *A* and *B* are congruent. Parallelogram *A* is the preimage of parallelogram *B*. Describe a possible sequence of transformations Dean could have used to map *A* onto *B*. 8.G.1, 8.G.2

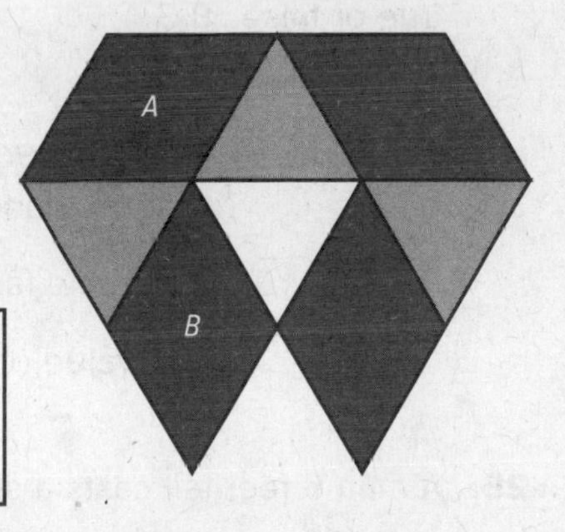

23. Triangle *KLM* is congruent to triangle *PQR*.
8.G.1, 8.G.1b, 8.G.2

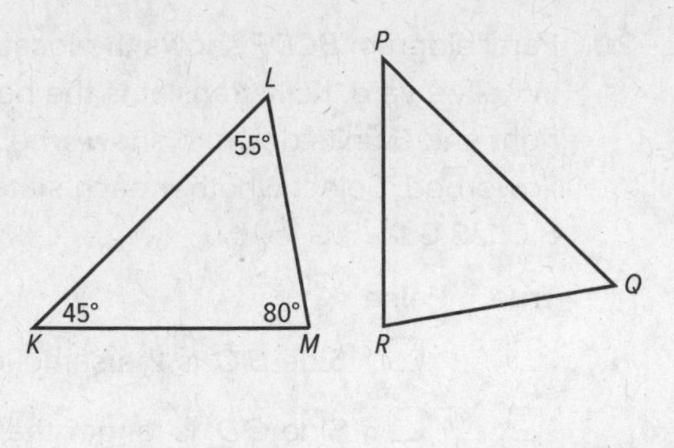

Part A: Describe possible transformations that could be used to prove $\triangle KLM \cong \triangle PQR$.

Part B: Find the value of each variable.

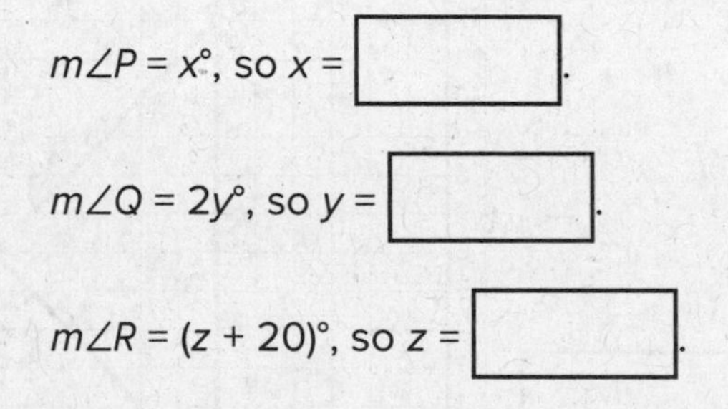

$m\angle P = x°$, so $x =$ ☐.

$m\angle Q = 2y°$, so $y =$ ☐.

$m\angle R = (z + 20)°$, so $z =$ ☐.

27.5	55	75	90	110
45	60	80	100	160

24. Triangle *ABC* was transformed to create similar triangle *FGH*. Select whether each statement is true or false. 8.G.4

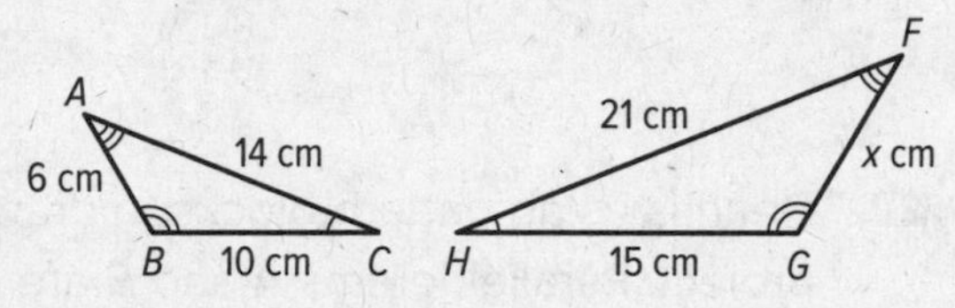

True	False	
☐	☐	Triangle *ABC* could be reflected, translated, and dilated to form triangle *FGH*.
☐	☐	The scale factor of the dilation from $\triangle ABC$ to $\triangle FGH$ is 1.5.
☐	☐	The value of *x* is 4.

25. A man 6 feet tall casts a shadow 8 feet long. At the same time, a nearby building casts a shadow 36 feet long. Write a proportion that can be used to find the height of the building. Then solve the proportion. 8.G.7

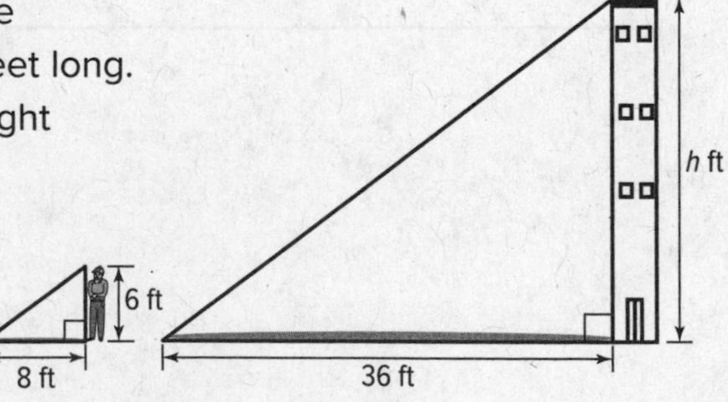

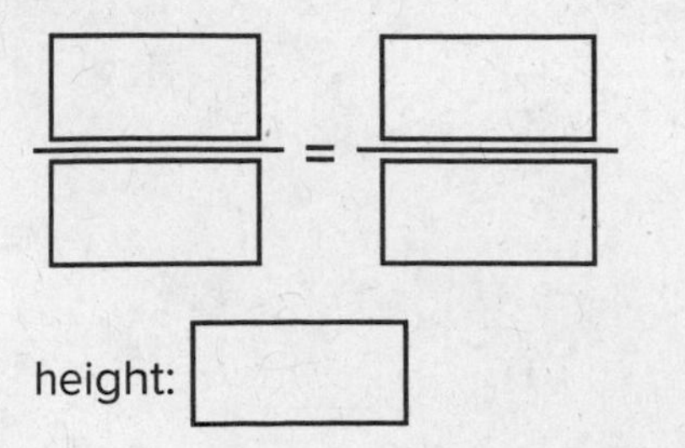

height: ☐

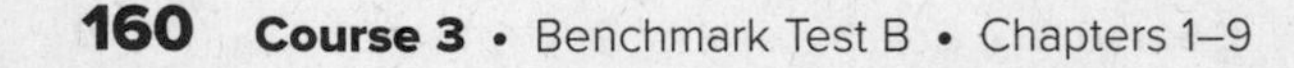

26. Four cones have the dimensions shown. Complete the table to order the cones from least to greatest lateral area. Round to the nearest tenth. 8.G.9

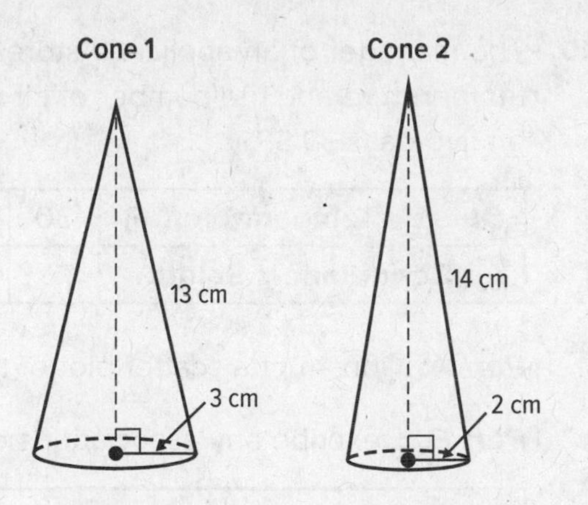

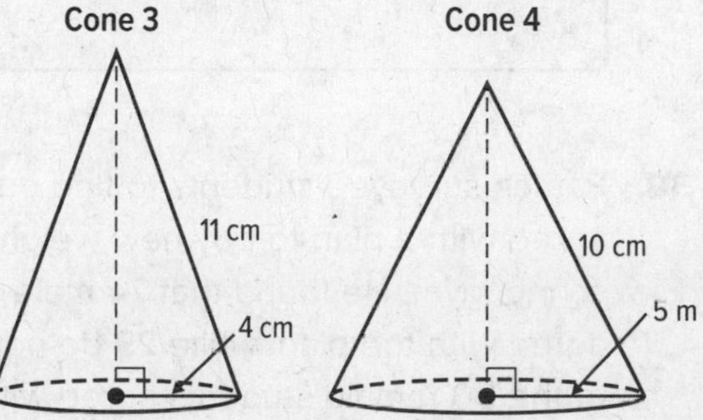

	Cone	Lateral Area (cm^2)
Least		
Greatest		

27. Mrs. Bauer rents a 24-foot-tall cylindrical oil tank and fills it with 504π cubic feet of oil. 8.G.9

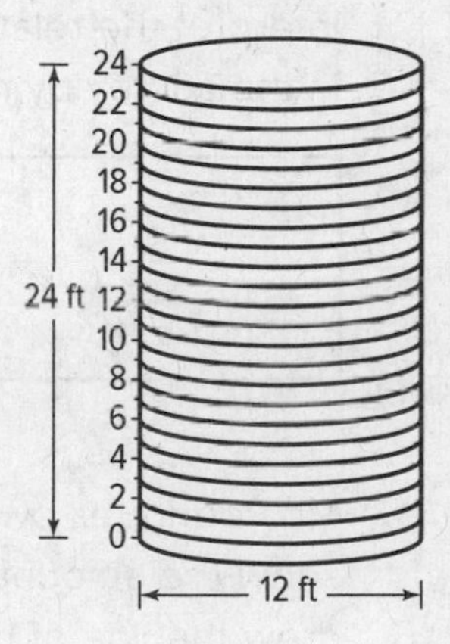

Part A: Shade the cylinder to represent the volume of oil in the tank.

Part B: How many more cubic feet of oil could be poured into the tank? Round to the nearest tenth.

28. Shaved ice completely fills the cone and the hemisphere above the cone. Select whether each statement is true or false. 8.G.9

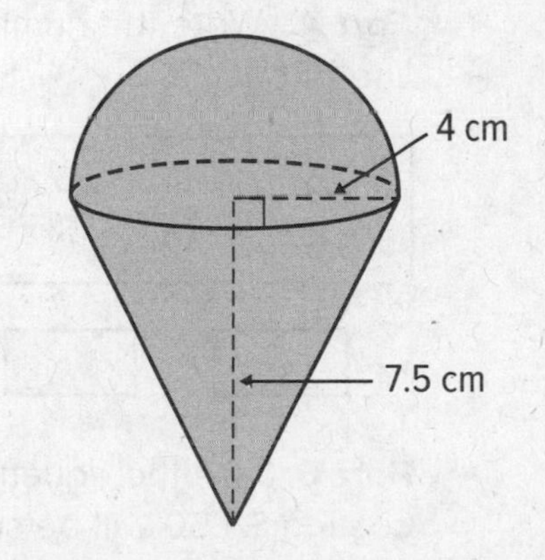

True	False	
☐	☐	The slant height of the cone is 8.5 cm.
☐	☐	The lateral area of the cone is approximately 125.7 cm^2.
☐	☐	The cone and the hemisphere contain approximately 259.7 cm^3 of shaved ice.

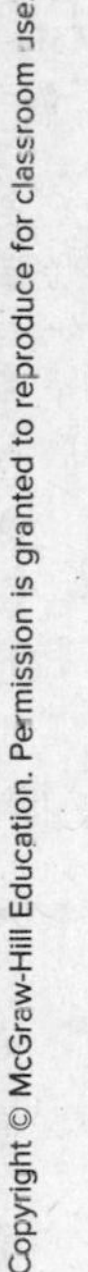

29. The manager of an appliance store recorded the outside temperature and the number of air conditioners sold on five days. 8.SP.1

Outside Temperature (°F)	30	40	50	60	70
Air Conditioners Sold	2	6	12	17	20

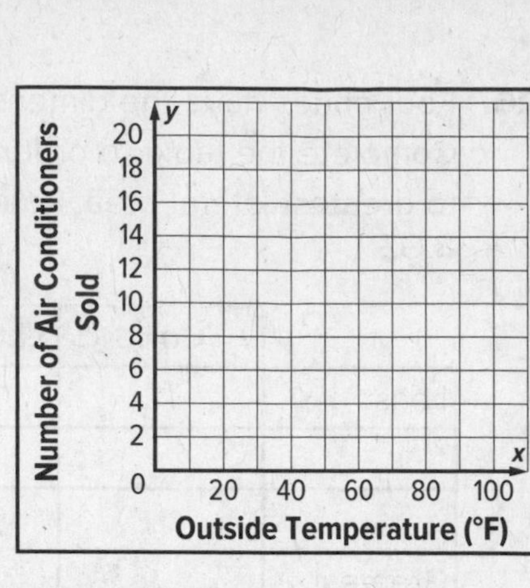

Part A: Construct a scatter plot of the data.

Part B: Describe any associations of the data.

30. Patrick surveyed students to find out if they agree with a plan to buy new weights for the school gym. He found that 74 male students agree with the plan, while 23 do not. Forty-six of the 90 female students agree with the plan. Complete the two-way table. Then find and interpret the relative frequencies of students in the survey by row. Round to the nearest hundredth. 8.SP.4

	Agree	Disagree	Total
Male	74;		
Female			
Total			

31. Mr. Rodriguez owns a restaurant. He made a scatter plot to show the amounts of soup sold at different prices. Then he drew the line of best fit. 8.SP.2, 8.SP.3

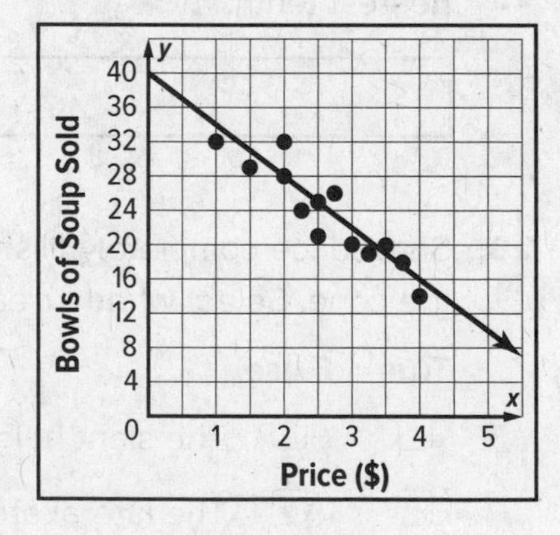

Part A: Write the numbers to represent the equation of the line of best fit.

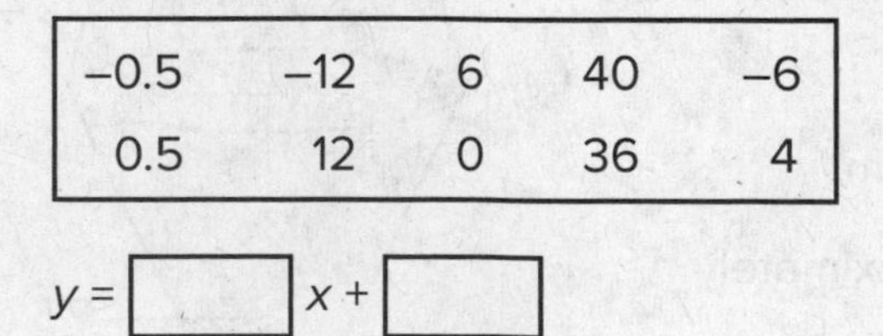

–0.5	–12	6	40	–6
0.5	12	0	36	4

$y =$ ☐ $x +$ ☐

Part B: Use the equation to predict about how many bowls of soup costing $4.50 will be sold.

Benchmark Test B, Performance Task, Chapters 1–9

Jewelry Makers

Anya and Taylor are starting a jewelry-making business. Anya will make necklaces, and Taylor will make earrings. They plan to sell them at the school craft fair.

Write your answers on another piece of paper. Show all your work to receive full credit.

Part A

Before they start making jewelry, the girls survey 200 students at their middle school. They ask whether students like to buy necklaces or earrings, either for themselves or as gifts for others. Of the 125 students who said they like to buy necklaces, 110 of them also like to buy earrings. However, 55 students said they do not buy either necklaces or earrings.

Create a two-way table to show the results of the survey. Label the columns "Necklace" and "No Necklace" and the rows "Earrings" and "No Earrings". Find the relative frequencies for the columns. Round to the nearest hundredth. Write at least two statements explaining what those frequencies show Anya and Taylor about their future customers.

Part B

Anya wants to make necklaces using beads and leather cord. The graph shows the cost of buying leather cord from the local craft store. What is the cost per yard for the cord?

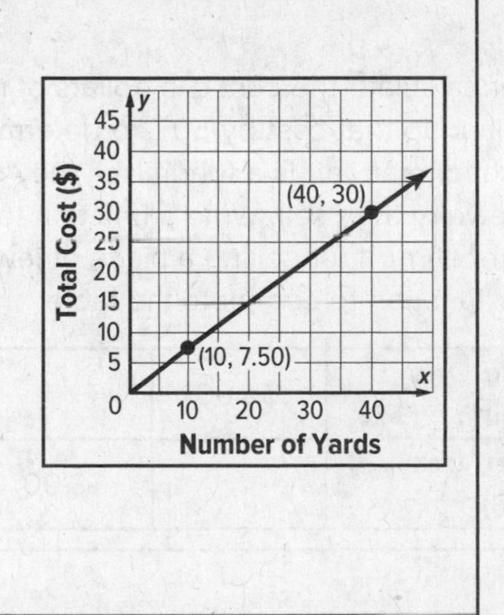

Taylor says that an online store sells the cord for a cheaper price. The equation $y = 5 + 0.50x$ can be used to determine the cost of buying x yards of cord from the online store. Graph the equation and explain whether Taylor is *always*, *sometimes*, or *never* correct.

Part C

Anya wants to make her own cylindrical clay beads for the necklaces. The height of each bead is 8 millimeters, and its total diameter is 3 millimeters. The hole in its center has a diameter of 2 millimeters. How many cubic millimeters of clay are needed to make 100 beads? Round to the nearest tenth.

Part D

Taylor carves wooden squares to make earrings. Each has an area of 7 cm^2. What is the side length of each wooden square to the nearest hundredth of a centimeter? Did you estimate the length or find an exact length? Explain.

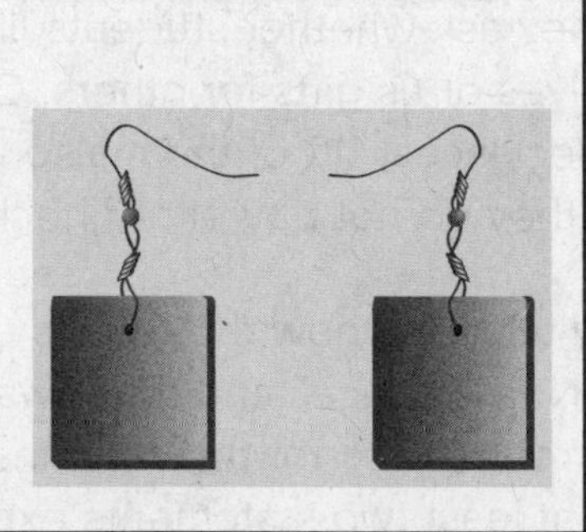

Part E

Anya and Taylor calculate the cost *c* in dollars of making each piece of jewelry. They mark up that cost by 50% to determine the selling price. Because the school craft fair is a fundraiser, they donate $1 to the school for each piece of jewelry they sell. Write a function to represent *P*, the total amount in dollars earned for selling a piece of jewelry that costs *c* dollars to make. Use your function to complete the table.

Cost of Making One Piece of Jewelry, *c* ($)	$4.00		$11.00	
Amount Earned from That Sale, *P* ($)		$8.00		$20.00

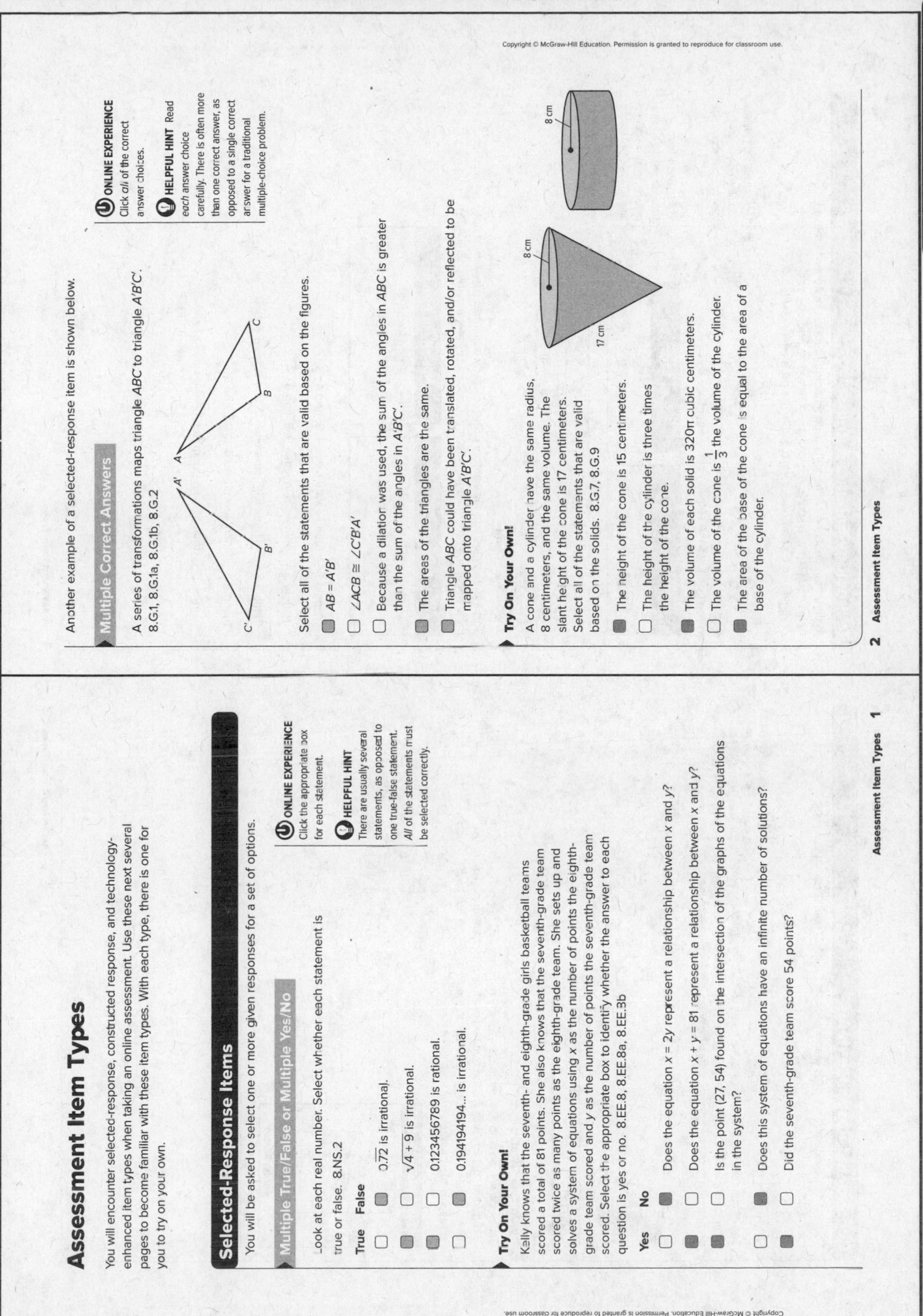

Assessment Item Types

You will encounter selected-response, constructed response, and technology-enhanced item types when taking an online assessment. Use these next several pages to become familiar with these item types. With each type, there is one for you to try on your own.

Selected-Response Items

You will be asked to select one or more given responses for a set of options.

Multiple True/False or Multiple Yes/No

ONLINE EXPERIENCE Click the appropriate box for each statement.

HELPFUL HINT There are usually several statements, as opposed to one true-false statement. *All* of the statements must be selected correctly.

Look at each real number. Select whether each statement is true or false. 8.NS.2

True	False	
□	■	$0.\overline{72}$ is irrational.
■	□	$\sqrt{4+9}$ is irrational.
■	□	0.123456789 is rational.
□	■	0.194194194... is irrational.

Try On Your Own!

Kelly knows that the seventh- and eighth-grade girls basketball teams scored a total of 81 points. She also knows that the seventh-grade team scored twice as many points as the eighth-grade team. She sets up and solves a system of equations using x as the number of points the eighth-grade team scored and y as the number of points the seventh-grade team scored. Select the appropriate box to identify whether the answer to each question is yes or no. 8.EE.8, 8.EE.8a, 8.EE.8b

Yes	No	
□	■	Does the equation $x = 2y$ represent a relationship between x and y?
■	□	Does the equation $x + y = 81$ represent a relationship between x and y?
■	□	Is the point (27, 54) found on the intersection of the graphs of the equations in the system?
□	■	Does this system of equations have an infinite number of solutions?
■	□	Did the seventh-grade team score 54 points?

Another example of a selected-response item is shown below.

Multiple Correct Answers

ONLINE EXPERIENCE Click *all* of the correct answer choices.

HELPFUL HINT Read *each* answer choice carefully. There is often more than one correct answer, as opposed to a single correct answer for a traditional multiple-choice problem.

A series of transformations maps triangle ABC to triangle $A'B'C'$. 8.G.1, 8.G.1a, 8.G.1b, 8.G.2

Select all of the statements that are valid based on the figures.

- ■ $AB = A'B'$
- □ $\angle ACB \cong \angle C'B'A'$
- □ Because a dilation was used, the sum of the angles in ABC is greater than the sum of the angles in $A'B'C'$.
- ■ The areas of the triangles are the same.
- ■ Triangle ABC could have been translated, rotated, and/or reflected to be mapped onto triangle $A'B'C'$.

Try On Your Own!

A cone and a cylinder have the same radius, 8 centimeters, and the same volume. The slant height of the cone is 17 centimeters. Select all of the statements that are valid based on the solids. 8.G.7, 8.G.9

- ■ The height of the cone is 15 centimeters.
- □ The height of the cylinder is three times the height of the cone.
- ■ The volume of each solid is 320π cubic centimeters.
- □ The volume of the cone is $\frac{1}{3}$ the volume of the cylinder.
- ■ The area of the base of the cone is equal to the area of a base of the cylinder.

Assessment Types

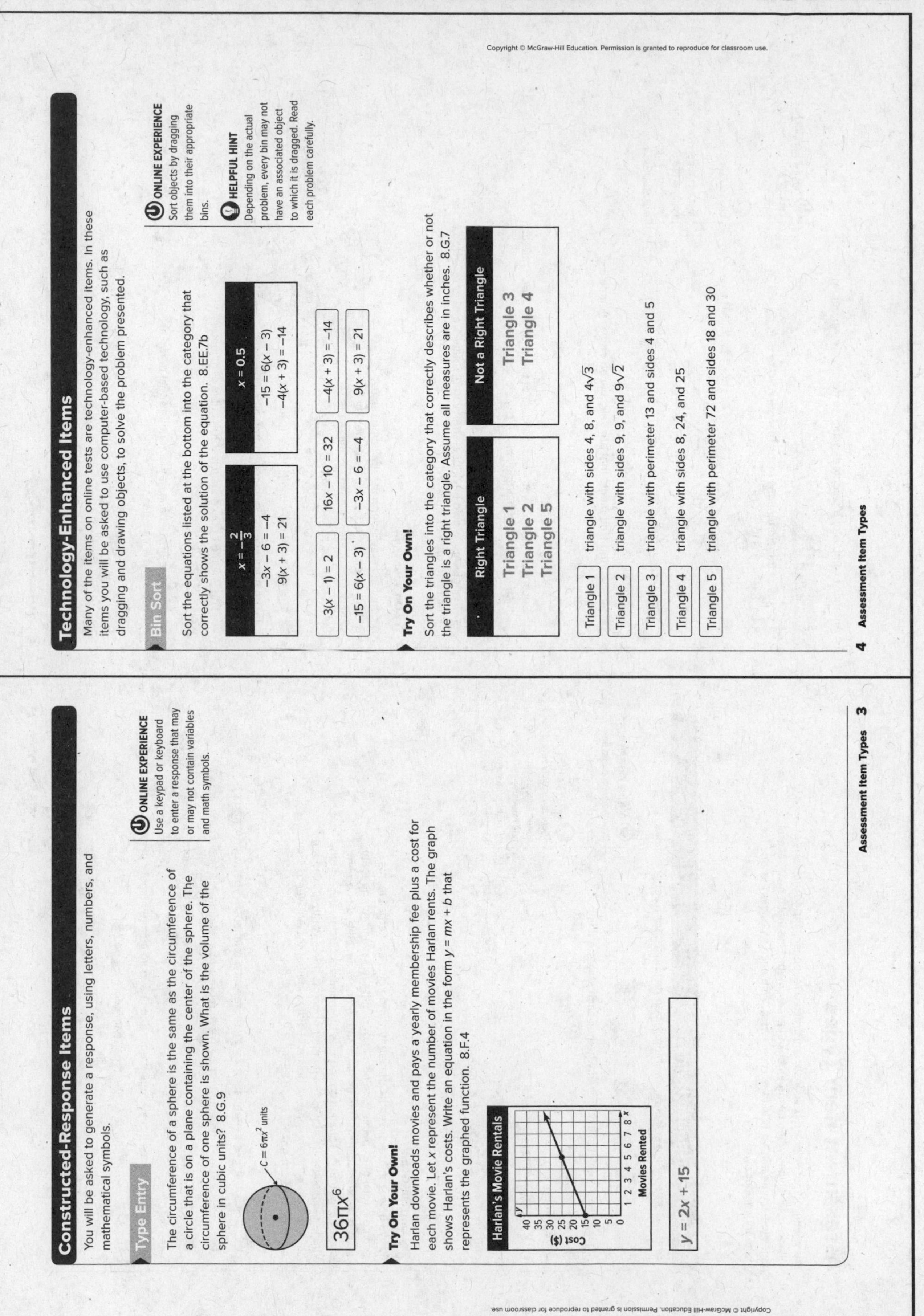

Constructed-Response Items

You will be asked to generate a response, using letters, numbers, and mathematical symbols.

Type Entry

The circumference of a sphere is the same as the circumference of a circle that is on a plane containing the center of the sphere. The circumference of one sphere is shown. What is the volume of the sphere in cubic units? 8.G.9

$C = 6\pi x^2$ units

$36\pi x^6$

ONLINE EXPERIENCE
Use a keypad or keyboard to enter a response that may or may not contain variables and math symbols.

Try On Your Own!

Harlan downloads movies and pays a yearly membership fee plus a cost for each movie. Let x represent the number of movies Harlan rents. The graph shows Harlan's costs. Write an equation in the form $y = mx + b$ that represents the graphed function. 8.F.4

Harlan's Movie Rentals

Cost ($): 0, 5, 10, 15, 20, 25, 30, 35, 40

Movies Rented: 1, 2, 3, 4, 5, 6, 7, 8

$y = 2x + 15$

Technology-Enhanced Items

Many of the items on online tests are technology-enhanced items. In these items you will be asked to use computer-based technology, such as dragging and drawing objects, to solve the problem presented.

Bin Sort

Sort the equations listed at the bottom into the category that correctly shows the solution of the equation. 8.EE.7b

$x = -\frac{2}{3}$	$x = 0.5$
$-3x - 6 = -4$	$-15 = 6(x - 3)$
$9(x + 3) = 21$	$-4(x + 3) = -14$

$3(x - 1) = 2$	$16x - 10 = 32$	$-4(x + 3) = -14$
$-15 = 6(x - 3)$	$-3x - 6 = -4$	$9(x + 3) = 21$

ONLINE EXPERIENCE
Sort objects by dragging them into their appropriate bins.

HELPFUL HINT
Depending on the actual problem, every bin may not have an associated object to which it is dragged. Read each problem carefully.

Try On Your Own!

Sort the triangles into the category that correctly describes whether or not the triangle is a right triangle. Assume all measures are in inches. 8.G.7

Right Triangle	Not a Right Triangle
Triangle 1 Triangle 2 Triangle 5	Triangle 3 Triangle 4

Triangle 1	triangle with sides 4, 8, and $4\sqrt{3}$
Triangle 2	triangle with sides 9, 9, and $9\sqrt{2}$
Triangle 3	triangle with perimeter 13 and sides 4 and 5
Triangle 4	triangle with sides 8, 24, and 25
Triangle 5	triangle with perimeter 72 and sides 18 and 30

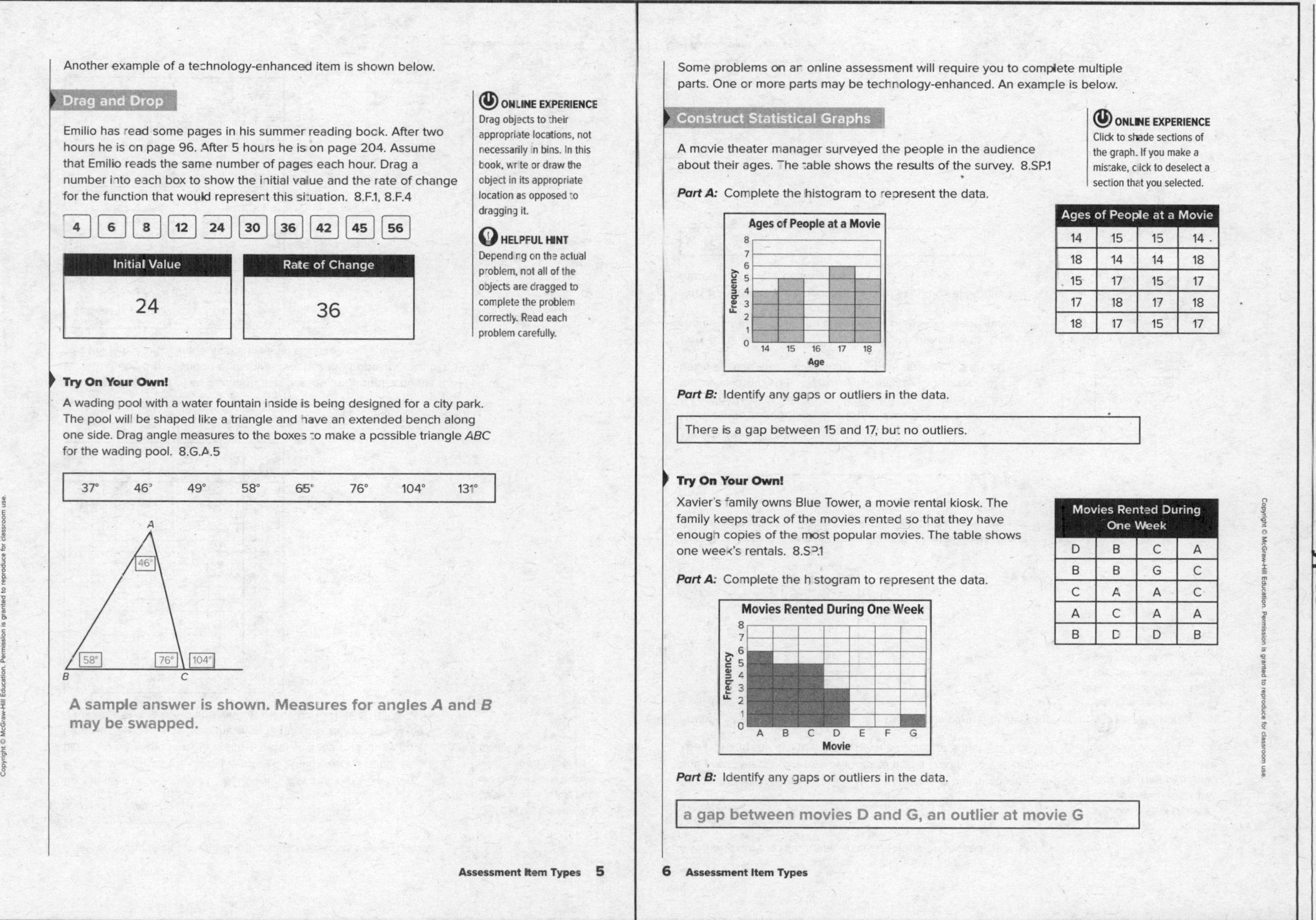

Another example of a technology-enhanced item is shown below.

Drag and Drop

Emilio has read some pages in his summer reading book. After two hours he is on page 96. After 5 hours he is on page 204. Assume that Emilio reads the same number of pages each hour. Drag a number into each box to show the initial value and the rate of change for the function that would represent this situation. 8.F.1, 8.F.4

4	6	8	12	24	30	36	42	45	56

Initial Value	Rate of Change
24	36

ONLINE EXPERIENCE
Drag objects to their appropriate locations, not necessarily in bins. In this book, write or draw the object in its appropriate location as opposed to dragging it.

HELPFUL HINT
Depending on the actual problem, not all of the objects are dragged to complete the problem correctly. Read each problem carefully.

Try On Your Own!

A wading pool with a water fountain inside is being designed for a city park. The pool will be shaped like a triangle and have an extended bench along one side. Drag angle measures to the boxes to make a possible triangle *ABC* for the wading pool. 8.G.A.5

37°	46°	49°	58°	65°	76°	104°	131°

A sample answer is shown. Measures for angles *A* and *B* may be swapped.

Some problems on an online assessment will require you to complete multiple parts. One or more parts may be technology-enhanced. An example is below.

Construct Statistical Graphs

A movie theater manager surveyed the people in the audience about their ages. The table shows the results of the survey. 8.SP.1

ONLINE EXPERIENCE
Click to shade sections of the graph. If you make a mistake, click to deselect a section that you selected.

Ages of People at a Movie			
14	15	15	14
18	14	14	18
15	17	15	17
17	18	17	18
18	17	15	17

Part A: Complete the histogram to represent the data.

Part B: Identify any gaps or outliers in the data.

There is a gap between 15 and 17, but no outliers.

Try On Your Own!

Xavier's family owns Blue Tower, a movie rental kiosk. The family keeps track of the movies rented so that they have enough copies of the most popular movies. The table shows one week's rentals. 8.SP.1

Movies Rented During One Week			
D	B	C	A
B	B	G	C
C	A	A	C
A	C	A	A
B	D	D	B

Part A: Complete the histogram to represent the data.

Part B: Identify any gaps or outliers in the data.

a gap between movies D and G, an outlier at movie G

Assessment Types

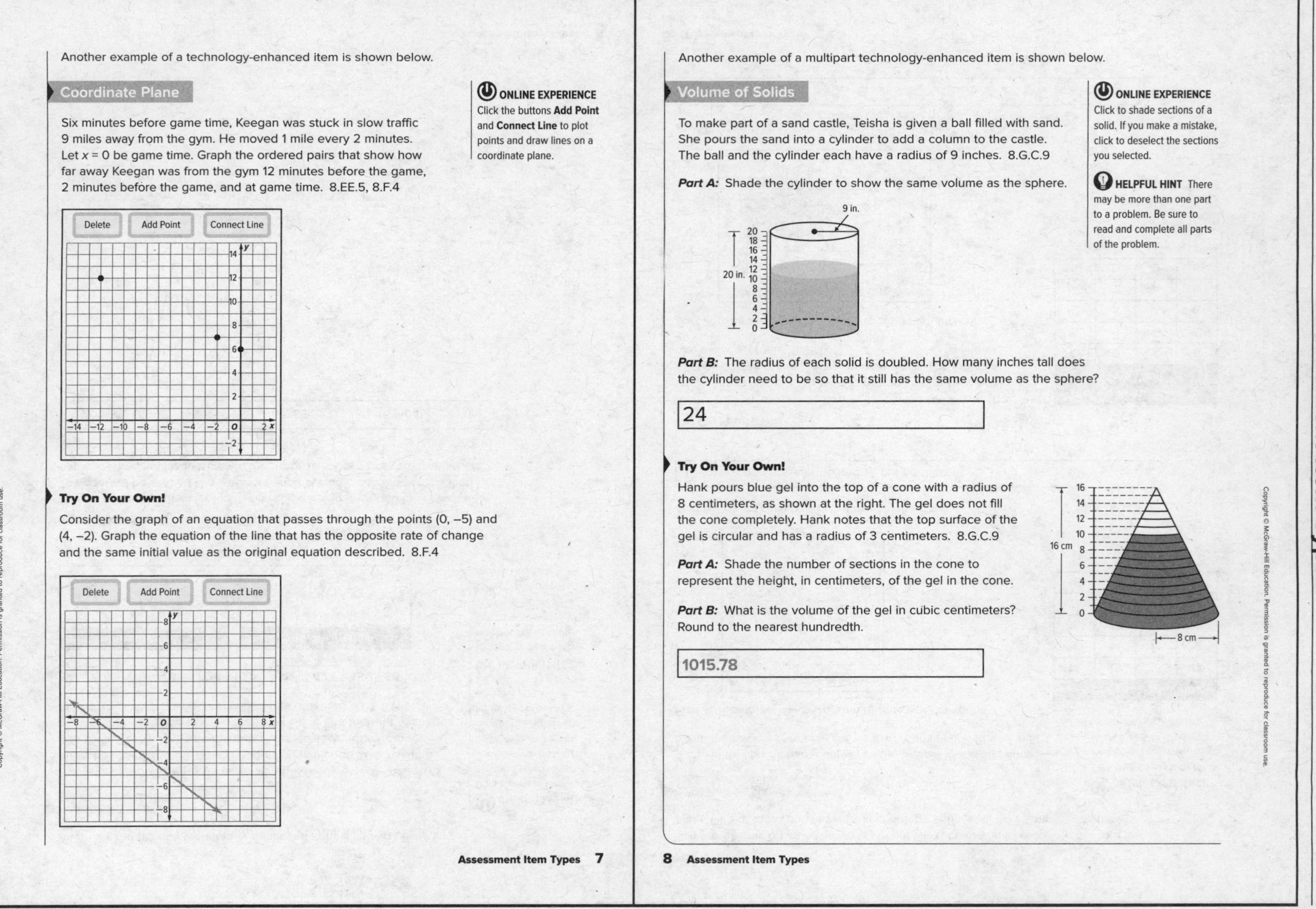

Another example of a technology-enhanced item is shown below.

Coordinate Plane

Six minutes before game time, Keegan was stuck in slow traffic 9 miles away from the gym. He moved 1 mile every 2 minutes. Let $x = 0$ be game time. Graph the ordered pairs that show how far away Keegan was from the gym 12 minutes before the game, 2 minutes before the game, and at game time. 8.EE.5, 8.F.4

ONLINE EXPERIENCE Click the buttons **Add Point** and **Connect Line** to plot points and draw lines on a coordinate plane.

Try On Your Own!

Consider the graph of an equation that passes through the points (0, −5) and (4, −2). Graph the equation of the line that has the opposite rate of change and the same initial value as the original equation described. 8.F.4

Another example of a multipart technology-enhanced item is shown below.

Volume of Solids

To make part of a sand castle, Teisha is given a ball filled with sand. She pours the sand into a cylinder to add a column to the castle. The ball and the cylinder each have a radius of 9 inches. 8.G.C.9

Part A: Shade the cylinder to show the same volume as the sphere.

Part B: The radius of each solid is doubled. How many inches tall does the cylinder need to be so that it still has the same volume as the sphere?

24

ONLINE EXPERIENCE Click to shade sections of a solid. If you make a mistake, click to deselect the sections you selected.

HELPFUL HINT There may be more than one part to a problem. Be sure to read and complete all parts of the problem.

Try On Your Own!

Hank pours blue gel into the top of a cone with a radius of 8 centimeters, as shown at the right. The gel does not fill the cone completely. Hank notes that the top surface of the gel is circular and has a radius of 3 centimeters. 8.G.C.9

Part A: Shade the number of sections in the cone to represent the height, in centimeters, of the gel in the cone.

Part B: What is the volume of the gel in cubic centimeters? Round to the nearest hundredth.

1015.78

Performance Tasks

These tasks measure your ability to integrate knowledge and skills across multiple topics, which helps prepare you for college and future careers. An example of a performance task is shown below, with guidance about how to complete it.

On the Road Again 8.EE.5, 8.F.1, 8.F.2, 8.F.3, 8.F.4, 8.F.5, 8.G.8, 8.SP.1, 8.SP.2, 8.SP.3

For economic and environmental reasons, Ronaldo has chosen to use his bike to get around town rather than a car.

This performance task has 5 parts, Parts A–E. Read each part and follow the guiding instructions for how to complete it.

Part A

Ronaldo uses a coordinate plane to map his town. Each gridline represents 1 mile. How far is the park from the grocery store? Explain how to find the distance. How does your solution relate to the Pythagorean Theorem?

Park

Grocery Store

How far is the park from the grocery store? Round to the nearest tenth.

21.3 mi

Explain how you found the distance.

Sample answer: Subtract the x-coordinates to get a horizontal change. Subtract the y-coordinates to get a vertical change. Find the sum of the squares of these numbers and take the square root; $\sqrt{452} \approx 21.3$.

How does your solution relate to the Pythagorean Theorem?

The horizontal and the vertical segments are the legs of a right triangle. The shortest distance between the points is the hypotenuse. Apply the Pythagorean Theorem to find the missing distance.

Part B

As Ronaldo travels from the park to the grocery store, he notes that after 1.5 hours he is still 1.8 miles from his destination. After 2 hours he would have gone 4.7 miles too far.

Write a function to relate Ronaldo's distance y to his time x. Show how you found the equation.

$y = 13x$; Sample answer: Use two points to find the slope. After 1.5 h, he went 21.3 – 1.8 = 19.5 mi; so (1.5, 19.5). After 2 h, he went 21.3 + 4.7 = 26 mi; so (2, 26).

Slope $= \frac{26 - 19.5}{2 - 1.5} = \frac{6.5}{0.5} = 13$

Use point-slope form: $y - 26 = 13(x - 2)$ becomes $y = 13x$.

Is this a linear function? Justify your answer.

Sample answer: Yes, it is in the form $y = mx + b$, where $m = 13$ and $b = 0$.

How long will it take Ronaldo to get to the grocery store from the park? Explain.

about 1.64 hours; The distance is 21.3 miles, so substitute 21.3 for y and solve for x; $21.3 = 13x$ and $x \approx 1.64$.

Part C

Another day, Ronaldo leaves home on his bike. He goes to his friend's house, which is halfway to work, at a slow pace. Ronaldo stays at his friend's house and then realizes that he left his bag at home. He quickly rides home to get it. He then bikes three times faster than his initial pace to get to work on time.

Sketch a graph that matches the scenario.

Distance from home

Time

Identify whether each part of the graph is increasing, decreasing, or neither.

The first part increases as Ronaldo bikes away from his home. The second part neither increases nor decreases because Ronaldo is at his friend's house and his distance to home does not change. The third part decreases as Ronaldo rides back home. The fourth part increases as Ronaldo again bikes away from home to get to work.

HELPFUL HINT
Questions may have more than one answer. This one requires four answers, one for each part of the graph.

Is this graph a function? Explain.

Yes; For every *x* value there is exactly one *y* value.

Part D
While Ronaldo rides his bike, his friend drives a car. She keeps track of how far she drives after filling the gas tank and how much gasoline is left in the tank after she drives. The table shows her results.

Distance Driven (mi)	20	40	100	120	160	240	300
Gas in the Tank (gal)	19	12	16	14	11	7	3

Use the data to construct a scatter plot of the distance driven and the amount of gas left in the tank.

Gasoline Usage

Gas in the Tank (gal): 0, 2, 4, 6, 8, 10, 12, 14, 16, 18, 20 (y)
Distance Driven (mi): 0, 20, 60, 100, 140, 180, 220, 260, 300, 340 (x)

The graph also shows a sample answer for the line of best fit in Part E.

Are there any outliers? If so, which point(s)? Explain your answer.

Yes; (40, 12) is an outlier because it does not follow the general trend of the rest of the data.

What kind of association, if any, is there with the data? Explain your answer.

Negative association; The number of gallons decreases as the number of miles increases.

Part E
Draw a line of best fit on the scatter plot. Write an equation for your line of best fit. What is the rate of change? What does it represent about the distance driven and the amount of gas left in the car? What is the initial value? What does the initial value represent about the distance driven and the amount of gas left in the car?

Draw a line of best fit for the data on your scatter plot.

A sample answer is shown on the scatter plot on the previous page.

Write an equation for your line of best fit.

Sample answer: $y = -\frac{2}{35}x + 20$

What is the rate of change? How is it shown on the graph? What does it represent about the distance driven and the amount of gas in the tank?

Sample answer: $-\frac{2}{35}$; It is the slope. For every 35 miles driven, the amount of gas in the tank decreases by 2 gallons.

What is the initial value? How is it shown on the graph? What does it represent about the distance driven and the amount of gas in the tank?

Sample answer: 20; It is the *y*-intercept. Before the car has been driven any miles (the distance is 0), the gas tank is full and it contains 20 gallons of gas.

NAME ____________ DATE ________ PERIOD ______ SCORE ______

Countdown: 20 Weeks

1. A supplier makes rulers that are supposed to be at least $0.\overline{78}$ inch wide. However, the machine that makes the rulers has been having problems. The table shows a sample of eight rulers and their widths. A supervisor states that if at least half of the samples are smaller than the desired width, he will call someone to fix the machine. Explain whether he needs to call. Convert $0.\overline{78}$ to a simplified fraction in your answer. 8.NS.1

Ruler Widths	
$\frac{39}{50}$ inch	$\frac{26}{33}$ inch
$\frac{4}{5}$ inch	$\frac{9}{10}$ inch
$\frac{76}{99}$ inch	$\frac{2}{3}$ inch
$\frac{1}{2}$ inch	$\frac{7}{9}$ inch

The repeating decimal $0.\overline{78}$ equals $\frac{78}{99} = \frac{26}{33}$. The ruler widths $\frac{39}{50}$, $\frac{76}{99}$, $\frac{2}{3}$, $\frac{1}{2}$, and $\frac{7}{9}$ are all less than that. So, more than half of the rulers are too small, and the supervisor needs to call someone to fix the machine.

2. A teacher wants to demonstrate π to her students, so she plans to cut a piece of wood exactly 2π feet in length and show it to them. Explain why she cannot do this. Then give an approximation for how long the piece of wood should be. 8.NS.2

Explanation:

Because π is an irrational number, it is a nonrepeating, nonterminating number and cannot be measured exactly.

Approximate Length:

Sample answer: 6.28 feet

3. A company makes square poster frames whose sides are integer lengths. Select all of the areas that would satisfy this requirement. 8.EE.2

- ■ 16 ft²
- □ 24 ft²
- □ 2.5 ft²
- ■ 4 ft²
- ■ 1 ft²
- ■ 36 ft²
- □ 48 ft²

Online Test Tip
On an online test, you might be asked to click all of the correct answer choices. In this book, you will be asked to shade a box next to each correct answer choice.

4. A school has a 20:2 student-teacher ratio. 8.EE.5

Part A: Graph a line representing this scenario.

Student-Teacher Ratio

Part B: What is the unit rate? How is it represented in the graph?

10:1, or 10 students for every 1 teacher; It is the slope of the line.

5. Veronica and Abdul are having a contest to see who can mow the greater area of lawn over the course of a week. The table shows the amount each person mowed on each day. 8.NS.1

Day	Veronica	Abdul
Monday	$\frac{1}{2}$ acre	0.65 acre
Tuesday	$\frac{1}{3}$ acre	20% of an acre
Wednesday	$\frac{6}{5}$ acres	$1\frac{1}{4}$ acres
Thursday	1 acre	100.5% of an acre
Friday	0.767 acre	$\frac{19}{25}$ acre
Saturday	33.3% of an acre	$\frac{1}{3}$ acre
Sunday	0.55 acre	$\frac{13}{25}$ acre

Part A: Sort the days into the bin of the person who mowed the greater area that day.

Monday | Tuesday | Wednesday | Thursday | Friday | Saturday | Sunday

Veronica Mowed More	Abdul Mowed More
Tuesday	**Monday**
Friday	**Wednesday**
Sunday	**Thursday**
	Saturday

Online Test Tip
On an online test, you might be asked to drag the days to a bin. In this book, you will be asked to write each day in the space provided.

Part B: Who won the contest?

Abdul

NAME ______________ DATE ________ PERIOD ______ SCORE ______

Countdown: 19 Weeks

1. A company sells only items that are in the shape of cubes. Select all of the volumes of cubes with rational number side lengths. 8.NS.1

- ■ 8 in^3
- □ 33 cm^3
- □ 1.5 ft^3
- ■ 9 ft^3
- ■ 1,000 m^3
- ■ $(4.12\ yd)^3$

Online Test Tip
On an online test, you might be asked to click all of the correct answer choices. In this book, you will be asked to shade a box next to each correct answer choice.

2. Sherron is writing a computer program that solves linear equations and displays a numerical answer for the solution. 8.EE.7, 8.EE.7a

Part A: When Sherron inputs the equation $4x + 3 = 4(1 + x) + 1$, she gets an error message. Explain why.

The equation simplifies to $4x + 3 = 4x + 5$, or $3 = 5$, which has no solutions. So, Sherron gets an error.

Part B: Sherron inputs the equation $5 + 6y = 9y + 2 + 3(1 - y)$. What is the result and why?

The equation simplifies to $5 + 6y = 5 + 6y$, or $5 = 5$, which has an infinite number of solutions. So, Sherron would get an error message.

3. A square picture frame encloses an area of 29 square inches. Its owner claims that the frame sides are between 5.25 and 5.35 inches long. Is the owner correct? Why or why not? 8.NS.2

No; Because the frame is a square, the sides must be the same length. The area $A = s^2 = 29$. So, the side length must equal $\sqrt{29} \approx 5.385$ inches. This does not fall between 5.25 and 5.35, so the owner is incorrect.

4. A cargo ship has a stack of shipping containers. The stack is x containers wide, x containers long, and x containers tall. Circle all of the equations that could represent the total number of containers on the ship. 8.EE.2

($x^3 = 64$)	$x^3 = 16$	$100 = x^3$
$x^3 = 9$	($27 = x^3$)	$x^3 = 0.125$
$0.343 = x^3$	($x^3 = 8$)	($216 = x^3$)

5. A ball rolls in a straight line roughly 3π yards before stopping. Then someone kicks it backward 0.5π yards. 8.NS.2

Part A: On the number line, plot a point to represent the distance from the ball's initial location at 0 to its final location. Each increment on the number line represents 1 yard.

0 1 2 3 4 5 6 7 8 9 10

Online Test Tip
On an online test, you might be asked to click the button to plot a point on the number line. In this book, you will be asked to draw the point on the number line.

Part B: Explain why you cannot illustrate the distance exactly. Then give the distance rounded to the nearest hundredth.

Because π is irrational, any multiple of π is also irrational. So, 2.5π is irrational. Irrational numbers never terminate or repeat, so they cannot be illustrated exactly. The distance from the initial location to the final location is 2.5π yd ≈ 7.85 yd.

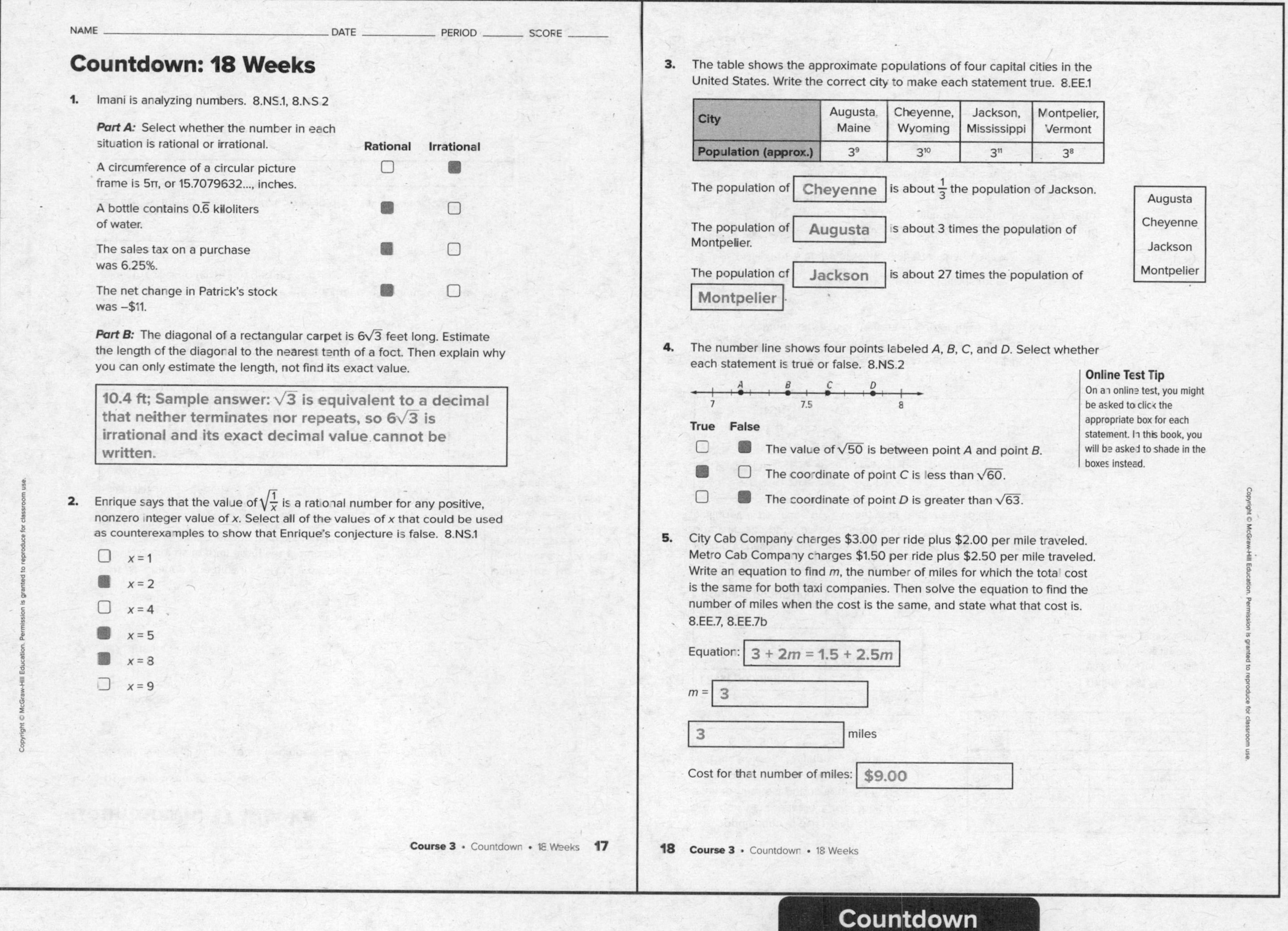

NAME ________________ DATE __________ PERIOD ______ SCORE ______

Countdown: 18 Weeks

1. Imani is analyzing numbers. 8.NS.1, 8.NS.2

Part A: Select whether the number in each situation is rational or irrational.

	Rational	Irrational
A circumference of a circular picture frame is 5π, or 15.7079632..., inches.	☐	■
A bottle contains $0.\overline{6}$ kiloliters of water.	■	☐
The sales tax on a purchase was 6.25%.	■	☐
The net change in Patrick's stock was –$11.	■	☐

Part B: The diagonal of a rectangular carpet is $6\sqrt{3}$ feet long. Estimate the length of the diagonal to the nearest tenth of a foot. Then explain why you can only estimate the length, not find its exact value.

10.4 ft; Sample answer: $\sqrt{3}$ is equivalent to a decimal that neither terminates nor repeats, so $6\sqrt{3}$ is irrational and its exact decimal value cannot be written.

2. Enrique says that the value of $\sqrt{\frac{1}{x}}$ is a rational number for any positive, nonzero integer value of *x*. Select all of the values of *x* that could be used as counterexamples to show that Enrique's conjecture is false. 8.NS.1

- ☐ $x = 1$
- ■ $x = 2$
- ☐ $x = 4$
- ■ $x = 5$
- ■ $x = 8$
- ☐ $x = 9$

3. The table shows the approximate populations of four capital cities in the United States. Write the correct city to make each statement true. 8.EE.1

City	Augusta, Maine	Cheyenne, Wyoming	Jackson, Mississippi	Montpelier, Vermont
Population (approx.)	3^9	3^{10}	3^{11}	3^8

The population of **Cheyenne** is about $\frac{1}{3}$ the population of Jackson.

The population of **Augusta** is about 3 times the population of Montpelier.

The population of **Jackson** is about 27 times the population of **Montpelier**.

Augusta
Cheyenne
Jackson
Montpelier

4. The number line shows four points labeled *A*, *B*, *C*, and *D*. Select whether each statement is true or false. 8.NS.2

True	False	
☐	■	The value of $\sqrt{50}$ is between point *A* and point *B*.
■	☐	The coordinate of point *C* is less than $\sqrt{60}$.
☐	■	The coordinate of point *D* is greater than $\sqrt{63}$.

Online Test Tip
On an online test, you might be asked to click the appropriate box for each statement. In this book, you will be asked to shade in the boxes instead.

5. City Cab Company charges $3.00 per ride plus $2.00 per mile traveled. Metro Cab Company charges $1.50 per ride plus $2.50 per mile traveled. Write an equation to find *m*, the number of miles for which the total cost is the same for both taxi companies. Then solve the equation to find the number of miles when the cost is the same, and state what that cost is. 8.EE.7, 8.EE.7b

Equation: $3 + 2m = 1.5 + 2.5m$

$m =$ 3

3 miles

Cost for that number of miles: $9.00

NAME ______________ DATE ________ PERIOD ______ SCORE ______

Countdown: 17 Weeks

1. The diagonal of a rectangular floor is $\sqrt{40}$ feet long. 8.NS.1

Part A: Select all of the sets of numbers to which $\sqrt{40}$ belongs.

- ■ real
- ☐ integer
- ☐ rational
- ■ irrational
- ☐ whole
- ☐ natural

Part B: Change one digit in $\sqrt{40}$ to a different digit so that the number belongs to a different set of numbers. Explain why changing that digit changes the sets to which the number belongs.

Sample answer: $\sqrt{49}$; The number is still a real number, but it is no longer irrational. Since 49 is a perfect square, and the square root of 49 is equal to 7, the number is now an integer, a rational number, a whole number, and a natural number.

Online Test Tip
On an online test, you might be asked to use a keypad with math symbols to enter the answer. In this book, you will be asked to write in the space provided.

2. The formula $t = \sqrt{\frac{h}{16}}$ represents the time t in seconds that it takes an object to fall from a height of h feet. A rock is dropped from a height of 80 feet. 8.NS.2

Part A: Graph on the number line a point that is an estimate of the time it takes the rock to fall to the ground.

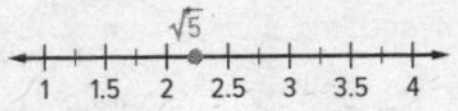

Part B: To the nearest second, how long did it take the rock to fall?

2 seconds

3. The populations of five Asian capital cities are shown in the table. Order the cities from least to greatest population. 8.EE.3, 8.EE.4

City	Population in 2012
Bangkok, Thailand	8.25×10^6
Beijing, China	2.02×10^7
Manila, Philippines	1.65×10^6
Suva, Fiji	8.44×10^5
Tokyo, Japan	1.32×10^7

Bangkok Beijing Manila Suva Tokyo

	City
Least population	**Suva**
	Manila
	Bangkok
	Tokyo
Greatest population	**Beijing**

Online Test Tip
On an online test, you might be asked to drag the city names into the spaces in the table. In this book, you will be asked to write in the table instead.

4. Anju purchased a storage cube that has a volume of 10 cubic feet. She wants to put it on a shelf on her wall that is 24 inches below the ceiling. Will the cube fit? Explain your reasoning. 8.EE.2

No; Sample answer: 24 in. = 2 ft, and the cube root of 8 is 2. The side length of the storage box is the cube root of 10, and the cube root of 10 is greater than the cube root of 8, or 2. So, the storage cube has a height greater than 2 ft. It will not fit.

5. Angelo and Deborah are landscapers. Angelo charges $45.50 for each job plus $15 an hour. Deborah charges $20.50 for each job plus $20 an hour. Select whether each statement is true or false. 8.EE.7, 8.EE.7b

True	False	
■	☐	For 2 hours of work, Angelo charges more.
☐	■	For 6 hours of work, Deborah charges less.
☐	■	The equation $45.5x + 15 = 20.5x + 20$ can be solved to find the number of hours for which the total cost is the same to hire either landscaper.
■	☐	Both landscapers charge the same amount for a 5-hour job.

NAME ______________ DATE ________ PERIOD ______ SCORE ______

Countdown: 16 Weeks

1. The radius of a circular fountain with area A can be approximated by solving the equation $\frac{A}{3} = r^2$. The area of the fountain is 84 square feet. 8.NS.2

Part A: Use a number line to estimate the value of the radius. Plot the square roots of the perfect squares between which the radius is located.

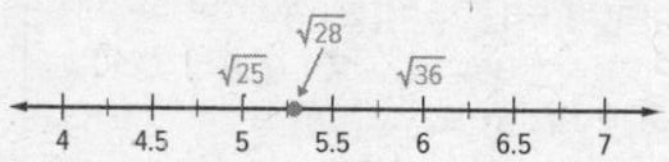

Part B: Find the estimate of the radius of the circular fountain to the nearest foot.

5 ft

2. Select whether the number in each situation is rational or irrational. 8.NS.1

	Rational	Irrational
The length of a ribbon is $23.08\overline{3}$ centimeters.	■	☐
The depth of a shark with respect to the surface of the water is −115.5 meters.	■	☐
Amy calculates that each side of a square measures $2\sqrt{9}$ inches.	■	☐
The circumference of a circular pie pan is 6π, or 18.8495559..., inches.	☐	■

3. Select all of the equations that have no real solution. 8.EE.7, 8.EE.7a

- ■ $5x - 1 - 2x = 3x - 7$
- ■ $6x - (x - 2) = 5x - 2$
- ☐ $-3(5x + 3) = -15x - 9$
- ☐ $2 - (7x - 1) = 5x - 1$
- ■ $10x + 4 + x = 4 + 11x - 1$

Online Test Tip
On an online test, you might be asked to click all of the correct answer choices. In this book, you will be asked to shade a box next to each correct answer choice.

4. Arturo is driving to a hotel. After 3 hours of driving, he is 135 miles from home. After 5 hours of driving, he is 225 miles from home. Arturo graphs his distance with respect to time as a line. What is the slope of the line? What does the slope tell us about Arturo's speed? 8.EE.5

Slope: 45

The slope is the unit rate, or his speed. Arturo drives an average of 45 miles per hour.

5. The table shows the number of people living in the United States and in each region of the country according to the 2010 census. Write the correct number to make each statement true. 8.EE.3, 8.EE.4

U.S. Region	Population (approx.)
Northeast	5.5×10^7
Midwest	6.7×10^7
South	1.1×10^8
West	7.2×10^7
United States (All)	3.1×10^8

2 3 4 5

20 30 40 50

The population of the South is about **2** times greater than the population of the Northeast.

The population of the entire United States is about **3** times greater than the population of the South alone.

The population of the entire United States is about **5** times greater than the population of the Midwest alone.

Countdown

NAME ______________________ DATE __________ PERIOD ________ SCORE ________

Countdown: 15 Weeks

1. Amy charges an hourly fee for each hour she babysits. The table shows how much Amy charges for different numbers of hours. 8.EE.5

Number of Hours	Charge ($)
2	12
3	18
4	24
5	30
6	36

Part A: Graph the points on the coordinate plane and connect them with a straight line.

Charge ($)

Number of Hours

Online Test Tip
On an online test, you might be asked to click the buttons to plot points and graph a line. In this book, you will be asked to draw the points and the line on the graph.

Part B: What is the constant rate of change? What does it mean?

6; Amy charges $6 per hour to babysit.

2. Write y-values for the empty cells in each table to make a linear function and a nonlinear function. Explain how you know your function is linear or nonlinear. 8.F.3

Linear Function

x	y
0	2
1	3
2	4
3	5

Nonlinear Function

x	y
1	6
2	7
3	5
4	2

Sample answers are given in the tables. For the nonlinear function, any numbers can be written, except for 8 and 9 consecutively.
Sample explanation: The linear function can be written as $y = x + 2$, which is in the form $y = mx + b$. The nonlinear function cannot be written in linear form and the points, when graphed, do not lie on a straight line.

3. The table shows the cost of buying different amounts of turkey. The total cost is a direct variation of the number of pounds purchased. Find the constant of proportionality and show how you found the answer. Then write an equation in $y = mx$ form to represent the situation. 8.F.4

Weight (lb), x	2	8	12
Cost ($), y	15	60	90

Constant of proportionality: **7.5; Sample answer: $\frac{60}{8} = \frac{15}{2} = \frac{7.5}{1}$**

Equation: **$y = 7.5x$**

4. Each member of the service club must complete 100 hours of community service during the year. So far, Kurt has completed 41.5% of his hours, Elias has completed $\sqrt{1,681}$ hours, Janina has completed $\frac{21}{50}$ of her hours, and Tasha has completed $\frac{3}{7}$ of her hours. Plot points on the number line to represent the number of hours of community service each club member has completed. 8.NS.1

Elias Kurt Janina Tasha

41 41.2 41.4 41.6 41.8 42 42.2 42.4 42.6 42.8 43

5. Ariel is filling a swimming pool. Three gallons of water flow into the pool every minute. 8.F.4

Part A: Complete the table to show the number of gallons of water in the pool several minutes after Ariel begins filling it.

Time Since Filling Started (min)	Water in Pool (gal)
1	3
2	6
3	9
4	12
5	15

Part B: How many gallons of water are in the pool 11 minutes after Ariel starts filling it?

33 gal

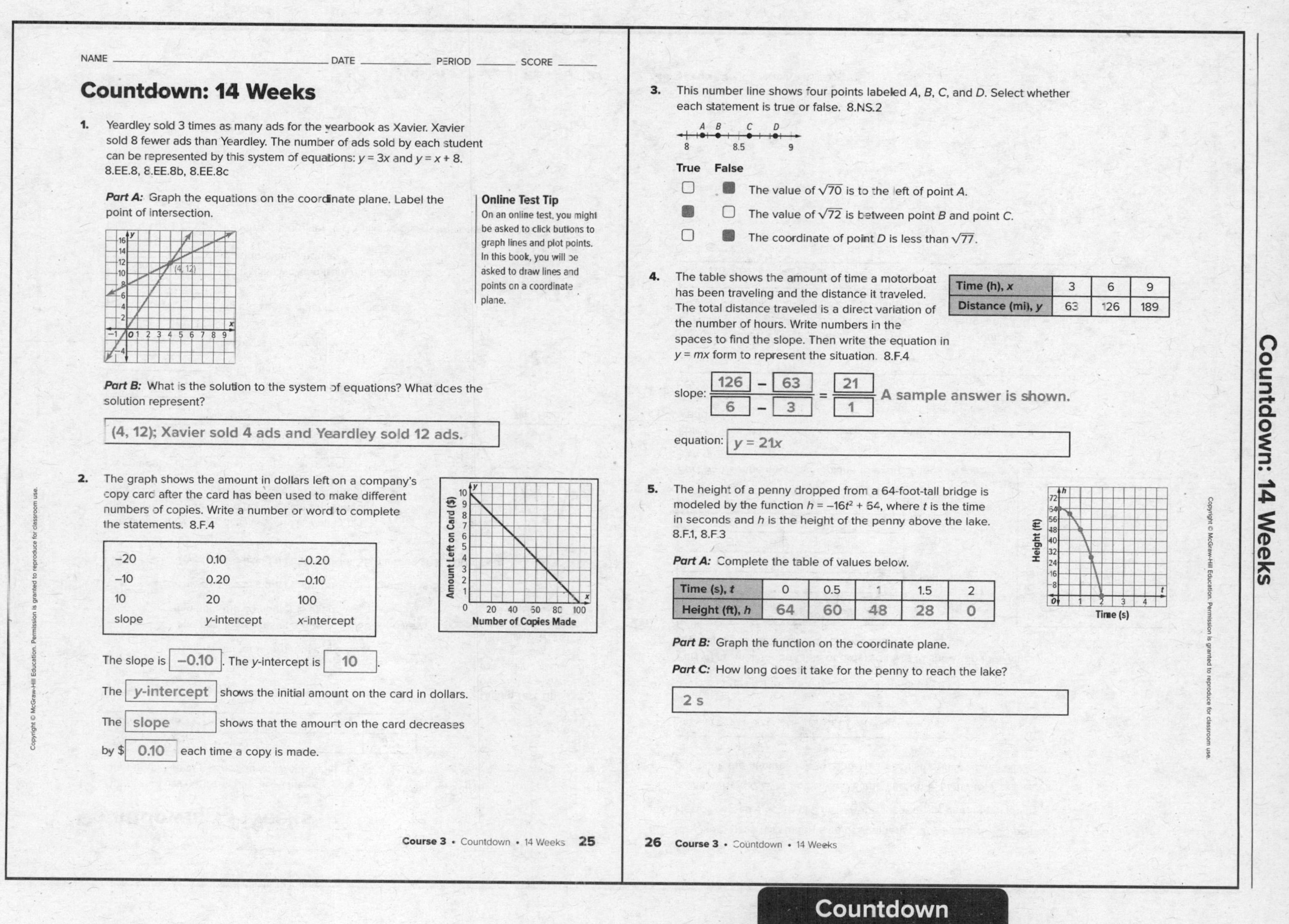

NAME ________ DATE ________ PERIOD ________ SCORE ________

Countdown: 14 Weeks

1. Yeardley sold 3 times as many ads for the yearbook as Xavier. Xavier sold 8 fewer ads than Yeardley. The number of ads sold by each student can be represented by this system of equations: $y = 3x$ and $y = x + 8$. 8.EE.8, 8.EE.8b, 8.EE.8c

Part A: Graph the equations on the coordinate plane. Label the point of intersection.

Online Test Tip
On an online test, you might be asked to click buttons to graph lines and plot points. In this book, you will be asked to draw lines and points on a coordinate plane.

Part B: What is the solution to the system of equations? What does the solution represent?

(4, 12); Xavier sold 4 ads and Yeardley sold 12 ads.

2. The graph shows the amount in dollars left on a company's copy card after the card has been used to make different numbers of copies. Write a number or word to complete the statements. 8.F.4

−20	0.10	−0.20
−10	0.20	−0.10
10	20	100
slope	y-intercept	x-intercept

The slope is −0.10. The y-intercept is 10.

The y-intercept shows the initial amount on the card in dollars.

The slope shows that the amount on the card decreases by $ 0.10 each time a copy is made.

3. This number line shows four points labeled A, B, C, and D. Select whether each statement is true or false. 8.NS.2

True	False	
☐	■	The value of $\sqrt{70}$ is to the left of point A.
■	☐	The value of $\sqrt{72}$ is between point B and point C.
☐	■	The coordinate of point D is less than $\sqrt{77}$.

4. The table shows the amount of time a motorboat has been traveling and the distance it traveled. The total distance traveled is a direct variation of the number of hours. Write numbers in the spaces to find the slope. Then write the equation in $y = mx$ form to represent the situation. 8.F.4

Time (h), x	3	6	9
Distance (mi), y	63	126	189

slope: $\frac{126 - 63}{6 - 3} = \frac{21}{1}$ A sample answer is shown.

equation: $y = 21x$

5. The height of a penny dropped from a 64-foot-tall bridge is modeled by the function $h = -16t^2 + 64$, where t is the time in seconds and h is the height of the penny above the lake. 8.F.1, 8.F.3

Part A: Complete the table of values below.

Time (s), t	0	0.5	1	1.5	2
Height (ft), h	64	60	48	28	0

Part B: Graph the function on the coordinate plane.

Part C: How long does it take for the penny to reach the lake?

2 s

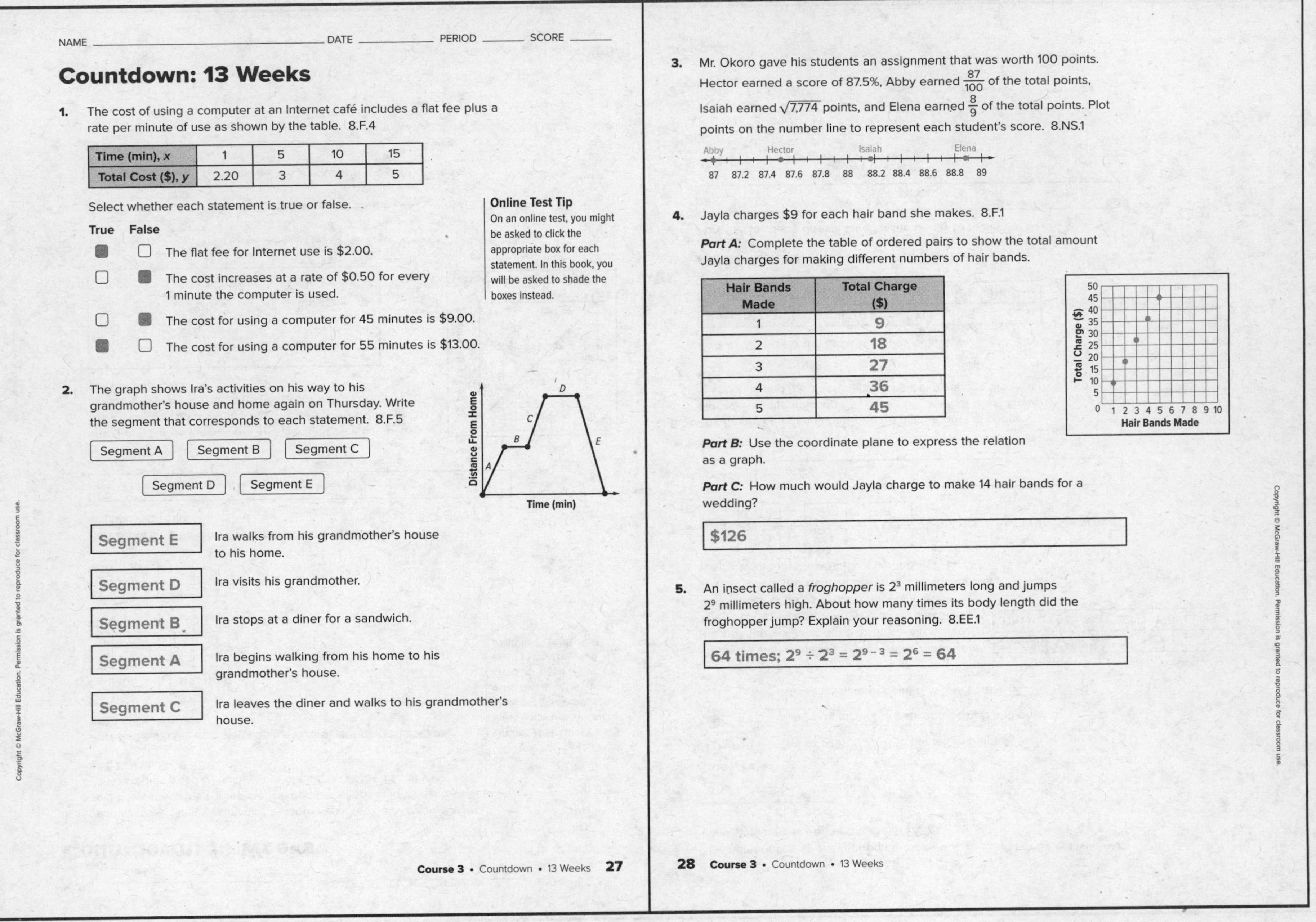

NAME ________ DATE ________ PERIOD ________ SCORE ________

Countdown: 13 Weeks

1. The cost of using a computer at an Internet café includes a flat fee plus a rate per minute of use as shown by the table. 8.F.4

Time (min), x	1	5	10	15
Total Cost ($), y	2.20	3	4	5

Select whether each statement is true or false.

True	False	
■	☐	The flat fee for Internet use is $2.00.
☐	■	The cost increases at a rate of $0.50 for every 1 minute the computer is used.
☐	■	The cost for using a computer for 45 minutes is $9.00.
■	☐	The cost for using a computer for 55 minutes is $13.00.

Online Test Tip
On an online test, you might be asked to click the appropriate box for each statement. In this book, you will be asked to shade the boxes instead.

2. The graph shows Ira's activities on his way to his grandmother's house and home again on Thursday. Write the segment that corresponds to each statement. 8.F.5

Segment A | Segment B | Segment C | Segment D | Segment E

Segment E	Ira walks from his grandmother's house to his home.
Segment D	Ira visits his grandmother.
Segment B	Ira stops at a diner for a sandwich.
Segment A	Ira begins walking from his home to his grandmother's house.
Segment C	Ira leaves the diner and walks to his grandmother's house.

3. Mr. Okoro gave his students an assignment that was worth 100 points. Hector earned a score of 87.5%, Abby earned $\frac{87}{100}$ of the total points, Isaiah earned $\sqrt{7{,}774}$ points, and Elena earned $\frac{8}{9}$ of the total points. Plot points on the number line to represent each student's score. 8.NS.1

4. Jayla charges $9 for each hair band she makes. 8.F.1

Part A: Complete the table of ordered pairs to show the total amount Jayla charges for making different numbers of hair bands.

Hair Bands Made	Total Charge ($)
1	9
2	18
3	27
4	36
5	45

Part B: Use the coordinate plane to express the relation as a graph.

Part C: How much would Jayla charge to make 14 hair bands for a wedding?

$126

5. An insect called a *froghopper* is 2^3 millimeters long and jumps 2^9 millimeters high. About how many times its body length did the froghopper jump? Explain your reasoning. 8.EE.1

64 times; $2^9 \div 2^3 = 2^{9-3} = 2^6 = 64$

NAME ______________ DATE ________ PERIOD ________ SCORE ________

Countdown: 12 Weeks

1. Quentin posted a video of his kitten on a Web site. The table shows the total number of "likes" his video had received by the end of each day over the course of a week. 8.F.4

Days Since Upload	1	3	5	7
Total Number of "Likes"	5,400	6,200	7,000	7,800

Quentin's Video
Total Number of Likes (thousands)
Days Since Upload

Part A: Graph the points on the coordinate plane to show the relationship.

Part B: The pattern shown in the graph continues. How many "likes" will Quentin's video have by the end of the 8th day since the upload?

8,200

2. Different types of functions have different characteristics.

Part A: Write what type of function is represented. 8.F.3

linear
nonlinear

x	y
−8	−2
−2	2.5
0	4
4	7
10	11.5

$y = -5x^2$

$y = -\frac{1}{2}x - 2$

linear	nonlinear	nonlinear	linear

Part B: Choose a linear function above. Describe how you could change the representation of that linear function to make it nonlinear.

Sample answer: I would square the variable x in the equation $y = -\frac{1}{2}x - 2$ to change it to $y = -\frac{1}{2}x^2 - 2$. The equation now will represent a nonlinear function.

3. The radius of a circle with area A can be approximated using the formula $r = \sqrt{\frac{A}{3}}$. A circular tabletop has an area of 42 ft². 8.NS.2

Part A: Use the number line to estimate the radius of the tabletop. What square root is the radius? Between which two points that represent the square roots of perfect squares is the radius located?

$\sqrt{4}$ $\sqrt{9}$ $\sqrt{16}$ $\sqrt{25}$
2 2.5 3 3.5 4 4.5 5

The radius is $\sqrt{14}$. It is located between $\sqrt{9} = 3$ and $\sqrt{16} = 4$.

Online Test Tip
On an online test, you might be asked to use a keypad with math symbols to enter the answer. In this book, you will be asked to write in the space provided.

Part B: What is the estimated radius of the tabletop to the nearest foot? Explain how you found your answer.

4 ft; Sample answer: $\sqrt{14}$ is closer to $\sqrt{16}$ than it is to $\sqrt{9}$, so the radius is closer to 4.

4. The Caspian Sea has an area of 371,000 square kilometers. Lake Superior has an area of 8.24×10^4 square kilometers. Complete each sentence to make a true statement 8.EE.4

The area of the Caspian Sea is greater than the area of Lake Superior.

The difference in the areas of the two lakes is 288,600 or 2.886×10^5 square kilometers.

5. A fish tank full of water is being emptied so it can be cleaned. The table shows how the volume of water in the tank changes over time. Select whether each statement is true or false. 8.F.4

Time (min)	0	4	8	12
Volume (gal)	20	18	16	14

True	False	
☐	■	The initial amount of water in the tank was 0 gallons.
■	☐	The amount of water in the tank decreases at a rate of 0.5 gallon every minute.
☐	■	There were 19 gallons of water in the tank after 1 minute.
■	☐	There were 15 gallons of water in the tank after 10 minutes.

Countdown

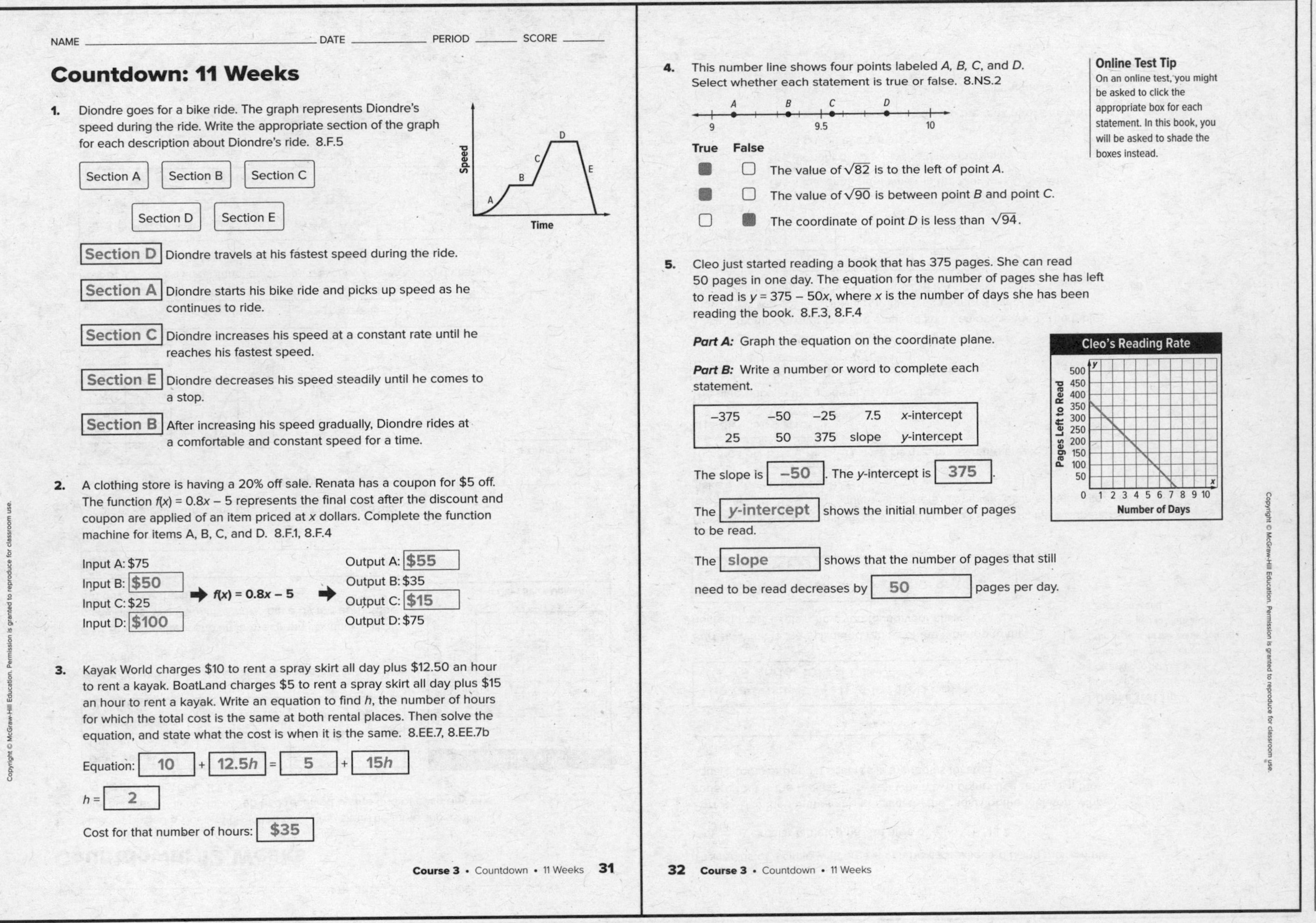

NAME ______________ DATE ________ PERIOD ______ SCORE ______

Countdown: 11 Weeks

1. Diondre goes for a bike ride. The graph represents Diondre's speed during the ride. Write the appropriate section of the graph for each description about Diondre's ride. 8.F.5

Section A | Section B | Section C | Section D | Section E

Section D Diondre travels at his fastest speed during the ride.

Section A Diondre starts his bike ride and picks up speed as he continues to ride.

Section C Diondre increases his speed at a constant rate until he reaches his fastest speed.

Section E Diondre decreases his speed steadily until he comes to a stop.

Section B After increasing his speed gradually, Diondre rides at a comfortable and constant speed for a time.

2. A clothing store is having a 20% off sale. Renata has a coupon for $5 off. The function $f(x) = 0.8x - 5$ represents the final cost after the discount and coupon are applied of an item priced at x dollars. Complete the function machine for items A, B, C, and D. 8.F.1, 8.F.4

Input A: $75 → Output A: $55
Input B: $50 → Output B: $35
Input C: $25 → $f(x) = 0.8x - 5$ → Output C: $15
Input D: $100 → Output D: $75

3. Kayak World charges $10 to rent a spray skirt all day plus $12.50 an hour to rent a kayak. BoatLand charges $5 to rent a spray skirt all day plus $15 an hour to rent a kayak. Write an equation to find h, the number of hours for which the total cost is the same at both rental places. Then solve the equation, and state what the cost is when it is the same. 8.EE.7, 8.EE.7b

Equation: $10 + 12.5h = 5 + 15h$

$h = 2$

Cost for that number of hours: $35

Course 3 • Countdown • 11 Weeks 31

4. This number line shows four points labeled A, B, C, and D. Select whether each statement is true or false. 8.NS.2

True	False	
■	□	The value of $\sqrt{82}$ is to the left of point A.
■	□	The value of $\sqrt{90}$ is between point B and point C.
□	■	The coordinate of point D is less than $\sqrt{94}$.

Online Test Tip
On an online test, you might be asked to click the appropriate box for each statement. In this book, you will be asked to shade the boxes instead.

5. Cleo just started reading a book that has 375 pages. She can read 50 pages in one day. The equation for the number of pages she has left to read is $y = 375 - 50x$, where x is the number of days she has been reading the book. 8.F.3, 8.F.4

Part A: Graph the equation on the coordinate plane.

Part B: Write a number or word to complete each statement.

−375	−50	−25	7.5	x-intercept
25	50	375	slope	y-intercept

The slope is −50. The y-intercept is 375.

The y-intercept shows the initial number of pages to be read.

The slope shows that the number of pages that still need to be read decreases by 50 pages per day.

32 Course 3 • Countdown • 11 Weeks

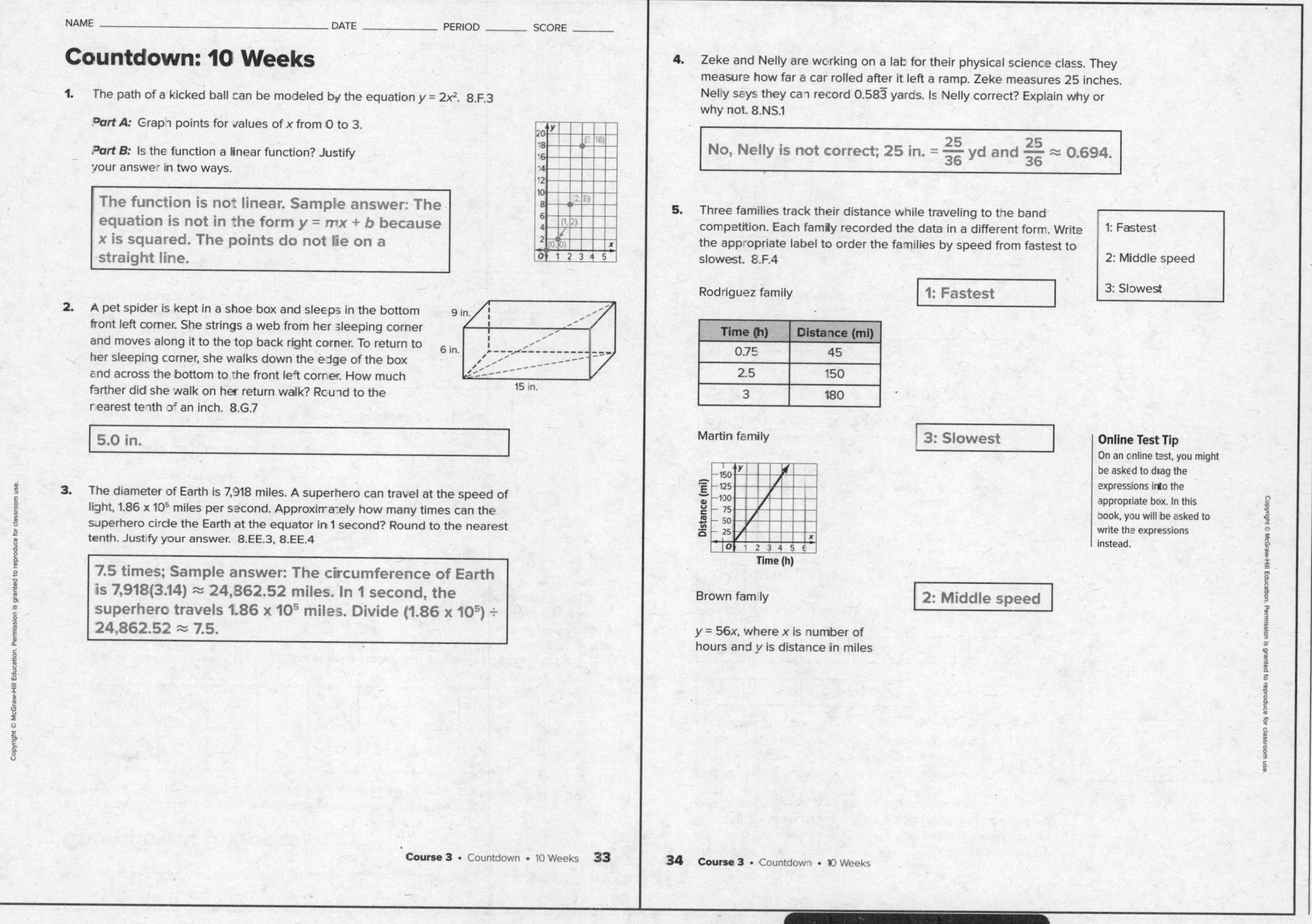

NAME ______________ DATE ________ PERIOD ______ SCORE ______

Countdown: 10 Weeks

1. The path of a kicked ball can be modeled by the equation $y = 2x^2$. 8.F.3

Part A: Graph points for values of x from 0 to 3.

Part B: Is the function a linear function? Justify your answer in two ways.

The function is not linear. Sample answer: The equation is not in the form $y = mx + b$ because x is squared. The points do not lie on a straight line.

2. A pet spider is kept in a shoe box and sleeps in the bottom front left corner. She strings a web from her sleeping corner and moves along it to the top back right corner. To return to her sleeping corner, she walks down the edge of the box and across the bottom to the front left corner. How much farther did she walk on her return walk? Round to the nearest tenth of an inch. 8.G.7

5.0 in.

3. The diameter of Earth is 7,918 miles. A superhero can travel at the speed of light, 1.86×10^5 miles per second. Approximately how many times can the superhero circle the Earth at the equator in 1 second? Round to the nearest tenth. Justify your answer. 8.EE.3, 8.EE.4

7.5 times; Sample answer: The circumference of Earth is $7{,}918(3.14) \approx 24{,}862.52$ miles. In 1 second, the superhero travels 1.86×10^5 miles. Divide $(1.86 \times 10^5) \div 24{,}862.52 \approx 7.5$.

4. Zeke and Nelly are working on a lab for their physical science class. They measure how far a car rolled after it left a ramp. Zeke measures 25 inches. Nelly says they can record $0.58\overline{3}$ yards. Is Nelly correct? Explain why or why not. 8.NS.1

No, Nelly is not correct; 25 in. = $\frac{25}{36}$ yd and $\frac{25}{36} \approx 0.694$.

5. Three families track their distance while traveling to the band competition. Each family recorded the data in a different form. Write the appropriate label to order the families by speed from fastest to slowest. 8.F.4

1: Fastest
2: Middle speed
3: Slowest

Rodriguez family — **1: Fastest**

Time (h)	Distance (mi)
0.75	45
2.5	150
3	180

Martin family — **3: Slowest**

Online Test Tip
On an online test, you might be asked to drag the expressions into the appropriate box. In this book, you will be asked to write the expressions instead.

Brown family — **2: Middle speed**

$y = 56x$, where x is number of hours and y is distance in miles

NAME ________________ DATE ________ PERIOD ______ SCORE ______

Countdown: 9 Weeks

1. Students build towers using marshmallows and toothpicks. They record the number of toothpicks used for the tower at different heights. 8.SP.1

Number of Toothpicks	5	15	25	30	40	45
Height (cm)	5	10	15	20	25	30

Part A: Use the data in the table to construct a scatter plot on the coordinate plane.

Online Test Tip
On an online test, you might be asked to click a button to plot points. In this book, you will be asked to draw the points on the coordinate plane.

Height (cm)
50 45 40 35 30 25 20 15 10 5 O
5 10 15 20 25 30 35 40 45 50
Number of Toothpicks

Part B: Describe patterns you see in the data.

The data set has a positive linear association. There are no clusters or outliers.

2. Elm Street and Oak Street are parallel. Avenue Z crosses each of them. The city planner needs to find the measures of the angles at each intersection. Find the measures of the labeled angles. 8.G.5

Avenue Z
$(2x + 2)°$
Elm Street
$(3x - 12)°$
Oak Street

angle between Avenue Z and Elm St.: **78°**

angle between Avenue Z and Oak St.: **102°**

3. The middle school choir had an outdoor concert to raise money for a field trip. The attendance was 350 people. A child's ticket cost \$1.50, and an adult's ticket cost \$5.00. The choir earned a total of \$917. 8.EE.8, 8.EE.8b, 8.EE.8c

Part A: Write the appropriate numbers, symbols, and variables to create a system of equations that would lead to finding the number of children and the number of adults at the concert.

a	*c*	1.50	5.00
350	917	+	–

$a + c = 350$

$5.00a + 1.50c = 917$

Part B: How many children and adults attended the concert?

112 adults

238 children

4. Adzo says the graph is of the function $y = 2^{-1}x - \sqrt{25}$. Ben says it is $y - 5 = 0.5x$. Who is correct? Explain your answer. 8.F.2

Adzo is correct. Both have the correct slope, $\frac{1}{2}$. The *y*-intercept on the graph is –5, but Ben's line has a *y*-intercept of 5. Adzo's line has the correct *y*-intercept.

5. Graph the numbers at their approximate locations on the number line. 8.NS.2

$\sqrt{70}$ $-\sqrt{55}$ $-\sqrt{20}$ $\sqrt{32}$

$-\sqrt{55}$ $-\sqrt{20}$ $\sqrt{32}$ $\sqrt{70}$
–10 –9 –8 –7 –6 –5 –4 –3 –2 –1 0 1 2 3 4 5 6 7 8 9 10

NAME ______________ DATE ________ PERIOD ______ SCORE ______

Countdown: 8 Weeks

1. Triangles *ABC* and *CDE* are slope triangles. 8.EE.6

Part A: Show that the slope triangles are similar.

Sample answer: $\angle ABC \cong \angle CDE$ and $\angle BCA \cong \angle DEC$, so the triangles are similar by the Angle-Angle Similarity.

Part B: Compare the rise to the run for each of the triangles. Write the reason next to each step in the solution.

Step	Reason
$\frac{ED}{CB} = \frac{CD}{AB}$	**Corresponding sides of similar triangles are proportional.**
$ED \cdot AB = CB \cdot CD$	**Find the cross products.**
$\frac{ED \cdot AB}{CD \cdot AB} = \frac{CB \cdot CD}{CD \cdot AB}$	**Division Property of Equality**
$\frac{ED}{CD} = \frac{CB}{AB}$	**Simplify.**

Part C: What conclusion can you draw from the work in Part B?

Sample answer: The slope between any two points on a non-vertical line is the same.

2. A tennis court is rectangular with a length of 120 feet and a width of 60 feet. For warm-up, a player runs along the diagonal of the court from one corner to the other. His partner runs the length and width of the court to the opposite corner. How much farther did the partner run? Explain your answer. Round to the nearest tenth. 8.G.7

45.8 ft farther; Sample answer: Add the length and width: 120 + 60 = 180 ft. Find the length of the diagonal by solving $d^2 = 120^2 + 60^2$ to get $d \approx 134.2$ ft. Subtract: 180 – 134.2 = 45.8 ft.

3. A student climbs up the ladder of a slide and slides down. Select all of the statements that are represented by the graph. 8.F.5

- ■ The student reaches the bottom of the slide at D.
- ■ The student slides faster at the top of the slide than at the bottom.
- ■ The student pauses at the top of the slide before sliding down.
- ☐ The student slows as he reaches the top of the ladder.
- ☐ The student is never more than 6 feet off the ground.

4. Every 15 minutes, the height of the water in the pool is measured and plotted. The data are shown in the table. 8.SP.2

Time (min)	15	30	45	75	90
Water Height (cm)	40	50	60	70	90

Part A: Construct a scatter plot of the data.

Part B: Would the equation $y = x + 40$ or the equation $y = 0.5x + 30$ better model the data? Explain.

$y = 0.5x + 30$; Sample answer: The data points are much closer to the line $y = 0.5x + 30$ than they are to the line $y = x + 40$, making the first equation a better model of the data.

5. Roberta plots coordinates to represent the corners of her garden: *A*(2.5, 1.5), *B*(–4, 3), and *C*(–2, –5). She decides to quadruple the length of each side using the origin as the center for the enlargement of her garden. Select all of the statements that are true about the new coordinates. 8.G.3

- ■ The perimeter of the garden is 4 times the original perimeter.
- ■ *A′* is located at (10, 6).
- ☐ *B′* is located at (–1, 0.75).
- ■ *C′* is located at (–8, –20).
- ☐ The area of the garden is 8 times greater than the original.

Online Test Tip
On an online test, you might be asked to click all of the correct answer choices. In this book, you will be asked to shade a box next to each correct answer choice.

NAME ____________ DATE ________ PERIOD ______ SCORE ______

Countdown: 7 Weeks

1. Jeremy takes his heart rate (in beats per minute) after running on the treadmill for different periods of time. Find and describe the constant rate of change for this function. Find and describe the initial value. 8.F.4

Time (min)	Heart Rate (bpm)
4	84
10	108

rate of change: **4; For every minute he runs, his heart rate increases by 4 beats per minute.**

initial value: **68; His heart rate is 68 bpm before he runs.**

2. Carrie creates triangular pendants to be worn as necklaces. Two pendants are shown. Select all of the statements that are true about the pendants. 8.G.4

- ☐ $\triangle ABC \cong \triangle DEF$ by the SAS Similarity Theorem.
- ■ Since there are two corresponding congruent angles, the third angles in the triangles must also be congruent.
- ■ $m\angle E \cong m\angle B$ and $m\angle C \cong m\angle F$
- ■ By the Angle-Angle Similarity, $\triangle ABC \sim \triangle DEF$.
- ☐ The measure of the third angle in each triangle can be found by subtracting the sum of the given angles from 360°.

3. Members of a book club pay lower prices for individual books and a flat shipping rate. One member graphs how much she spends and draws a line of best fit. Write an equation for the line of best fit. What does the slope represent? What does the y-intercept represent? 8.SP.3

$y = 3.5x + 4$; The slope represents the average cost of a book, \$3.50. The y-intercept represents the shipping rate of \$4.

4. A road divides the neighborhood park into two parts. Calvin plots one part in a coordinate plane. The part of the park shown is a reflection over the x-axis of the other part. 8.G.3

Part A: Draw the other part of the park.

Part B: Write the coordinates of the vertices of the part that you drew. Then describe the effects of a reflection across the x-axis on the coordinates.

$A(4, -4)$, $B(-4, -7)$, and $C(-3, -1)$; The y-coordinate of the reflection is the opposite of the initial y-coordinate, while the x-coordinates do not change.

5. The choir started selling CDs of their concerts as a fundraiser in 2008. The table shows the number of CDs sold each year. 8.SP.2

Years Since 2008	1	2	3	4	5	6
Number of CDs Sold	460	380	370	310	225	175

Part A: Draw a line of best fit. **A sample line of best fit is shown.**

Part B: Write the equation of the line of best fit. According to the model, how many CDs were sold in 2008? Predict how many CDs will be sold in 2016. Justify your answer.

Sample answer: $y = -50x + 500$; 500 CDs in 2008, because it is the y-intercept, which represents 0 years since 2008; 100 CDs in 2016, because 2016 is 8 years after 2008, so substitute 8 for x into the equation and solve for y.

Online Test Tip
On an online test, you might be asked to click a button to graph a line. In this book, you will be asked to draw the line in the coordinate plane.

NAME ______________ DATE ________ PERIOD ______ SCORE ______

Countdown: 6 Weeks

1. Chloe has started a new business where she ships books to her customers. She records the number of books shipped in a box and the cost to ship the box for her first five orders. 8.SP.1

Number of Books	1	2	4	5	8
Shipping Cost ($)	3	5	6	8	10

Part A: Construct a scatter plot of the data.

Shipping Cost ($)
Number of Books

Part B: Interpret the scatter plot based on the shape of its distribution.

positive, linear association; no outliers or clusters

2. A square table *PQRS* is mapped in a coordinate plane. The table is rotated 270° clockwise about the origin. Select whether each statement is true or false. 8.G.3

True	False	
■	☐	The image of point *P* is *P*′(−4, 4).
■	☐	The image of point *Q* is *Q*′(−1, 4).
☐	■	The image of point *R* is *R*′(−4, 1).
☐	■	Square *PQRS* can also be mapped onto *P*′*Q*′*R*′*S*′ by translating it 5 units left.
■	☐	*PQRS* and its image are congruent polygons.

3. Kali maps two flower beds in a coordinate plane. Use transformations to show that the flower beds are congruent. 8.G.2

Sample answer: Start with triangle *LMN*. Translate the triangle 3 units up and 4 units left. Then rotate the triangle 90° counterclockwise about the origin to map onto *RST*.

4. A town is laid out so that L Street and M Street are parallel. L Street and N Street are perpendicular, as are M Street and P Street. Select all of the statements that are true about the streets in this town. 8.G.1

L Street
N Street
Main Street
M Street
P Street

■ L Street and M Street can be mapped onto N Street and P Street by a reflection across Main Street.

☐ N Street and P Street have the same slope as L Street and M Street.

■ N Street and P Street must be parallel.

5. Juan learns to make soap and studies its density. He uses a scatter plot to map its volume and mass. He models his data with the linear equation $y = 1.25x + 1$, where x is the volume of the soap in cubic centimeters, and y is the mass of the soap in grams. 8.SP.3

Online Test Tip
On an online test, you might be asked to use a keypad with math symbols to enter the answer. In this book, you will be asked to write the answer in the space provided.

Part A: What is the slope of the line that models the data? What does it represent?

1.25; For every 1 cm^3 of volume that a piece of soap has, its mass increases by 1.25 g.

Part B: What is the y-intercept? What does it represent? Explain why the model does not work for very small volumes of soap.

1; It represents that a piece of soap with volume 0 cm^3 would have a mass of 1 g. The model does not work at this point because when the volume is 0, the mass would be 0.

Countdown

NAME ______________________ DATE ____________ PERIOD ________ SCORE ________

Countdown: 5 Weeks

1. Abby is collecting data for her science fair project about nutrition. She gathers data about the number of grams of fat and the number of calories in a serving of fruit. 8.SP.1

Fruit	Apple	Banana	Kiwi	Orange	Pear	Strawberry
Fat (g)	0.1	0.3	0.5	0.3	0.7	0.9
Calories	48	95	49	62	98	28

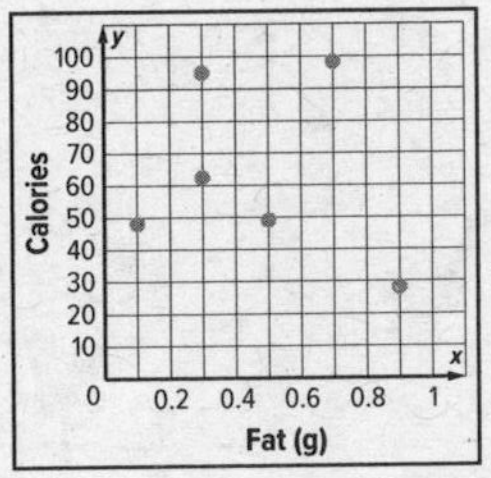

Part A: Make a scatter plot of the data.

Part B: Describe any patterns in the data.

Sample answer: no association between the number of fat grams and number of calories; no outliers or clusters

2. $\overline{AB}$ and $\overline{CD}$ are plotted on a coordinate plane. Select whether each statement is true or false. 8.G.1, 8.G.1a

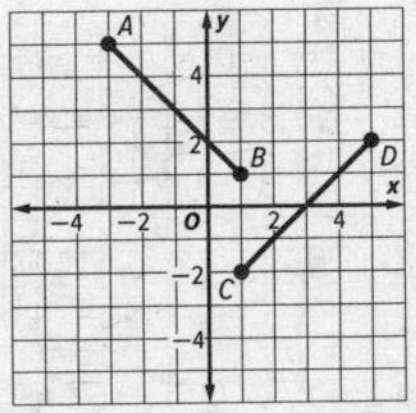

True	False	
■	☐	$AB = CD$
☐	■	The image of point *A* reflected across the *y*-axis is *D*(5, 2).
■	☐	$\overline{AB}$ can be mapped onto $\overline{CD}$ by a reflection and a translation.
☐	■	$\overline{AB}$ can be mapped onto $\overline{CD}$ by a rotation about the origin.

3. Michael maps two triangular courtyards on a coordinate plane. Write numbers to describe the effects of the translation of $\triangle ABC$ onto $\triangle DEF$. What can you conclude about these triangles? Explain. 8.G.3

$(x, y) \rightarrow (x + \boxed{5}, y + \boxed{3})$

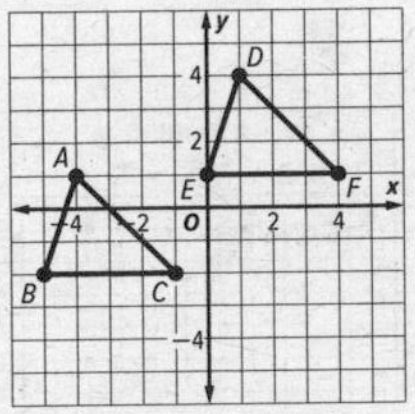

Sample answer: The triangles are congruent because a translation maps $\triangle ABC$ onto $\triangle DEF$, and images produced by a translation are congruent.

4. Lucia invites 48 friends, including 20 boys, to a party. There are a total of 32 who were on time, and of those, 18 are girls. 8.SP.4

Part A: Complete the two-way table to summarize the data.

	On Time	Late	Total
Boys	14	6	20
Girls	18	10	28
Total	32	16	48

Part B: Select each valid conclusion using the table in Part A.

- ■ There are 4 more girls who are on time than boys.
- ☐ The number of boys who are late is half the number of girls who are late.
- ■ There are 6 guests who are boys and are late.
- ■ To find the total number of late guests, subtract 32 from 48.

Online Test Tip
On an online test, you might be asked to click all of the correct answer choices. In this book, you will be asked to shade a box next to each correct answer choice.

5. A company produces a new key pocket that is in the shape of a triangle. They plot the shapes on a coordinate plane. 8.G.4

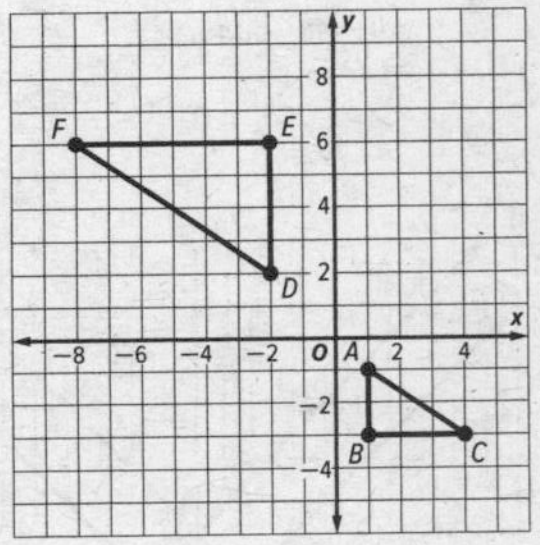

Part A: Describe two sequences that could map triangle *ABC* onto triangle *DEF*.

Sample answer: 1) A rotation of 180° followed by a dilation with a scale factor of 2, or 2) A reflection across the *x*-axis, a reflection across the *y*-axis, and then a dilation with a scale factor of 2.

Part B: What conclusion can you draw about the triangles?

The triangles are similar.

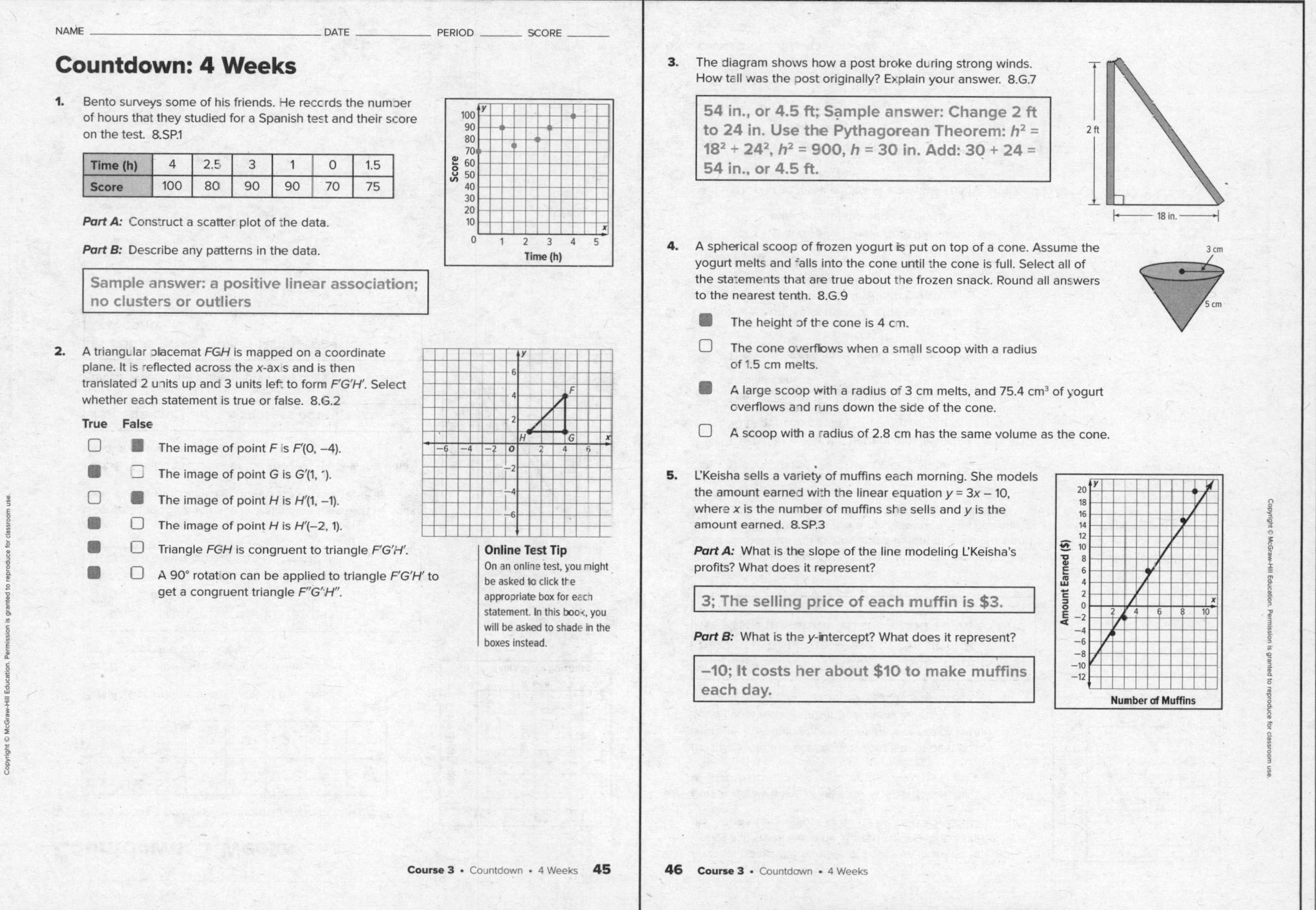

NAME ______________________ DATE ________ PERIOD ______ SCORE ______

Countdown: 4 Weeks

1. Bento surveys some of his friends. He records the number of hours that they studied for a Spanish test and their score on the test. 8.SP.1

Time (h)	4	2.5	3	1	0	1.5
Score	100	80	90	90	70	75

Part A: Construct a scatter plot of the data.

Part B: Describe any patterns in the data.

Sample answer: a positive linear association; no clusters or outliers

2. A triangular placemat FGH is mapped on a coordinate plane. It is reflected across the x-axis and is then translated 2 units up and 3 units left to form $F'G'H'$. Select whether each statement is true or false. 8.G.2

True	False	
☐	■	The image of point F is $F'(0, -4)$.
■	☐	The image of point G is $G'(1,$ [illegible]$)$.
☐	■	The image of point H is $H'(1, -1)$.
■	☐	The image of point H is $H'(-2, 1)$.
■	☐	Triangle FGH is congruent to triangle $F'G'H'$.
■	☐	A 90° rotation can be applied to triangle $F'G'H'$ to get a congruent triangle $F''G''H''$.

Online Test Tip
On an online test, you might be asked to click the appropriate box for each statement. In this book, you will be asked to shade in the boxes instead.

3. The diagram shows how a post broke during strong winds. How tall was the post originally? Explain your answer. 8.G.7

54 in., or 4.5 ft; Sample answer: Change 2 ft to 24 in. Use the Pythagorean Theorem: $h^2 = 18^2 + 24^2$, $h^2 = 900$, $h = 30$ in. Add: 30 + 24 = 54 in., or 4.5 ft.

4. A spherical scoop of frozen yogurt is put on top of a cone. Assume the yogurt melts and falls into the cone until the cone is full. Select all of the statements that are true about the frozen snack. Round all answers to the nearest tenth. 8.G.9

- ■ The height of the cone is 4 cm.
- ☐ The cone overflows when a small scoop with a radius of 1.5 cm melts.
- ■ A large scoop with a radius of 3 cm melts, and 75.4 cm³ of yogurt overflows and runs down the side of the cone.
- ☐ A scoop with a radius of 2.8 cm has the same volume as the cone.

5. L'Keisha sells a variety of muffins each morning. She models the amount earned with the linear equation $y = 3x - 10$, where x is the number of muffins she sells and y is the amount earned. 8.SP.3

Part A: What is the slope of the line modeling L'Keisha's profits? What does it represent?

3; The selling price of each muffin is $3.

Part B: What is the y-intercept? What does it represent?

−10; It costs her about $10 to make muffins each day.

NAME ________ DATE ________ PERIOD ______ SCORE ______

Countdown: 3 Weeks

1. Bruce records how his car depreciated over time. 8.SP.1

Years Since Purchase	0	1	4	5	8
Value (Thousands of $)	20	13	9	8	7

Part A: Construct a scatter plot of the data.

Part B: Describe the association. Then write a statement that is supported by the data.

There is a negative nonlinear association. Sample answer: The car's value decreases very quickly at first and then more slowly as the car gets older.

2. George conducts a science investigation for which he rolls a toy car down a ramp. He graphs his results. 8.SP.3

Part A: What is the slope of the line that models the data? What does it represent?

1.5; The car rolls 1.5 meters every second.

Part B: What is the y-intercept? What does it represent?

0; The car had moved 0 meters after 0 seconds.

3. A waiter tracks the number of hours he is asked to work each week since he started his job. The scatter plot shows the number of hours he worked. 8.SP.2

Part A: Draw a line of best fit. **A sample line is shown.**

Part B: Write the equation of your line of best fit. On average, how many hours does he work each week? Justify your answer. After how many weeks will he have worked 80 hours? Explain your answer.

Sample answer: $y = 10x$; 10 hours per week, because 10 is the slope of the line; 8 weeks; Substitute 80 for y and solve to find $x = 8$.

4. Baked beans are available in two different-sized cans. One can has a diameter of 2.5 inches and a height of 4.5 inches and sells for $2.87. The other can has a diameter of 4.5 inches and a height of 2.5 inches and sells for $5.95. Select all of the correct conclusions. 8.G.9

- ■ The volume of the smaller can is about 22.1 cubic inches.
- ☐ The larger can is the better buy because it costs about $0.12 per cubic inch.
- ■ The volume of the larger can is about 1.8 times the volume of the smaller can.
- ■ The smaller can costs about $0.13 per cubic inch.

Online Test Tip
On an online test, you might be asked to click all of the correct answer choices. In this book, you will be asked to shade a box next to each correct answer choice.

5. Leanna tears off the corners of a triangle and aligns them as shown. Select whether each statement is true or false. 8.G.5

True	False	
■	☐	This diagram shows that the sum of the measures of the angles of a triangle is 180°.
■	☐	The three angles of a triangle can be arranged to form a straight angle.
☐	■	This experiment would have different results with a right triangle.

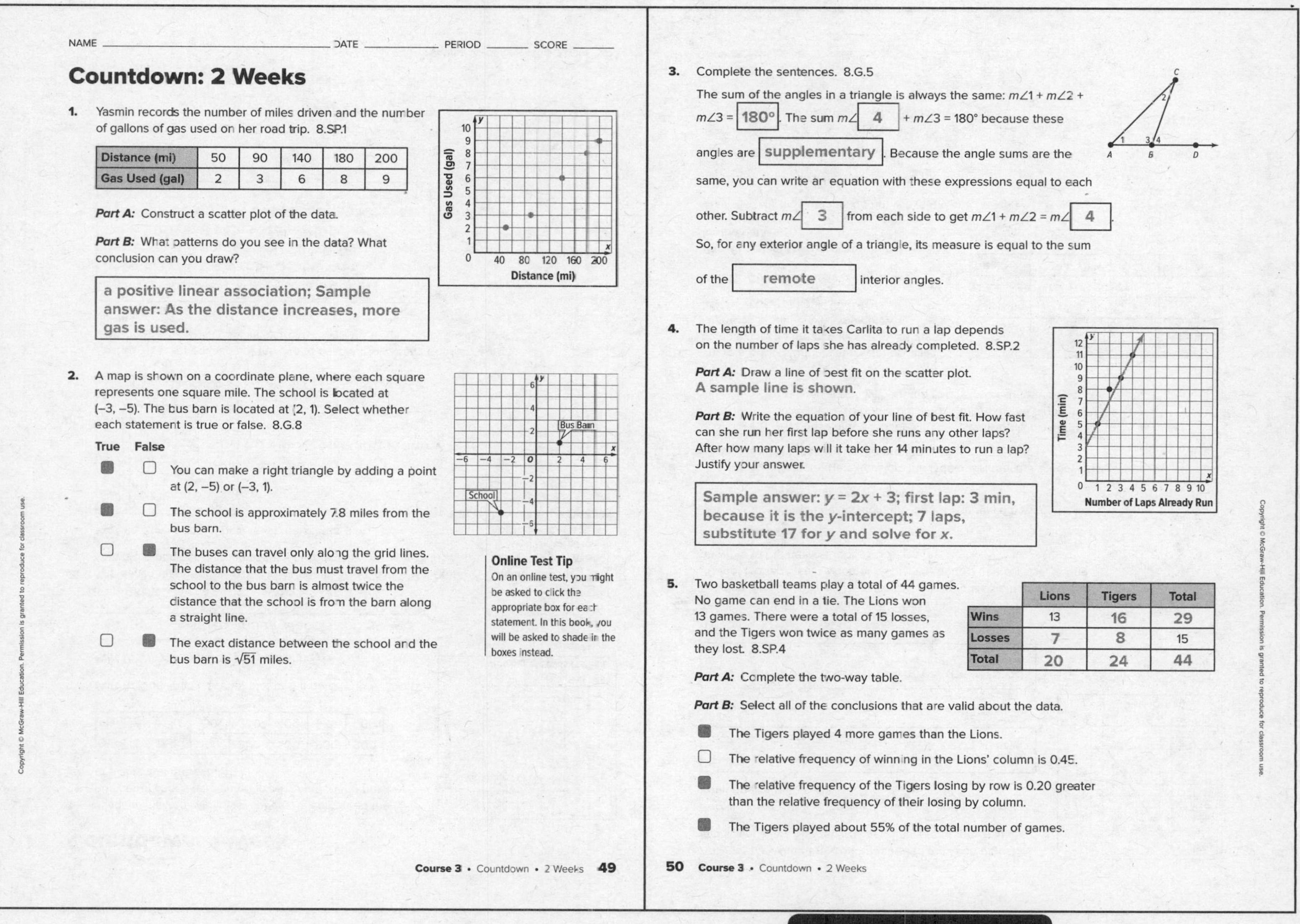

NAME ________________ DATE ________ PERIOD ______ SCORE ______

Countdown: 2 Weeks

1. Yasmin records the number of miles driven and the number of gallons of gas used on her road trip. 8.SP.1

Distance (mi)	50	90	140	180	200
Gas Used (gal)	2	3	6	8	9

Part A: Construct a scatter plot of the data.

Part B: What patterns do you see in the data? What conclusion can you draw?

a positive linear association; Sample answer: As the distance increases, more gas is used.

2. A map is shown on a coordinate plane, where each square represents one square mile. The school is located at (–3, –5). The bus barn is located at (2, 1). Select whether each statement is true or false. 8.G.8

True	False	
■	☐	You can make a right triangle by adding a point at (2, –5) or (–3, 1).
■	☐	The school is approximately 7.8 miles from the bus barn.
☐	■	The buses can travel only along the grid lines. The distance that the bus must travel from the school to the bus barn is almost twice the distance that the school is from the barn along a straight line.
☐	■	The exact distance between the school and the bus barn is $\sqrt{51}$ miles.

Online Test Tip
On an online test, you might be asked to click the appropriate box for each statement. In this book, you will be asked to shade in the boxes instead.

3. Complete the sentences. 8.G.5

The sum of the angles in a triangle is always the same: $m\angle 1 + m\angle 2 + m\angle 3 =$ **180°**. The sum $m\angle$ **4** $+ m\angle 3 = 180°$ because these angles are **supplementary**. Because the angle sums are the same, you can write an equation with these expressions equal to each other. Subtract $m\angle$ **3** from each side to get $m\angle 1 + m\angle 2 = m\angle$ **4**.

So, for any exterior angle of a triangle, its measure is equal to the sum of the **remote** interior angles.

4. The length of time it takes Carlita to run a lap depends on the number of laps she has already completed. 8.SP.2

Part A: Draw a line of best fit on the scatter plot.
A sample line is shown.

Part B: Write the equation of your line of best fit. How fast can she run her first lap before she runs any other laps? After how many laps will it take her 14 minutes to run a lap? Justify your answer.

Sample answer: $y = 2x + 3$; first lap: 3 min, because it is the y-intercept; 7 laps, substitute 17 for y and solve for x.

5. Two basketball teams play a total of 44 games. No game can end in a tie. The Lions won 13 games. There were a total of 15 losses, and the Tigers won twice as many games as they lost. 8.SP.4

	Lions	Tigers	Total
Wins	13	16	29
Losses	7	8	15
Total	20	24	44

Part A: Complete the two-way table.

Part B: Select all of the conclusions that are valid about the data.

- ■ The Tigers played 4 more games than the Lions.
- ☐ The relative frequency of winning in the Lions' column is 0.45.
- ■ The relative frequency of the Tigers losing by row is 0.20 greater than the relative frequency of their losing by column.
- ■ The Tigers played about 55% of the total number of games.

Countdown

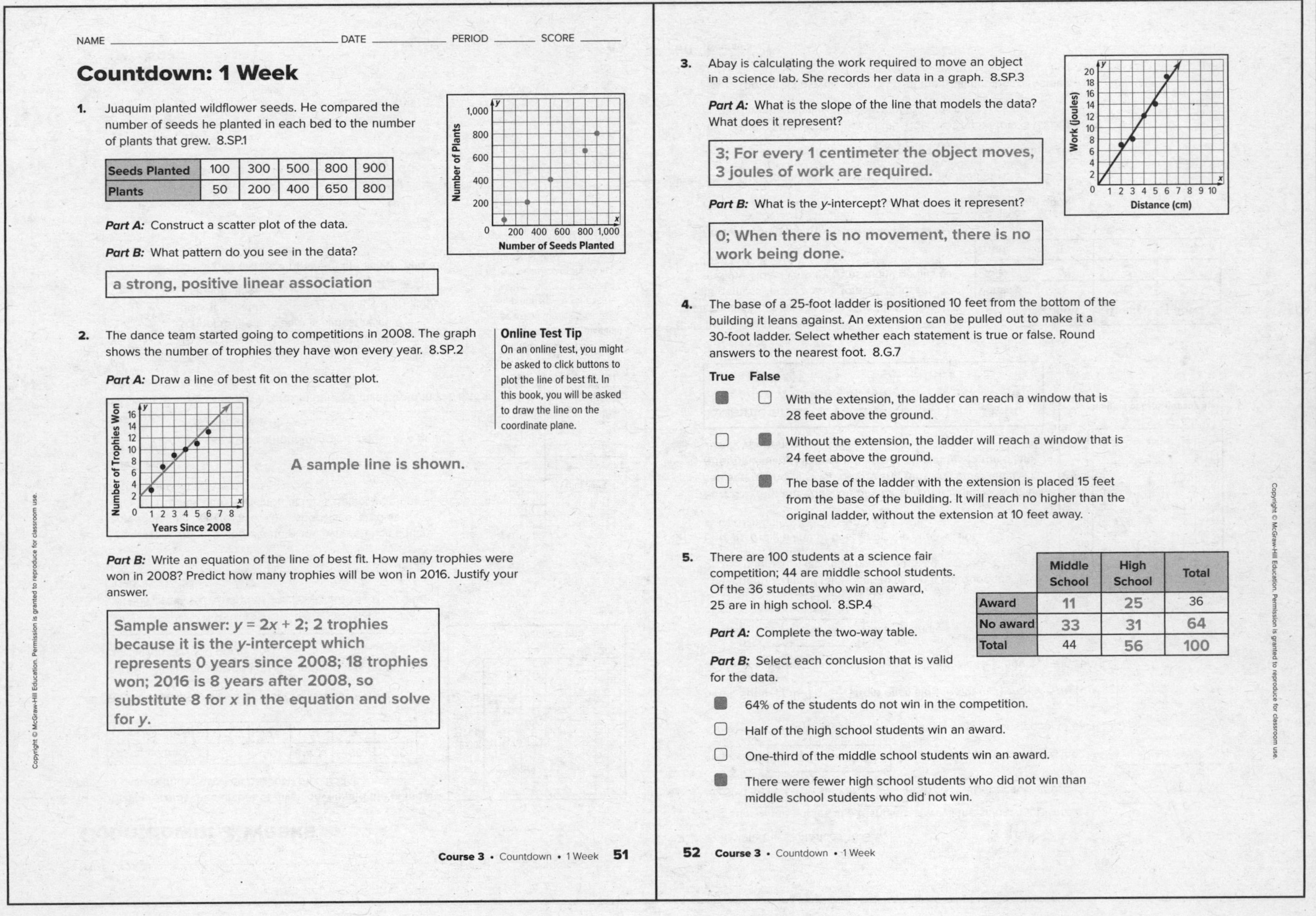

NAME ________ DATE ________ PERIOD ________ SCORE ________

Countdown: 1 Week

1. Juaquim planted wildflower seeds. He compared the number of seeds he planted in each bed to the number of plants that grew. 8.SP.1

Seeds Planted	100	300	500	800	900
Plants	50	200	400	650	800

Part A: Construct a scatter plot of the data.

Part B: What pattern do you see in the data?

a strong, positive linear association

2. The dance team started going to competitions in 2008. The graph shows the number of trophies they have won every year. 8.SP.2

Part A: Draw a line of best fit on the scatter plot.

A sample line is shown.

Online Test Tip
On an online test, you might be asked to click buttons to plot the line of best fit. In this book, you will be asked to draw the line on the coordinate plane.

Part B: Write an equation of the line of best fit. How many trophies were won in 2008? Predict how many trophies will be won in 2016. Justify your answer.

Sample answer: $y = 2x + 2$; 2 trophies because it is the y-intercept which represents 0 years since 2008; 18 trophies won; 2016 is 8 years after 2008, so substitute 8 for x in the equation and solve for y.

3. Abay is calculating the work required to move an object in a science lab. She records her data in a graph. 8.SP.3

Part A: What is the slope of the line that models the data? What does it represent?

3; For every 1 centimeter the object moves, 3 joules of work are required.

Part B: What is the y-intercept? What does it represent?

0; When there is no movement, there is no work being done.

4. The base of a 25-foot ladder is positioned 10 feet from the bottom of the building it leans against. An extension can be pulled out to make it a 30-foot ladder. Select whether each statement is true or false. Round answers to the nearest foot. 8.G.7

True	False	
■	☐	With the extension, the ladder can reach a window that is 28 feet above the ground.
☐	■	Without the extension, the ladder will reach a window that is 24 feet above the ground.
☐	■	The base of the ladder with the extension is placed 15 feet from the base of the building. It will reach no higher than the original ladder, without the extension at 10 feet away.

5. There are 100 students at a science fair competition; 44 are middle school students. Of the 36 students who win an award, 25 are in high school. 8.SP.4

Part A: Complete the two-way table.

	Middle School	High School	Total
Award	11	25	36
No award	33	31	64
Total	44	56	100

Part B: Select each conclusion that is valid for the data.

- ■ 64% of the students do not win in the competition.
- ☐ Half of the high school students win an award.
- ☐ One-third of the middle school students win an award.
- ■ There were fewer high school students who did not win than middle school students who did not win.

NAME ______________ DATE ________ PERIOD ______ SCORE ______

Chapter 1 Test

1. Arnaldo is analyzing numbers. 8.NS.1, 8.NS.2

Part A: Select whether the number in each situation is rational or irrational.

	Rational	Irrational
A bottle contains $0.\overline{6}$ kiloliters of water.	■	☐
The area of the floor covered by a circular rug is 8π, or 25.1327412..., square feet.	☐	■
Each side of a square measures $\sqrt{9}$ centimeters.	■	☐

Part B: The diagonal of rectangular tile A is $3\sqrt{2}$ inches long. The diagonal of rectangular tile B is $2\sqrt{3}$ inches long. Which tile has a longer diagonal? Explain how you got your answer.

Tile A; $3\sqrt{2} \approx 4.24$ and $2\sqrt{3} \approx 3.46$, so $3\sqrt{2} > 2\sqrt{3}$.

2. The table shows the approximate populations of four countries. Write the correct country to make each statement true. 8.EE.1

Country	Austria	Lesotho	Netherlands	Surinam
Population	2^{23}	2^{21}	2^{24}	2^{19}

Austria
Lesotho
the Netherlands
Surinam

The population of **Austria** is about $\frac{1}{2}$ that of the Netherlands.

The population of **Surinam** is about $\frac{1}{4}$ that of Lesotho.

The population of **the Netherlands** is about 8 times the population of **Lesotho**.

3. Sort the expressions into the appropriate bins based on their values compared to 9. 8.EE.1

Less than 9	Equal to 9	Greater than 9
$\frac{9^{10}}{9^{11}}$, $(3^2 \cdot 3)^0$	$\frac{9^{11}}{9^{10}}$, $\frac{3^{-2}}{3^{-4}}$, $(-3)^2$	$3^6 \cdot 3^{-3}$

$\frac{9^{10}}{9^{11}}$ $\frac{9^{11}}{9^{10}}$ $3^6 \cdot 3^{-3}$ $(3^2 \cdot 3)^0$ $(-3)^2$ $\frac{3^{-2}}{3^{-4}}$

4. The table shows the diameters, in kilometers, of the five planets in the solar system that are farther from the sun than Earth. Write the five planets in order from largest to smallest planet by diameter. 8.EE.3

Planet	Diameter (km)
Jupiter	1.43×10^5
Mars	6.79×10^3
Neptune	4.95×10^4
Saturn	1.21×10^5
Uranus	5.11×10^4

	Planet	Diameter (km)
Largest	Jupiter	1.43×10^5
	Saturn	1.21×10^5
	Uranus	5.11×10^4
	Neptune	4.95×10^4
Smallest	Mars	6.79×10^3

5. The metric system uses prefixes to describe different lengths. 8.EE.1

Part A: Complete the table by writing the correct power of 10.

10^0	10^1	10^2
10^3	10^4	10^5
10^6	10^7	10^{-1}
10^{-2}	10^{-3}	10^{-5}
10^{-4}	10^{-6}	10^{-7}

Metric Unit	Number of Meters	
	Standard Form	Power of 10
megameter	1,000,000	10^6
kilometer	1,000	10^3
meter	1	10^0
millimeter	0.001	10^{-3}
micrometer	0.000001	10^{-6}

Part B: In the table, look for a pattern in the powers of 10. Describe the relationship between the exponents and place value.

Sample answer: Each time the place value decreases by 3 places (or each time the number in standard form is divided by 1,000), the exponent of the 10 decreases by 3.

6. A jumping spider that is 3^{-4} meters long jumps 3^{-1} meters high. About how many times its body length did the spider jump? Explain your reasoning. 8.EE.1

27 times; $3^{-1} \div 3^{-4} = 3^{-1-(-4)} = 3^3 = 27$

Copyright © McGraw-Hill Education. Permission is granted to reproduce for classroom use.

7. Keisha is writing a report on state capitals. She notes that in 2010, Frankfurt, Kentucky, had a population of about 26,000, while Montgomery, Alabama, had a population of about 2.3×10^5. Write in the spaces provided to make each statement true. 8.EE.4

The population of **Montgomery** is greater than the population of **Frankfurt**.

In scientific notation, the difference in the number of people living in the two capitals is **2.04×10^5**.

8. Oceanographers divide the oceans into layers, as shown in the table. Depths below sea level are represented as negative integers. Select whether each statement is true or false. 8.EE.4

Ocean Zones	
Zone	**Depth**
Sunlight Zone	0 ft to –660 ft
Twilight Zone	–660 ft to –3,300 ft
Midnight Zone	–3,300 ft to –13,000 ft
Abyssal Zone	–13,000 ft and below

True	False	Statement
■	☐	A whale swimming at a depth of -5.9×10^2 feet is in the sunlight zone.
■	☐	A jellyfish swimming at a depth of -3.4×10^3 feet is in the midnight zone.
☐	■	A crab swimming at a depth of -6.4×10^2 feet is in the twilight zone.
■	☐	A squid swimming at a depth of -1.8×10^4 feet is in the abyssal zone.

9. Ling is finding the volume of a cube with an edge length of $5ab^3$. Her work is shown. 8.EE.1

Part A: Circle the step(s) that show an error.

Part B: Find the correct volume for the cube.

Part C: Describe Ling's error(s) and how she should correct her work.

Part A:

Step 1 $V = (5ab^3)^3$

Step 2 $V = 5^3(a)^3(b^3)^3$

(Step 3 $V = 15a^3b^6$) (circled)

Part B: $V = 125a^3b^9$

Ling multiplied 5 by 3 instead of cubing 5. She also added the exponent of b^3 to the exponent outside the parentheses, 3, instead of multiplying them.

10. Density is a measure of how compact a substance is. To calculate density, divide mass by volume. Calculate the density of each liquid shown in the table. Write the four liquids in order from least to greatest density. 8.EE.4

Liquids	Mass (g)	Volume (cm³)
Honey	1.19×10^3	8.5×10^2
Mercury	6.8×10^{-1}	5×10^{-2}
Milk	3.09×10^3	3.0×10^3
Olive Oil	9.1×10^2	1×10^3

	Liquid	Density (g/cm³)
Least	**Olive Oil**	**0.91**
	Milk	**1.03**
	Honey	**1.40**
Greatest	**Mercury**	**13.6**

11. Golden Gate Park in San Francisco, California, is rectangular in shape and measures approximately 1.6×10^4 feet by 2.7×10^3 feet. One acre is equal to 4.356×10^4 feet. About how many acres does Golden Gate Park cover? Round to the nearest hundredth. Explain your answer. 8.EE.4

991.74 acres; Sample answer: First I found the area in square feet: $(1.6 \times 10^4) \cdot (2.7 \times 10^3) = 4.32 \times 10^7$. Then I found the number of acres: $\frac{4.32 \times 10^7}{4.356 \times 10^4} \approx 0.99174 \times 10^3 \approx 991.74$.

12. Dayshawn has a storage cube with a volume of 7 cubic feet. What is the shortest space in feet in which the cube will fit? Explain. 8.EE.2

2 ft; Sample answer: The height of the cube is $\sqrt[3]{7}$ ft. Since $\sqrt[3]{8} = 2$, $\sqrt[3]{7}$ is less than 2. So the cube will fit in 2 feet of space.

13. The table shows the land areas of the five continents that are not islands. Write the continents in order from least to greatest land area. 8.EE.3

Continent	Land Area (mi²)
Africa	1.16×10^7
Asia	1.72×10^7
Europe	3.84×10^6
North America	9.37×10^6
South America	6.88×10^6

	Continent
Least Land Area	**Europe**
	South America
	North America
	Africa
Greatest Land Area	**Asia**

14. The diagonal of a rectangular quilt is $\sqrt{324}$ feet long. 8.NS.1

Part A: Select all of the sets of numbers to which $\sqrt{324}$ belongs.

(real) (rational) (whole)
(integer) irrational (natural)

Part B: Change one digit in $\sqrt{324}$ to a different digit. Explain how and why changing that digit changes the set of numbers to which it belongs.

Sample answer: $\sqrt{325}$; Because 325 is not a perfect square, $\sqrt{325}$ is a decimal with digits that never repeat and never terminate, so it is irrational. The number is no longer an integer, a rational number, a whole number, or a natural number.

15. The table shows several planets and their distances from the sun. Write the correct number to make each statement true. 8.EE.3, 8.EE.4

Planet	Distance from Sun (km)
Mercury	5.8×10^7
Venus	1.1×10^8
Saturn	1.43×10^9
Neptune	4.5×10^9

2	3	4	5
20	25	40	250

Neptune is about **3** times farther from the sun than Saturn.

Neptune is about **40** times farther from the sun than Venus.

Saturn is about **25** times farther from the sun than Mercury.

Venus is about **2** times farther from the sun than Mercury.

16. Lori found this information while doing research on stars. Select whether the answer to each question is yes or no. 8.EE.3, 8.EE.4

- The sun is approximately 1.4×10^6 kilometers across.
- A low-mass star can be approximately 700 thousand kilometers across.
- A red giant star can be approximately 1×10^8 kilometers across.

Yes	No	
☐	■	Is a red giant star about 700 times larger than the sun?
☐	■	Is the sun about 20 times larger than a low-mass star?
■	☐	Is a red giant star about 143 times larger than a low-mass star?
■	☐	Is a low-mass star about half the size of the sun?

17. The area of each small square in the figures is 64 square units. 8.EE.2

Part A: Write the perimeter of each figure.

84 units	104 units
88 units	112 units
96 units	132 units

Figure 1: **96 units** Figure 2: **112 units** Figure 3: **112 units**

Part B: Do any of the figures have the same perimeter? If so, identify the figures and explain why.

Yes, Figures 2 and 3; Sample answer: Each side of a square is $\sqrt{64} = 8$ units long. The outside border of Figures 2 and 3 each contain 14 segments. So each has a perimeter of 8 • 14, or 112 units.

18. The number line shows four points labeled *A*, *B*, *C*, and *D*. Select whether each statement is true or false. 8.NS.2, 8.EE.2

True	False	
☐	■	The value of $\sqrt{28}$ is to the left of point *A*.
■	☐	The value of $\sqrt{30}$ is between point *B* and point *C*.
☐	■	The coordinate of point *D* is less than $\sqrt{32}$.

19. The table shows the masses of the particles in an atom. The numbers are from a calculator. Write the particles in order from least to greatest mass. 8.EE.3, 8.EE.4

Subatomic Particles	Mass (g)
Proton	1.673 E–24
Electron	9.109 E–28
Neutron	1.674 E–24

Least Mass: **Electron**, **Proton**, **Neutron** :Greatest Mass

20. Ms. Diaz gave her students a project that was worth 100 points. Jacey earned a 92%, Omar earned $\sqrt{8,649}$ points, Keiko earned $\frac{182}{200}$ of the total points, and Matt earned $\frac{11}{12}$ of the total points. Plot points on the number line to represent each student's score. 8.NS.1

NAME ____________ DATE ________ PERIOD ______ SCORE ______

Chapter 2 Test

1. Sort the equations into the bin that correctly describes its solution. 8.EE.7, 8.EE.7a

$0.25n + 4 = 0.4(n + 4)$	$-3(6n - 1) = -18n + 3$	$8n - 28 - n = 7(n - 4)$
$5(2z + 4) = 7z + 8$	$17 - 3(2n - 5) = 30 - 6n$	$-2(8x + 2) = -16x + 2$

No Solution	One Solution	Infinitely Many Solutions
$-2(8x + 2) = -16x + 2$	$5(2z + 4) = 7z + 8$	$-3(6n - 1) = -18n + 3$
$17 - 3(2n - 5) = 30 - 6n$	$0.25n + 4 = 0.4(n + 4)$	$8n - 28 - n = 7(n - 4)$

2. Yuriko ran 3 more than twice as many miles as Paul did yesterday. Yuriko ran 7 miles yesterday. Let x represent the number of miles Paul ran. 8.EE.7, 8.EE.7b

Part A: Draw algebra tiles on the equation mat to model this situation.

x | −1 | 1

x x 1 1 1 = 1 1 1 1 1 1 1

Part B: Solve to find x. How many miles did Paul run?

$x = 2$; 2 miles

3. Jorge buys two magnets. Each magnet is shaped like an equilateral polygon, and they have the same perimeter. Select whether each statement is true or false. 8.EE.7, 8.EE.7b

$(x + 7)$ cm

$(x + 3)$ cm

True	False	
☐	■	The value of x is 4.
☐	■	The perimeter of the triangular magnet is 30 centimeters.
■	☐	The perimeter of the rhombus magnet is 48 centimeters.
■	☐	The equation $3(x + 7) - 4(x + 3) = 0$ can be solved to find the value of x.

4. Write a number in each box to make an equation that has exactly one real solution. 8.EE.7, 8.EE.7a

1 2 3 4 5 6 7 8 9 10

$3(2a + 1) - a = \boxed{4}\,a + \boxed{5}$

A sample answer is shown. The first box can be any number except 5. The second box can be any number.

5. In one physical education class, $\frac{5}{8}$ of the students were playing basketball. After 3 more students joined, 18 students were playing basketball. How many students are in the class? Circle all the equations that could represent this situation. Then find the answer. 8.EE.7, 8.EE.7b

$\frac{5}{8}x = 18 + 3x$	$\frac{5}{8}(x + 3) = 18$	(circled) $\frac{5}{8}x = 18 - 3$
$18 = \frac{5}{8}x - 3$	(circled) $\frac{5}{8}x + 3 = 18$	$\frac{5}{8}x + 3x = 18$

There are **24** students in the class.

6. SkateWorld charges $10.00 for admission plus $2.50 per hour to rent ice skates. IceLand charges $7.00 for admission plus $4.00 per hour to rent ice skates. Write an equation to find h, the number of hours for which the total cost is the same at both skating rinks. Then solve the equation and state what the cost is for that number of hours. 8.EE.7, 8.EE.7b

Equation: **$10 + 2.5h$** = **$7 + 4h$**

h = **2**

Cost for that number of hours: **$15.00**

7. Jonah is 20 inches shorter than 2 times Shayna's height. Aisha is 1.5 times as tall as Shayna. Jonah and Aisha are the same height. Let s represent Shayna's height in inches. Select whether each statement is true or false. 8.EE.7, 8.EE.7b

True	False	
☐	■	Jonah's height, in inches, can be represented as $20 - 2s$.
■	☐	Aisha's height, in inches, can be represented as $1.5s$.
☐	■	Shayna's height is 33 inches.
■	☐	Jonah and Aisha are each 60 inches tall.

8. Select all of the equations that have infinitely many solutions. 8.EE.7, 8.EE.7a

- ☐ $6x + 7 - 2x = 4x - 7$
- ■ $9x - (2x + 5) = 7x - 5$
- ☐ $-5(2x + 3) = -10x + 15$
- ☐ $5 - (3x - 2) = 2x + 2$
- ■ $12x + 3 + x = 4 + 13x - 1$

9. Write a number in each box to make an equation with a solution of 5. 8.EE.7, 8.EE.7a, 8.EE.7b

1 2 3 4 5

$2(3b - 4) =$ **4** $b +$ **2**

10. The table shows expressions to represent the number of eighth-grade students enrolled in different world language classes. The number of students enrolled in French and German is equal to the number of students enrolled in Chinese and Spanish. 8.EE.7, 8.EE.7b

Class	Number of Students
Chinese	$2n$
French	$7n + 6$
German	$4n - 2$
Spanish	$2(4n + 6)$

Part A: Model the situation with an equation. Write the appropriate expression in each box.

$2n$ $7n + 6$ $4n - 2$ $2(4n + 6)$

$7n + 6$ + **$4n - 2$** = **$2n$** + **$2(4n + 6)$**

Part B: Solve the equation. Then identify the number of students enrolled in each language class.

$n =$ **8**

Chinese: **16** students German: **30** students

French: **62** students Spanish: **76** students

11. Complete the equation so that it has an infinite number of solutions. Write one number in each box. 8.EE.7, 8.EE.7a

$2(4k - 2) - 2k =$ **6** $k -$ **4**

12. Pearl is making a quilt. One quilt piece is shaped like the trapezoid shown. The fabric to make the quilt piece has an area of 22.5 square inches. The formula for the area of a trapezoid is $A = \frac{1}{2}h(b_1 + b_2)$. 8.EE.7, 8.EE.7b

4.5 in.
6 in.

Part A: Write an equation you can use to find the length of the top base in the quilt piece. Then find the base length.

Equation: **$22.5 = \frac{1}{2}(4.5)(b_1 + 6)$**

Base length: **4 in.**

Part B: Steve wants to make a quilt piece like Pearl's but with a bottom base that is twice as long. He claims that the area of his quilt piece will be double the area of Pearl's piece. Is Steve's claim accurate? Why or why not?

Steve's claim is not correct. Doubling the bottom base makes it 2(6) = 12 in. The area will be $\frac{1}{2}(4.5)(12 + 4) =$ 36 in², which is not twice 22.5 in².

13. Select the correct equation for each situation. Then solve each problem. 8.EE.7, 8.EE.7b

$\frac{10}{x} = 75$ $75 = 1.1x$ $75x = 10$ $0.1x = 75$ $0.01x = 75$ $10x = 75$

Part A: Dorian deposits $75 in his bank account. It is 10% of the total amount of money he earned last month working part-time. How much money did Dorian earn last month?

Equation: **$0.1x = 75$** Solution: **$750**

Part B: A rope is 75 feet long. It is 10 times the length Carmen needs for her jump rope. How many feet of rope does Carmen need?

Equation: **$10x = 75$** Solution: **7.5 ft**

14. Angles *A* and *B* are supplementary. The measure of angle *B* is 5 less than 4 times the measure of angle *A*. Write an equation to represent this situation and define the variable you choose. Then find the measures of the angles. 8.EE.7, 8.EE.7b

$a + (4a - 5) = 180$, where a is the measure of angle *A*. The measure of angle *A* is 37° and the measure of angle *B* is (4)(37) − 5 = 143°.

15. Jacob is solving an equation. His work is shown. 8.EE.7, 8.EE.7b

Equation: $-0.5(20x - 10) - 2 = 13$	
Step 1: (circled)	$-10x - 5 - 2 = 13$
Step 2:	$-10x - 7 = 13$
Step 3:	$-10x - 7 = 13$; $+7\ +7$; $-10x = 20$
Step 4:	$\frac{-10x}{-10} = \frac{20}{-10}$; $x = -2$

Part A: Circle the first step in which Jacob's work shows an error.

Part B: Describe Jacob's error(s) and how he should correct his work.

Jacob did not multiply two negative numbers correctly when using the distributive property. He should have simplified $-0.5(20x - 10)$ as $-10x + 5$.

Part C: Find the correct value of x.

$x =$ **−1**

16. Sylvia and Raul are computer technicians who make house calls. Sylvia charges a flat fee of $35.50 plus $16 per hour. Raul charges a $15.50 flat fee plus $20 per hour. Select whether each statement is true or false. 8.EE.7, 8.EE.7b

True	False	
■	☐	For 2 hours of work, Sylvia charges more than Raul.
☐	■	For 6 hours of work, Raul charges less than Sylvia.
☐	■	The equation $35.5x + 16 = 15.5x + 20$ can be solved to find the number of hours for which the total cost is the same to hire either technician.
■	☐	Both technicians charge the same amount for a 5-hour job.

17. The table shows the total distance Mr. Wilder drove each day last week. The total distance Mr. Wilder drove last week is two thirds of the distance he drove this week. Write and solve an equation to show how far Mr. Wilder drove this week. 8.EE.7, 8.EE.7b

Day	Sunday	Monday	Tuesday	Wednesday	Thursday	Friday	Saturday
Miles	9.5	12.5	5.5	7.8	5.5	3.2	10.0

Equation: $\frac{2}{3}x = 54$

Miles this week: **81 miles**

18. Write a number in each box to make an equation that has no real solution. 8.EE.7, 8.EE.7a

1 2 3 4 5 6 7 8 9 0

$4(a - 2) + a =$ **5** $a -$ **6**

A sample answer is shown. The second box can be any number except 8.

19. The perimeter of a rectangular carpet is 44 feet. The length of the carpet is $(3n + 3)$ feet and the width is $(2n - 1)$ feet. Select whether each statement is true or false. 8.EE.7, 8.EE.7b

True	False	
☐	■	The equation $3n + 3 + 2n - 1 = 44$ can be solved to find the value of n.
☐	■	The width of the carpet is 4 feet.
■	☐	The length of the carpet is 15 feet.
☐	■	The carpet is a square.
■	☐	The equation $44 - 2(2n - 1) = 2(3n + 3)$ can be solved to find the dimensions of the carpet.

20. An online shopping company uses boxes like the one shown to ship purchases to customers. 8.EE.7, 8.EE.7b

12 in.
24 in.

Part A: The shipping box needs 1,224 square inches of cardboard to make its six sides, without overlap. What is the height of the box? Use the formula for surface area of a prism $S.A. = 2wh + 2\ell w + 2\ell h$ to write an equation. Then find the box height.

Equation: $1{,}224 = 2(12)h + 2(24)(12) + 2(24)h$

Height of box: **9 in.**

Part B: Would packing material with volume 2500 cubic inches fit into this shipping box? Explain.

Yes, it would fit. The volume of the box is $(24)(12)(9) = 2{,}592\ in^3$. Because $2{,}500 < 2{,}592$, the packing material would fit.

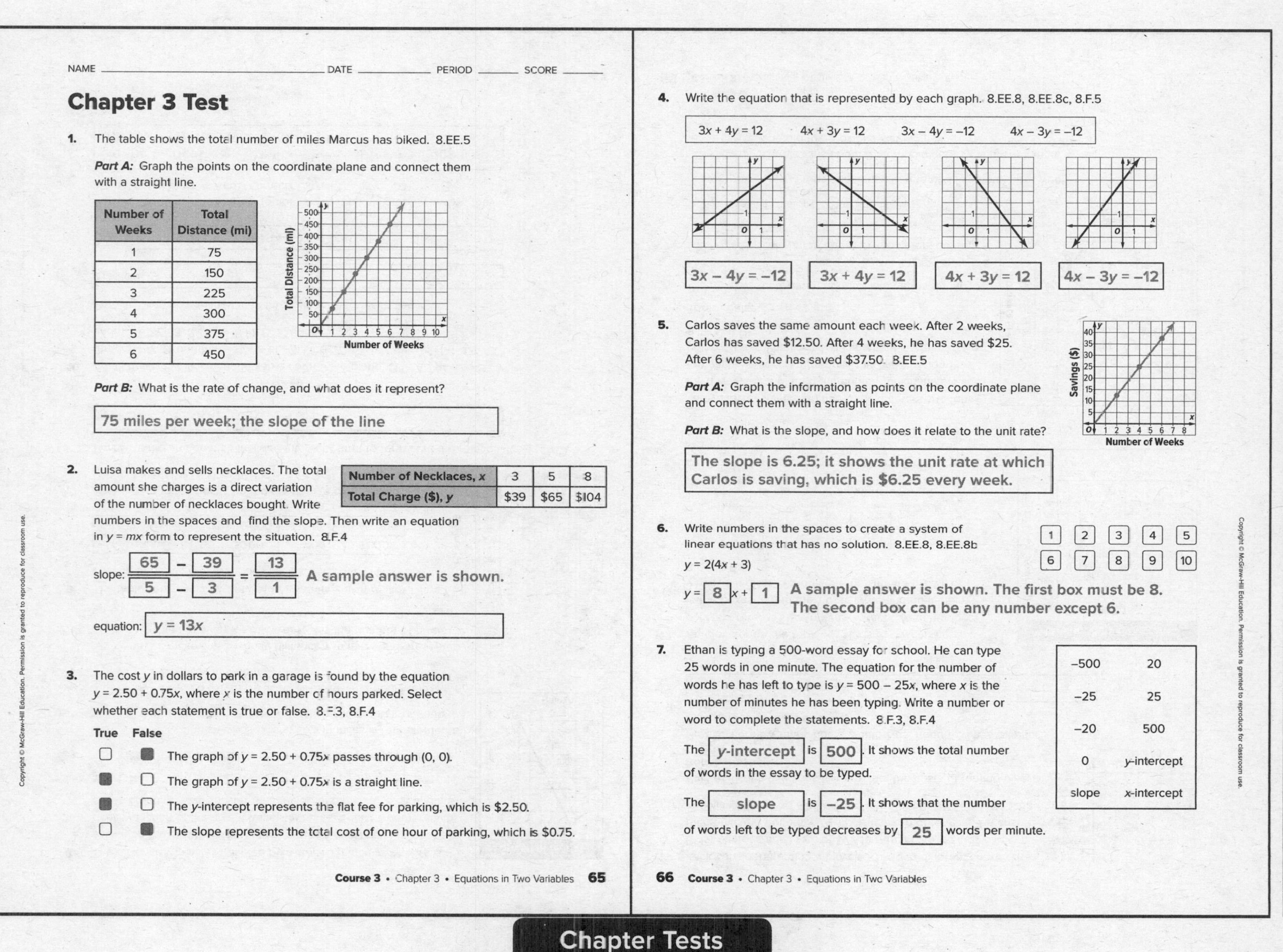

NAME ______________ DATE ________ PERIOD ______ SCORE ______

Chapter 3 Test

1. The table shows the total number of miles Marcus has biked. 8.EE.5

Part A: Graph the points on the coordinate plane and connect them with a straight line.

Number of Weeks	Total Distance (mi)
1	75
2	150
3	225
4	300
5	375
6	450

Part B: What is the rate of change, and what does it represent?

75 miles per week; the slope of the line

2. Luisa makes and sells necklaces. The total amount she charges is a direct variation of the number of necklaces bought. Write numbers in the spaces and find the slope. Then write an equation in $y = mx$ form to represent the situation. 8.F.4

Number of Necklaces, x	3	5	8
Total Charge ($), y	$39	$65	$104

slope: $\frac{65 - 39}{5 - 3} = \frac{13}{1}$ **A sample answer is shown.**

equation: $y = 13x$

3. The cost y in dollars to park in a garage is found by the equation $y = 2.50 + 0.75x$, where x is the number of hours parked. Select whether each statement is true or false. 8.F.3, 8.F.4

True	False	
☐	■	The graph of $y = 2.50 + 0.75x$ passes through (0, 0).
■	☐	The graph of $y = 2.50 + 0.75x$ is a straight line.
■	☐	The y-intercept represents the flat fee for parking, which is $2.50.
☐	■	The slope represents the total cost of one hour of parking, which is $0.75.

4. Write the equation that is represented by each graph. 8.EE.8, 8.EE.8c, 8.F.5

$3x + 4y = 12$ $4x + 3y = 12$ $3x - 4y = -12$ $4x - 3y = -12$

$3x - 4y = -12$ **$3x + 4y = 12$** **$4x + 3y = 12$** **$4x - 3y = -12$**

5. Carlos saves the same amount each week. After 2 weeks, Carlos has saved $12.50. After 4 weeks, he has saved $25. After 6 weeks, he has saved $37.50. 8.EE.5

Part A: Graph the information as points on the coordinate plane and connect them with a straight line.

Part B: What is the slope, and how does it relate to the unit rate?

The slope is 6.25; it shows the unit rate at which Carlos is saving, which is $6.25 every week.

6. Write numbers in the spaces to create a system of linear equations that has no solution. 8.EE.8, 8.EE.8b

1 2 3 4 5 6 7 8 9 10

$y = 2(4x + 3)$

$y =$ **8** $x +$ **1** **A sample answer is shown. The first box must be 8. The second box can be any number except 6.**

7. Ethan is typing a 500-word essay for school. He can type 25 words in one minute. The equation for the number of words he has left to type is $y = 500 - 25x$, where x is the number of minutes he has been typing. Write a number or word to complete the statements. 8.F.3, 8.F.4

−500	20
−25	25
−20	500
0	y-intercept
slope	x-intercept

The **y-intercept** is **500**. It shows the total number of words in the essay to be typed.

The **slope** is **−25**. It shows that the number of words left to be typed decreases by **25** words per minute.

Chapter Tests

8. The distance y in miles traveled by a striped marlin in x hours is shown on the graph. Each ocean creature's distance in miles is a direct variation of the time it travels in hours. Select whether each ocean creature travels faster than the striped marlin. 8.EE.5, 8.F.2

Yes	No	
□	■	a tuna that travels at a speed of 43.5 miles per hour
■	□	a swordfish whose distance y in miles is represented by the equation $y = 60x$, where x is the number of hours
□	■	a wahoo fish that travels 144 miles in 3 hours and 192 miles in 4 hours
□	■	a mako shark whose distance y in miles is represented by the equation $y = 31x$, where x is the number of hours

Speed of Marlin

Distance (mi); Time (h); (1, 50); (2, 100)

9. The table shows how Ms. Mwanda's earnings as a realtor change depending on her house sales. 8.EE.6, 8.F.4

Sales (thousands), x	$200	$400	$600
Total Earnings, y	$20,000	$30,000	$40,000

Part A: Graph the points on the coordinate plane and connect them with a straight line.

Earnings ($); Sales (thousands of $)

Part B: Write an equation in slope-intercept form to represent the relationship.

$y = 50x + 10,000$

10. Anoki draws two lines on the same coordinate plane. Line AB passes through (–2, 9) and has a slope of –5. Line CD passes through (–1, 12) and (1, 4). 8EE.8, 8.EE.8a, 8.EE.8c

Part A: Write an equation in point-slope form for each line.

$\overleftrightarrow{AB}$: $y - 9 = -5(x + 2)$

$\overleftrightarrow{CD}$: $y - 4 = -4(x - 1)$ OR $y - 12 = -4(x + 1)$

Part B: The lines Anoki drew do not intersect on his graph. He says they will never intersect. Is Anoki correct? Explain.

No, he is incorrect. The lines have different slopes, so they will eventually intersect.

11. Zack considers renting a bicycle from two different shops. The Rider charges a flat rate of $72 to rent a bike for a day. At Bikerama, the equation $y = 12x$ is used to determine the cost y in dollars of renting a bike for x hours. 8.EE.8, 8.EE.8a, 8.EE.8b

Part A: Graph two lines to represent the costs of renting bikes from both shops.

Cost ($); Time (h); The Rider; Bikerama; (6, 72)

Part B: For how many hours would Zack need to rent a bike for Bikerama to be the better deal?

fewer than 6 hours

12. An elevator on the top floor starts to descend at a constant rate, as shown by the graph. Write numbers in the boxes to find the slope. Write an equation in $y = mx + b$ form to represent the situation. 8.EE.6, 8.F.3, 8.F.4

Elevator during Descent

Height Above Ground (ft); Time (s); (5, 160); (10, 120)

slope: $\frac{120 - 160}{10 - 5} = \frac{-8}{1}$ **A sample answer is shown.**

equation: $y = -8x + 200$

13. Latoya increases the number of kilometers she runs each week. She plotted the number of kilometers she ran each week and then drew this line through the points. Select whether each statement is true or false. 8.EE.5, 8.F.5

Distance Run (km); Week

True	False	
□	■	Latoya ran about 2 kilometers during week 6.
■	□	Latoya ran about 21 kilometers during week 7.
□	■	The slope of the line is $\frac{1}{3}$.
□	■	Latoya runs at a constant rate of 3 kilometers per week.
■	□	Latoya runs about 3 more kilometers each week than she did the previous week.

14. There are 5 times as many girls as boys taking French this year. Sixty students are taking French this year. Let g represent the number of girls and b represent the number of boys. 8.EE.8, 8.EE.8b, 8.EE.8c

b
g
boys
girls
60

Part A: Write labels into the bar diagram to model the situation.

b	boys				
g	girls	girls	girls	girls	girls
	60				

Part B: Use the bar diagram to write and solve a system of equations. How many boys and girls are taking French this year?

System of equations: **$g = 5b$; $g + b = 60$**

Solution: **$g = 50$; $b = 10$; 10 boys and 50 girls are taking French this year.**

15. Sort the systems of equations into the appropriate bins that describe their solutions. 8.EE.8, 8.EE.8b

$y = 2(x + 3)$, $y = 2x + 6$ | $y = 4x + 4$, $y = 4x + 1$ | $y = -x$, $y = x - 1$

No Solution	One Solution	Infinitely Many Solutions
$y = 4x + 4$ $y = 4x + 1$	$y = -x$ $y = x - 1$	$y = 2(x + 3)$ $y = 2x + 6$

16. Line m has a slope of $\frac{3}{2}$ and passes through $(0, -1)$. Luz and Demetrius each point to $(0, -1)$. Luz then moves her finger 6 units to the right. From there, how many units up is line m? Demetrius moves his finger 6 units down. From there, how many units left is line m? 8.EE.6

line m

Luz: **9 units**

Demetrius: **4 units**

17. The width of a rectangular dance floor is 5 meters less than the length. The perimeter of the floor is 38 meters. Set up a system of equations to represent the length ℓ and the width w. Then solve the system of equations to find the dimensions of the dance floor. 8.EE.8, 8.EE.8b, 8.EE.8c

System of equations: **Sample answer: $w = \ell - 5$; $2\ell + 2w = 38$**

Dimensions of the dance floor: **12 m by 7 m**

18. The total cost in dollars y of buying peanuts at a health food store varies directly with x, the number of pounds purchased. Macadamia nuts cost 4 times as much as peanuts at the store. Write an equation to represent the cost y of buying x pounds of macadamia nuts. 8.EE.5

Peanuts (lb), x	2	4	6	8
Cost ($), y	9	18	27	36

$y = 18x$

19. The table shows how the height of a candle y changes x hours after it has been lit. Select whether each statement is true or false. 8.F.4

Time (h), x	Candle Height (in.), y
0	16
2	12
4	8
6	4

True	False	
■	☐	The initial height of the candle was 16 inches.
■	☐	The height of the candle decreases by 2 inches every 1 hour.
☐	■	The height of the candle after 3 hours is 6 inches.
■	☐	The height of the candle after 7 hours is 2 inches.

20. Yuri wrote twice as many poems as Xenia. Yuri wrote 3 more poems than Xenia. The number of poems written can be represented by the system of equations: $y = 2x$ and $y = x + 3$. 8.EE.8, 8.EE.8b, 8.EE.8c

Part A: Graph these equations on the coordinate plane. Label the point of intersection.

(3, 6)

Part B: What is the solution to the system of equations? What does the solution represent?

(3, 6); Xenia wrote 3 poems and Yuri wrote 6 poems.

NAME ______________ DATE ________ PERIOD ______ SCORE ______

Chapter 4 Test

1. The table shows the number of students enrolled in a community college over the course of several years. 8.F.4

Semester	1	3	5	7
Enrollment	1,800	1,950	2,100	2,250

Part A: Graph the relationship on the coordinate plane.

Community College

Enrollment: 0, 500, 1,000, 1,500, 2,000, 2,500
Semester: 0, 1, 2, 3, 4, 5, 6, 7, 8, 9

Part B: The pattern shown in the graph continues. How many students will be enrolled in the school by the eighth semester?

2,325 students

2. An electronics store is having a 10% off sale. Dante has a coupon for $20 off. The function $f(x) = 0.9x - 20$ represents the final cost after the discount and coupon are applied for an item priced at x dollars. Complete the function machine for items A, B, C, and D. 8.F.1, 8.F.4

$18	$65
$25	$70
$27	$80
$40	$90

Input A: $50
Input B: **$70**
Input C: $100
Input D: **$80**

➜ $f(x) = 0.9x - 20$ ➜

Output A: **$25**
Output B: $43
Output C: **$70**
Output D: $52

3. Members of the softball team order custom sweatshirts. They must pay a $45 design fee for the entire order plus $18.50 per shirt. Complete the table to show the cost of buying n shirts. 8.F.1, 8.F.4

Number of Sweatshirts, n	1	3	6	9	10
Total Cost ($), $c(n)$	63.50	100.50	156.00	211.50	230.00

4. The bookstore sells used books for $2 each and bookmarks for $1 each. Gabriela has $7 to spend. The function $y = 7 - 2x$ represents the number of used books x and the number of bookmarks y she can buy. Select whether each statement is true or false. 8.F.3, 8.F.4

True	False	
☐	■	She can buy 0 bookmarks and 7 used books.
■	☐	She can buy 2 used books and 3 bookmarks.
☐	■	She can buy 4 used books and 1 bookmark.

5. Neveah earns a profit of $6 for each necklace she sells. 8.F.1

Part A: Complete the table of ordered pairs to show her total profits for making several necklaces.

Necklaces Sold	Total Profits ($)
1	6
2	12
3	18
4	24

Part B: What would be Neveah's total profit after selling 13 necklaces?

$78

6. Antoine has some money saved. He plans to start saving a certain amount each week to add to his savings, as shown in the graph. Find the slope and y-intercept. Then describe what the y-intercept and slope represent. 8.F.4

Antoine's Savings

Total Saved ($): 0, 10, 20, 30, 40, 50, 60, 70, 80
Number of Weeks: 1, 2, 3, 4, 5, 6, 7

y-intercept: **20** slope: **15**

The y-intercept represents the initial amount, $20, that Antoine had before he started saving. The slope is the rate of change, which is the amount, $15, he saves each week.

7. The graph shows Ella's activities on her way home from camp one summer day. Write the segment that corresponds with each statement. 8.F.5

Distance from Home
Time
A B C D E

Segment A Segment B Segment C Segment D Segment E

Segment A	Ella walks from camp to the library.
Segment E	Ella gets a ride home from Maria's house.
Segment B	Ella spends time at the library.
Segment D	Ella spends time at Maria's house.
Segment C	Ella goes from the library to Maria's house.

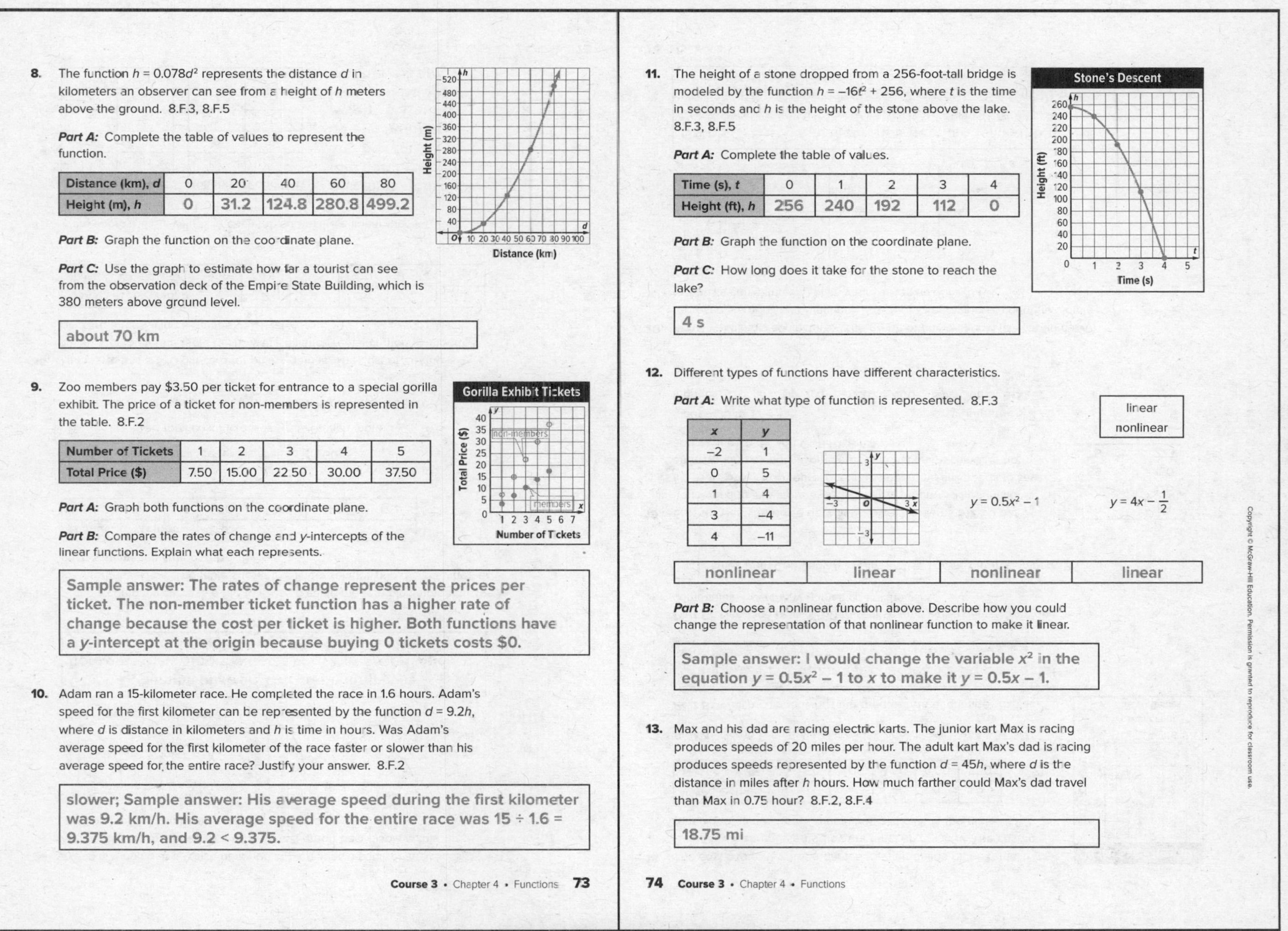

8. The function $h = 0.078d^2$ represents the distance d in kilometers an observer can see from a height of h meters above the ground. 8.F.3, 8.F.5

Part A: Complete the table of values to represent the function.

Distance (km), d	0	20	40	60	80
Height (m), h	0	31.2	124.8	280.8	499.2

Part B: Graph the function on the coordinate plane.

Part C: Use the graph to estimate how far a tourist can see from the observation deck of the Empire State Building, which is 380 meters above ground level.

about 70 km

9. Zoo members pay $3.50 per ticket for entrance to a special gorilla exhibit. The price of a ticket for non-members is represented in the table. 8.F.2

Number of Tickets	1	2	3	4	5
Total Price ($)	7.50	15.00	22.50	30.00	37.50

Part A: Graph both functions on the coordinate plane.

Part B: Compare the rates of change and y-intercepts of the linear functions. Explain what each represents.

Sample answer: The rates of change represent the prices per ticket. The non-member ticket function has a higher rate of change because the cost per ticket is higher. Both functions have a y-intercept at the origin because buying 0 tickets costs $0.

10. Adam ran a 15-kilometer race. He completed the race in 1.6 hours. Adam's speed for the first kilometer can be represented by the function $d = 9.2h$, where d is distance in kilometers and h is time in hours. Was Adam's average speed for the first kilometer of the race faster or slower than his average speed for the entire race? Justify your answer. 8.F.2

slower; Sample answer: His average speed during the first kilometer was 9.2 km/h. His average speed for the entire race was $15 \div 1.6 = 9.375$ km/h, and $9.2 < 9.375$.

11. The height of a stone dropped from a 256-foot-tall bridge is modeled by the function $h = -16t^2 + 256$, where t is the time in seconds and h is the height of the stone above the lake. 8.F.3, 8.F.5

Part A: Complete the table of values.

Time (s), t	0	1	2	3	4
Height (ft), h	256	240	192	112	0

Part B: Graph the function on the coordinate plane.

Part C: How long does it take for the stone to reach the lake?

4 s

12. Different types of functions have different characteristics.

Part A: Write what type of function is represented. 8.F.3

linear
nonlinear

x	y
−2	1
0	5
1	4
3	−4
4	−11

$y = 0.5x^2 - 1$ $\quad$ $y = 4x - \frac{1}{2}$

nonlinear	linear	nonlinear	linear

Part B: Choose a nonlinear function above. Describe how you could change the representation of that nonlinear function to make it linear.

Sample answer: I would change the variable x^2 in the equation $y = 0.5x^2 - 1$ to x to make it $y = 0.5x - 1$.

13. Max and his dad are racing electric karts. The junior kart Max is racing produces speeds of 20 miles per hour. The adult kart Max's dad is racing produces speeds represented by the function $d = 45h$, where d is the distance in miles after h hours. How much farther could Max's dad travel than Max in 0.75 hour? 8.F.2, 8.F.4

18.75 mi

14. A dog is running at a constant speed. It then sees a squirrel and races after it, picking up speed as it runs. Which graph best displays this relationship? Explain your reasoning. 8.F.5

Graph A Graph B Graph C Graph D

Graph D; Sample answer: The graph initially is horizontal, showing the dog's constant speed, and then curves upward, showing the speed increasing.

15. A cable company charges a fee to install a cable modem plus a monthly fee for Internet service. The table shows this linear relationship. Select whether each statement is true or false. 8.F.4

Number of Months	0	2	4	6
Total Cost ($)	50	90	130	170

True	False	
■	☐	The initial fee for installation is $50.
■	☐	The total cost increases by $20 each month.
☐	■	The total cost for a year of service would be $340.

16. Humberto has a $30 gift card for online games. The cost of 1 game is $2.95. Complete the table to show the balance remaining on Humberto's gift card after buying n games. 8.F.1, 8.F.4

Games Purchased, n	2	4	5	7	10
Balance Remaining ($), $g(n)$	24.10	18.20	15.25	9.35	0.50

17. Write appropriate y-values in each table to make a linear function and a nonlinear function.

Linear Function

x	y
0	3
1	5
2	7
3	9

Nonlinear Function

x	y
0	3
1	5
2	6
3	7

A sample nonlinear function is shown. The box for 2 can be any number except 7. The box for 3 can be any number except 9.

0	1	2
3	4	5
6	7	8
9	10	11

18. The cost c to rent v video games from an online game rental Company A is represented by the function $c = 2.5v$. The cost to rent video games from Company B is shown in the table. 8.F.2

Video Games, v	1	2	3	4	5
Total Cost ($), c	1.50	3.00	4.50	6.00	7.50

Video Game Rentals

Total Cost ($)

Company A

Company B

Number of Video Games

Part A: Graph both functions on the coordinate plane.

Part B: Which company has the greater rate of change? Explain.

Company A; Company A charges $2.50 per rental. Company B charges $1.50 per rental; 2.5 > 1.5.

Part C: Naquana pays $7.50 to rent several video games from one of the companies. How many games could she rent?

3 games from Company A OR **5** games from Company B

19. Ernesto wants to buy a new $400 bike. He earns $12.50 per hour working at a store and saves all his money. The function $f(x) = -12.50x + 400$ represents the amount he still needs to save after working x hours. Complete the function machine for hours and savings A, B, and C. 8.F.1, 8.F.4

20	88
30	125
65	150
75	275

Input A: 10 h
Input B: **30** h
Input C: 26 h

➡ $f(x) = -12.5x + 400$ ➡

Output A: $ **275**
Output B: $25
Output C: $ **75**

20. Anna makes this conjecture: "The graph of any parabola (U-shaped curve) represents a nonlinear function." Which graph provides a counterexample to Anna's conjecture? Explain your reasoning. 8.F.1, 8.F.3

Graph A Graph B Graph C

Graph C; Sample answer: In a function, each input corresponds to only one output. In Graph C, all x-values greater than 0 correspond to 2 outputs. So Graph C is a parabola that is a relation but not a function.

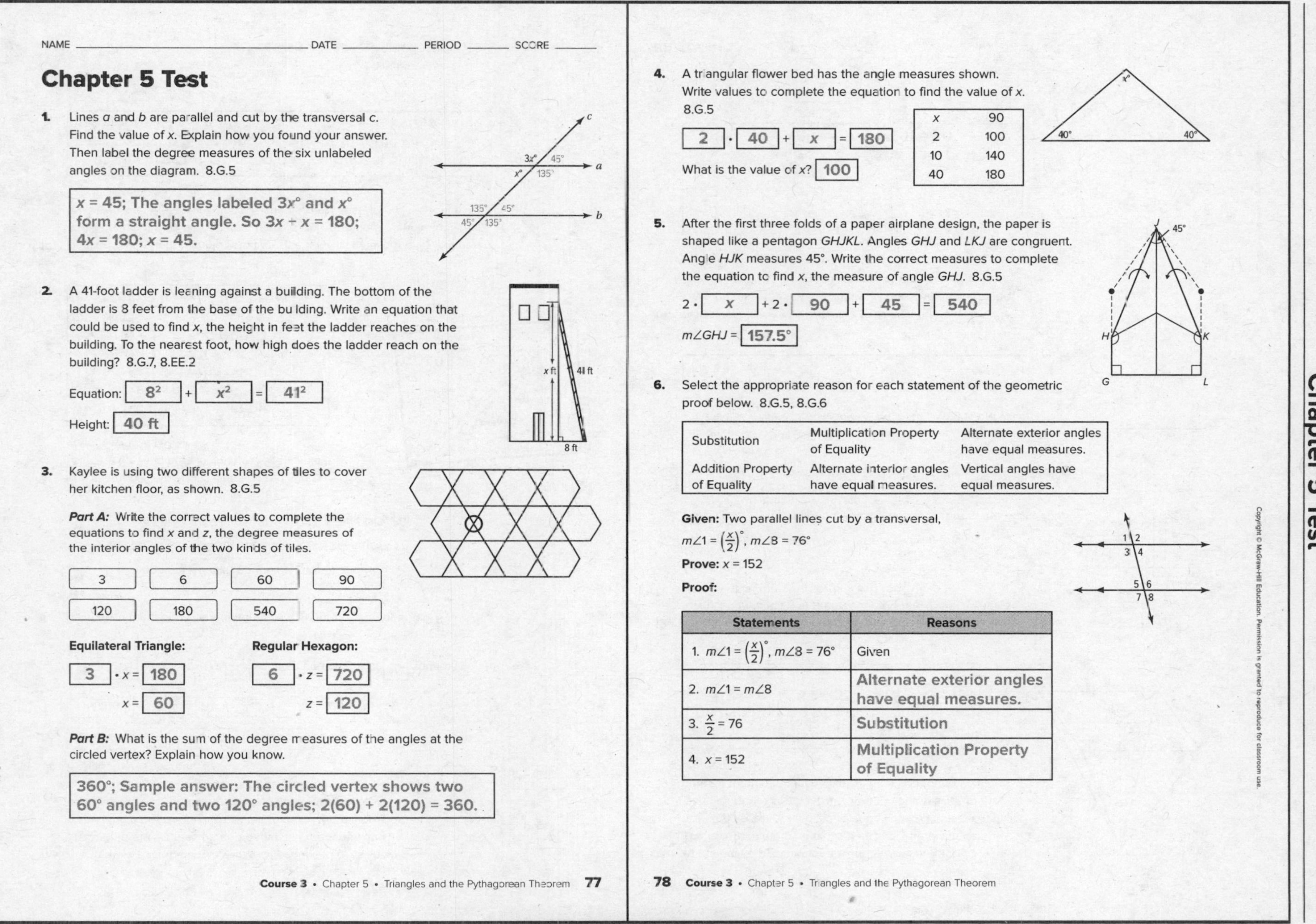

NAME ________ DATE ________ PERIOD ________ SCORE ________

Chapter 5 Test

1. Lines a and b are parallel and cut by the transversal c. Find the value of x. Explain how you found your answer. Then label the degree measures of the six unlabeled angles on the diagram. 8.G.5

$x = 45$; The angles labeled $3x°$ and $x°$ form a straight angle. So $3x + x = 180$; $4x = 180$; $x = 45$.

2. A 41-foot ladder is leaning against a building. The bottom of the ladder is 8 feet from the base of the building. Write an equation that could be used to find x, the height in feet the ladder reaches on the building. To the nearest foot, how high does the ladder reach on the building? 8.G.7, 8.EE.2

Equation: 8^2 + x^2 = 41^2

Height: 40 ft

3. Kaylee is using two different shapes of tiles to cover her kitchen floor, as shown. 8.G.5

Part A: Write the correct values to complete the equations to find x and z, the degree measures of the interior angles of the two kinds of tiles.

3	6	60	90
120	180	540	720

Equilateral Triangle: 3 · x = 180; x = 60

Regular Hexagon: 6 · z = 720; z = 120

Part B: What is the sum of the degree measures of the angles at the circled vertex? Explain how you know.

360°; Sample answer: The circled vertex shows two 60° angles and two 120° angles; $2(60) + 2(120) = 360$.

4. A triangular flower bed has the angle measures shown. Write values to complete the equation to find the value of x. 8.G.5

2 · 40 + x = 180

x	90
2	100
10	140
40	180

What is the value of x? 100

5. After the first three folds of a paper airplane design, the paper is shaped like a pentagon $GHJKL$. Angles GHJ and LKJ are congruent. Angle HJK measures 45°. Write the correct measures to complete the equation to find x, the measure of angle GHJ. 8.G.5

2 · x + 2 · 90 + 45 = 540

$m\angle GHJ$ = 157.5°

6. Select the appropriate reason for each statement of the geometric proof below. 8.G.5, 8.G.6

Substitution	Multiplication Property of Equality	Alternate exterior angles have equal measures.
Addition Property of Equality	Alternate interior angles have equal measures.	Vertical angles have equal measures.

Given: Two parallel lines cut by a transversal, $m\angle 1 = \left(\frac{x}{2}\right)°$, $m\angle 8 = 76°$

Prove: $x = 152$

Proof:

Statements	Reasons
1. $m\angle 1 = \left(\frac{x}{2}\right)°$, $m\angle 8 = 76°$	Given
2. $m\angle 1 = m\angle 8$	Alternate exterior angles have equal measures.
3. $\frac{x}{2} = 76$	Substitution
4. $x = 152$	Multiplication Property of Equality

Chapter Tests

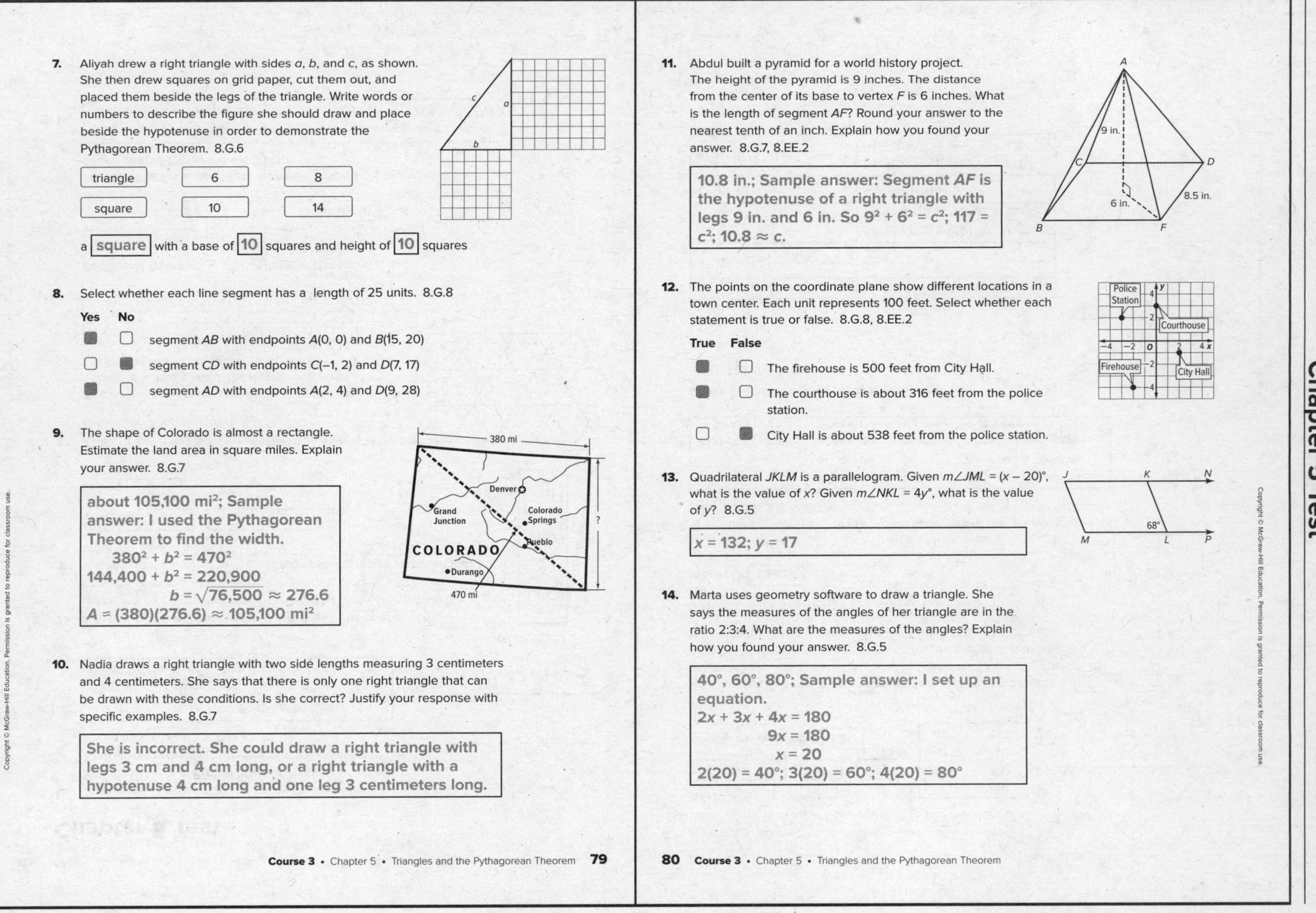

7. Aliyah drew a right triangle with sides *a*, *b*, and *c*, as shown. She then drew squares on grid paper, cut them out, and placed them beside the legs of the triangle. Write words or numbers to describe the figure she should draw and place beside the hypotenuse in order to demonstrate the Pythagorean Theorem. 8.G.6

triangle	6	8
square	10	14

a **square** with a base of **10** squares and height of **10** squares

8. Select whether each line segment has a length of 25 units. 8.G.8

Yes	No	
■	☐	segment *AB* with endpoints *A*(0, 0) and *B*(15, 20)
☐	■	segment *CD* with endpoints *C*(–1, 2) and *D*(7, 17)
■	☐	segment *AD* with endpoints *A*(2, 4) and *D*(9, 28)

9. The shape of Colorado is almost a rectangle. Estimate the land area in square miles. Explain your answer. 8.G.7

about 105,100 mi²; Sample answer: I used the Pythagorean Theorem to find the width.
$$380^2 + b^2 = 470^2$$
$$144{,}400 + b^2 = 220{,}900$$
$$b = \sqrt{76{,}500} \approx 276.6$$
$$A = (380)(276.6) \approx 105{,}100 \text{ mi}^2$$

10. Nadia draws a right triangle with two side lengths measuring 3 centimeters and 4 centimeters. She says that there is only one right triangle that can be drawn with these conditions. Is she correct? Justify your response with specific examples. 8.G.7

She is incorrect. She could draw a right triangle with legs 3 cm and 4 cm long, or a right triangle with a hypotenuse 4 cm long and one leg 3 centimeters long.

11. Abdul built a pyramid for a world history project. The height of the pyramid is 9 inches. The distance from the center of its base to vertex *F* is 6 inches. What is the length of segment *AF*? Round your answer to the nearest tenth of an inch. Explain how you found your answer. 8.G.7, 8.EE.2

10.8 in.; Sample answer: Segment *AF* is the hypotenuse of a right triangle with legs 9 in. and 6 in. So $9^2 + 6^2 = c^2$; $117 = c^2$; $10.8 \approx c$.

12. The points on the coordinate plane show different locations in a town center. Each unit represents 100 feet. Select whether each statement is true or false. 8.G.8, 8.EE.2

True	False	
■	☐	The firehouse is 500 feet from City Hall.
■	☐	The courthouse is about 316 feet from the police station.
☐	■	City Hall is about 538 feet from the police station.

13. Quadrilateral *JKLM* is a parallelogram. Given $m\angle JML = (x - 20)°$, what is the value of *x*? Given $m\angle NKL = 4y°$, what is the value of *y*? 8.G.5

$x = 132$; $y = 17$

14. Marta uses geometry software to draw a triangle. She says the measures of the angles of her triangle are in the ratio 2:3:4. What are the measures of the angles? Explain how you found your answer. 8.G.5

40°, 60°, 80°; Sample answer: I set up an equation.
$$2x + 3x + 4x = 180$$
$$9x = 180$$
$$x = 20$$
$$2(20) = 40°;\ 3(20) = 60°;\ 4(20) = 80°$$

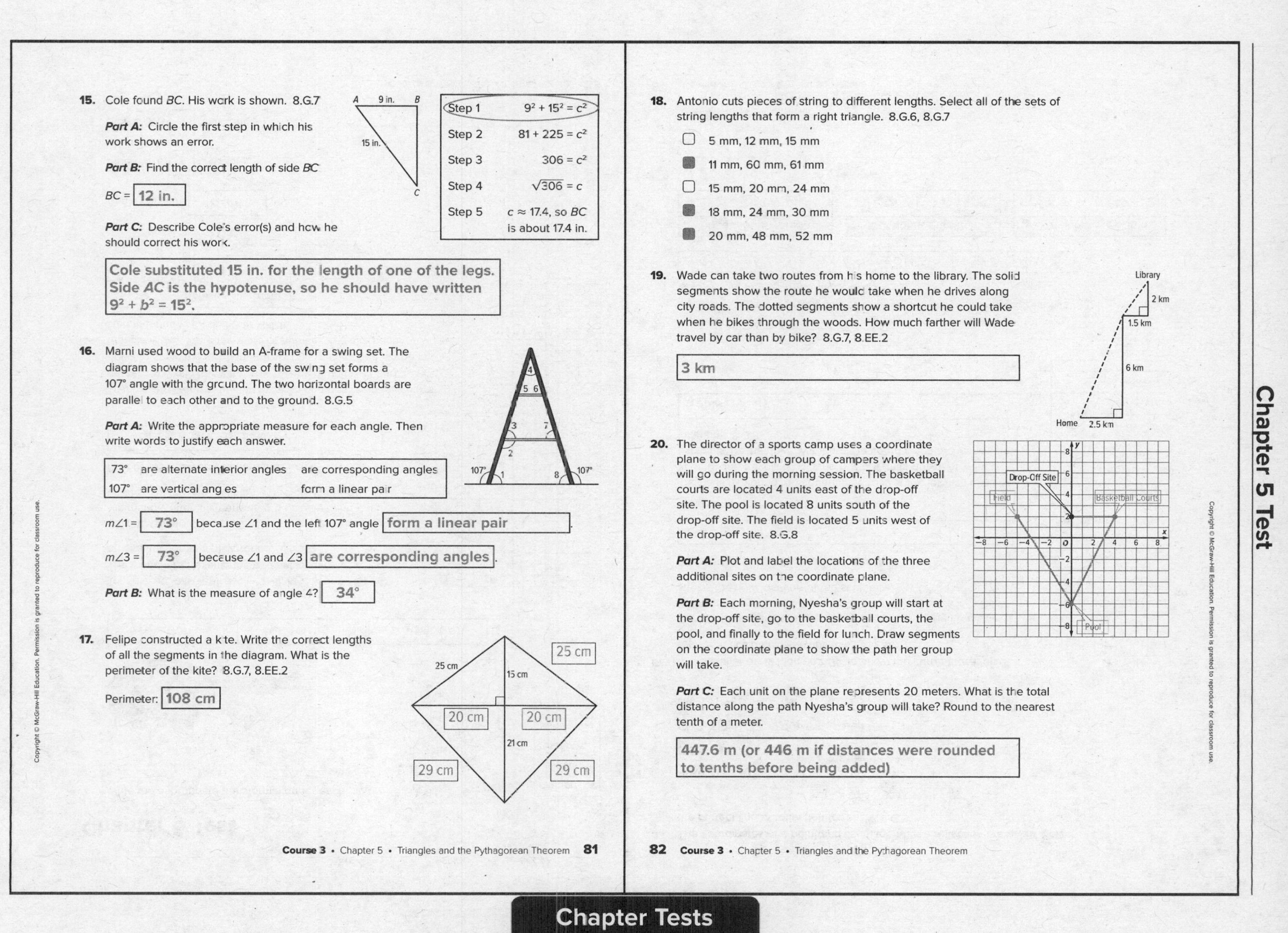

15. Cole found *BC*. His work is shown. 8.G.7

Step 1	$9^2 + 15^2 = c^2$
Step 2	$81 + 225 = c^2$
Step 3	$306 = c^2$
Step 4	$\sqrt{306} = c$
Step 5	$c \approx 17.4$, so *BC* is about 17.4 in.

Part A: Circle the first step in which his work shows an error.

Part B: Find the correct length of side *BC*

BC = 12 in.

Part C: Describe Cole's error(s) and how he should correct his work.

Cole substituted 15 in. for the length of one of the legs. Side *AC* is the hypotenuse, so he should have written $9^2 + b^2 = 15^2$.

16. Marni used wood to build an A-frame for a swing set. The diagram shows that the base of the swing set forms a 107° angle with the ground. The two horizontal boards are parallel to each other and to the ground. 8.G.5

Part A: Write the appropriate measure for each angle. Then write words to justify each answer.

73°	are alternate interior angles	are corresponding angles
107°	are vertical angles	form a linear pair

$m\angle 1$ = 73° because ∠1 and the left 107° angle form a linear pair.

$m\angle 3$ = 73° because ∠1 and ∠3 are corresponding angles.

Part B: What is the measure of angle ∠4? 34°

17. Felipe constructed a kite. Write the correct lengths of all the segments in the diagram. What is the perimeter of the kite? 8.G.7, 8.EE.2

Perimeter: 108 cm

18. Antonio cuts pieces of string to different lengths. Select all of the sets of string lengths that form a right triangle. 8.G.6, 8.G.7

- ☐ 5 mm, 12 mm, 15 mm
- ■ 11 mm, 60 mm, 61 mm
- ☐ 15 mm, 20 mm, 24 mm
- ■ 18 mm, 24 mm, 30 mm
- ■ 20 mm, 48 mm, 52 mm

19. Wade can take two routes from his home to the library. The solid segments show the route he would take when he drives along city roads. The dotted segments show a shortcut he could take when he bikes through the woods. How much farther will Wade travel by car than by bike? 8.G.7, 8.EE.2

3 km

20. The director of a sports camp uses a coordinate plane to show each group of campers where they will go during the morning session. The basketball courts are located 4 units east of the drop-off site. The pool is located 8 units south of the drop-off site. The field is located 5 units west of the drop-off site. 8.G.8

Part A: Plot and label the locations of the three additional sites on the coordinate plane.

Part B: Each morning, Nyesha's group will start at the drop-off site, go to the basketball courts, the pool, and finally to the field for lunch. Draw segments on the coordinate plane to show the path her group will take.

Part C: Each unit on the plane represents 20 meters. What is the total distance along the path Nyesha's group will take? Round to the nearest tenth of a meter.

447.6 m (or 446 m if distances were rounded to tenths before being added)

Chapter Tests

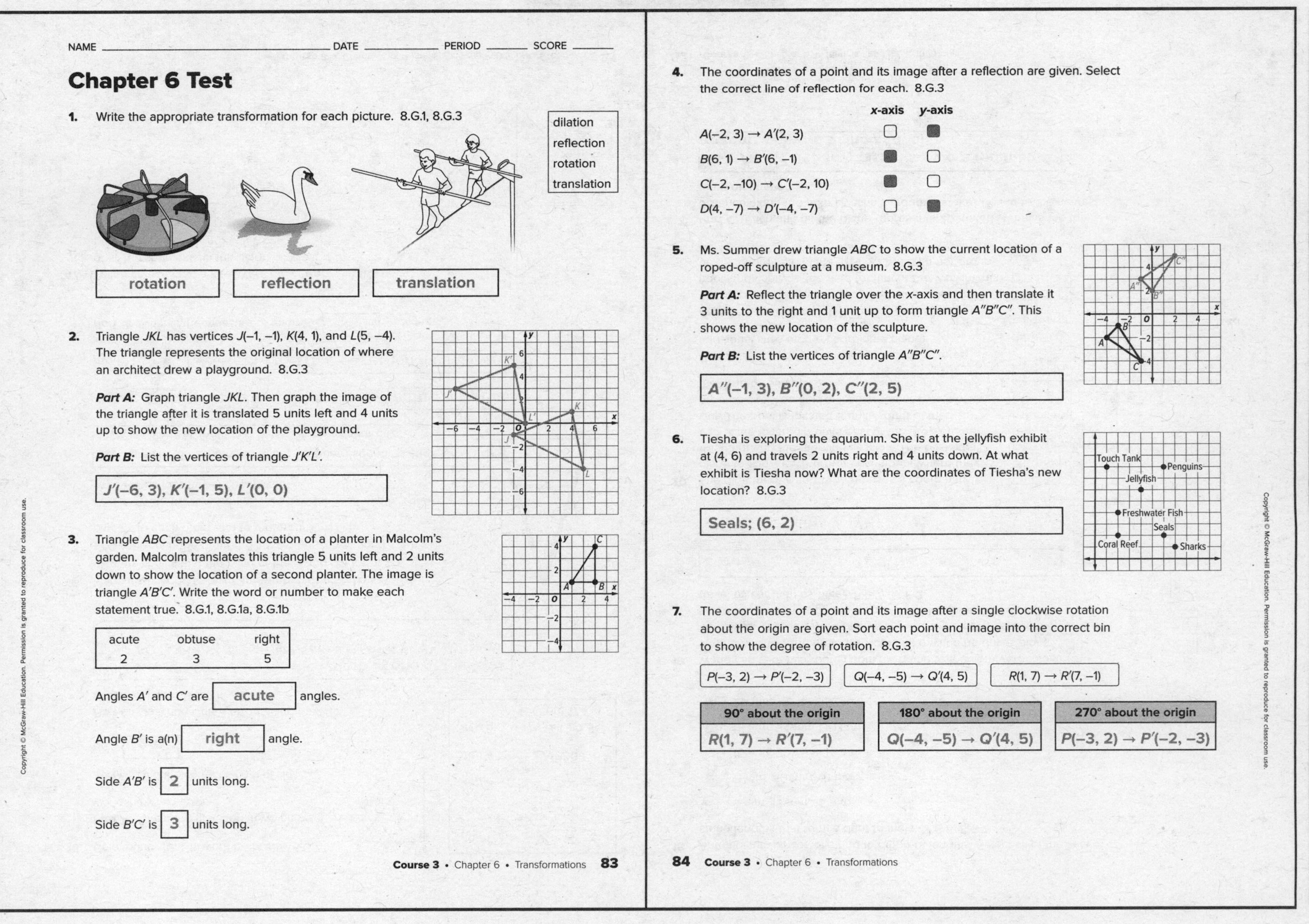

NAME ______________ DATE ________ PERIOD ______ SCORE ______

Chapter 6 Test

1. Write the appropriate transformation for each picture. 8.G.1, 8.G.3

dilation
reflection
rotation
translation

rotation | reflection | translation

2. Triangle *JKL* has vertices *J*(–1, –1), *K*(4, 1), and *L*(5, –4). The triangle represents the original location of where an architect drew a playground. 8.G.3

Part A: Graph triangle *JKL*. Then graph the image of the triangle after it is translated 5 units left and 4 units up to show the new location of the playground.

Part B: List the vertices of triangle *J′K′L′*.

J′(–6, 3), K′(–1, 5), L′(0, 0)

3. Triangle *ABC* represents the location of a planter in Malcolm's garden. Malcolm translates this triangle 5 units left and 2 units down to show the location of a second planter. The image is triangle *A′B′C′*. Write the word or number to make each statement true. 8.G.1, 8.G.1a, 8.G.1b

acute	obtuse	right
2	3	5

Angles *A′* and *C′* are **acute** angles.

Angle *B′* is a(n) **right** angle.

Side *A′B′* is **2** units long.

Side *B′C′* is **3** units long.

4. The coordinates of a point and its image after a reflection are given. Select the correct line of reflection for each. 8.G.3

	x-axis	*y*-axis
A(–2, 3) → *A′*(2, 3)	☐	■
B(6, 1) → *B′*(6, –1)	■	☐
C(–2, –10) → *C′*(–2, 10)	■	☐
D(4, –7) → *D′*(–4, –7)	☐	■

5. Ms. Summer drew triangle *ABC* to show the current location of a roped-off sculpture at a museum. 8.G.3

Part A: Reflect the triangle over the *x*-axis and then translate it 3 units to the right and 1 unit up to form triangle *A″B″C″*. This shows the new location of the sculpture.

Part B: List the vertices of triangle *A″B″C″*.

A″(–1, 3), B″(0, 2), C″(2, 5)

6. Tiesha is exploring the aquarium. She is at the jellyfish exhibit at (4, 6) and travels 2 units right and 4 units down. At what exhibit is Tiesha now? What are the coordinates of Tiesha's new location? 8.G.3

Seals; (6, 2)

7. The coordinates of a point and its image after a single clockwise rotation about the origin are given. Sort each point and image into the correct bin to show the degree of rotation. 8.G.3

P(–3, 2) → *P′*(–2, –3) | *Q*(–4, –5) → *Q′*(4, 5) | *R*(1, 7) → *R′*(7, –1)

90° about the origin	180° about the origin	270° about the origin
R(1, 7) → R′(7, –1)	**Q(–4, –5) → Q′(4, 5)**	**P(–3, 2) → P′(–2, –3)**

8. Aaron is experimenting with geometry software. He dilates triangle *DEF* so that the image of point *F* is *F*′(10, 5). 8.G.3

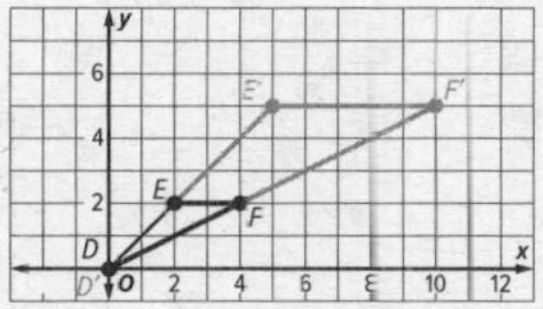

Part A: Draw the image, triangle *D′E′F′*.

Part B: What is the scale factor of the dilation? Is the dilation a reduction or an enlargement?

2.5; enlargement

9. Triangle *R′S′T′* is the image of triangle *RST* after one or more transformations. Select whether each transformation or sequence of transformations produces triangle *R′S′T′*. 8.G.3

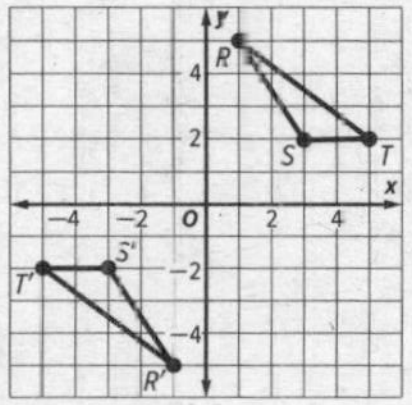

Yes	No	
■	☐	Triangle *RST* is rotated 180° about the origin.
■	☐	Triangle *RST* is reflected across the *y*-axis and then reflected across the *x*-axis.
☐	■	Triangle *RST* is reflected across the *y*-axis and then translated 4 units down.

10. Julissa drew a partial cloverleaf with point *C* at (2, 2) on the coordinate plane. She then rotated this figure 90°, 180°, and 270° clockwise about the origin to complete the design. Plot and label the locations of points *C′*, *C″*, and *C‴*. 8.G.3

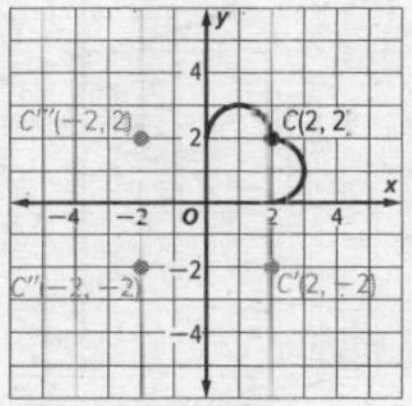

C‴(−2, 2) C(2, 2) C″(−2, −2) C′(2, −2)

11. Darren draws triangle *XYZ* with vertices *X*(−4, −4), *Y*(−2, 6), and *Z*(10, 2). He then translates it by $(x + 8, y - 12)$ to form triangle *X′Y′Z′*. Write symbols and numbers to show how Darren could translate triangle *X′Y′Z′* so it completely covers the original triangle *XYZ*. 8.G.3

− + 2 4 6 8 10 12

translation: $(x - 8, y + 12)$

12. On a floor plan, rectangle *FGHJ* with vertices *F*(−5, 3), *G*(−5, 1), *H*(−1, 1), and *J*(−1, 3) represents the location of a table in Marta's dining room. Marta would like to rotate the table 90° clockwise about point *H* to see if she likes the new placement. 8.G.1, 8.G.3

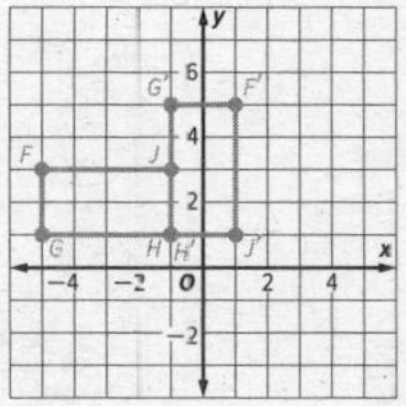

Part A: Draw the rectangle and the rotated image on the coordinate plane.

Part B: List the vertices of the corners of the rotated table.

***F′*(1, 5), *G′*(−1, 5), *H′*(−1, 1), *J′*(1, 1)**

13. Alyssa cuts two congruent pieces of felt. She glues one piece of felt where triangle *BCD* is located. She moves and glues the other at the location of triangle *B′C′D′*. Select all of the sequences of transformations that Alyssa could use to move triangle *BCD* to triangle *B′C′D′*. 8.G.3

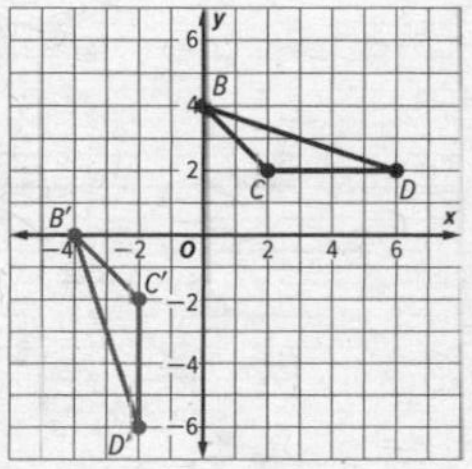

- ☐ a reflection across the *x*-axis followed by a reflection across the *y*-axis
- ■ a 90° clockwise rotation about the origin followed by a reflection across the *y*-axis
- ☐ a 270° clockwise rotation about the origin followed by a reflection across the *y*-axis
- ■ a 270° clockwise rotation about the origin followed by a reflection across the *x*-axis
- ☐ a reflection across the *y*-axis followed by a translation of 2 units down

14. Triangle *KLM* has vertices *K*(4, 3), *L*(6, −1), and *M*(−1, 0). Ellis is finding the coordinates of the image of triangle *KLM* after a reflection across the *x*-axis. His answers are shown. Circle the part(s) of his answer that contain errors. Then describe and correct the error(s). 8.G.3

K(4, 3) → *K′*(4, −3)
L(6, −1) → *L′*(6, 1)
M(−1, 0) → *M′*(1, 0)

Sample answer: Ellis did not need to change the *x*-coordinate. When a point (*x*, *y*) is reflected across the *x*-axis, its image is (*x*, −*y*). Since the *y*-coordinate of point *M* is 0, points *M* and *M′* are both located at (−1, 0).

15. Parallelogram *FGHJ* shows the location of several parking spaces that were painted in a parking lot. Bernardo translates this parallelogram 3 units to the right and 4 units up to show where several other parking spaces will be painted. Select whether each statement about the new parallelogram is true or false. 8.G.1, 8.G.1a, 8.G.1c

True	False	
☐	■	Side *F′J′* is longer than side *FJ*.
■	☐	Side *G′H′* has the same length as side *FJ*.
■	☐	Lines *F′G′* and *H′J′* are parallel.
■	☐	Lines *F′J′* and *G′H′* are parallel.

16. Triangle *PQR* shows a pennant Brittany designed and placed on her wall in support of her school's baseball team. She wants to enlarge the pennant by a scale factor of 2, with (0, 0) as the center of dilation, and then move it 7 units higher on her wall. 8.G.3

Part A: Graph triangle *P″Q″R″* to show the new size and location of the pennant.

Part B: List the coordinates of the vertices of the image.

P″(−6, 1), Q″(−6, 9), R″(8, 5)

17. Nick will move a storage bin from its current location to the new location shown on the coordinate plane. Describe how Nick could do this, using transformations. 8.G.3

Using One or More Translations	**Sample answer: a translation of 9 units left and 7 units down**
Using One or More Reflections	**Sample answer: a reflection across the *x*-axis followed by a reflection across the *y*-axis**
Using One or More Rotations	**Sample answer: a 180° clockwise rotation about the origin**

18. Cami drew part of a jet on the coordinate plane and then reflected what she had drawn over the *y*-axis to complete the drawing. Identify the coordinates of the images of points *A*, *B*, and *C*. 8.G.3

A′(1, 2), B′(4, −3), C′(2, −6)

19. Triangle *STV* has vertices *S*(−2, 5), *T*(2, −4), and *V*(7, 3). Mia found the coordinates of the vertices of the image of triangle *STV* after a 90° clockwise rotation about the origin. Her answers are shown. Describe and correct the error(s) that Mia made. 8.G.3

S(2, 5) → *S′*(−5, 2)
T(2, −4) → *T′*(4, 2)
V(7, 3) → *V′*(−3, 7)

Mia rotated triangle *STV* 270° clockwise about the origin to get (*x*, *y*) → (−*y*, *x*). She should have rotated 90° clockwise about the origin to get (*x*, *y*) → (*y*, −*x*). The correct coordinates are *S′*(5, −2), *T′*(−4, −2), and *V′*(3, −7).

20. Trapezoid *JKLM* shows a swimming pool at a community center. The center will build a second children's swimming pool, represented by trapezoid *J′K′L′M′*. Select all of the transformations or sequences of transformations that would produce trapezoid *J′K′L′M′* when applied to trapezoid *JKLM*. 8.G.3

- ■ a 180° rotation about the origin followed by a dilation by a factor of 0.5
- ■ a dilation by a factor of 0.5 followed by a 180° rotation about the origin
- ☐ a reflection across both axes followed by a dilation by a factor of 2
- ☐ a translation of 4 units down and 6 units to the left followed by a dilation by a factor of 2
- ■ a dilation by a factor of −0.5

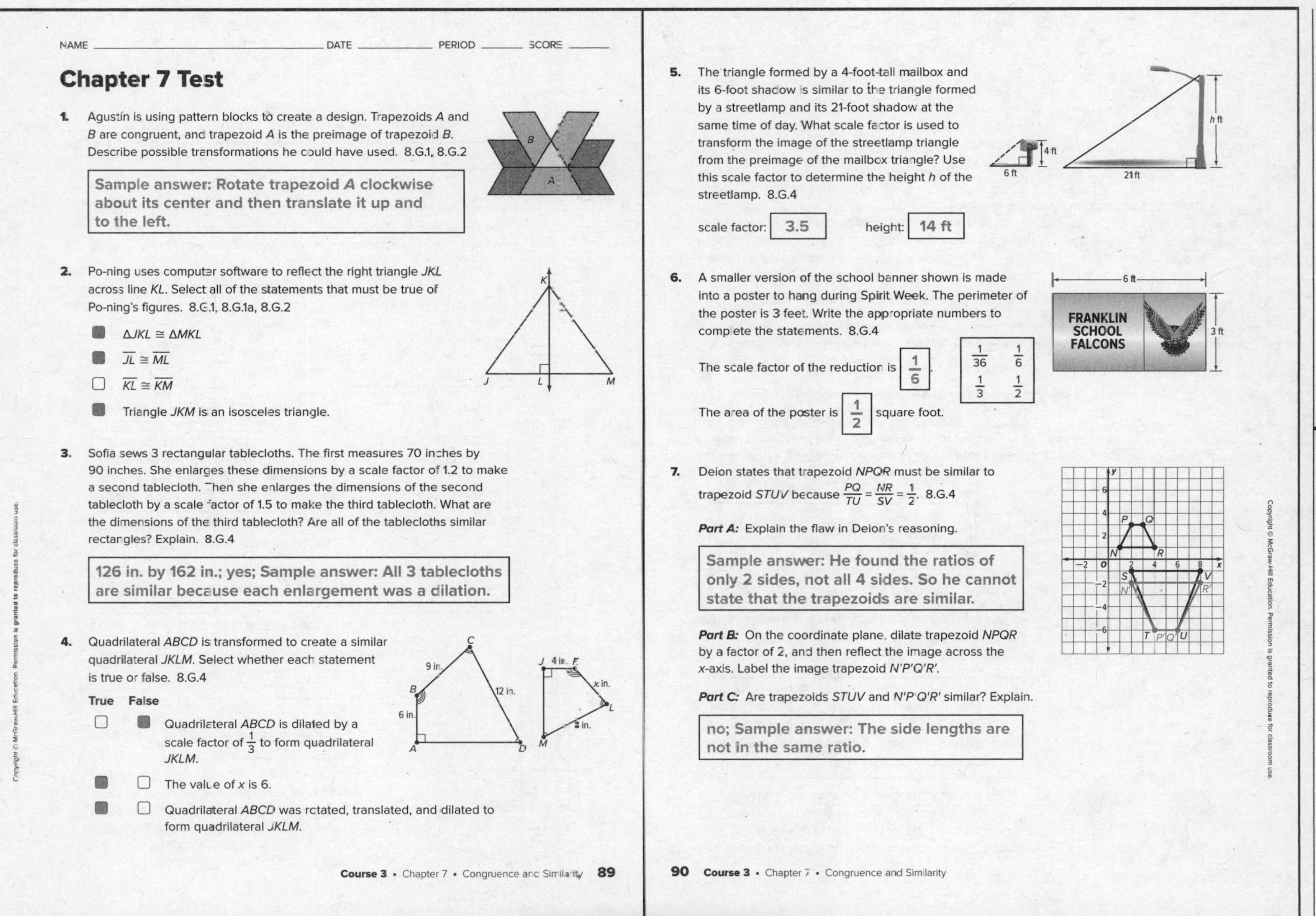

NAME ____________________ DATE __________ PERIOD ______ SCORE ______

Chapter 7 Test

1. Agustín is using pattern blocks to create a design. Trapezoids *A* and *B* are congruent, and trapezoid *A* is the preimage of trapezoid *B*. Describe possible transformations he could have used. 8.G.1, 8.G.2

Sample answer: Rotate trapezoid *A* clockwise about its center and then translate it up and to the left.

2. Po-ning uses computer software to reflect the right triangle *JKL* across line *KL*. Select all of the statements that must be true of Po-ning's figures. 8.G.1, 8.G.1a, 8.G.2

- ■ $\Delta JKL \cong \Delta MKL$
- ■ $\overline{JL} \cong \overline{ML}$
- ☐ $\overline{KL} \cong \overline{KM}$
- ■ Triangle *JKM* is an isosceles triangle.

3. Sofia sews 3 rectangular tablecloths. The first measures 70 inches by 90 inches. She enlarges these dimensions by a scale factor of 1.2 to make a second tablecloth. Then she enlarges the dimensions of the second tablecloth by a scale factor of 1.5 to make the third tablecloth. What are the dimensions of the third tablecloth? Are all of the tablecloths similar rectangles? Explain. 8.G.4

126 in. by 162 in.; yes; Sample answer: All 3 tablecloths are similar because each enlargement was a dilation.

4. Quadrilateral *ABCD* is transformed to create a similar quadrilateral *JKLM*. Select whether each statement is true or false. 8.G.4

True	False	
☐	■	Quadrilateral *ABCD* is dilated by a scale factor of $\frac{1}{3}$ to form quadrilateral *JKLM*.
■	☐	The value of *x* is 6.
■	☐	Quadrilateral *ABCD* was rotated, translated, and dilated to form quadrilateral *JKLM*.

Course 3 • Chapter 7 • Congruence and Similarity 89

5. The triangle formed by a 4-foot-tall mailbox and its 6-foot shadow is similar to the triangle formed by a streetlamp and its 21-foot shadow at the same time of day. What scale factor is used to transform the image of the streetlamp triangle from the preimage of the mailbox triangle? Use this scale factor to determine the height *h* of the streetlamp. 8.G.4

scale factor: **3.5** height: **14 ft**

6. A smaller version of the school banner shown is made into a poster to hang during Spirit Week. The perimeter of the poster is 3 feet. Write the appropriate numbers to complete the statements. 8.G.4

$\frac{1}{36}$ $\frac{1}{6}$ $\frac{1}{3}$ $\frac{1}{2}$

The scale factor of the reduction is $\frac{1}{6}$.

The area of the poster is $\frac{1}{2}$ square foot.

7. Deion states that trapezoid *NPQR* must be similar to trapezoid *STUV* because $\frac{PQ}{TU} = \frac{NR}{SV} = \frac{1}{2}$. 8.G.4

Part A: Explain the flaw in Deion's reasoning.

Sample answer: He found the ratios of only 2 sides, not all 4 sides. So he cannot state that the trapezoids are similar.

Part B: On the coordinate plane, dilate trapezoid *NPQR* by a factor of 2, and then reflect the image across the *x*-axis. Label the image trapezoid *N'P'Q'R'*.

Part C: Are trapezoids *STUV* and *N'P'Q'R'* similar? Explain.

no; Sample answer: The side lengths are not in the same ratio.

90 Course 3 • Chapter 7 • Congruence and Similarity

Chapter Tests

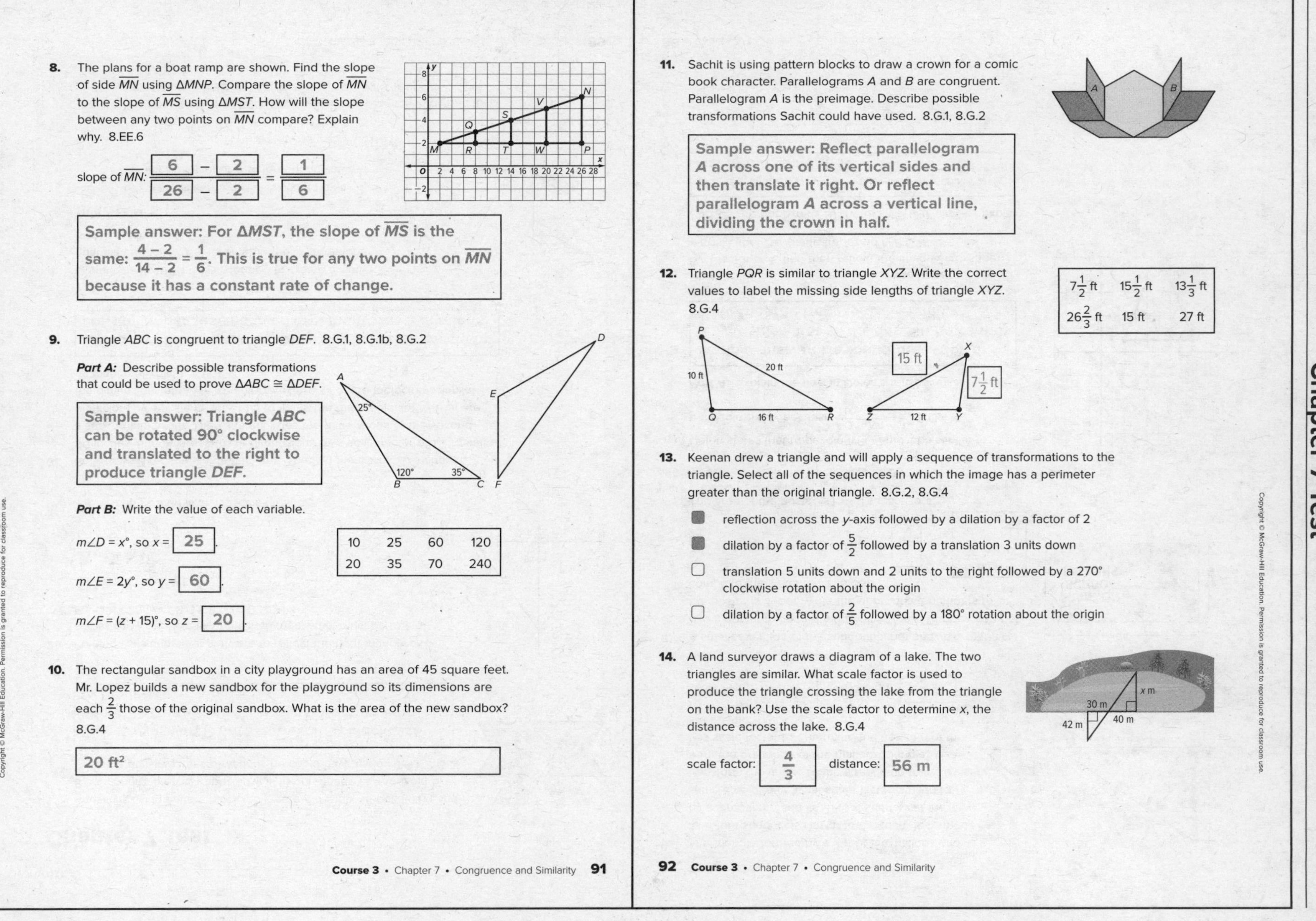

8. The plans for a boat ramp are shown. Find the slope of side $\overline{MN}$ using ΔMNP. Compare the slope of $\overline{MN}$ to the slope of $\overline{MS}$ using ΔMST. How will the slope between any two points on $\overline{MN}$ compare? Explain why. 8.EE.6

slope of $\overline{MN}$: $\frac{6 - 2}{26 - 2} = \frac{1}{6}$

Sample answer: For ΔMST, the slope of $\overline{MS}$ is the same: $\frac{4-2}{14-2} = \frac{1}{6}$. This is true for any two points on $\overline{MN}$ because it has a constant rate of change.

9. Triangle ABC is congruent to triangle DEF. 8.G.1, 8.G.1b, 8.G.2

Part A: Describe possible transformations that could be used to prove $\Delta ABC \cong \Delta DEF$.

Sample answer: Triangle ABC can be rotated 90° clockwise and translated to the right to produce triangle DEF.

Part B: Write the value of each variable.

$m\angle D = x°$, so $x =$ 25.

$m\angle E = 2y°$, so $y =$ 60.

$m\angle F = (z + 15)°$, so $z =$ 20.

10	25	60	120
20	35	70	240

10. The rectangular sandbox in a city playground has an area of 45 square feet. Mr. Lopez builds a new sandbox for the playground so its dimensions are each $\frac{2}{3}$ those of the original sandbox. What is the area of the new sandbox? 8.G.4

20 ft²

11. Sachit is using pattern blocks to draw a crown for a comic book character. Parallelograms A and B are congruent. Parallelogram A is the preimage. Describe possible transformations Sachit could have used. 8.G.1, 8.G.2

Sample answer: Reflect parallelogram A across one of its vertical sides and then translate it right. Or reflect parallelogram A across a vertical line, dividing the crown in half.

12. Triangle PQR is similar to triangle XYZ. Write the correct values to label the missing side lengths of triangle XYZ. 8.G.4

$7\frac{1}{2}$ ft	$15\frac{1}{2}$ ft	$13\frac{1}{3}$ ft
$26\frac{2}{3}$ ft	15 ft	27 ft

13. Keenan drew a triangle and will apply a sequence of transformations to the triangle. Select all of the sequences in which the image has a perimeter greater than the original triangle. 8.G.2, 8.G.4

- ■ reflection across the y-axis followed by a dilation by a factor of 2
- ■ dilation by a factor of $\frac{5}{2}$ followed by a translation 3 units down
- ☐ translation 5 units down and 2 units to the right followed by a 270° clockwise rotation about the origin
- ☐ dilation by a factor of $\frac{2}{5}$ followed by a 180° rotation about the origin

14. A land surveyor draws a diagram of a lake. The two triangles are similar. What scale factor is used to produce the triangle crossing the lake from the triangle on the bank? Use the scale factor to determine x, the distance across the lake. 8.G.4

scale factor: $\frac{4}{3}$ distance: 56 m

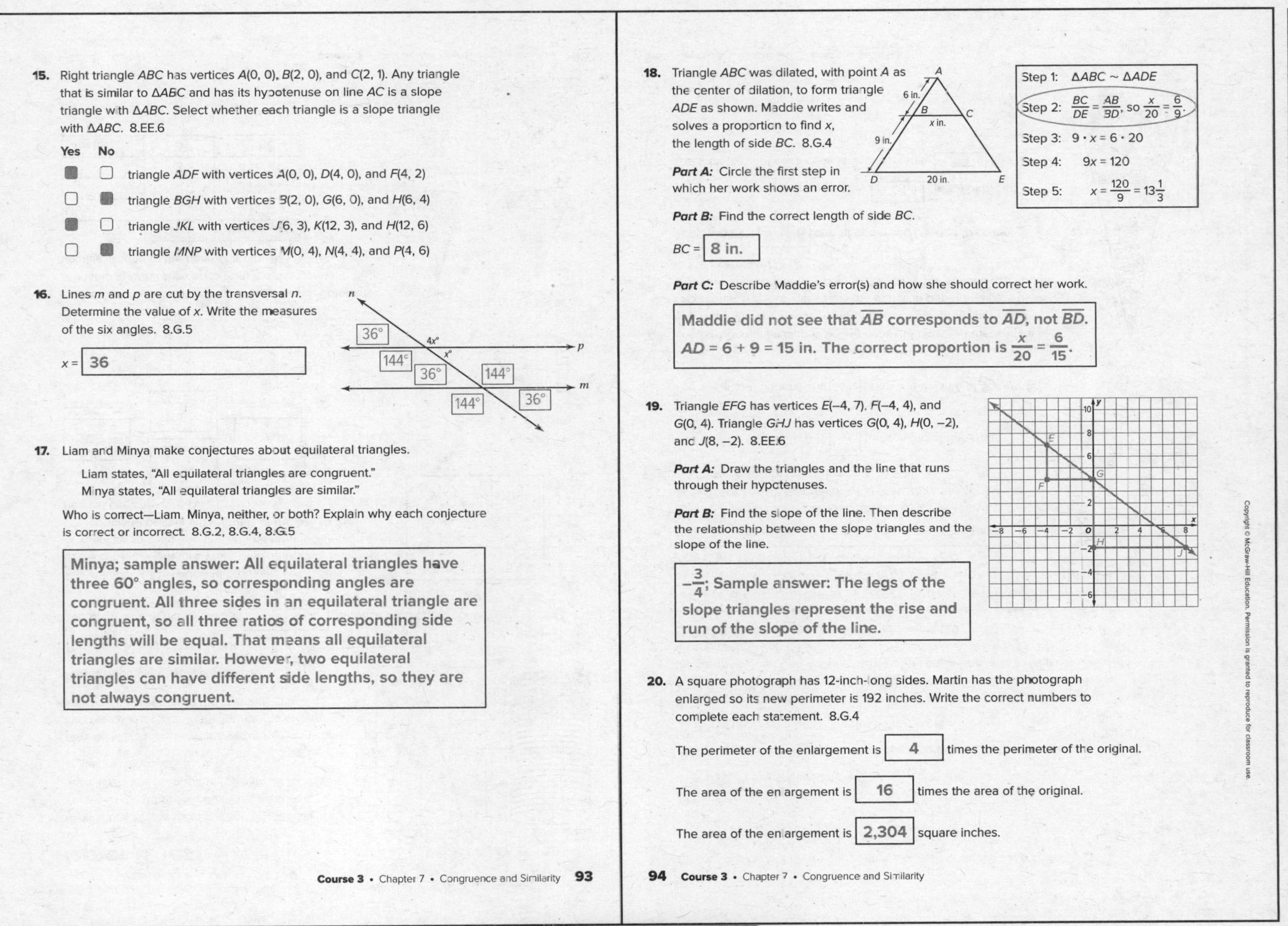

15. Right triangle ABC has vertices $A(0, 0)$, $B(2, 0)$, and $C(2, 1)$. Any triangle that is similar to ΔABC and has its hypotenuse on line AC is a slope triangle with ΔABC. Select whether each triangle is a slope triangle with ΔABC. 8.EE.6

Yes	No	
■	☐	triangle ADF with vertices $A(0, 0)$, $D(4, 0)$, and $F(4, 2)$
☐	■	triangle BGH with vertices $B(2, 0)$, $G(6, 0)$, and $H(6, 4)$
■	☐	triangle JKL with vertices $J(6, 3)$, $K(12, 3)$, and $H(12, 6)$
☐	■	triangle MNP with vertices $M(0, 4)$, $N(4, 4)$, and $P(4, 6)$

16. Lines m and p are cut by the transversal n. Determine the value of x. Write the measures of the six angles. 8.G.5

$x =$ **36**

17. Liam and Minya make conjectures about equilateral triangles.

Liam states, "All equilateral triangles are congruent."
Minya states, "All equilateral triangles are similar."

Who is correct—Liam, Minya, neither, or both? Explain why each conjecture is correct or incorrect. 8.G.2, 8.G.4, 8.G.5

Minya; sample answer: All equilateral triangles have three 60° angles, so corresponding angles are congruent. All three sides in an equilateral triangle are congruent, so all three ratios of corresponding side lengths will be equal. That means all equilateral triangles are similar. However, two equilateral triangles can have different side lengths, so they are not always congruent.

18. Triangle ABC was dilated, with point A as the center of dilation, to form triangle ADE as shown. Maddie writes and solves a proportion to find x, the length of side BC. 8.G.4

Step 1: $\Delta ABC \sim \Delta ADE$
Step 2: $\frac{BC}{DE} = \frac{AB}{BD}$, so $\frac{x}{20} = \frac{6}{9}$.
Step 3: $9 \cdot x = 6 \cdot 20$
Step 4: $9x = 120$
Step 5: $x = \frac{120}{9} = 13\frac{1}{3}$

Part A: Circle the first step in which her work shows an error.

Part B: Find the correct length of side BC.

$BC =$ **8 in.**

Part C: Describe Maddie's error(s) and how she should correct her work.

Maddie did not see that $\overline{AB}$ corresponds to $\overline{AD}$, not $\overline{BD}$. $AD = 6 + 9 = 15$ in. The correct proportion is $\frac{x}{20} = \frac{6}{15}$.

19. Triangle EFG has vertices $E(-4, 7)$, $F(-4, 4)$, and $G(0, 4)$. Triangle GHJ has vertices $G(0, 4)$, $H(0, -2)$, and $J(8, -2)$. 8.EE.6

Part A: Draw the triangles and the line that runs through their hypotenuses.

Part B: Find the slope of the line. Then describe the relationship between the slope triangles and the slope of the line.

$-\frac{3}{4}$; Sample answer: The legs of the slope triangles represent the rise and run of the slope of the line.

20. A square photograph has 12-inch-long sides. Martin has the photograph enlarged so its new perimeter is 192 inches. Write the correct numbers to complete each statement. 8.G.4

The perimeter of the enlargement is **4** times the perimeter of the original.

The area of the enlargement is **16** times the area of the original.

The area of the enlargement is **2,304** square inches.

NAME ______ DATE ______ PERIOD ______ SCORE ______

Chapter 8 Test

1. Mykelti has two containers—one shaped like a cone and the other shaped like a cylinder. Mykelti fills the cone to the top with 392π cubic inches of water. 8.G.9

Part A: Mykelti pours all the water from the cone into the cylinder. Shade the cylinder to show the volume of water now in the cylinder.

14 in.
24 in.
14 in.
24 in.
24 22 20 18 16 14 12 10 8 6 4 2 0

Part B: Complete each statement.

The water height of the cylinder is **one third** the height of the cone.

The base area of the cylinder is **equal to** the base area of the cone.

2. The volume of a playground ball is approximately $523\frac{1}{3}$ cubic centimeters. Write the appropriate numbers or variables to complete the volume formula. Then use the formula to calculate the radius of the ball to the nearest centimeter. 8.G.9

2	5
3	125
4	r
$392\frac{1}{2}$	$523\frac{1}{3}$

$$523\frac{1}{3} = \frac{4}{3}\pi r^{3}$$

radius: **5** cm

3. Four cones have heights and radii as shown. Complete the table to order the cones from least to greatest volume. Round to the nearest tenth. 8.G.9

	Cone	Volume (m³)
Least	1	217.8
	2	314.2
	3	414.7
Greatest	4	461.8

Cone 1: 4 m, 13 m
Cone 2: 5 m, 12 m
Cone 3: 6 m, 11 m
Cone 4: 7 m, 9 m

4. Alejandro is buying paper cups in the shapes of cylinders and cones. Select whether each shape and size of cup has a volume of at least 200 cubic centimeters. 8.G.9

Yes	No	
☐	■	cone with diameter 8 cm, height 8 cm
■	☐	cylinder with diameter 7 cm, height 6 cm
☐	■	cylinder with diameter 6 cm, height 7 cm

5. A canned foods company makes two different cylindrical cans, each with the same volume. Can A has a height of 9 centimeters and a radius of 4 centimeters. Can B has a radius of 6 centimeters. What is the height of Can B? Explain how you found your answer. 8.G.9

4 cm; Sample answer: I wrote expressions for the two volumes, set them equal, and solved for h, the height of Can B. $\pi(4)^2(9) = \pi(6)^2h$; $144 = 36h$; $4 = h$.

6. Sphere A has a radius of r feet. Sphere B has a radius of $2r$ feet. Sphere C has a radius of $3r$ feet. Write the appropriate values to complete the statements. 8.G.9

$\frac{1}{27}$	$\frac{1}{9}$	$\frac{1}{8}$	$\frac{1}{4}$
2	8	9	27

The volume of Sphere A is $\frac{1}{8}$ the volume of Sphere B.

The volume of Sphere C is **27** times the volume of Sphere A.

7. The environmental club is selling cones of birdseed that can be hung outside. The birdseed weighs about 3.5 grams per cubic centimeter. The club gift-wraps the cones in paper and sells them. Write the appropriate numbers to complete the statements. Round to the nearest tenth. 8.G.9

Approximately **353.4** cm² of paper are needed to cover each cone.

Each cone contains approximately **424.1** cm³ of birdseed.

The total mass of each cone is approximately **1.5** kg.

20.5 cm
20 cm
9 cm

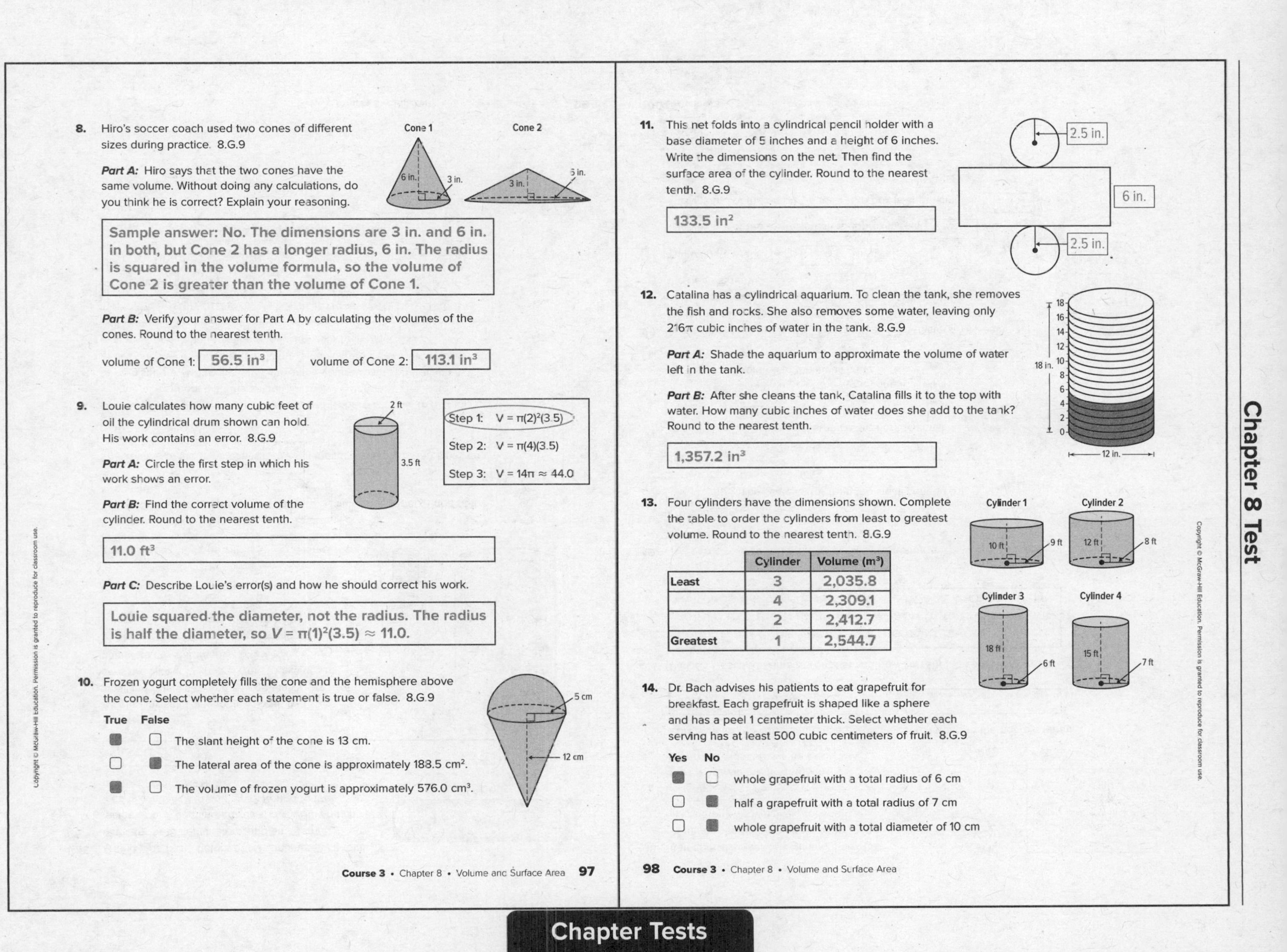

8. Hiro's soccer coach used two cones of different sizes during practice. 8.G.9

Part A: Hiro says that the two cones have the same volume. Without doing any calculations, do you think he is correct? Explain your reasoning.

Sample answer: No. The dimensions are 3 in. and 6 in. in both, but Cone 2 has a longer radius, 6 in. The radius is squared in the volume formula, so the volume of Cone 2 is greater than the volume of Cone 1.

Part B: Verify your answer for Part A by calculating the volumes of the cones. Round to the nearest tenth.

volume of Cone 1: **56.5 in³** volume of Cone 2: **113.1 in³**

9. Louie calculates how many cubic feet of oil the cylindrical drum shown can hold. His work contains an error. 8.G.9

Step 1: $V = \pi(2)^2(3.5)$ (circled)

Step 2: $V = \pi(4)(3.5)$

Step 3: $V = 14\pi \approx 44.0$

Part A: Circle the first step in which his work shows an error.

Part B: Find the correct volume of the cylinder. Round to the nearest tenth.

11.0 ft³

Part C: Describe Louie's error(s) and how he should correct his work.

Louie squared the diameter, not the radius. The radius is half the diameter, so $V = \pi(1)^2(3.5) \approx 11.0$.

10. Frozen yogurt completely fills the cone and the hemisphere above the cone. Select whether each statement is true or false. 8.G.9

True	False	
■	☐	The slant height of the cone is 13 cm.
☐	■	The lateral area of the cone is approximately 188.5 cm².
■	☐	The volume of frozen yogurt is approximately 576.0 cm³.

11. This net folds into a cylindrical pencil holder with a base diameter of 5 inches and a height of 6 inches. Write the dimensions on the net. Then find the surface area of the cylinder. Round to the nearest tenth. 8.G.9

133.5 in²

12. Catalina has a cylindrical aquarium. To clean the tank, she removes the fish and rocks. She also removes some water, leaving only 216π cubic inches of water in the tank. 8.G.9

Part A: Shade the aquarium to approximate the volume of water left in the tank.

Part B: After she cleans the tank, Catalina fills it to the top with water. How many cubic inches of water does she add to the tank? Round to the nearest tenth.

1,357.2 in³

13. Four cylinders have the dimensions shown. Complete the table to order the cylinders from least to greatest volume. Round to the nearest tenth. 8.G.9

	Cylinder	Volume (m³)
Least	3	2,035.8
	4	2,309.1
	2	2,412.7
Greatest	1	2,544.7

14. Dr. Bach advises his patients to eat grapefruit for breakfast. Each grapefruit is shaped like a sphere and has a peel 1 centimeter thick. Select whether each serving has at least 500 cubic centimeters of fruit. 8.G.9

Yes	No	
■	☐	whole grapefruit with a total radius of 6 cm
☐	■	half a grapefruit with a total radius of 7 cm
☐	■	whole grapefruit with a total diameter of 10 cm

Chapter Tests

15. A lead pipe has a height of 40 centimeters, a total diameter of 10 centimeters, and an internal diameter of 8 centimeters, as shown. How much lead is contained in one pipe? Round to the nearest tenth. 8.G.9

8 cm
10 cm
40 cm

1,131.0 cm^3

16. A company sells pineapple juice in two sizes—a small individual size and a large family size. Both cans are similar in shape. Write the values to complete the statements. 8.G.9

Family Size
32 cm
24 cm
Individual Size
8 cm
6 cm

$\frac{1}{64}$	$\frac{1}{27}$	$\frac{1}{16}$	$\frac{1}{4}$
4	16	27	64

The height of the large can is **4** times the height of the small can.

The surface area of the small can is $\frac{1}{16}$ times the surface area of the large can.

The volume of the large can is **64** times the volume of the small can.

17. Dominique knows that the volume of a hemisphere is equal to half the volume of a sphere with the same radius. Based on that, she states, "A hemisphere with radius r has the same volume as a sphere with a radius one-half as long." Is Dominique's conjecture true or false? Use examples or a counterexample to justify your response. 8.G.9

false; Sample answer: A hemisphere with radius r has a volume of $\left(\frac{4}{3}\pi r^3\right)\left(\frac{1}{2}\right) = \frac{2}{3}\pi r^3$ cubic units. A sphere with radius $\frac{1}{2}r$ has a volume of $\frac{4}{3}\pi\left(\frac{1}{2}r\right)^3 = \frac{1}{6}\pi r^3$ cubic units. The two volumes are not equivalent.

18. Kamara calculates the minimum amount of paper needed to make a paper cone like the one shown. Her work contains an error. 8.G.9

3 in.
4 in.

Step 1: $L.A. = \pi r \ell$
Step 2: $L.A. = \pi(3)(4)$
Step 3: $L.A. = 12\pi \approx 37.7$

Part A: Circle the first step in which her work shows an error.

Part B: Find the correct lateral area of the cone. Round to the nearest tenth.

47.1 in^2

Part C: Describe Kamara's error(s) and how she should correct her work.

Kamara used the height, not the slant height. She should use the Pythagorean Theorem to find the slant height is 5 inches and substitute 5 for ℓ in the formula.

19. The two cones shown are similar. Select whether each statement is true or false. 8.G.9

10 in.
4 in.

True	False	
■	☐	The scale factor from the small cone to the large cone is $\frac{5}{2}$.
■	☐	The surface area of the large cone is $\frac{25}{4}$ times the surface area of the small cone.
☐	■	The volume of the large cone is $\frac{25}{4}$ the volume of the small cone.

20. A pet store sells a spherical exercise ball for hamsters. The ball fits in the cube-shaped box, touching the top, bottom, and sides of the box. Write values to complete each statement. Round to the nearest tenth. 8.G.9

7 in.
7 in.

The volume of the box is **343** in^3.

The volume of the exercise ball is approximately **179.6** in^3.

The volume of the empty space in the box is approximately **163.4** in^3.

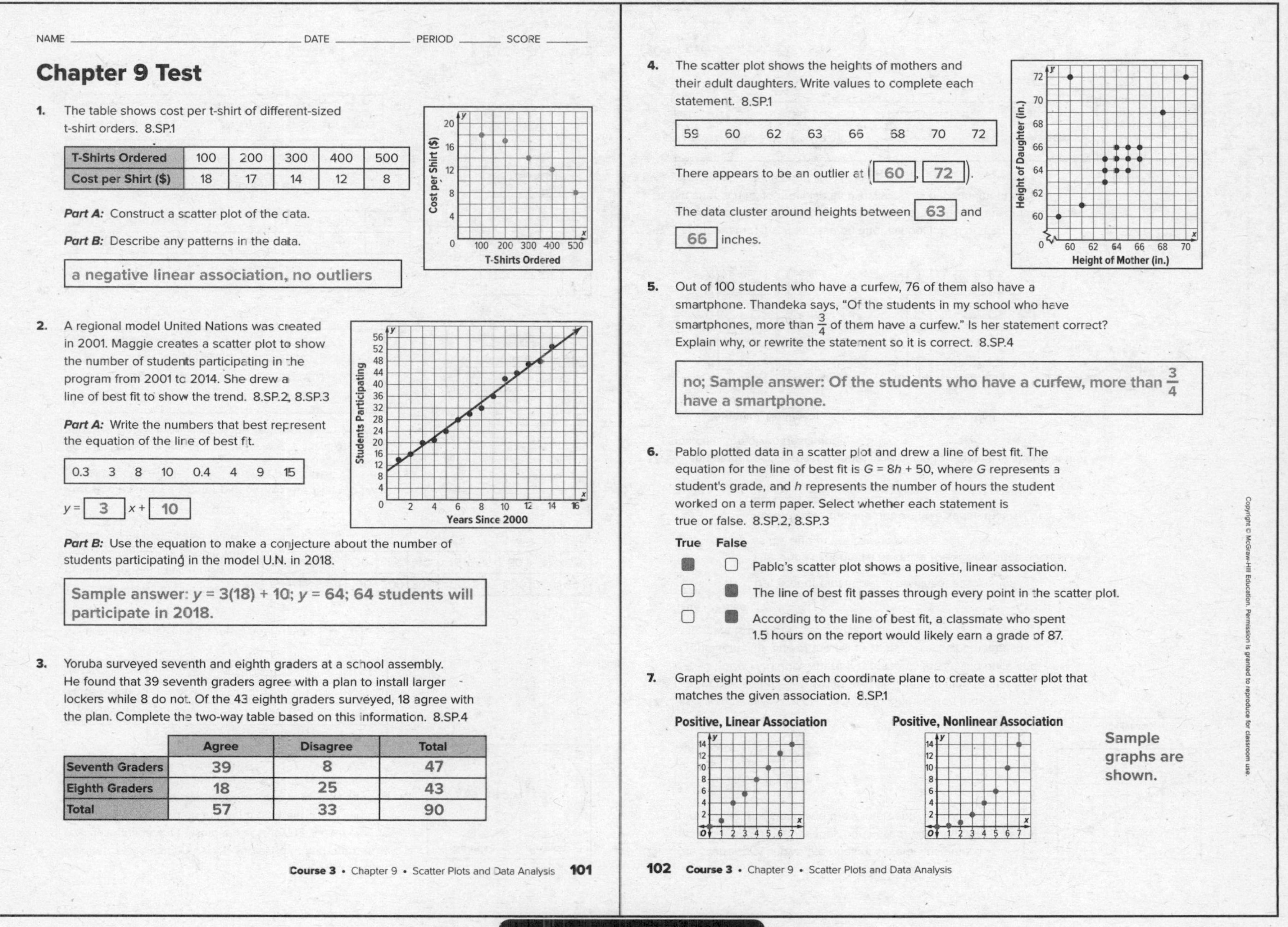

NAME ______________________ DATE ________ PERIOD ______ SCORE ______

Chapter 9 Test

1. The table shows cost per t-shirt of different-sized t-shirt orders. 8.SP.1

T-Shirts Ordered	100	200	300	400	500
Cost per Shirt ($)	18	17	14	12	8

Part A: Construct a scatter plot of the data.

Part B: Describe any patterns in the data.

a negative linear association, no outliers

2. A regional model United Nations was created in 2001. Maggie creates a scatter plot to show the number of students participating in the program from 2001 to 2014. She drew a line of best fit to show the trend. 8.SP.2, 8.SP.3

Part A: Write the numbers that best represent the equation of the line of best fit.

0.3 3 8 10 0.4 4 9 15

$y =$ **3** $x +$ **10**

Part B: Use the equation to make a conjecture about the number of students participating in the model U.N. in 2018.

Sample answer: $y = 3(18) + 10$; $y = 64$; 64 students will participate in 2018.

3. Yoruba surveyed seventh and eighth graders at a school assembly. He found that 39 seventh graders agree with a plan to install larger lockers while 8 do not. Of the 43 eighth graders surveyed, 18 agree with the plan. Complete the two-way table based on this information. 8.SP.4

	Agree	Disagree	Total
Seventh Graders	39	8	47
Eighth Graders	18	25	43
Total	57	33	90

4. The scatter plot shows the heights of mothers and their adult daughters. Write values to complete each statement. 8.SP.1

59 60 62 63 66 68 70 72

There appears to be an outlier at (**60**, **72**).

The data cluster around heights between **63** and **66** inches.

5. Out of 100 students who have a curfew, 76 of them also have a smartphone. Thandeka says, "Of the students in my school who have smartphones, more than $\frac{3}{4}$ of them have a curfew." Is her statement correct? Explain why, or rewrite the statement so it is correct. 8.SP.4

no; Sample answer: Of the students who have a curfew, more than $\frac{3}{4}$ have a smartphone.

6. Pablo plotted data in a scatter plot and drew a line of best fit. The equation for the line of best fit is $G = 8h + 50$, where G represents a student's grade, and h represents the number of hours the student worked on a term paper. Select whether each statement is true or false. 8.SP.2, 8.SP.3

True	False	
■	☐	Pablo's scatter plot shows a positive, linear association.
☐	■	The line of best fit passes through every point in the scatter plot.
☐	■	According to the line of best fit, a classmate who spent 1.5 hours on the report would likely earn a grade of 87.

7. Graph eight points on each coordinate plane to create a scatter plot that matches the given association. 8.SP.1

Sample graphs are shown.

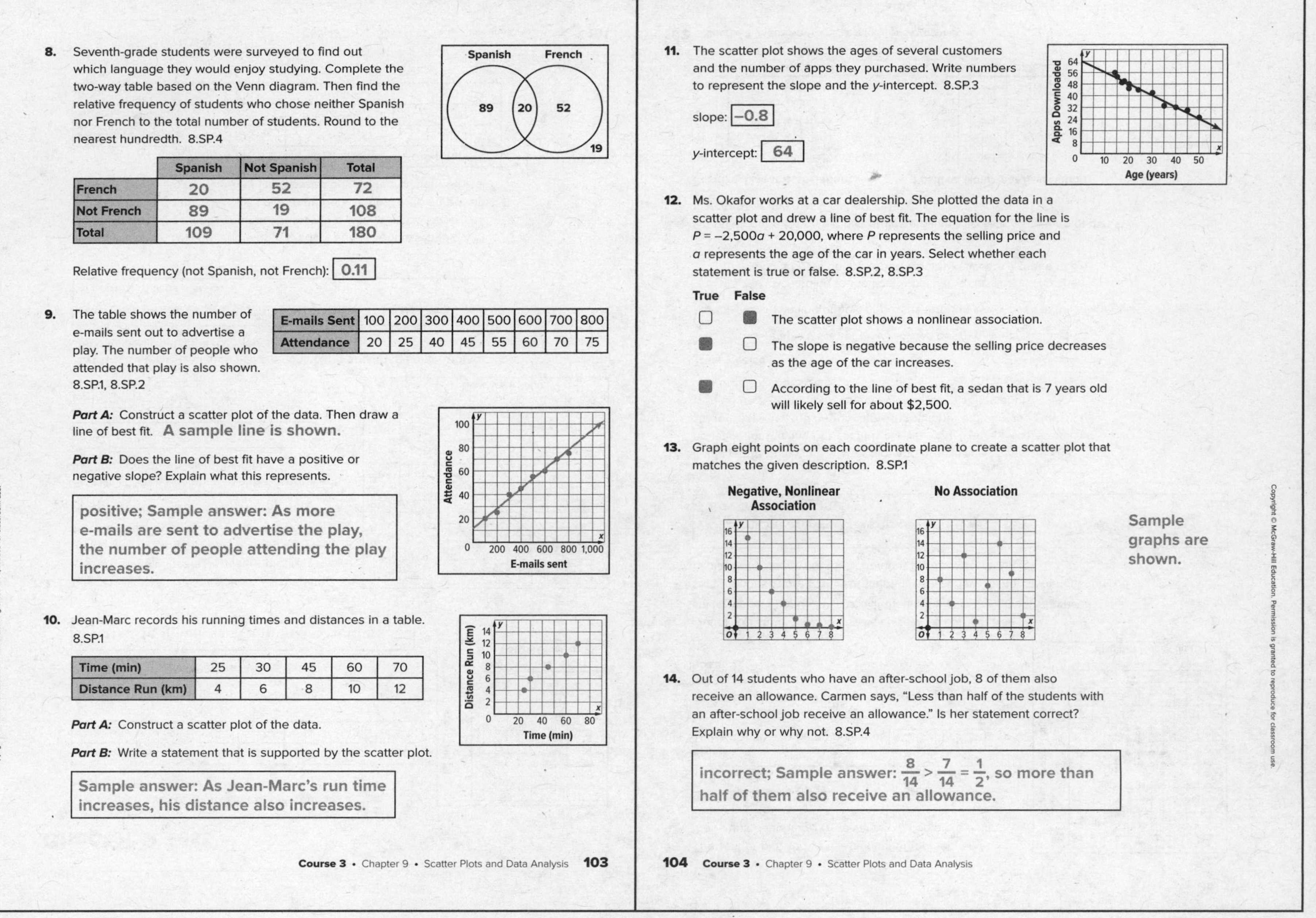

8. Seventh-grade students were surveyed to find out which language they would enjoy studying. Complete the two-way table based on the Venn diagram. Then find the relative frequency of students who chose neither Spanish nor French to the total number of students. Round to the nearest hundredth. 8.SP.4

	Spanish	Not Spanish	Total
French	20	52	72
Not French	89	19	108
Total	109	71	180

Relative frequency (not Spanish, not French): 0.11

9. The table shows the number of e-mails sent out to advertise a play. The number of people who attended that play is also shown. 8.SP.1, 8.SP.2

E-mails Sent	100	200	300	400	500	600	700	800
Attendance	20	25	40	45	55	60	70	75

Part A: Construct a scatter plot of the data. Then draw a line of best fit. **A sample line is shown.**

Part B: Does the line of best fit have a positive or negative slope? Explain what this represents.

positive; Sample answer: As more e-mails are sent to advertise the play, the number of people attending the play increases.

10. Jean-Marc records his running times and distances in a table. 8.SP.1

Time (min)	25	30	45	60	70
Distance Run (km)	4	6	8	10	12

Part A: Construct a scatter plot of the data.

Part B: Write a statement that is supported by the scatter plot.

Sample answer: As Jean-Marc's run time increases, his distance also increases.

11. The scatter plot shows the ages of several customers and the number of apps they purchased. Write numbers to represent the slope and the y-intercept. 8.SP.3

slope: **−0.8**

y-intercept: **64**

12. Ms. Okafor works at a car dealership. She plotted the data in a scatter plot and drew a line of best fit. The equation for the line is $P = -2{,}500a + 20{,}000$, where P represents the selling price and a represents the age of the car in years. Select whether each statement is true or false. 8.SP.2, 8.SP.3

True	False	
☐	■	The scatter plot shows a nonlinear association.
■	☐	The slope is negative because the selling price decreases as the age of the car increases.
■	☐	According to the line of best fit, a sedan that is 7 years old will likely sell for about $2,500.

13. Graph eight points on each coordinate plane to create a scatter plot that matches the given description. 8.SP.1

Sample graphs are shown.

14. Out of 14 students who have an after-school job, 8 of them also receive an allowance. Carmen says, "Less than half of the students with an after-school job receive an allowance." Is her statement correct? Explain why or why not. 8.SP.4

incorrect; Sample answer: $\frac{8}{14} > \frac{7}{14} = \frac{1}{2}$, so more than half of them also receive an allowance.

15. Arturo recorded the number of years of experience and the hourly wages of store employees in the scatter plot. He then used all the points to draw the line shown. 8.SP.1, 8.SP.2

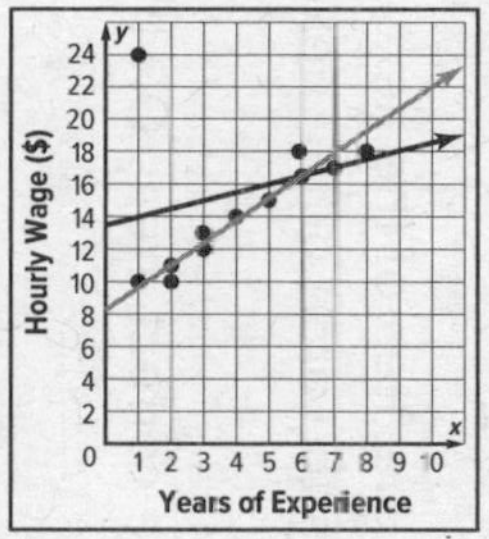

Part A: Explain why Arturo's line is not a good fit for the data and what error he may have made.

Sample answer: The line does not have as many points above it as below it. Arturo may have been considering the outlier (1, 24).

Part B: Draw a line that better fits the data. **A sample line is shown.**

16. The two-way table shows the number of eighth-grade students who participate in school sports and clubs. Complete the table to find the relative frequencies of students in the survey by columns. Round to the nearest hundredth. Then interpret the relative frequencies. 8.SP.4

	Sport	No Sport	Total
Club	52; **0.76**	35; **0.49**	87
No Club	16; **0.24**	37; **0.51**	53
Total	68	72	140

Sample answer: Most students who participate in sports also belong to clubs. Nearly half of the students who do not participate in sports do belong to clubs.

17. Fatima lit a quick-burning candle and recorded its height every 10 minutes as it burned. She created a scatter plot of the data and drew a line of best fit to show the trend. Select whether each statement is true or false. 8.SP.2, 8.SP.3

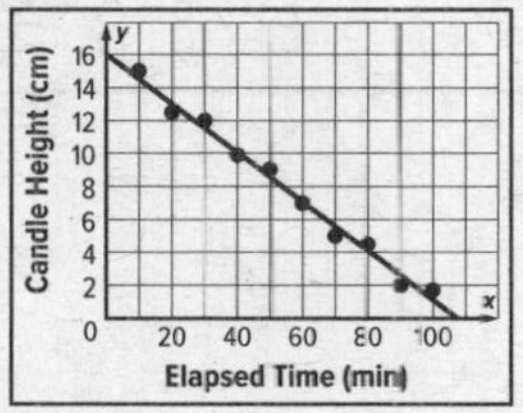

True	False	
■	☐	The y-intercept of the line of best fit is about 16.
■	☐	The candle's height decreases by approximately 0.15 centimeter for each minute the candle burns.
☐	■	After 90 minutes, the height of the candle is approximately 1 centimeter.

18. Seventh-grade students were surveyed to find out if they might be interested in joining the band or chorus. Complete the table based on the Venn diagram. What is the relative frequency of students who chose only chorus to the total number of students? Round to the nearest hundredth. 8.SP.4

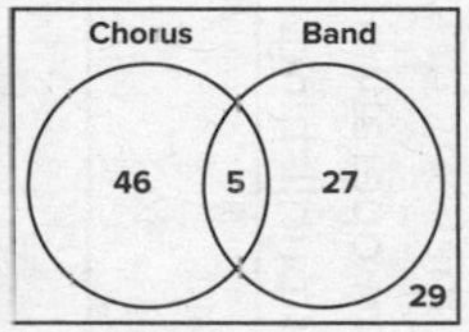

	Chorus	No Chorus	Total
Band	5	27	32
No Band	46	29	75
Total	51	56	107

Relative frequency (only chorus): **0.43**

19. The scatter plot shows the number of hot pretzels and the number of drinks sold each day at a snack stand during baseball games. 8.SP.2, 8.SP.3

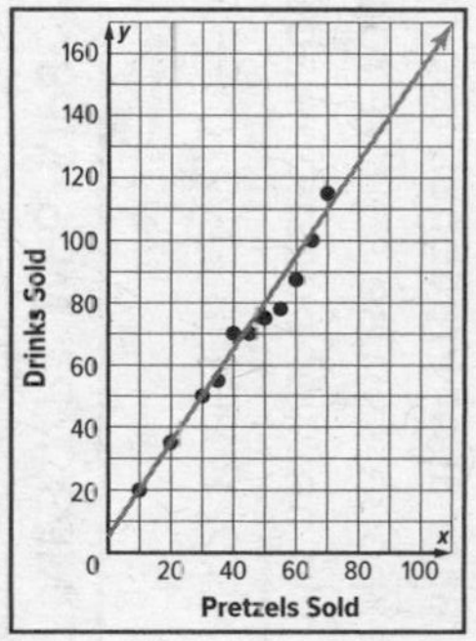

Part A: Graph a line of best fit for these data. **A sample line is shown.**

Part B: Use your line of best fit to find the number of drinks that will be sold when 90 pretzels are sold.

Sample answer: 140 drinks

20. Julieta surveyed eighth-grade students. She found that 35 male students agree with a plan to set aside part of the school yard for a garden, while 23 do not. Of the 83 female students, 61 agree with the plan. Complete the two-way table based on this information. Round to the nearest hundredth. Then find and interpret the relative frequencies of students by column. 8.SP.4

	Agree	Disagree	Total
Male	35; 0.36	**23; 0.51**	**58**
Female	**61; 0.64**	**22; 0.49**	**83**
Total	**96**	**45**	**141**

Sample answer: About two-thirds of the students who agree with the proposal are female. About half of the students who disagree are female, and half are male.

Page 107 • Designing a Newspaper

Task Scenario		
Students will determine if numbers are rational or irrational, use rational approximations of irrational numbers, apply properties of exponents, use square roots, and perform operations with numbers expressed in scientific notation to answer questions about newspaper publishing.		
CCSS Content Standard(s)		8.NS.1, 8.NS.2, 8.EE.1, 8.EE.2, 8.EE.3, 8.EE.4
Mathematical Practices		MP1, MP2, MP3, MP4, MP6, MP8
Depth of Knowledge		DOK2, DOK3, DOK4
Part	**Maximum Points**	**Scoring Rubric**
A	2	Full Credit: $4r^2 = 196$; $r^2 = 49$; $\sqrt{r^2} = \sqrt{49}$; $r = 7$ Each square section has 7 rows with 7 seats in each row. Partial Credit (1 point) will be given for the correct equation OR the correct answer. No credit will be given for an incorrect answer.
B	2	Full Credit: A3: $420 \times 297 = 124{,}740$ mm^2 A4: $297 \times 210 = 62{,}370$ mm^2 A5: $210 \times 148.5 = 31{,}185$ mm^2 $\frac{A5}{A4}: \frac{31{,}185}{62{,}370} = \frac{1}{2} = 2^{-1}$; $\frac{A5}{A3}: \frac{31{,}185}{124{,}740} = \frac{1}{4} = 4^{-1}$ or 2^{-2} Each paper size is one-half (or 2^{-1} times) the area of the next larger size. (Or each paper size is 2 times the area of the next smaller size.) Partial Credit (1 point) will be given for the correct areas OR the correct relationships between the areas. No credit will be given for an incorrect answer.
C	2	Full Credit: The size of A1 will be 2 times the size of A2, and the size of A2 will be 2 times the size of A3. So A1 size = (2)(2)(A3 size) = 4(124,740) = 498,960 mm^2. The size of A7 will be 2^{-1} times the size of A6, and the size of A6 will be 2^{-1} times the size of A5. So A7 size = $(2^{-1})(2^{-1})$(A5 size) = $\frac{1}{4}$(31,185) = 7,796.25 mm^2. Partial Credit (1 point) will be given for correctly calculating one of the areas. No credit will be given for an incorrect answer.

Part	Maximum Points	Scoring Rubric
D	3	Full Credit: The aspect ratio $\sqrt{2}$ is irrational because 2 is not a perfect square. Estimate: $\sqrt{2} \approx 1.41$. The estimate makes sense, because each page size has the same aspect ratio; A3: $\frac{L}{W} \approx \frac{420}{297} \approx 1.41$; A4: $\frac{L}{W} \approx \frac{297}{210} \approx 1.41$; A5: $\frac{L}{W} \approx \frac{210}{148.5} \approx 1.41$ Partial Credit (1 point each) will be given for correctly describing the aspect ratio OR approximating the aspect ratio OR comparing the aspect ratios of the A-series. No credit will be given for an incorrect answer.
E	2	Full Credit: Aspect ratio for letter-sized paper: $\frac{L}{W} = \frac{11}{8.5} \approx 1.29$ Aspect ratio for legal-sized paper: $\frac{L}{W} = \frac{14}{8.5} \approx 1.65$ Sample answer: Since the aspect ratios are different, it will be difficult to use the pages together for a newspaper. The aspect ratio for each paper size is rational because it can be written as a fraction. Partial Credit (1 point) will be given for determining whether the pages can be used together OR whether the aspect ratios are rational or irrational. No credit will be given for an incorrect answer.
F	2	Full Credit: $\frac{\textit{The Sun}}{\textit{Daily Telegraph}}: \frac{2.1 \times 10^6}{5.2 \times 10^5} \approx 0.4 \times 10^1 = 4$ *The Sun's* circulation is about 4 times greater than that of the *Daily Telegraph*. $(9.7 \times 10^5) - (2.2 \times 10^5) = 7.5 \times 10^5$ The *Daily Mirror* sold 7.5×10^5, or 750,000, more copies than the *Financial Times*. Partial Credit (1 point) will be given for the correct circulation comparison OR the correct number of copies. No credit will be given for incorrect answers.
TOTAL	**13**	

Chapter 1 Performance Task

Part A

$\frac{4r^2}{4} = \frac{196}{4}$

$\sqrt{r^2} = \sqrt{49}$

$r = 7$

r = number of rows = 7

Number of seats in each row = 7

Part B

A_3
A = l·w
A = 420(297)
A = 124,740 mm²

A_4
A = l·w
A = 297×210
A = 62,370 mm²

A_5
A = l·w
A = 210(148.5)
A = 31,185 mm²

$A_5 : A_3$
31,185 : 124,740
1 : 4 or $\frac{1}{4}$ or 2^{-2}

$A_5 : A_4$
31185 : 62,370
1 : 2 or $\frac{1}{2}$ or 2^{-1}

If you compare a larger paper to the next smaller size, the area is twice as big as the next smaller size.

Part C

A_1	498,960	$2 \cdot 2 \cdot 2 \cdot 2x = 2^4 x$
A_2	249,480	$2 \cdot 2 \cdot 2x = 2^3 x$
A_3	124,740	$2 \cdot 2x = 2^2 x$
A_4	62,370	$2x = 2^1 x$
A_5	31,185	$x = 2^0 x$
A_6	15592.5	$2^{-1} \cdot x$
A_7	7796.25	$2^{-1} \cdot 2^{-1} \cdot x = 2^{-2} x$

Let x represent the area of A_5

Part D

The aspect ratio of $\sqrt{2}$ is irrational because it cannot be expressed as the ratio of two integers. Rounding, its decimal approximation is 1.41.

A_3 : 420 ÷ 297 = 1.41
A_4 : 297 ÷ 210 = 1.41
A_5 : 210 ÷ 148.5 = 1.41

All of these have an aspect ratio of 1.41.

Part E

Letter : 11 ÷ 8.5 = 1.294
Legal : 14 ÷ 8.5 = 1.647

These two sizes cannot be easily used together because their aspect ratios are different. The aspect ratio for letter paper is rational because it can be expressed as a ratio of 22:17. The aspect ratio of the legal paper is also rational because it is the ratio 28:17.

Part F

The Sun : 2.1×10^6 = 2,100,000 = 2,100,000
The Daily Telegraph = 5.20000 = 520,000
2,100,000 ÷ 520,000 ≈ 4

The circulation of The Sun is about 4 times the circulation of The Daily Telegraph.

Daily Mirror 970,000
Financial Times 220,000

970,000 − 220,000 = 750,000

Approximately 750,000 more issues of the Daily Mirror were sold than the Financial Times.

Chapter 1 Performance Task

Part A

$\frac{196}{4} = \frac{4r^2}{4}$

$49 = r^2$

$24.5 = r$

25 seats in each section with 5 rows each

Part B

Area of $A_3 = 124,740 = 353^2$ ↑ x2 Bigger

Area of $A_4 = 62,370 = 250^2$ ↑ x2 Bigger

Area of $A_5 = 31,185 = 177^2$

Part C

$A_1 = 2 \cdot 2 \cdot (124,740) = 498,960$

$A_7 = 31185 \left(\frac{1}{2}\right)\left(\frac{1}{2}\right) = 7796.25$

Part D

$\sqrt{2}$ is irrational because it never repeats and never ends. $\sqrt{2} = 1.414213562$

Part E

Letter

$\frac{11}{8.5} = 1.294$

irrational
never
repeats
never ends

Legal

$\frac{14}{8.5} = 1.647$

irrational
never repeats
never ends

Part F

Paper	Circulation
The Son	2,100,000
Daily Mirror	970,000
Daily Telegraph	520,000
Financial Times	220,000
The Independent	63,000

Chapter 1 Performance Task

Part A

$196 \div 4 = 49$

7 rows, 7 seats in each row

Part B

$\frac{A_5}{A_3}$ $\frac{31,185}{124,740} = \frac{1}{4} = 4^{-1}$

$\frac{A_5}{A_4}$ $\frac{31,185}{62,370} = \frac{1}{2} = 2^{-1}$

Part C

$\frac{A_5}{A_1}$ $\frac{1}{16}$ $31,185 \times 16 = 498,960 \text{ mm}^2$

$\frac{A_5}{A_7}$ $\frac{1}{\frac{1}{4}}$ $31,185 \times \frac{1}{4} = 7796.25 \text{ mm}^2$

Part D

$\sqrt{2} \approx 1.41$ R

$A_3: 297 \times 1.41 \approx 418.77$ ✓
$A_4: 210 \times 1.41 \approx 296.1$ ✓
$A_5: 148.5 \times 1.41 \approx 209.4$ ✓
} Yes, the A.R. works.

Part E

No, they wouldn't work together because their aspect ratio is not the same.

Part F

Sun + D.T
$2.1 \div .52 = 4$

DM FT
$9.7 \div 2.2 \approx 4.4$

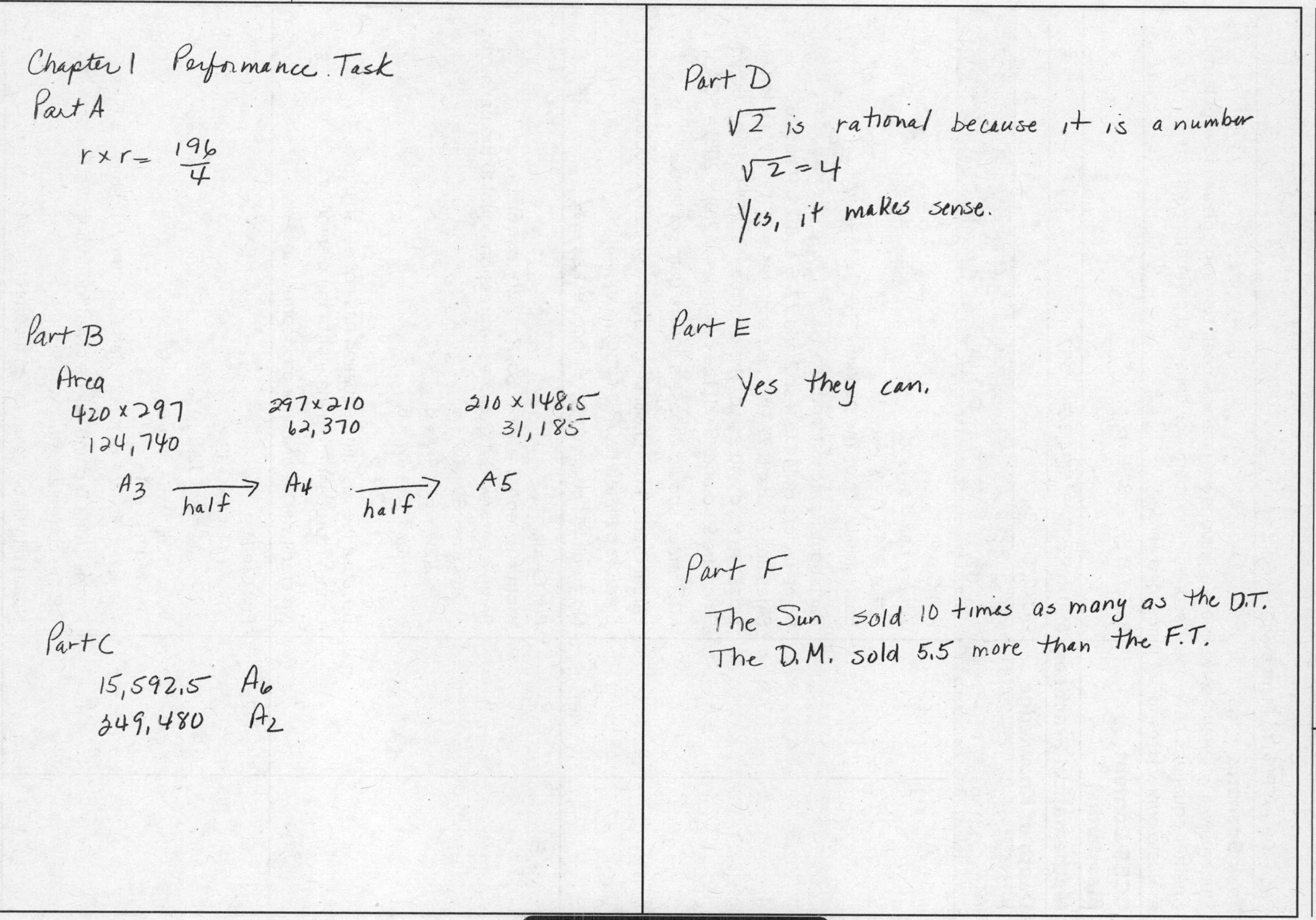
Chapter 1 Performance Task
Part A
r x r = 196/4
Part B
Area
420 x 297
124,740
297 x 210
62,370
210 x 148.5
31,185
A3 half A4 half A5
Part C
15,592.5 A6
249,480 A2
Part D
√2 is rational because it is a number
√2 = 4
Yes, it makes sense.
Part E
Yes they can.
Part F
The Sun sold 10 times as many as the D.T.
The D.M. sold 5.5 more than the F.T.

Student Work Sample

Page 109 • A Plan to Plant a School Garden

Task Scenario Students will write and solve linear equations with rational coefficients in one variable; determine whether equations have one, no, or infinitely many solutions; find perimeters and areas; and evaluate conjectures to set plans for a garden.		
CCSS Content Standard(s)		8.EE.7, 8.EE7a, 8.EE.7b
Mathematical Practices		MP1, MP2, MP3, MP4, MP6, MP7
Depth of Knowledge		DOK2, DOK3
Part	**Maximum Points**	**Scoring Rubric**
A	2	Full Credit: Square patch of land: $A = s^2 = 144$; $s = \sqrt{144} = 12$ Each side is 12 yd. The perimeter is $4(12) = 48$ yd. Rectangular patch of land: Some factors of 144 to test: 2 and 72, 6 and 24, 9 and 16 Sides are 2 yd and 72 yd. The perimeter is $2(2) + 2(72) = 148$ yd. Sides are 6 yd and 24 yd. The perimeter is $2(6) + 2(24) = 60$ yd. Sides are 9 yd and 16 yd. The perimeter is $2(9) + 2(16) = 50$ yd. Ms. Denton should choose a square patch of land. Partial Credit (1 point) will be given for correctly calculating possible perimeters OR a correct explanation. No credit will be given for an incorrect answer.
B	1	Full Credit: width = w, length = $w + 6$; So, $P = 2(w + w + 6)$. Sample answer: Set Corinna's expression equal to the perimeter. $2(w + w + 6) = 4w + 6$ $2(2w + 6) = 4w + 6$ $4w + 12 = 4w + 6$ $12 \neq 6$ Because the resulting equation has no real solutions, $4w + 6$ cannot represent the perimeter of the planter bed. No credit will be given for an incorrect answer.
C	2	Full Credit: $3w + 14 = 4w + 12$ $14 = w + 12$ $2 = w$ The width is 2 ft. The length is $(w + 6)$ ft from Part B. So the length is $2 + 6$, or 8 ft. Partial Credit (1 point) will be given for finding the correct width OR the correct length. No credit will be given for an incorrect answer.

Part	Maximum Points	Scoring Rubric
D	2	Full Credit: Company A: $12.5b + 50$; Company B: $11b + 95$ $12.5b + 50 = 11b + 95$ $1.5b + 50 = 95$ $1.5b = 45$ $b = 30$ Cost of 30 bags: A: $12.5(30) + 50 = 425$; B: $11(30) + 95 = 425$ Both companies charge $425 for 30 bags of compost. Partial Credit (1 point) will be given for correct number of bags OR the total cost. No credit will be given for an incorrect answer.
E	2	Full Credit: The fencing is the perimeter. $2(2x + 1) + 3x + 1 = 52$ $4x + 2 + 3x + 1 = 52$ $7x + 3 = 52$ $7x = 49$ $x = 7$ Leg length: $2(7) + 1 = 15$ feet Area of 1 flower bed: $A = \frac{1}{2}bh = \frac{1}{2}(15)(15) = 112.5$ ft^2 Area of 4 corner flower beds: $112.5(4) = 450$ ft^2 Partial Credit (1 point) will be given for the correct leg length OR correct area of 4 flower beds. No credit will be given for an incorrect answer.
F	2	Full Credit: Company B: $11b + 95$, where b represents number of bags $11b + 95 = 304$ $11b = 209$ $b = 19$ 19 bags are needed to cover the flower beds. $19 \div 4 = 4.75$; Each flower bed needs 4.75 bags. Cost from Company A for 19 bags: $12.5b + 50 = 12.5(19) + 50 = 237.5 + 50 = 287.5$ It costs $287.50 from Company A for 19 bags. $287.50 < $304, so, Company A is less expensive. Partial Credit (1 point) will be given for the correct number of bags for each flower bed OR the final answer and explanation. No credit will be given for an incorrect answer.
TOTAL	**11**	

Chapter 2 Performance Task

Part A

Area is 144 square yards.

Square land:
$A = s^2 = 144$; $s = \sqrt{144} = 12$
Side is 12 yd.
Perimeter is $4(12) = 48$ yd.

Rectangular land:
Factors of 144:
2 and 72: Perimeter is $2(2) + 2(72) = 148$ yd.
6 and 24: Perimeter is $2(6) + 2(24) = 60$ yd.
9 and 16: Perimeter is $2(9) + 2(16) = 50$ yd.

A square patch of land has smaller perimeter.

Part B

width = w; length = w + 6; so, $P = 2(w + w + 6)$.

perimeter $\stackrel{?}{=}$ Corinna's expression

$$2(w+w+6) = 4w + 6$$
$$2(2w+6) = 4w + 6$$
$$4w + 12 = 4w + 6$$
$$-4w \quad -4w$$
$$12 \neq 6$$

Expressions are not equal.

Part C

Perimeters are equal.

$$3w + 14 = 4w + 12$$
$$-3w \quad -3w$$
$$14 = w + 12$$
$$-12 \quad -12$$
$$2 = w$$

The width is 2 ft.
The length is (w+6) ft from Part B.
The length is 2+6, or 8 ft.

Part D

Company A: $12.5b + 50$; Company B: $11b + 95$

$$12.5b + 50 = 11b + 95$$
$$-11b \quad -11b$$
$$1.5b + 50 = 95$$
$$-50 \quad -50$$
$$1.5b = 45$$
$$\frac{1.5b}{1.5} = \frac{45}{1.5}$$
$$b = 30 \text{ bags}$$

Cost of 30 bags:
A: $12.5(30) + 50 = 425$
B: $11(30) + 95 = 425$

Both companies charge $425 for 30 bags of compost.

Part E

The fencing is the perimeter.

$$2(2x+1) + 3x + 1 = 52$$
$$4x + 2 + 3x + 1 = 52$$
$$7x + 3 = 52$$
$$-3 \quad -3$$
$$7x = 49$$
$$x = 7$$

Leg length: $2(7) + 1 = 15$ feet

Area of 1 flowerbed:
$A = \frac{1}{2}bh = \frac{1}{2}(15)(15) = 112.5 \text{ ft}^2$

Area of 4 flowerbeds:
$112.5(4) = 450 \text{ ft}^2$

Total area of flowerbeds: 450 ft^2

Part F

Company B: $11b + 95$

$$11b + 95 = 304$$
$$-95 \quad -95$$
$$11b = 209$$
$$b = 19$$

19 bags are needed to cover the 4 flowerbeds.

$19 \div 4 = 4.75$

Each flowerbed needs 4.75 bags.

Cost from Company A for 19 bags:
$12.5b + 50 = 12.5(19) + 50 = 237.5 + 50 = 287.5$

Company A costs $287.50.

$287.50 < 304$, so Company A is less expensive.

Chapter 2 Performance Task

(Part A)

Area = 144 sq ft

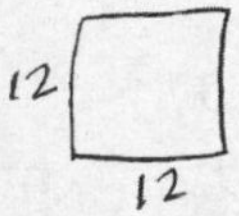

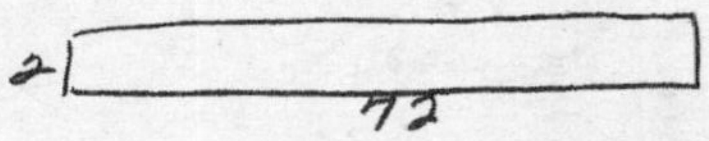

$P = 4(12) = 48$ $\quad$ $P = 2 + 72 + 2 + 72 = 148$

Square has shorter perimeter.

(Part B)

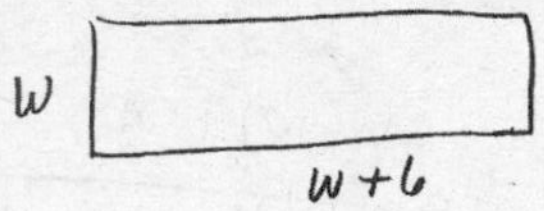

Perimeter $= w + w + (w+6) + (w+6)$
$= (4w+12)$ feet

(Part C)

$3w + 14 = 4w + 12$
$-4w$
$-1w + 14 = 12$
-14
$-1w = -2$
$w = 2$

Width is 2 ft.
Perimeter is
$3(2)+14 = 6+14 = 20$ ft.

(Part D)

b = number of bags

$11b + 95 = 12.5b + 50$
$-12.5b \qquad -12.5b$
$-1.5b + 95 = 50$
$-95 \qquad -95$
$-1.5b = -45$
$b = 30$

30 bags

(Part E)

Perimeter = 52
$(2x+1) + (2x+1) + (3x+1) = 52$
$7x + 3 = 52$
$7x = 49$
$x = 7$

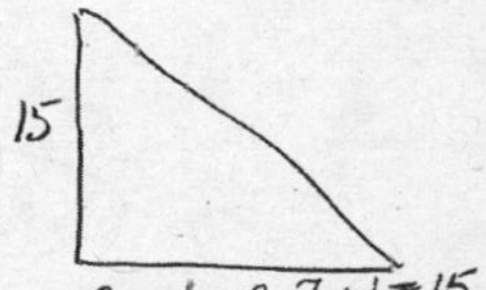

$2x+1 = 2 \cdot 7 + 1 = 15$

area $= \frac{1}{2}(15)(15) = 112.5$
area of 4 Δs $= 4(112.5)$
$= 450$

450 square feet

(Part F)

$11b + 95 = 304$
-95
$\frac{11b}{11} = \frac{209}{11}$
$b = 19$

19 bags

Student Work Sample

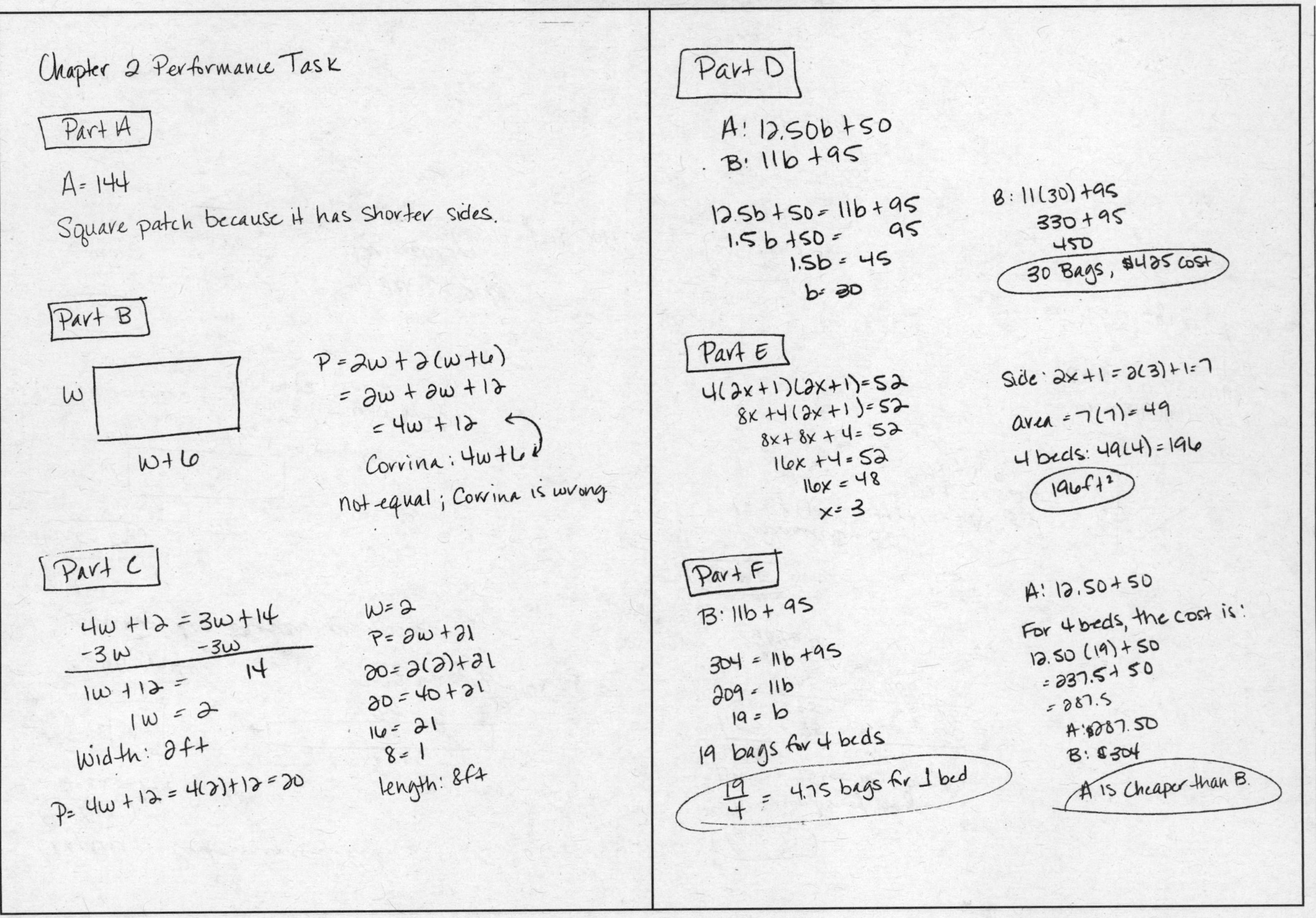
Chapter 2 Performance Task
Part A
A = 144
Square patch because it has shorter sides.
Part B
w
w + 6
P = 2w + 2(w + 6)
= 2w + 2w + 12
= 4w + 12
Corrina: 4w + 6
not equal; Corrina is wrong
Part C
4w + 12 = 3w + 14
-3w -3w
1w + 12 = 14
1w = 2
Width: 2 ft
P = 4w + 12 = 4(2) + 12 = 20
w = 2
P = 2w + 2l
20 = 2(2) + 2l
20 = 4 + 2l
16 = 2l
8 = l
length: 8 ft
Part D
A: 12.50b + 50
B: 11b + 95
12.5b + 50 = 11b + 95
1.5b + 50 = 95
1.5b = 45
b = 30
B: 11(30) + 95
330 + 95
450
30 Bags, $425 cost
Part E
4(2x + 1)(2x + 1) = 52
8x + 4(2x + 1) = 52
8x + 8x + 4 = 52
16x + 4 = 52
16x = 48
x = 3
Side: 2x + 1 = 2(3) + 1 = 7
area = 7(7) = 49
4 beds: 49(4) = 196
196 ft²
Part F
B: 11b + 95
304 = 11b + 95
209 = 11b
19 = b
19 bags for 4 beds
19/4 = 4.75 bags fr 1 bed
A: 12.50 + 50
For 4 beds, the cost is:
12.50 (19) + 50
= 237.5 + 50
= 287.5
A: $287.50
B: $304
A is cheaper than B.

Chapter 2 Performance Task

PART A

Area = 144

rectangle

PART B

width: w
length: w + 6

perimeter: 2(w) + 2(w) + 6
4w + 6

Corrina: (4w + 6) = 4w + 6 ✓

PART C

4w + 12
−3w + 14
1w − 2

width: w − 2 ft

PART D

$(12.5 + 50)b = (11 + 95)b$

$\frac{62.5b}{62.5} = \frac{106b}{62.5}$

$b = 1.696$

2 bags
(12.50 + 50)(2)
(62.5)(2)
125
$125

PART E

54
× 4
208

208 sq ft

PART F

f = flowerbed
4f = $304
f = $304 ÷ 4 = $76

$76 for 1 flowerbed from Company B

Comp B: $(11 + 95)b = 76$

$\frac{106b}{106} = \frac{76}{106}$

$b \approx 0.72$

0.72 bag for 1 flowerbed

Comp. A: (12.5 + 50)(0.72)
= 62.5(0.72)
= 45
$45

Page 111 • Managing a Team

Task Scenario		
Students will write, analyze, and graph linear equations and systems of linear equations to solve problems involving data related to a basketball team.		
CCSS Content Standard(s)		8.EE.5, 8.EE.6, 8.EE.8, 8.EE.8a, 8.EE.8b, 8.EE.8c, 8.F.2, 8.F.3, 8.F.4, 8.F.5
Mathematical Practices		MP1, MP2, MP3, MP4, MP6, MP7
Depth of Knowledge		DOK2, DOK3
Part	**Maximum Points**	**Scoring Rubric**
A	3	Full Credit: Slope: Any 2 points in the table can be used to compute the slope. A sample is shown. $\frac{900-0}{5-0} = 180$ *y*-intercept: 0 Equation: $y = 180x$ Sample graph: 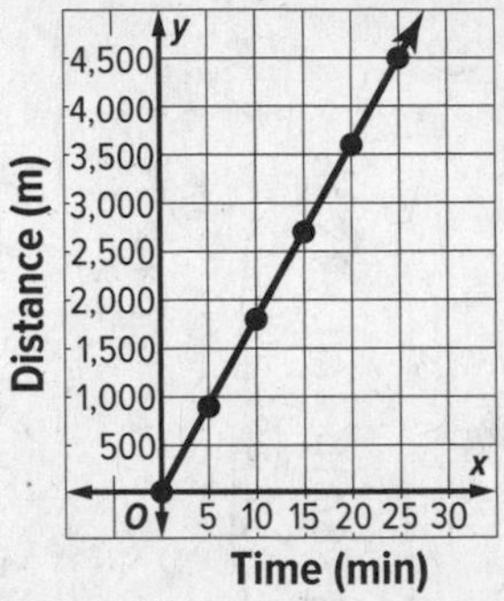 Sample answer: The graph and the equation show that the slope is the same for any two points. So Damon ran at the same speed during the entire run, not faster in the beginning. Partial Credit (2 points) will be given for 2 of these 3 answers: the correct equation OR the correct graph OR an appropriate explanation for why Damon is incorrect. Partial Credit (1 point) will be given for 1 of the 3 answers listed above. No credit will be given for an incorrect answer.
B	2	Full Credit: The slope of the line is $\frac{5-2}{20-8} = \frac{3}{12} = \frac{1}{4}$. The slope represents points scored per minute. For every 4 minutes Talia plays, she scores about 1 point. Partial Credit (1 point) will be given for the correct slope without an explanation. No credit will be given for an incorrect answer.

Part	Maximum Points	Scoring Rubric
C	3	Full Credit: System of equations: $y = 22x + 100$, $y = 30x$ Sample graph: Sports Shoppe offers a lower price for 11 uniforms. Sample check by substitution: $30x = 22x + 100$; $8x = 100$; $x = 12.5$ $y = 30(12.5) = 375$ The solution is (12.5, 375), where the costs are the same. The Sports Shoppe is cheaper for 12 or fewer uniforms. Partial Credit (1 point) will be given for each of these 3 answers: the correct system OR the correct graph OR the correct store to use and checking the answer. No credit will be given for an incorrect answer.
D	2	Full Credit: 11(2) = 22 uniforms will be needed. The solution of the system is (12.5, 375). When 13 or more uniforms are ordered, the Uni-Forme Company is cheaper. Uni-Forme: $y = 22x + 100 = 22(22) + 100 = \$584$ Sports Shoppe: $y = 30x = 30(22) = \$660$ Amount saved: 660 – 584 = \$76 Partial Credit (1 point) will be given for the correct company OR the correct amount of money saved. No credit will be given for an incorrect answer.
E	3	Full Credit: slope $= \frac{30 - 0}{40 - 20} = \frac{3}{2} = 1.5$, y-intercept $= -30$ equation: $y = 1.5x - 30$ slope: the selling price per muffin, \$1.50 y-intercept: the \$30 debt for buying 60 muffins The x-intercept at (20, 0) shows that José must sell more than 20 muffins to make a profit. Partial Credit (1 point) will be given for each of these 3 answers: the correct equation OR descriptions of slope and y-intercept OR the correct profit point. No credit will be given for an incorrect answer.
TOTAL	**13**	

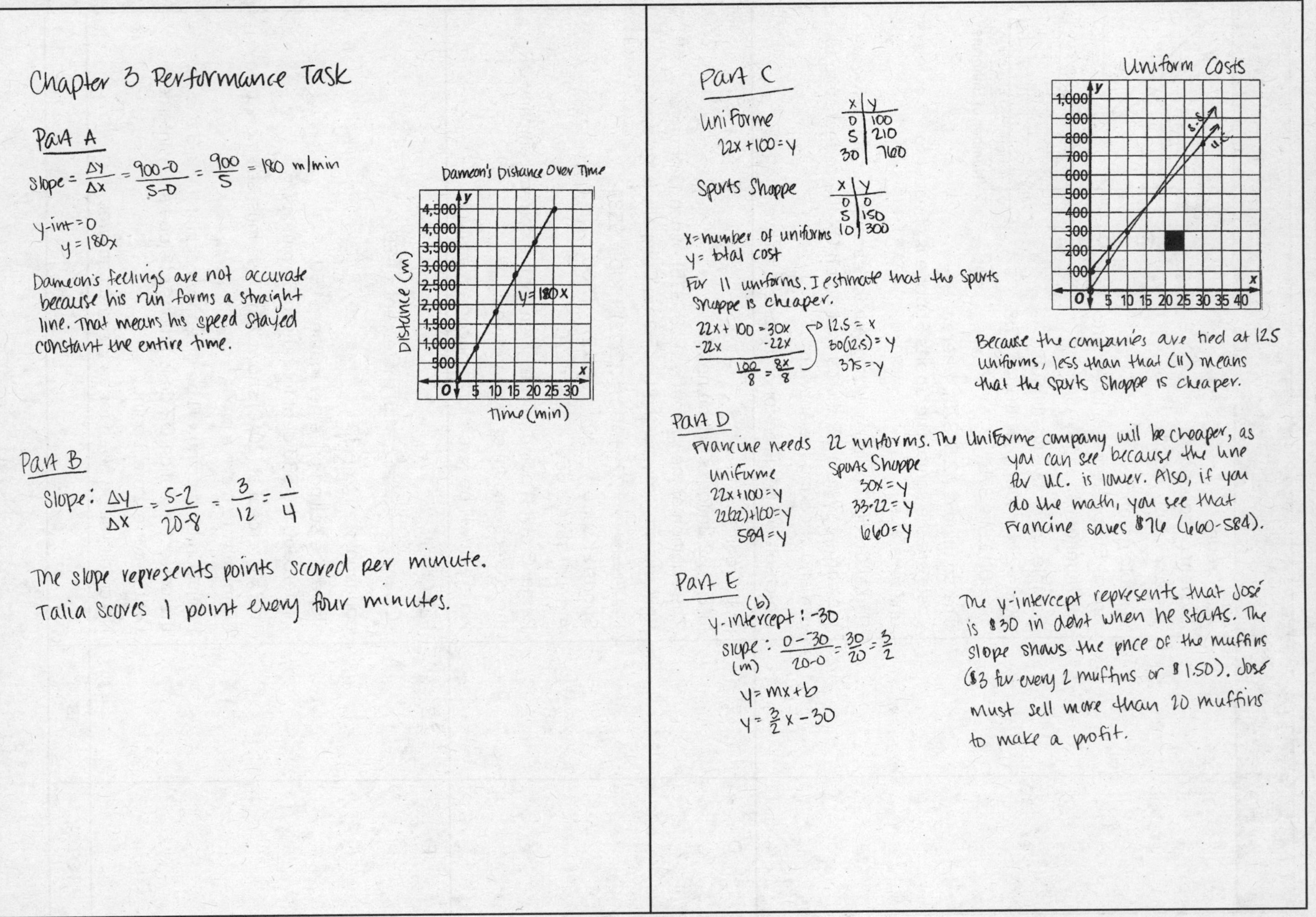

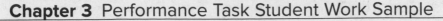

Chapter 3 Performance Task

Part A

slope = $\frac{\Delta y}{\Delta x} = \frac{900-0}{5-0} = \frac{900}{5} = 180$ m/min

y-int = 0
y = 180x

Dameon's feelings are not accurate because his run forms a straight line. That means his speed stayed constant the entire time.

Part B

Slope: $\frac{\Delta y}{\Delta x} = \frac{5-2}{20-8} = \frac{3}{12} = \frac{1}{4}$

The slope represents points scored per minute.
Talia scores 1 point every four minutes.

Part C

Uniforme
22x + 100 = y

x	y
0	100
5	210
30	760

Sports Shoppe

x	y
0	0
5	150
10	300

x = number of uniforms
y = total cost

For 11 uniforms, I estimate that the Sports Shoppe is cheaper.

22x + 100 = 30x
−22x −22x
$\frac{100}{8} = \frac{8x}{8}$
12.5 = x
30(12.5) = y
375 = y

Because the companies are tied at 12.5 uniforms, less than that (11) means that the Sports Shoppe is cheaper.

Part D

Francine needs 22 uniforms. The Uniforme company will be cheaper, as you can see because the line for U.C. is lower. Also, if you do the math, you see that Francine saves \$76 (660−584).

Uniforme
22x + 100 = y
22(22) + 100 = y
584 = y

Sports Shoppe
30x = y
33·22 = y
660 = y

Part E

(b) y-intercept: −30
slope (m): $\frac{0-(-30)}{20-0} = \frac{30}{20} = \frac{3}{2}$
y = mx + b
y = $\frac{3}{2}$x − 30

The y-intercept represents that José is \$30 in debt when he starts. The slope shows the price of the muffins (\$3 for every 2 muffins or \$1.50). José must sell more than 20 muffins to make a profit.

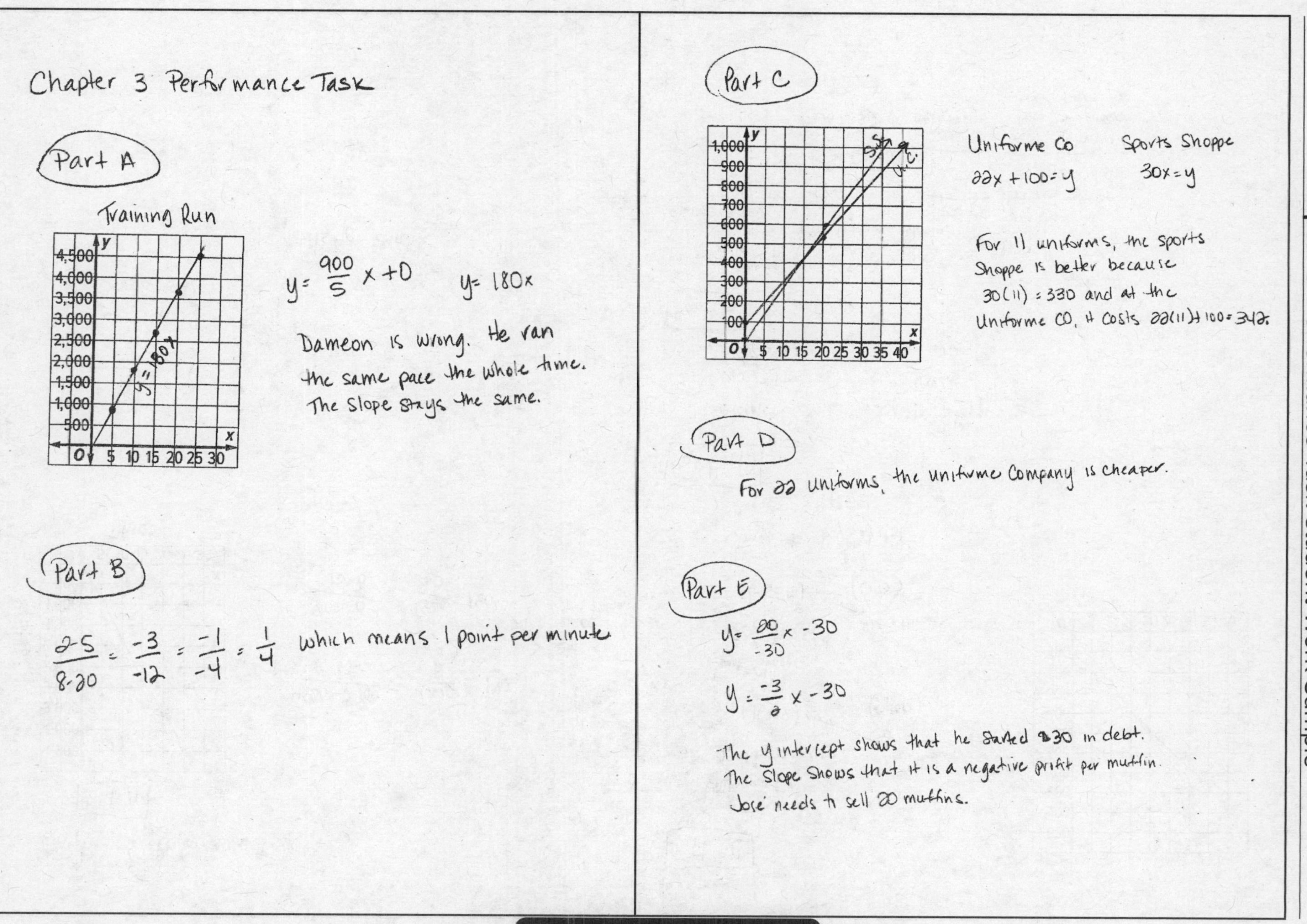
Chapter 3 Performance Task

Part A

Training Run

$y = \frac{900}{5}x + 0$ $y = 180x$

Dameon is wrong. He ran the same pace the whole time. The slope stays the same.

Part B

$\frac{2-5}{8-20} = \frac{-3}{-12} = \frac{-1}{-4} = \frac{1}{4}$ which means 1 point per minute

Part C

Uniforme Co   Sports Shoppe

$22x + 100 = y$ $30x = y$

For 11 uniforms, the Sports Shoppe is better because $30(11) = 330$ and at the Uniforme Co, it costs $22(11) + 100 = 342$.

Part D

For 22 uniforms, the Uniforme Company is cheaper.

Part E

$y = \frac{20}{-30}x - 30$

$y = \frac{-3}{2}x - 30$

The y intercept shows that he started $30 in debt. The slope shows that it is a negative profit per muffin. Jose needs to sell 20 muffins.

Student Work Sample

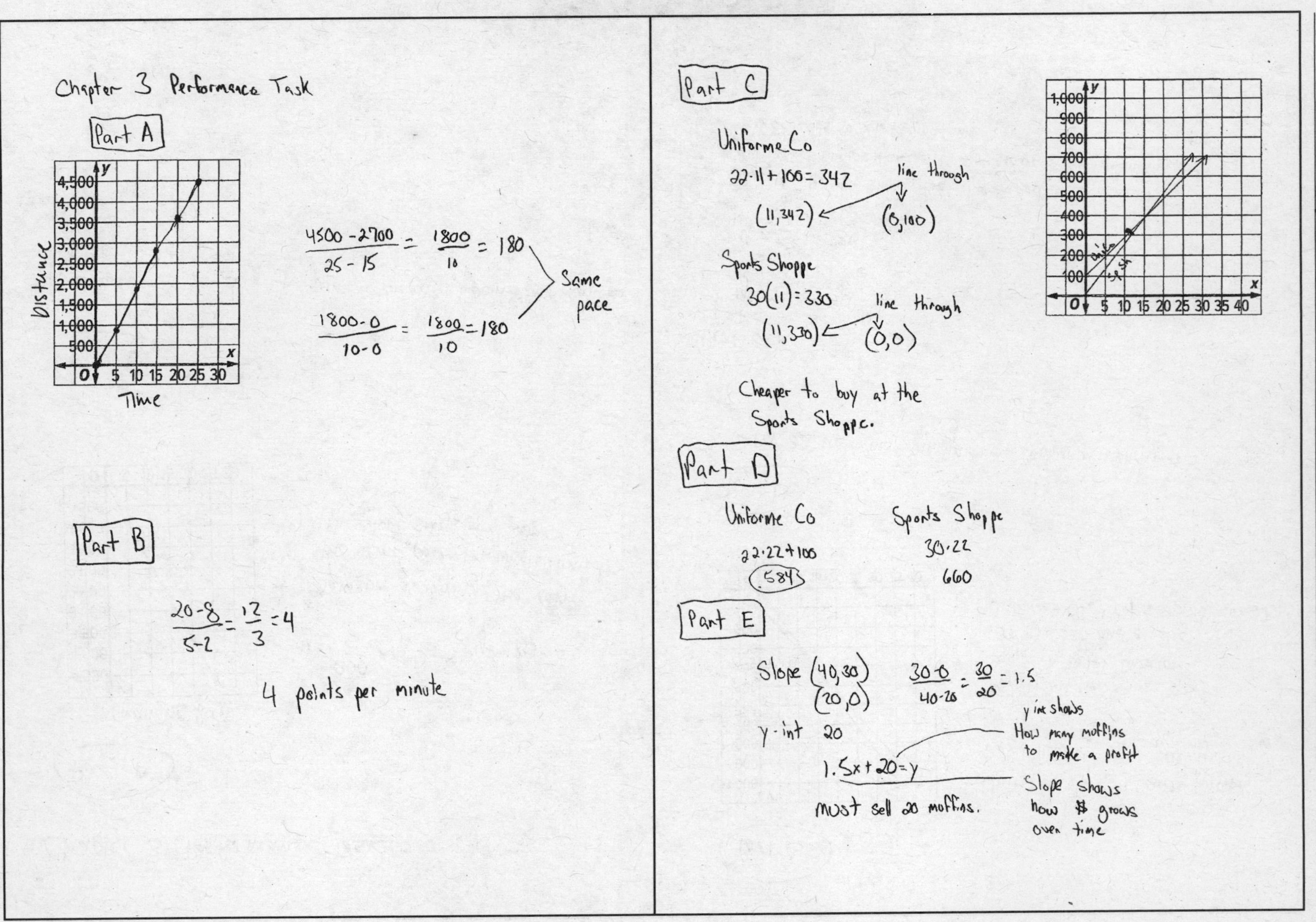
Chapter 3 Performance Task
Part A
Distance
Time
4500 - 2700 / 25 - 15 = 1800 / 10 = 180
1800 - 0 / 10 - 0 = 1800 / 10 = 180
Same pace
Part B
20 - 8 / 5 - 2 = 12 / 3 = 4
4 points per minute
Part C
Uniforme Co
22·11 + 100 = 342
(11,342)
line through (0,100)
Sports Shoppe
30(11) = 330
(11,330)
line through (0,0)
Cheaper to buy at the Sports Shoppe.
Part D
Uniforme Co
22·22+100
584
Sports Shoppe
30·22
660
Part E
Slope (40,30) (20,0)
30-0 / 40-20 = 30 / 20 = 1.5
y-int 20
1.5x + 20 = y
y int shows How many muffins to make a profit
Slope shows how $ grows over time
Must sell 20 muffins.

Chapter 3 Performance Task

Part A

Yes, Damcon gets faster because the numbers keep going up.

Up 2 over 1 $\quad y = \frac{2}{1}x$

Part B

over 6 up 3 $\quad$ slope $= \frac{6}{3} = 2$

The slope is the rise over the run.

Part C

U.C. = $100x + 22 = 100 \times 11 + 22 = 1122$

S.S. = $30x = 30 \times 11 = 330$ (circled)

Cheaper

Part D

U.C. $100(22) + 22 = 2200 + 22 = 2222$

S.S. $= 30(22) = 660$ ★

Part E

$\frac{2}{3}$ = slope

$30 + \frac{2}{3}y = x$

Must sell 60 muffins to make $60.

Student Work Sample

Page 113 • Saving for College

<table>
<tr><td colspan="3">Task Scenario
Students will interpret the equation $y = mx + b$ as defining a linear function, create tables of values and graphs to represent linear functions, compare two functions represented in different ways, determine and interpret the rate of change and initial value of a function, and make a qualitative graph to solve problems about saving money for a college education.</td></tr>
<tr><td colspan="2">CCSS Content Standard(s)</td><td>8.F.1, 8.F.2, 8.F.3, 8.F.4, 8.F.5</td></tr>
<tr><td colspan="2">Mathematical Practices</td><td>MP1, MP2, MP3, MP4, MP6</td></tr>
<tr><td colspan="2">Depth of Knowledge</td><td>DOK2, DOK3</td></tr>
<tr><th>Part</th><th>Maximum Points</th><th>Scoring Rubric</th></tr>
<tr><td>A</td><td>2</td><td>Full Credit:
Sample answer: The equation shows that $500 is the initial amount in the bank account. The interest is added to that amount to get the total amount in the account after x years.

The equation simplifies to $y = 20x + 500$, which is in the form $y = mx + b$. So, it is a linear function.

Partial Credit (1 point) will be given for explaining the equation OR reasoning that it is a linear function.

No credit will be given for an incorrect answer.</td></tr>
<tr><td>B</td><td>3</td><td>Full Credit:
Sample table:
<table>
<tr><th colspan="2">Simple Interest</th></tr>
<tr><th>x (years)</th><th>y (total $)</th></tr>
<tr><td>0</td><td>500</td></tr>
<tr><td>1</td><td>520</td></tr>
<tr><td>3</td><td>560</td></tr>
<tr><td>6</td><td>620</td></tr>
<tr><td>12</td><td>740</td></tr>
<tr><td>18</td><td>860</td></tr>
</table>
Savings Accounts
Compound Interest
Simple Interest
Amount in Account ($)
Time (years)

The simple interest graph is increasing and is a linear function. It has a constant rate of change ($m = 20$). The compound interest graph is also increasing but is a nonlinear function and has a variable rate of change (for example: $m_{0-1} = 20.37$, $m_{3-6} = 23.91$).

Partial Credit (1 point) will be given for each of these 3: the correct table OR the correct graph OR an accurate comparison.

No credit will be given for an incorrect answer.</td></tr>
</table>

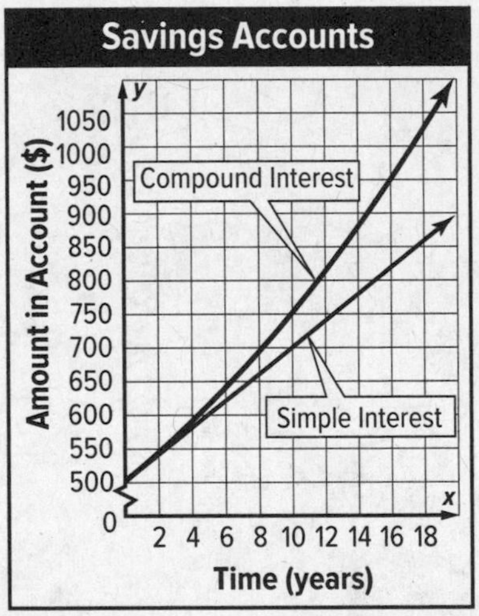

<table>
<tr><th>Part</th><th>Maximum Points</th><th>Scoring Rubric</th></tr>
<tr><td>C</td><td>2</td><td>Full Credit:
Sample answer:
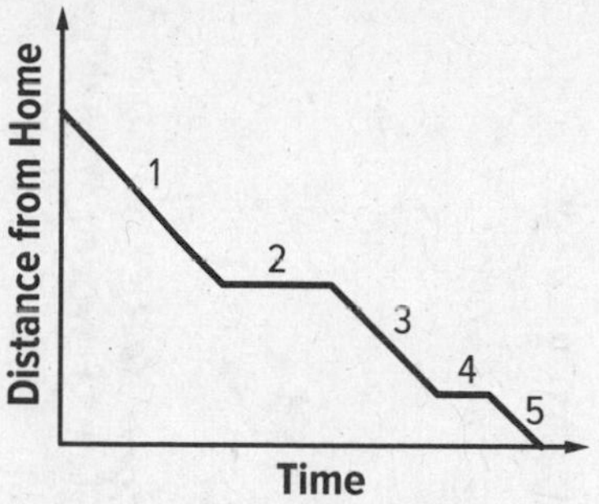

Key:
1. Mrs. Sanchez drives halfway home to get to the crafts store.
2. She spends time at the crafts store shopping.
3. She continues on to the bank, which is close to home.
4. She spends less time at the bank than at the crafts store.
5. Finally, she drives the rest of the way home.
Partial Credit (1 point) will be given for creating the graph but failing to create a key.
No credit will be given for an incorrect answer.</td></tr>
<tr><td>D</td><td>4</td><td>Full Credit:
Sample answer:
The slope represents the profit for selling each bracelet: $2.25. The y-intercept represents the amount spent to start the business: –$200.
Break even: $y = 0$, so $0 = 2.25x - 200$ and $x \approx 88.89$; they must sell 89 bracelets.
Make $1,000: $y = 1{,}000$, so $1{,}000 = 2.25x - 200$ and $x \approx 533.3$; they must sell 534 bracelets.
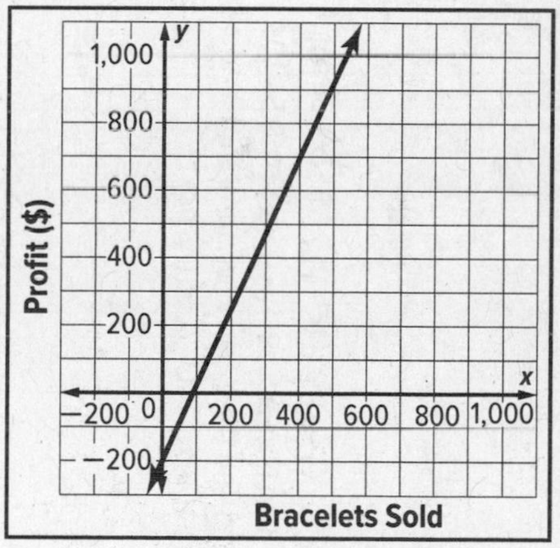

Sell 1,000 bracelets: $y = 2.25(1{,}000) - 200 = 2{,}050$; they will make $2,050.
Partial Credit (1 point) will be given for each of these 4: the correct graph and explanation of slope and y-intercept OR the correct break-even sales OR the correct number of bracelets for $1,000 OR the correct sales on 1,000 bracelets.
No credit will be given for an incorrect answer.</td></tr>
<tr><td>TOTAL</td><td>11</td><td></td></tr>
</table>

Performance Task Rubrics

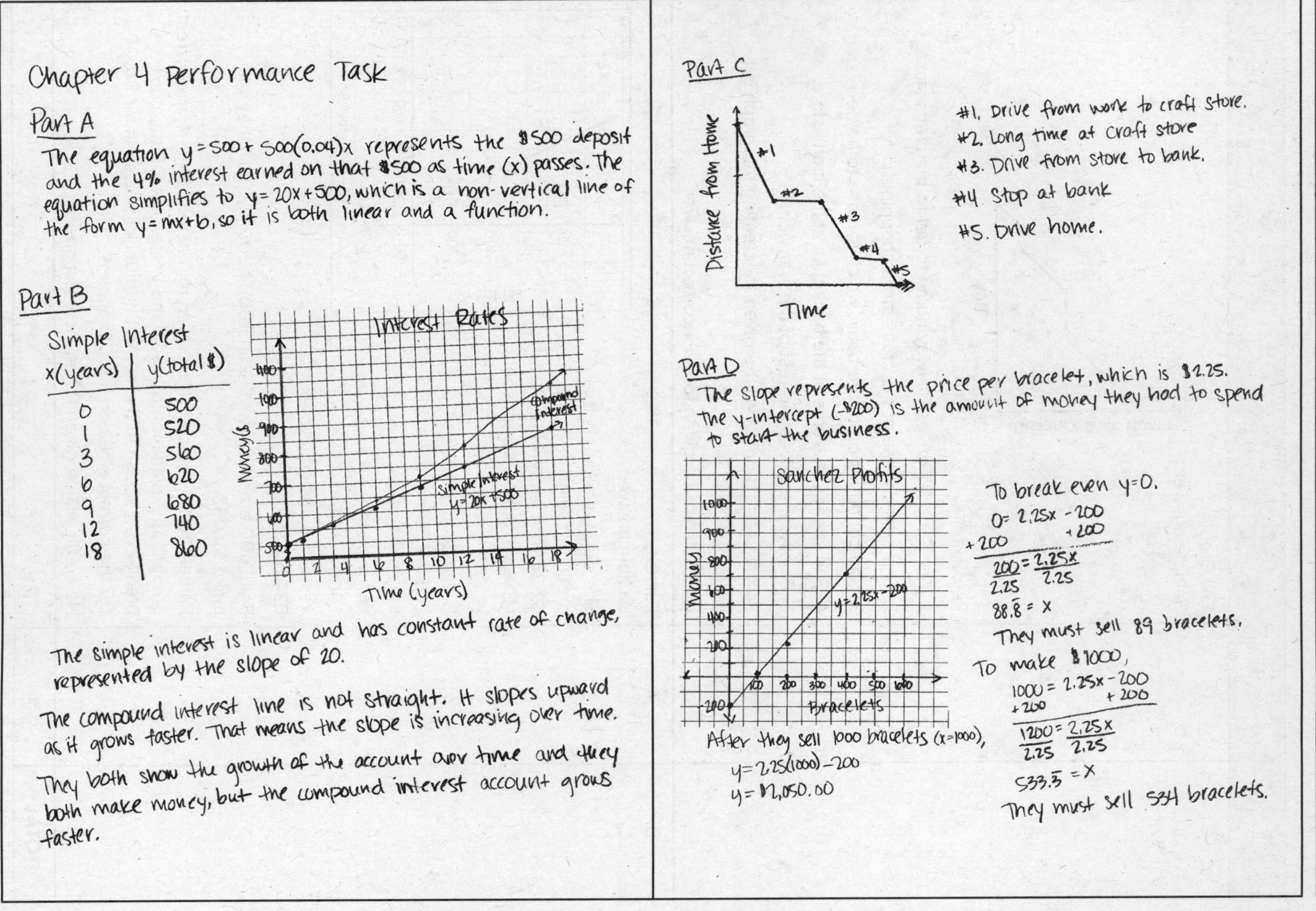
Chapter 4 Performance Task
Part A
The equation y = 500 + 500(0.04)x represents the $500 deposit and the 4% interest earned on that $500 as time (x) passes. The equation simplifies to y = 20x + 500, which is a non-vertical line of the form y = mx + b, so it is both linear and a function.
Part B
Simple Interest
x(years) | y(total $)
0 | 500
1 | 520
3 | 560
6 | 620
9 | 680
12 | 740
18 | 860
Interest Rates
Money($)
Time (years)
Compound Interest
Simple Interest
y = 20x + 500
The simple interest is linear and has constant rate of change, represented by the slope of 20.
The compound interest line is not straight. It slopes upward as it grows faster. That means the slope is increasing over time.
They both show the growth of the account over time and they both make money, but the compound interest account grows faster.
Part C
Distance from Home
Time
#1. Drive from work to craft store.
#2. Long time at craft store
#3. Drive from store to bank.
#4 Stop at bank
#5. Drive home.
Part D
The slope represents the price per bracelet, which is $2.25.
The y-intercept (-$200) is the amount of money they had to spend to start the business.
Sanchez Profits
Money
Bracelets
y = 2.25x - 200
To break even y = 0.
0 = 2.25x - 200
+200 +200
200/2.25 = 2.25x/2.25
88.8̄ = x
They must sell 89 bracelets.
To make $1000,
1000 = 2.25x - 200
+200 +200
1200/2.25 = 2.25x/2.25
533.3̄ = x
They must sell 534 bracelets.
After they sell 1000 bracelets (x=1000),
y = 2.25(1000) - 200
y = $2,050.00

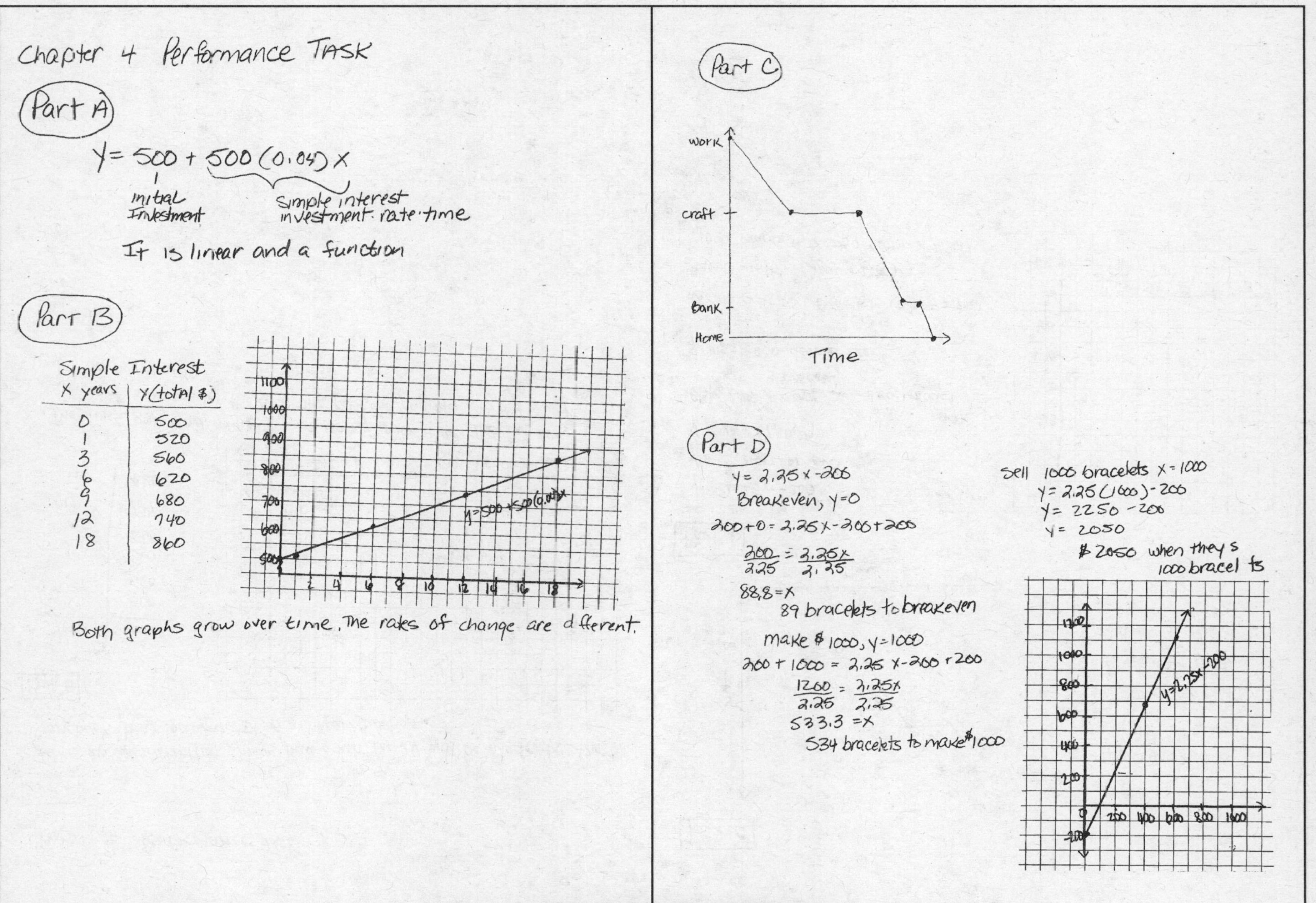

Chapter 4 Performance Task
Part A
y = 500 + 500 (0.04) x
initial Investment
simple interest
investment · rate · time
It is linear and a function
Part B
Simple Interest
x years
y (total $)
0 500
1 520
3 560
6 620
9 680
12 740
18 860
y=500+500(0.04)x
Both graphs grow over time. The rates of change are different.
Part C
work
craft
Bank
Home
Time
Part D
y = 2.25x − 200
Breakeven, y=0
200+0 = 2.25x − 200 + 200
200/2.25 = 2.25x/2.25
88.8 = x
89 bracelets to breakeven
make $1000, y=1000
200 + 1000 = 2.25x − 200 + 200
1200/2.25 = 2.25x/2.25
533.3 = x
534 bracelets to make $1000
sell 1000 bracelets x=1000
y = 2.25(1000) − 200
y = 2250 − 200
y = 2050
$2050 when they s
1000 bracel ts
y=2.25x−200

Student Work Sample

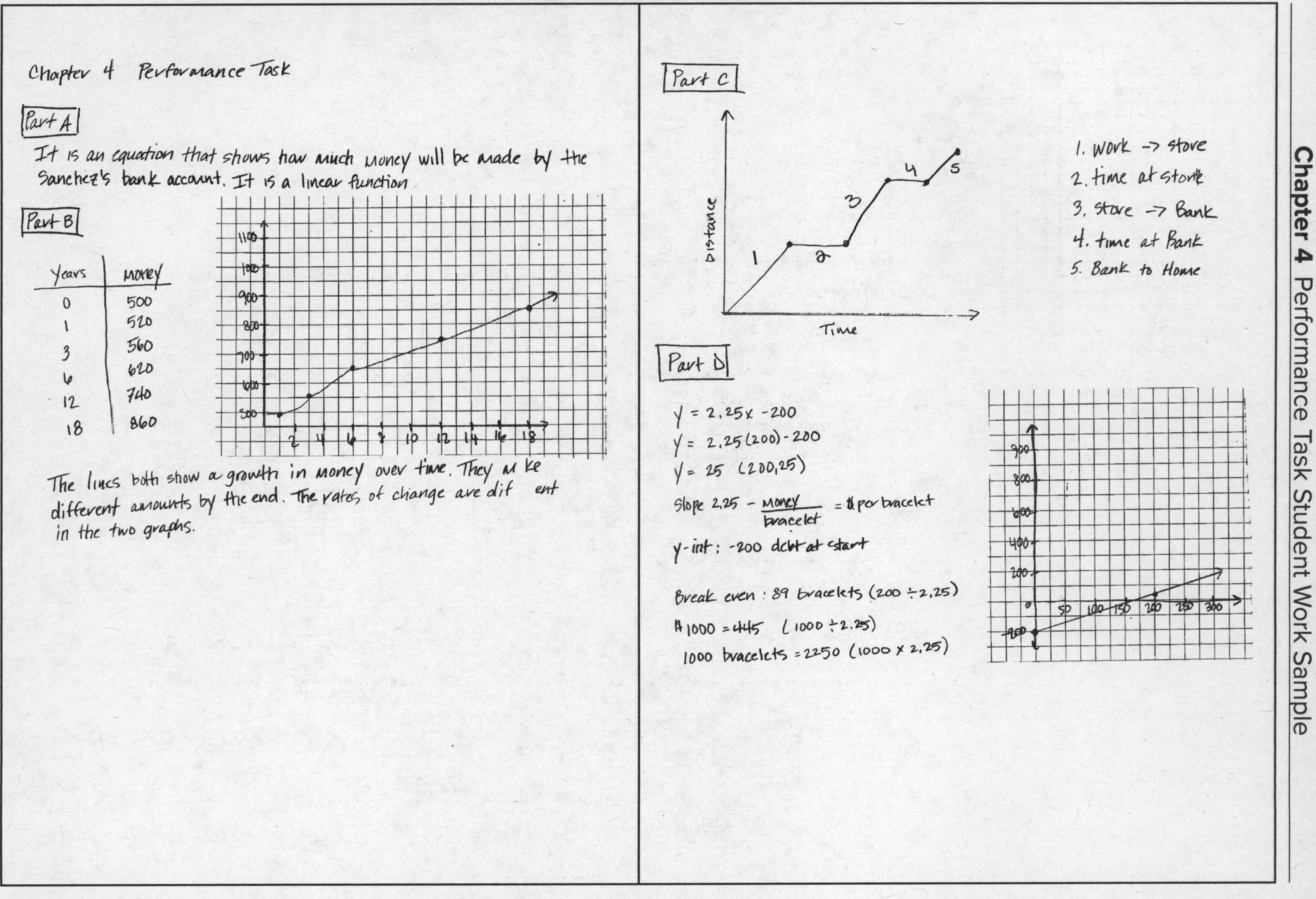
Chapter 4 Performance Task
Part A
It is an equation that shows how much money will be made by the Sanchez's bank account. It is a linear function
Part B
Years Money
0 500
1 520
3 560
6 620
12 740
18 860
1100
1000
900
800
700
600
500
2 4 6 8 10 12 14 16 18
The lines both show a growth in money over time. They m ke different amounts by the end. The rates of change are dif ent in the two graphs.
Part C
Distance
Time
1
2
3
4
5
1. Work -> store
2. time at store
3. Store -> Bank
4. time at Bank
5. Bank to Home
Part D
y = 2.25x - 200
y = 2.25(200) - 200
y = 25 (200,25)
Slope 2.25 - money/bracelet = $ per bracelet
y-int: -200 debt at start
Break even: 89 bracelets (200 ÷ 2.25)
$1000 = 445 (1000 ÷ 2.25)
1000 bracelets = 2250 (1000 x 2.25)
900
800
600
400
200
0
-200
50 100 150 200 250 300

Chapter 4 Performance Task

PART A

$I = p \cdot r \cdot t$

$I = 500 \times 4\% \times t$

yes, it is a line.

yes, it is a function.

PART B

x years	y total $
0	0
1	20
3	60
6	120
9	180
12	240
18	360

The graph would all be underneath the squiggle mark.

The other bank account makes a lot more money. I changes faster, so it has a faster rate of change.

PART C

① Distance to crafts store

② Crafts store

③ Distance to bank

④ Bank

⑤ Distance Home

PART D

y int: 200

slope: 225

They start at $200, so they are already ahead.

To make $1000, about 675 bracelets.

If they sell 1000 bracelets, they will make around $1400.

Student Work Sample

Page 115 • Park Redesign

Task Scenario		
Students will find missing angle measures and side lengths, prove a triangle is a right triangle, and find distances on the coordinate plane. Students will use parallel lines cut by transversals and the Pythagorean Theorem and its converse to solve problems about a park and a music festival.		
CCSS Content Standard(s)	8.EE.2, 8.G.5, 8.G.7, 8.G.8	
Mathematical Practices	MP1, MP2, MP3, MP4, MP6	
Depth of Knowledge	DOK2, DOK3	

Part	Maximum Points	Scoring Rubric
A	2	Full Credit: $x° = 55°$ The angle labeled 55° and the angle labeled $x°$ are alternate interior angles, so they are congruent. $y° = 100.4°$ The three angles along Boat Boulevard form a straight angle, so their measures add to 180°. $24.6 + x + y = 180$; $24.6 + 55 + y = 180$; $79.6 + y = 180$; $y = 100.4$ Partial Credit (1 point) will be given for one correct angle. No credit will be given for an incorrect answer.
B	1	Full Credit: $a^2 + b^2 = c^2$ $2^2 + (\sqrt{21})^2 \stackrel{?}{=} 5^2$ $4 + 21 \stackrel{?}{=} 25$ $25 = 25$ By the converse of the Pythagorean Theorem, the triangle must be a right triangle, and the right angle is opposite the longest side; $5 > \sqrt{21} > 2$. So, Right Road is perpendicular to Shore Street, and was designed correctly. No credit will be given for an incorrect or incomplete answer.
C	2	Full Credit: $z° = 65.4°$ The angle adjacent to the $z°$ angle and between Wild Way and Boat Boulevard is an alternate exterior angle with the angle labeled 24.6°. Alternate exterior angles are congruent, so those two angles have the same measure. Because Right Road and Boat Boulevard form a 90° angle, $z = 90 - 24.6 = 65.4$. Partial Credit (1 point) will be given for the correct angle measure OR a correct explanation. No credit will be given for an incorrect answer.

Part	Maximum Points	Scoring Rubric
D	2	Full Credit: Sample answer: From the food stands at (2, 8) to the nearest restrooms at (0, 5), the distance is: $d = \sqrt{2^2 + 3^2} = \sqrt{13} \approx 3.61$ units Each unit is 0.2 mile: 3.61(0.2) = 0.722 mi 0.722 mi > 0.5 mi, so the restrooms are not close enough to the food stands. Partial Credit (1 point) will be given for the correct distance OR an appropriate explanation. No credit will be given for an incorrect answer.
E	3	Full Credit: Golf cart: 8 units + 15 units = 23 units 23 units × 0.2 mi/unit = 4.6 mi $4.6 \text{ mi} \times \frac{1 \text{ h}}{12 \text{ mi}} \approx 0.38 \text{ h}$ Walking distance: $d = \sqrt{8^2 + 15^2} = \sqrt{289} = 17$ units 17 units × 0.2 mi/unit = 3.4 mi $3.4 \text{ mi} \times \frac{1 \text{ h}}{4 \text{ mi}} = 0.85 \text{ h}$ Valeria should take the golf cart because 0.38 h < 0.85 h. Partial Credit (2 points) will be given for both correct distances and times without a final answer. Partial Credit (1 point) will be given for one correct distance and time. No credit will be given for an incorrect answer.
F	2	Full Credit: $1 \text{ mi} \times \frac{1 \text{ unit}}{0.2 \text{ mi}} = 5$ units, so the station must be 5 units from each stage. The station should be at (–1, 2). The stages are at (–4, 6), (3, –1), and (–4, –2). From each stage to (–1, 2), a right triangle can be drawn with sides of 3 units and 4 units, and a hypotenuse of 5 units. $a^2 + b^2 = c^2$ $3^2 + 4^2 = c^2$ $\sqrt{25} = c$ $5 = c$; So the first aid station is 1 mi from each stage. Partial Credit (1 point) will be given for identifying the location OR for proving the location is the correct distance from the stages. No credit will be given for an incorrect answer.
TOTAL	**12**	

Chapter 5 Performance Task

Part A

$x = 55°$ because it is the alternate interior angle to the one labeled 55°.

$y = 100.4°$ I know this because ∢ between Lake Lane and Shore Street is 125° (180°−55°). However, that angle is split, but we know the angle between Boat Blvd and Shore St is 24.6° because they are vertical angles. So $125° - 24.6° = 100.4°$

Part B

Boat Blvd 5 km; Right Rd 2 km; Shore St $\sqrt{21}$ km; ?

$a^2 + b^2 = c^2$

$(2)^2 + (\sqrt{21})^2 \stackrel{?}{=} 5^2$

$4 + 21 \stackrel{?}{=} 25$

$25 = 25$ True

Yes, Right Rd is perpendicular to Shore St. I know this because when I substitute the side lengths into the Pythagorean Theorem, it checks. Also, 2km is the longest side, so that is supposed to be across from the right ∢.

Part C

The measure of ∢ 2 is 65.4°. I know this because the angle labeled 24.6° is a vertical angle to the angle between Boat Blvd and Shore St, so its measure is also 24.6°. That is an alternate interior angle to the angle between Wild Way and Boat Blvd, so it also is 24.6°. That is a vertical angle with the angle that is ∢ 2's complement (because Right Rd and Wild Way are perpendicular). So $90° - 24.6° = 65.4°$.

Part D

Food; 3 units; RR; 2 units

The distance between the Food Stands and the restrooms can be found using the Pythagorean Thm.

$a^2 + b^2 = c^2$

$2^2 + 3^2 = c^2$

$4 + 9 = c^2$

$\sqrt{13} = \sqrt{c^2}$

$3.61u = c$

$\frac{1 \text{ unit}}{.2 \text{ miles}} = \frac{3.61u}{x \text{ mi}}$

$x = 0.722$ miles

No, the distance is 0.722 miles, which is greater than 0.5 miles, so they are not close enough.

Part E

Solid lines: 8 un + 15 un = 23 units $\quad 23(0.2) = 4.6$ miles

$\frac{12 \text{ mi}}{1 \text{ hr}} = \frac{4.6 \text{ mi}}{x}$

$\frac{12x}{12} = \frac{4.6}{12}$

$x = 0.38\overline{3}$ hrs

It will be faster to drive on the solid than walk on the dashed.

Dashed line: Find length with Pythagorean Thm

$a^2 + b^2 = c^2$

$8^2 + 15^2 = c^2$

$64 + 225 = c^2$

$\sqrt{289} = \sqrt{c^2}$

$17 = c$

17 units (0.2) = 3.4 miles

$3.4 \div 4 = 0.85$ hrs

Part F

$1 \text{ mi} \div 0.2 = 5$ units from each stage

Because the First Aid Station will be diagonal from the stages, I need a right triangle with a hypotenuse of 5.

$a^2 + b^2 = 5^2$

$3^2 + 4^2 = 25$

$9 + 16 = 25$

$a = 3$ and $b = 4$

4; 5; 3

F.S. and K.S. are 7 units apart, so if I arrange the △s correctly, they both can have a vertex at (1, 2). L.S. and K.S. are 8 units apart, so again, if I lay out the △s right, they share a vertex at (−1, 2). That is the correct spot for the First Aid Station.

Chapter 5 Performance Task

Part A

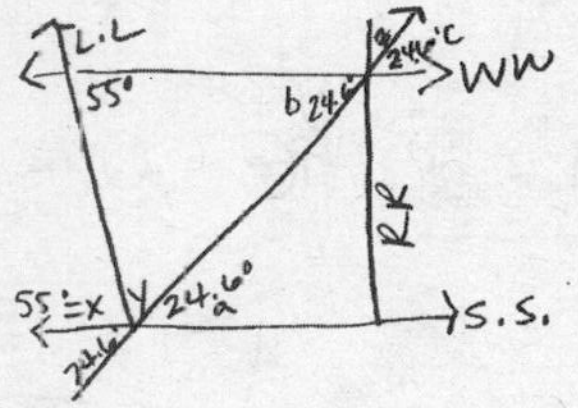

$55° + y + 24.6° = 180°$
$y = 100.4°$
$x = 55°$

Part B

$a^2 + b^2 = c^2$
$2^2 + (\sqrt{21})^2 = c^2$
$4 + 21 = c^2$
$\sqrt{25} = \sqrt{c^2}$
$5 = c$

c = hypotenuse = labeled as 2km
So yes, it is a perpendicular intersection.

Part C

Angles a, b, and c = 24.6° (see drawing above for labels).
(a: vertical angle; b: alt. int. ∠; c: vert. ∠)

$24.6° + z = 90°$
$-24.6° \quad -24.6°$
$z = 65.4°$

(SS and WW are ∥, RR and SS are ⊥ so RR and WW are ⊥)

Part D

F.S. (2, 8)
R.R. (0, 5)

2un = 0.4mi
3un = 0.6mi

$a^2 + b^2 = c^2$
$(0.4)^2 + (0.6)^2 = c^2$
$0.16 + 0.36 = c^2$
$\sqrt{0.52} = \sqrt{c^2}$
$0.72\text{mi} = c$

No, not close enough

Part E

23 un = 4.6
12 mi/hr × 4.6 = 55.2

$1.6^2 + 3^2 = c^2$
$\sqrt{11.56} = \sqrt{c^2}$
$3.4 = c$
$3.4 \times 4 = 13.6$

She should use the hypotenuse.

Part F

1mi = 5un

I drew three circles with a hypotenuse of 5. centered on each stage. They intersect at approximately (-1, 2), so that is where she should put the stage.

Student Work Sample

Chapter 5 Performance Task

Part A

$x = 55°$

$y = 24.6°$

Part B

$a^2 + b^2 = c^2$

$(\sqrt{21})^2 + 2^2 \stackrel{?}{=} 5^2$

$441 + 4 \stackrel{?}{=} 25$

$445 \neq 25$

No, it is not a right angle.

Part C

$90° - 24.6° = 65.4°$

$z = 65.4°$

Part D

$3^2 + 2^2 = c^2$

$9 + 4 = c^2$

$\sqrt{13} = \sqrt{c^2}$

$3.6 = c$

No, too far.

Part E

$8 + 15 = 23$

$23 \times .2 \div 12 = 0.383$

$8^2 + 15^2 = w^2$

$64 + 225 = w^2$

$17 = w$

$17 \times .2 \div 12 = 0.283$

Walk!

Part F

There is not a spot that is 1 mile from any of the stages because it would be 5 squares away but you can't do that staying on the lines.

Chapter 5 Performance Task

Part A

$180 - 55 = 125^\circ = y^\circ$

$180 - 125 = 55^\circ = x$

Part B

$a^2 + b^2 = c^2$

$2 + \sqrt{21} = 5$

$\sqrt{23} \neq 5$

Part C

$Z = 90^\circ$ because it is $\perp$.

Part D

No $3 + 2 = 5$

$5 \times .2 = 1$ mile

Too far away

Part E

The hypotenuse will be shorter, but she walks slower. The longer way she gets to drive 3 times faster and it doesn't look 3 times as long, so I say drive.

Part F

$1 \times .2 = .2$

There is no place to put the Aid Station because the stages are too far apart.

Student Work Sample

Page 117 • Geometry at the Gym

Task Scenario	
Students will use what they know about translations, reflections, and rotations to describe the effects of transformations; draw images on the coordinate plane; and explain that these transformations preserve segment length, angle measure, and distance between segments. Students will also use dilations to enlarge figures.	
CCSS Content Standard(s)	8.G.1, 8.G.1a, 8.G.1b, 8.G.1c, 8.G.3
Mathematical Practices	MP1, MP3, MP4, MP5, MP6
Depth of Knowledge	DOK2, DOK3, DOK4

Part	Maximum Points	Scoring Rubric
A	1	Full Credit: Sample answer: First poster: a translation of students along balance beams Second poster: a rotation of a gymnast about the high bar Third poster: one gymnast reflecting the position of another gymnast No credit will be given for an incorrect or incomplete answer.
B	2	Full Credit: Sample graph: 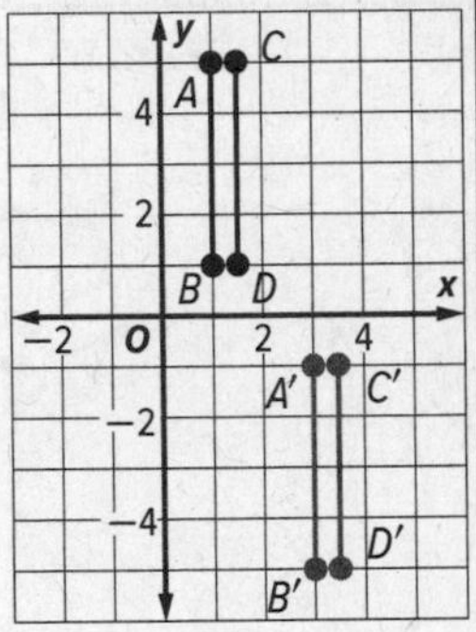 Sample answer: The image segments are parallel and still have the same length because in a translation, parallel line segments are taken to parallel line segments of the same length. Partial Credit (1 point) will be given for a correct graph OR a correct explanation. No credit will be given for an incorrect or incomplete answer.
C	2	Full Credit: After a 90° clockwise rotation: $(x, y) \rightarrow (y, -x)$. The vertices are $F'(-2, 5)$, $G'(-1, 5)$, $H'(-1, 3)$, and $J'(-2, 3)$. Sample answer: Rotations do not change the side lengths or the angle measures. So, rectangle *FGHJ* and its image are congruent rectangles. Partial credit (1 point) will be given for the correct vertices OR the correct answer about the rotated image. No credit will be given for an incorrect or incomplete answer.

Part	Maximum Points	Scoring Rubric
D	1	Full Credit: Students graph the reflection of the obstacle course. 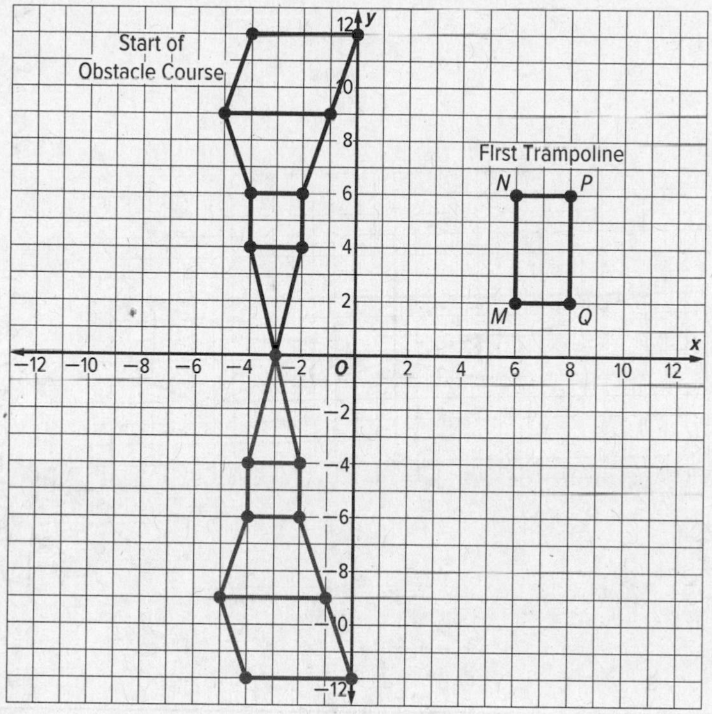 Start of Obstacle Course; First Trampoline; N, P, M, Q No credit will be given for an incorrect or incomplete answer.
E	3	Full Credit: The coordinates of $M(6, 2)$ and $N(6, 6)$ are multiplied by –1.5 to produce $M'(-9, -3)$ and $N'(-9, -9)$. So, multiply the coordinates of P and Q by –1.5: $(8)(-1.5) = -12$, $(6)(-1.5) = -9$, $(2)(-1.5) = -3$. The other vertices are $P'(-12, -9)$ and $Q'(-12, -3)$. Sample transformations (all dilations have the origin as the center of dilation): reflections across both axes followed by a dilation by 1.5 OR a dilation by 1.5 followed by a 180° rotation about the origin OR a dilation by –1.5 The scale factor is 1.5, or –1.5, depending on the transformations used. Because $1.5 > 1$, the image is an enlargement. The second trampoline is larger than the first. Partial credit (2 points) will be given for 2 of these 3: correct vertices OR correct transformation(s) OR correct interpretation of the scale factor. Partial credit (1 point) will be given for 1 of the 3 above. No credit will be given for an incorrect and incomplete answer.
TOTAL	**9**	

Chapter 6 Performance Task

Part A

The balance beam shows a translation of gymnasts as they walk. The high beam shows a rotation as they go around the bar.
The pairs floor shows a reflection of the gymnasts.

Part B

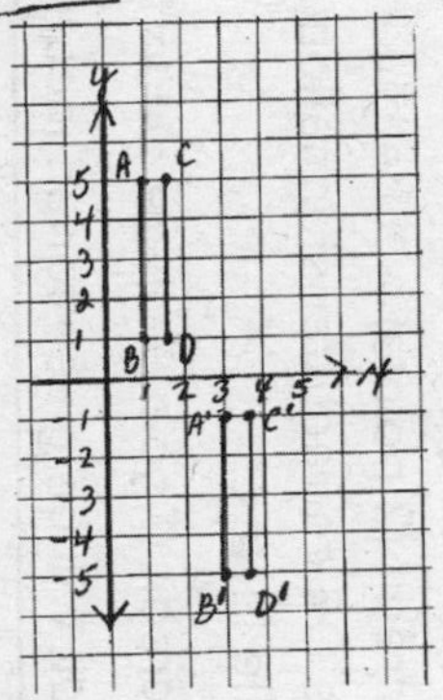

They are still parallel and still the same length.
Transformations preserve those characteristics because all the points are moved an equal distance.

Part C

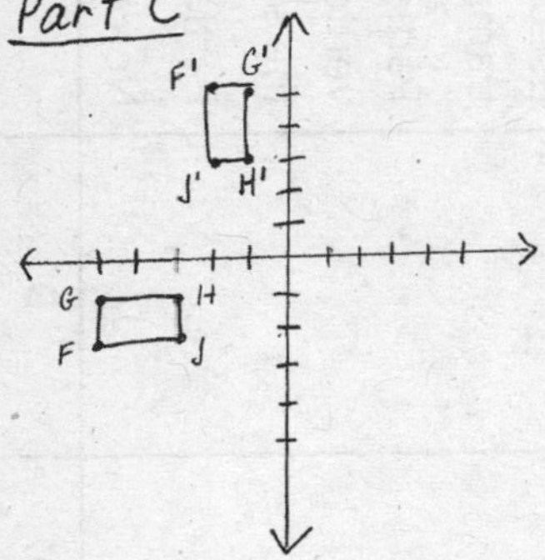

F' (-2, 5)
G' (-1, 5)
H' (-1, 3)
J' (-2, 3)

The rectangle is the same size and shape but a different orientation.
Rotation keeps the side lengths and angle measures the same.

Part D

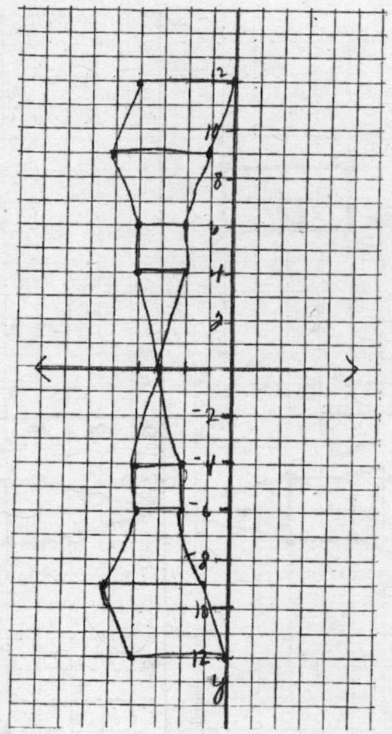

Part E

M (6, 2) → M' (-9, -3)
N (6, 6) → N' (-9, -9)

P (8, 6) → P' (-12, -9)
Q (8, 2) → Q' (-12, -3)

$-9 \div 6 = -1.5$

Scale factor is -1.5

It is a dilation and enlarges the original trampoline because we multiply by a factor of 1.5 (the negative moves it to the third quadrant).

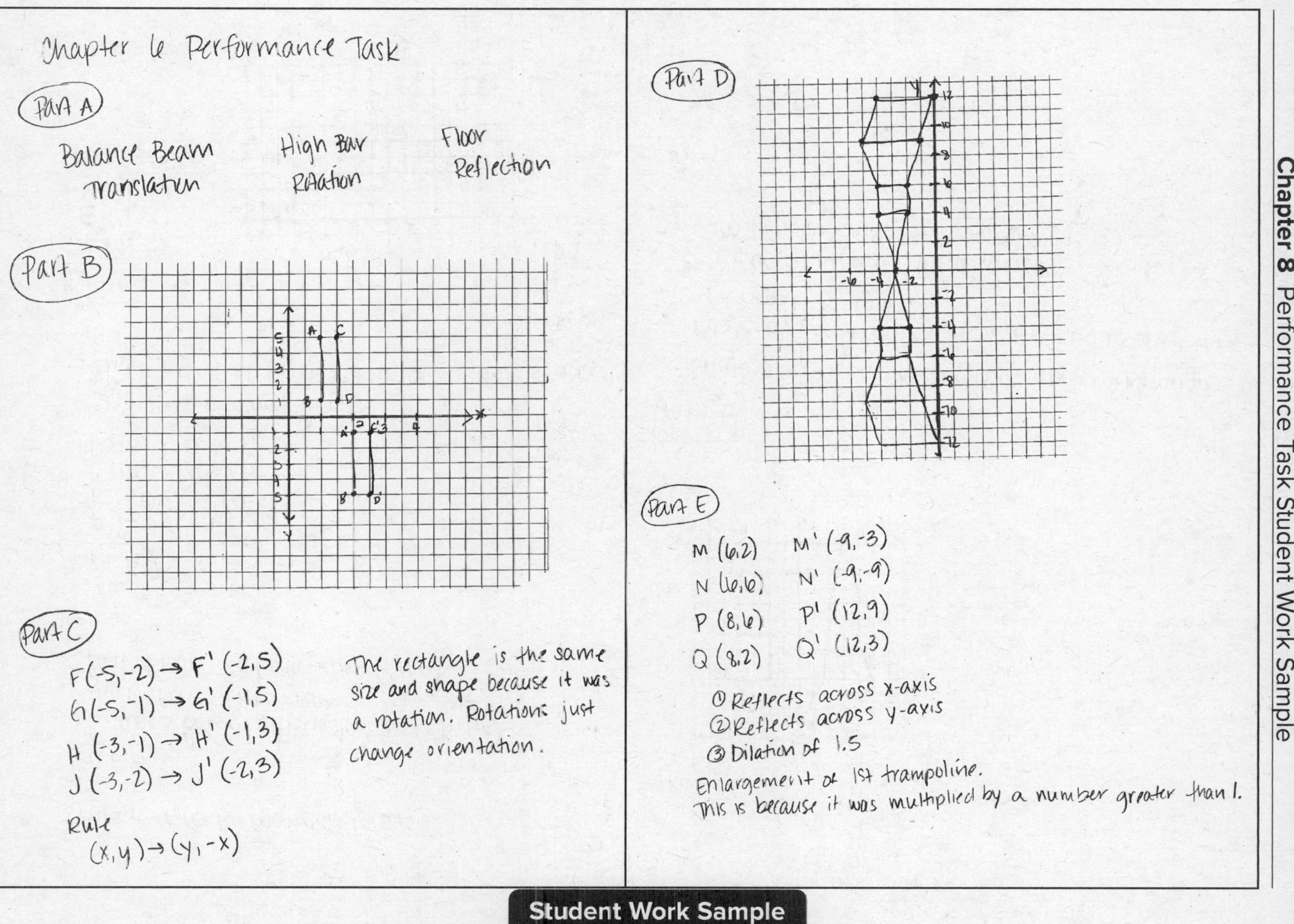

Chapter 6 Performance Task
Part A
Balance Beam
Translation
High Bar
Rotation
Floor
Reflection
Part B
Part C
F(-5,-2) → F' (-2,5)
G(-5,-1) → G' (-1,5)
H (-3,-1) → H' (-1,3)
J (-3,-2) → J' (-2,3)
Rule
(x,y) → (y,-x)
The rectangle is the same size and shape because it was a rotation. Rotations just change orientation.
Part D
Part E
M (6,2) M' (-9,-3)
N (6,6) N' (-9,-9)
P (8,6) P' (12,9)
Q (8,2) Q' (12,3)
① Reflects across x-axis
② Reflects across y-axis
③ Dilation of 1.5
Enlargement of 1st trampoline.
This is because it was multiplied by a number greater than 1.

Student Work Sample

Chapter 6 Performance Task

Part A

Balance Beam: Translation (slide)
High Bar: Rotation
Pair Floor: Reflection (flip)

Part B

OLD	New
A (1,5)	A' (3,-1)
B (1,1)	B' (3,-5)
C (1.5,5)	C' (3.5,-1)
D (1.5,1)	D' (3.5,-5)

Still ∥ and same length
Slides move all points the same distance.

Part C

F' (2,-5)
G' (1,-5)
H' (1,-3)
J' (2,-3)

Part D

Part E

- Dilate and then rotate 180° about the origin
- Dilate by multiplying each point by 1.5 and then add negative signs.

M(6,2) N(6,6) P(8,6) Q(8,2)
M'(-9,-3) N'(-9,-9) P'(-12,-9) Q'(-12,-3)

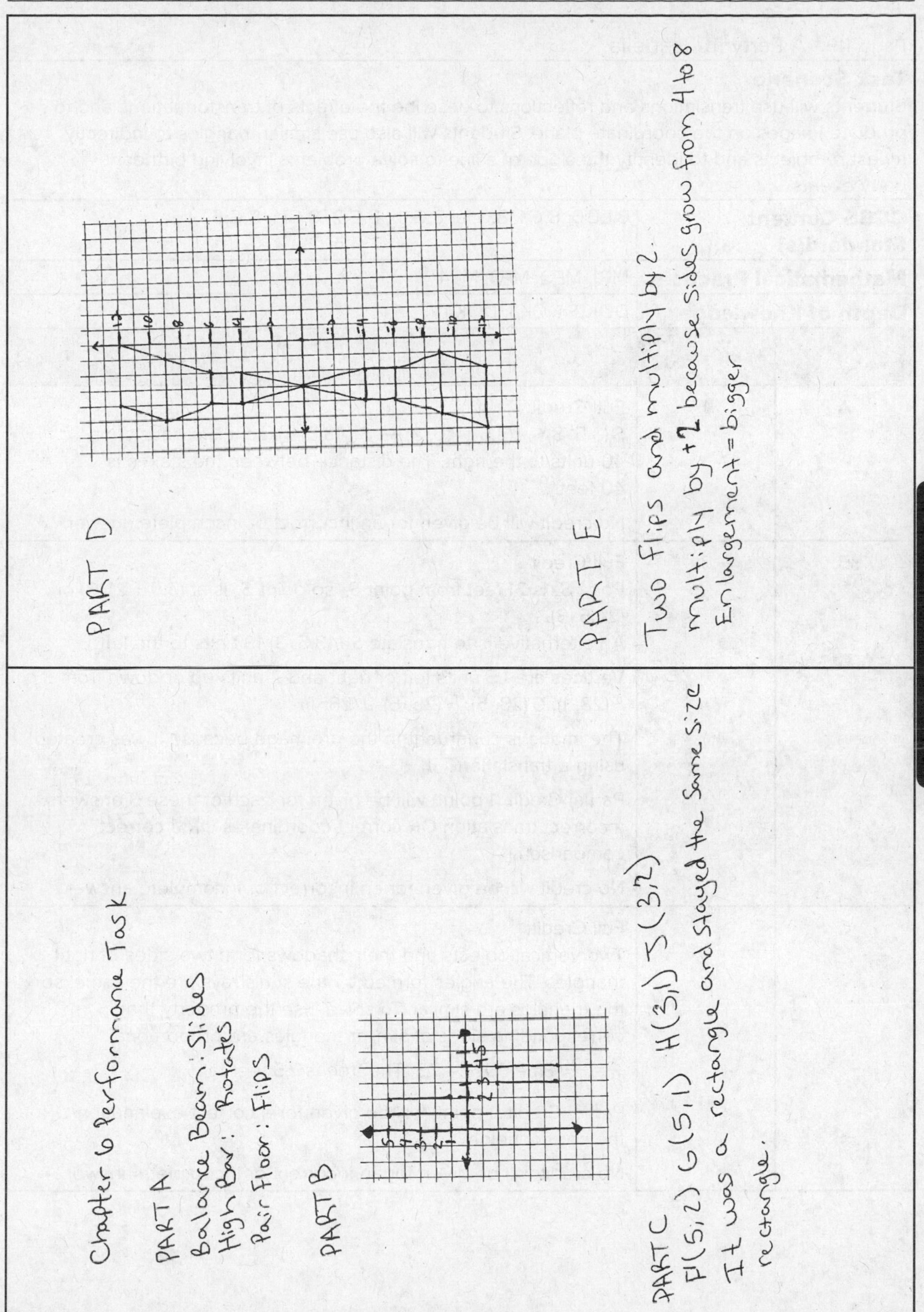
Chapter 6 Performance Task
PART A
Balance Beam: Slides
High Bar: Rotates
Pair Floor: Flips
PART B
PART C
F(5,2) G(5,1) H(3,1) J(3,2)
It was a rectangle and stayed the same size rectangle.
PART D
PART E
Two flips and multiply by 2.
multiply by 2 because sides grow from 4 to 8
Enlargement = bigger

Student Work Sample

Page 119 • A Party for Isabella

Task Scenario Students will use translations and reflections to describe the effects of transformations and to produce images on the coordinate plane. Students will also use similar triangles to indirectly measure objects and to identify the slope of a line to solve problems involving birthday party events.		
CCSS Content Standard(s)		8.EE.6, 8.G.1, 8.G.1a, 8.G.1b, 8.G.2, 8.G.4, 8.G.5
Mathematical Practices		MP1, MP2, MP3, MP4
Depth of Knowledge		DOK2, DOK3, DOK4
Part	**Maximum Points**	**Scoring Rubric**
A	1	Full Credit: $S_1(3.5, 3) \rightarrow (3.5 + 40, 3) \rightarrow S_2(43.5, 3)$, so it is a translation 40 units to the right. The distance between the stakes is 40 feet. No credit will be given for an incorrect or incomplete answer.
B	3	Full Credit: Point S_3 is 21 feet from point S_1, so point S_3 is at (3.5 + 21, 3) or (24.5, 3). An alternative is to translate $S_2(43.5, 3)$ 19 units to the left. Vertices are 1.5 units left or right and 2 units up or down from S_3: $F'(23, 1)$, $G'(23, 5)$, $H'(26, 5)$, $J'(26, 1)$. The image is congruent to the preimage because it was created using a translation. Partial Credit (1 point) will be given for each of these 3 answers: a correct translation OR correct coordinates OR a correct comparison. No credit will be given for an incorrect or incomplete answer.
C	2	Full Credit: Two vertical objects and their shadows form two sides of right triangles. The angles formed by the sun's rays are the same, so the triangles are similar. To solve, use the property that corresponding sides of similar triangles are proportional. $\frac{5}{h} = \frac{8}{12}$, $8h = 60$, $h = 7.5$; The tree is 7.5 feet tall. Partial Credit (1 point) will be given for a correct explanation OR the correct height. No credit will be given for an incorrect or incomplete answer.

Part	Maximum Points	Scoring Rubric
D	2	Full Credit: 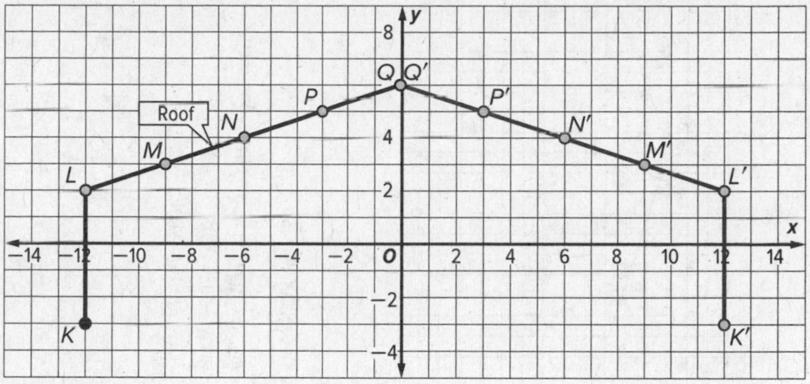 Reflections do not change segment length, so $KL = K'L'$ and $LQ = L'Q'$. Partial Credit (1 point) will be given for a correct graph OR a correct comparison. No credit will be given for an incorrect or incomplete answer.
E	2	Full Credit: Sample answer: $L(-12, 2)$ and $Q(0, 6)$: slope $= \frac{6-2}{0-(-12)} = \frac{4}{12} = \frac{1}{3}$ $M(-9, 3)$ and $N(-6, 4)$: slope $= \frac{4-3}{-6-(-9)} = \frac{1}{3}$ The slope is the same for any two points on the line, so it does not matter which points are chosen. Partial Credit (1 point) will be given for the correct slopes for two sets of points but no explanation OR the correct slopes for only one set of points with a correct explanation. No credit will be given for an incorrect and incomplete answer.
F	3	Full Credit: $L'(12, 2)$ and $Q'(0, 6)$: slope $= \frac{6-2}{0-12} = -\frac{1}{3}$ The slope shows the same relationship between the rise and run, 1:3, as for $\overline{LQ}$, but because it is a reflection, the sign of the slope is the opposite. Sample answer: Conjecture/support: Reflecting a line with slope m across the y-axis results in a line with slope $-m$. When line $y = 2x$ is reflected across the y-axis, it forms line $y = -2x$. Partial credit (1 point) will be given for each of 3 answers: the correct slope OR an accurate comparison of the slopes OR a valid a conjecture with a supporting example. No credit will be given for an incorrect and incomplete answer.
TOTAL	**13**	

Chapter 7 Performance Task

Part A

$S_1(3.5, 3) \rightarrow (3.5+40, 3) \rightarrow S_2(43.5, 3)$

- This means we had to add 40 units to the x-value, so it is a translation 40 units to the right.
- This also means the stakes are 40 ft apart.

Part B

$S_2(43.5, 3) \rightarrow (43.5-19, 3) \rightarrow S_3(24.5, 3)$

- Perform a translation of S_2 19 units to the left.

$F(42, 1) \rightarrow F'(23, 1)$
$G(42, 5) \rightarrow G'(23, 5)$
$H(45, 5) \rightarrow H'(26, 5)$
$J(45, 1) \rightarrow J'(26, 1)$

- The image and preimage have the exact same dimensions and orientation.
- It is just shifted 19 units over to the left.

Part C

$\frac{5\text{ ft}}{h} = \frac{8\text{ ft}}{12\text{ ft}}$

$\frac{8 \cdot h}{8} = \frac{60}{8}$

$h = 7.5$

The tree is 7.5 ft tall. I knew the triangles would be similar because the angles are all the same, so I set up a proportion using corresponding sides.

Part D

- Because the image is a reflection, the lengths of the segments will remain the same.

Part E

$Q(0, 6)$ $N(-6, 4)$

$\frac{y_2 - y_1}{x_2 - x_1} = \frac{4-6}{-6-0} = \frac{-2}{-6} = \frac{1}{3}$

$M(-9, 3)$ $L(-12, 2)$

$\frac{2-3}{-12-(-9)} = \frac{-1}{-3} = \frac{1}{3}$

- The slope is $\frac{1}{3}$.
- No, it does not matter because the pitch does not change on the left side of the roof.

Part F

$L'(12, 2)$ $Q'(0, 6)$

$\frac{y_2 - y_1}{x_2 - x_1} = \frac{6-2}{0-12} = \frac{4}{-12} = -\frac{1}{3}$

- The slope is the opposite of $\overline{LQ}$. Same numbers, but different sign because it is going downhill instead of uphill.
- I think that whenever a line is reflected over the y-axis, it will have the opposite sign of the original but the same number. Example

slope of left line: $\frac{5-1}{-5-0} = \frac{4}{-5} = -\frac{4}{5}$

slope of right line: $\frac{5-1}{5-0} = \frac{4}{5} = \frac{4}{5}$

Chapter 7 Performance Task

Part A

Slides 40 units right
40 ft apart

Part B

Add 21 units to S_1 to make a new point S_3

S_3 (24.5, 3)

F' (23,1) G' (23,5) H' (26,5) J' (26,1)

It is exactly the same as the pre-image.

Part C

$\frac{8}{12} = \frac{5}{h}$

$\frac{8h}{8} = \frac{60}{8}$

$h = 7.5$ ft

Part D

Q'(3,5) N'(6,4) H'(9,3) L'(12,2) (12,-3)K'

They are all the same as before.

Part E

$\frac{6-2}{0-{}^-12} = \frac{4}{12} = \frac{1}{3}$

$\frac{5-4}{-3-{}^-6} = \frac{1}{3}$

No, it doesn't matter.

Part F

L'Q' will be $-\frac{1}{3}$ because it sinks 1 for every 3 over.

It is the opposite. All reflections of lines have opposite slopes.

Student Work Sample

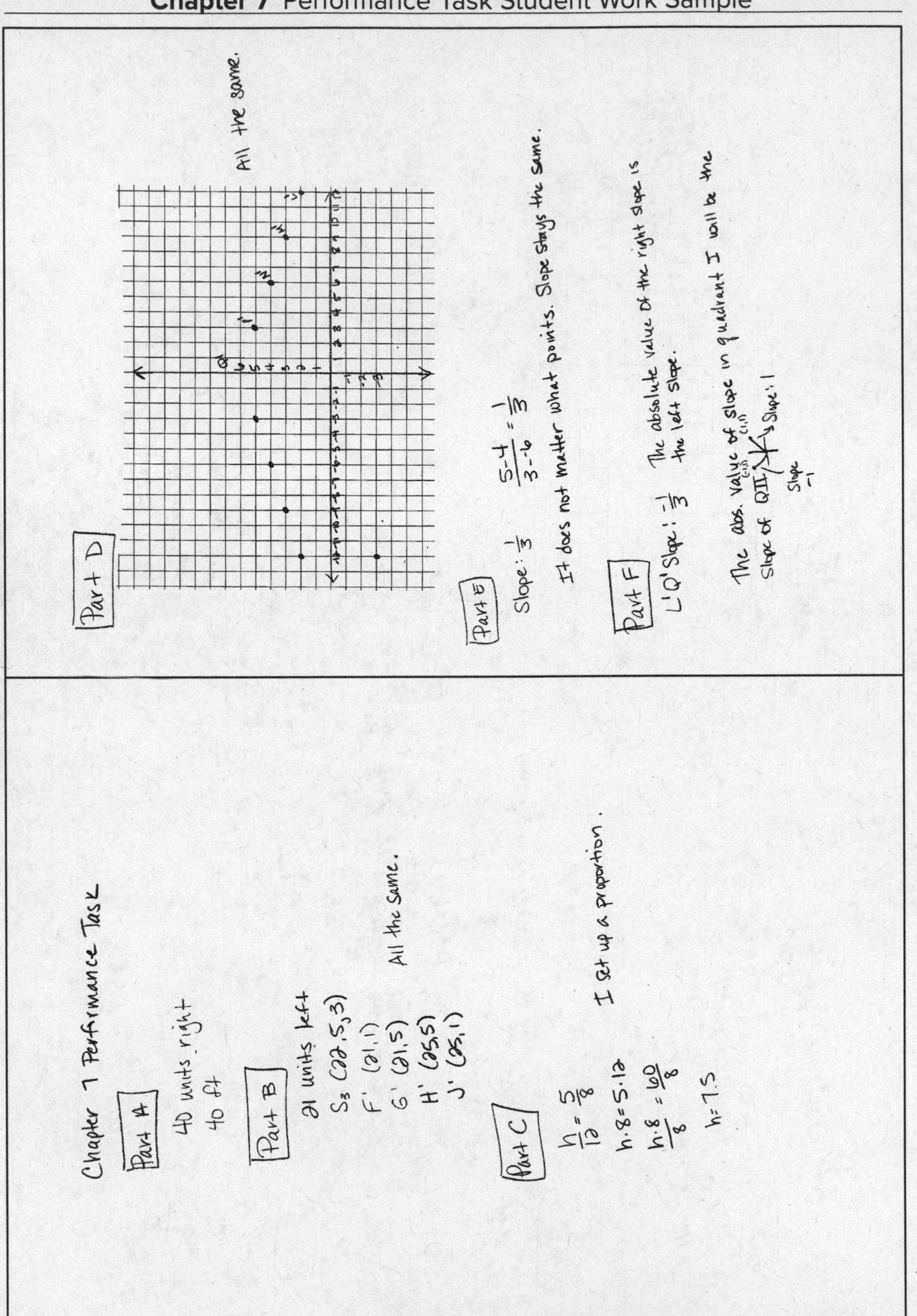
Chapter 7 Performance Task
Part A
40 units right
40 ft
Part B
21 units left
S3 (22.5,3)
F' (21,1)
G' (21,5)
H' (25,5)
J' (25,1)
All the same.
Part C
h/12 = 5/8
h·8 = 5·12
h·8/8 = 60/8
h = 7.5
I set up a proportion.
Part D
All the same.
Part E
Slope: 1/3
(5-4)/(3-6) = -1/3
It does not matter what points. Slope stays the same.
Part F
L'Q' Slope: -1/3
The absolute value of the right slope is the left slope.
The abs. value of slope in quadrant I will be the slope of QII
Slope: 1
Slope -1

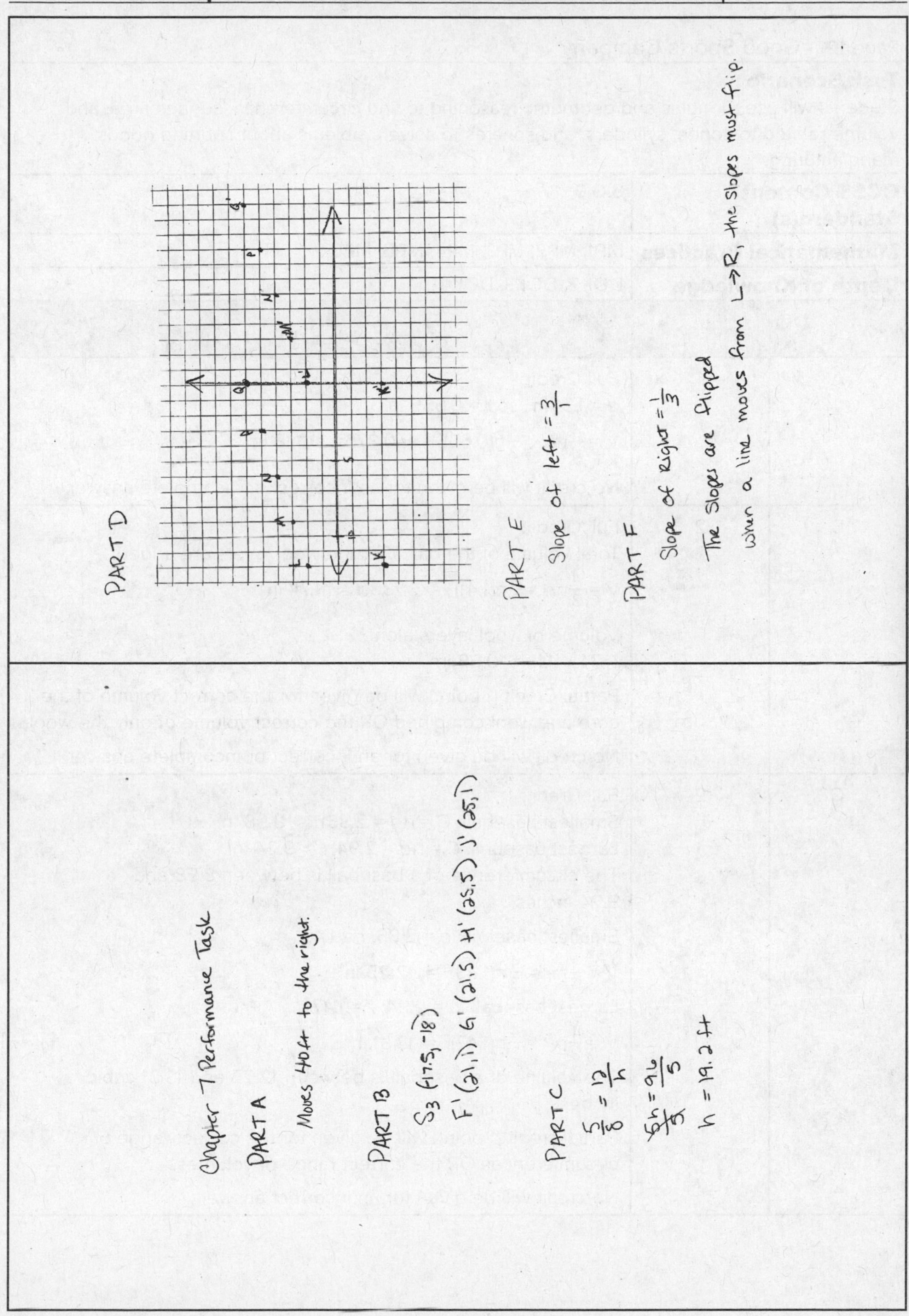

Chapter 7 Performance Task
PART A
Moves 40 ft to the right.
PART B
S_3 (17.5, -18)
F' (21,1) G' (21,5) H' (25,5) J' (25,1)
PART C
$\frac{5}{8} = \frac{12}{h}$
$\frac{5h}{5} = \frac{96}{5}$
h = 19.2 ft
PART D
PART E
Slope of left = $\frac{3}{1}$
PART F
Slope of right = $-\frac{1}{3}$
The slopes are flipped when a line moves from L→R, the slopes must flip.

Student Work Sample

Page 121 • Good Sports Company

Task Scenario Students will use formulas and geometric reasoning to find circumference, surface area, and volume related to cones, cylinders, and spheres to solve problems about sporting goods manufacturing.		
CCSS Content Standard(s)		8.G.9
Mathematical Practices		MP1, MP2, MP3, MP4, MP5, MP6
Depth of Knowledge		DOK2, DOK3, DOK4
Part	**Maximum Points**	**Scoring Rubric**
A	1	Full Credit: $d = 1.31$ in., so $r = 0.655$ in. $V = \frac{4}{3}\pi r^3 = \frac{4}{3}\pi(0.655)^3 \approx 0.375\pi \approx 1.18$ in^3 No credit will be given for an incorrect or incomplete answer.
B	2	Full Credit: Total volume of the ball after the wool layers are added: $V = \frac{4}{3}\pi r^3 = \frac{4}{3}\pi(1.41)^3 \approx 3.738\pi \approx 11.74$ in^3 Volume of wool layers alone: $11.74 - 1.18 = 10.56$ in^3 Partial Credit (1 point) will be given for the correct volume of the core and wool combined OR the correct volume of only the wool. No credit will be given for an incorrect or incomplete answer.
C	2	Full Credit: Smallest baseball: $C = \pi d = 2.86\pi \approx 8.98$ in. Largest baseball: $C = \pi d = 2.94\pi \approx 9.24$ in. The circumference of a baseball is between 8.98 and 9.24 inches. Smallest baseball: $d = 2.86$, $r = 1.43$ $V = \frac{4}{3}\pi r^3 = \frac{4}{3}\pi(1.43)^3 \approx 12.25$ in^3 Largest baseball: $d = 2.94$, $r = 1.47$ $V = \frac{4}{3}\pi r^3 = \frac{4}{3}\pi(1.47)^3 \approx 13.31$ in^3 The volume of a baseball is between 12.25 and 13.31 cubic inches. Partial credit (1 point) will be given for the correct range of circumferences OR the correct range of volumes. No credit will be given for an incorrect answer.

Part	Maximum Points	Scoring Rubric
D	2	Full Credit: Because both cones are open at the bottom, the amount of plastic used is equal to the lateral area. Current cone: $d = 3.5$, $r = 1.75$ $L.A. = \pi r\ell = \pi(1.75)(8) = 14\pi \approx 43.98$ in^2 New cone: $d = 7$, $r = 3.5$ Lateral area is equal to the current cone's lateral area. $L.A. = \pi r\ell$ $14\pi = \pi(3.5)(x)$ $14 = 3.5x$ $4 = x$, so the slant height of the new cone is 4 in. Partial credit (1 point) will be given for the correct lateral area OR the correct slant height. No credit will be given for an incorrect or incomplete answer.
E	4	Full Credit: Maximum diameter of a tennis ball = 2.7 in. Diameter of can = diameter of ball = 2.7 in. Height of can = height of 3 tennis balls = 3(2.7) = 8.1 in. Radius of can or tennis ball: $2.7 \div 2 = 1.35$ in. Can: $V = \pi r^2 h = \pi(1.35)^2(8.1) \approx 46.377$ in^3 1 tennis ball: $V = \frac{4}{3}\pi r^3 = \frac{4}{3}\pi(1.35)^3 \approx 10.306$ in^3 3 tennis balls: $V = 3(10.306) = 30.918$ in^3 Percentage of the can filled by tennis balls: $\frac{30.918}{46.377} \approx 0.667$, or 66.7% Empty space in can: $46.377 - 30.918 \approx 15.46$ in^3 Partial Credit (1 point) will be given for each of 4 answers: the correct can dimensions OR the correct percentage of can filled by tennis balls OR the correct mathematical reasoning and process for finding the percentage but based on incorrect calculations OR the correct amount of empty space in the can. No credit will be given for an incorrect and incomplete answer.
TOTAL	**11**	

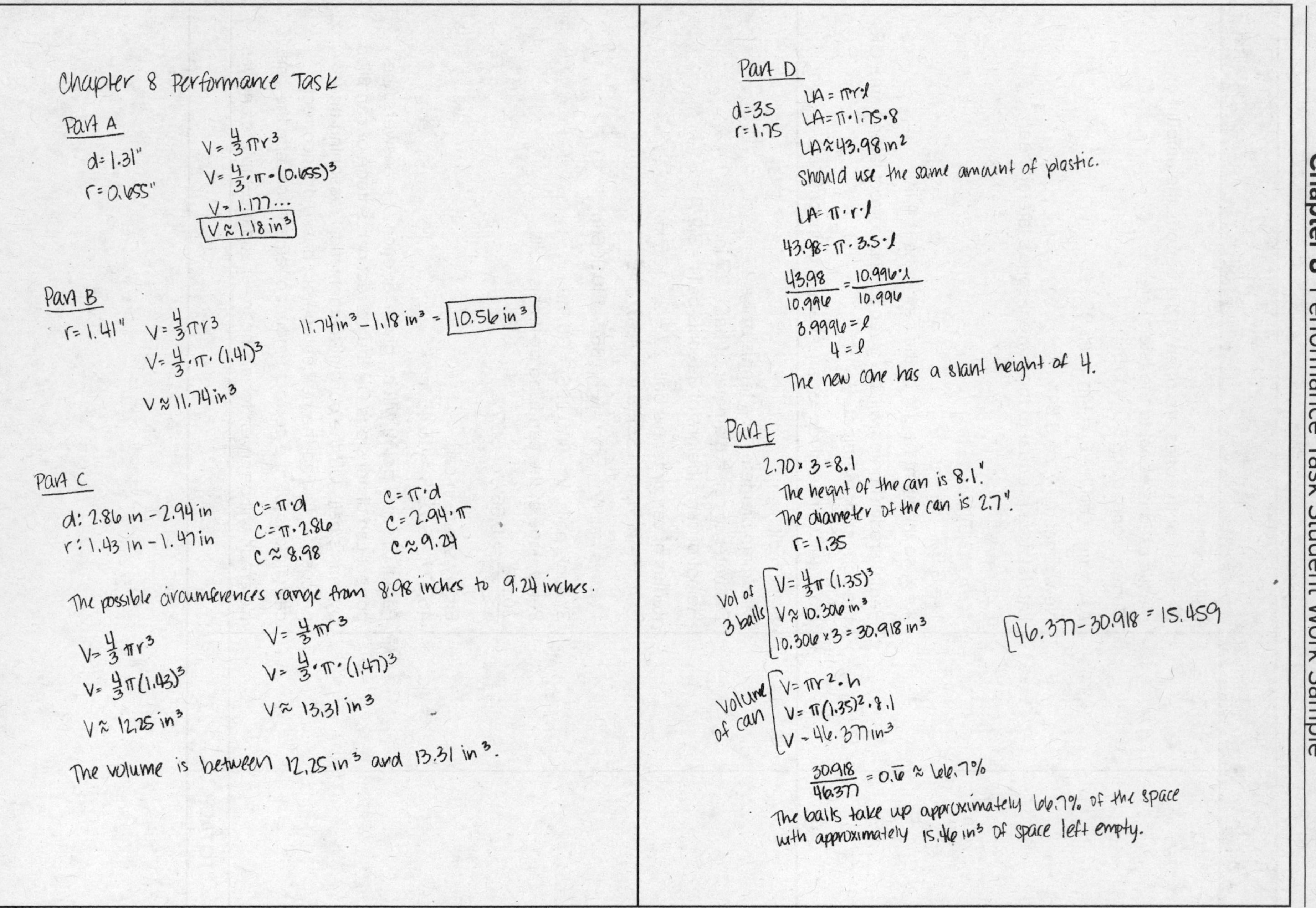

Chapter 8 Performance Task

Part A

d = 1.31"
r = 0.655"

$V = \frac{4}{3}\pi r^3$
$V = \frac{4}{3} \cdot \pi \cdot (0.655)^3$
$V = 1.177...$
$V \approx 1.18 \text{ in}^3$

Part B

r = 1.41"

$V = \frac{4}{3}\pi r^3$
$V = \frac{4}{3} \cdot \pi \cdot (1.41)^3$
$V \approx 11.74 \text{ in}^3$

$11.74 \text{ in}^3 - 1.18 \text{ in}^3 = 10.56 \text{ in}^3$

Part C

d: 2.86 in – 2.94 in
r: 1.43 in – 1.47 in

$C = \pi \cdot d$
$C = \pi \cdot 2.86$
$C \approx 8.98$

$C = \pi \cdot d$
$C = 2.94 \cdot \pi$
$C \approx 9.24$

The possible circumferences range from 8.98 inches to 9.24 inches.

$V = \frac{4}{3}\pi r^3$
$V = \frac{4}{3}\pi (1.43)^3$
$V \approx 12.25 \text{ in}^3$

$V = \frac{4}{3}\pi r^3$
$V = \frac{4}{3} \cdot \pi \cdot (1.47)^3$
$V \approx 13.31 \text{ in}^3$

The volume is between 12.25 in³ and 13.31 in³.

Part D

d = 3.5
r = 1.75

$LA = \pi r \ell$
$LA = \pi \cdot 1.75 \cdot 8$
$LA \approx 43.98 \text{ in}^2$

Should use the same amount of plastic.

$LA = \pi \cdot r \cdot \ell$
$43.98 = \pi \cdot 3.5 \cdot \ell$
$\frac{43.98}{10.996} = \frac{10.996 \cdot \ell}{10.996}$
$3.9996 = \ell$
$4 = \ell$

The new cone has a slant height of 4.

Part E

$2.70 \times 3 = 8.1$
The height of the can is 8.1".
The diameter of the can is 2.7".
r = 1.35

Vol of 3 balls:
$V = \frac{4}{3}\pi (1.35)^3$
$V \approx 10.306 \text{ in}^3$
$10.306 \times 3 = 30.918 \text{ in}^3$

Volume of can:
$V = \pi r^2 \cdot h$
$V = \pi (1.35)^2 \cdot 8.1$
$V = 46.377 \text{ in}^3$

$46.377 - 30.918 = 15.459$

$\frac{30.918}{46.377} = 0.\overline{6} \approx 66.7\%$

The balls take up approximately 66.7% of the space with approximately 15.46 in³ of space left empty.

Chapter 8 Performance Task

Part A

$V = \frac{4}{3}\pi(0.655)^3$

$V \approx 1.18 \text{ in}^3$

Part B

$V = \frac{4}{3}\pi(1.41)^3 - \frac{4}{3}\pi(0.655)^3$

$V \approx 10.56 \text{ in}^3$

Part C

Circumference: between 8.98 in and 9.24 inches.
Volume: between 12.25 in^3 and 13.31 in^3.

$\pi(2.86) = 8.98$

$\pi(2.94) = 9.24$

$\frac{4}{3} \cdot \pi \cdot 1.43^3 = 12.25$

$\frac{4}{3}\pi\ 1.47^3 = 13.31$

Part D

$LA = \pi(3.5)8$

$LA = 87.96 \text{ in}^2$

$\frac{87.96}{7\pi} = \frac{\pi \cdot 7 \cdot x}{7\pi}$

$3.999 = x$

$4 \text{ in} = x$

Part E

Can: H: 8.1, D: 2.7

$V = \frac{4}{3}\pi(1.35)^3 \times 3$

$V = 30.92 \text{ in}^3$ ← volume of balls

$V = \pi r^2 h$

$V = \pi(1.35)^2 \cdot 8.1$

$V = 46.38 \text{ in}^3$ ← volume of can

Left over Space $= 46.38 - 30.92 = 15.46 \text{ in}^3$

Student Work Sample

Chapter 8 Performance Task

Part A

$V = \frac{4}{3} \cdot \pi \cdot r^3$

$V = \frac{4}{3} \cdot \pi \cdot 1.31^3$

$V = \frac{4}{3} \cdot \pi \cdot 2.248091$

$V = 9.42$ cubic inches

Part B

$V = \frac{4}{3} \cdot \pi \cdot r^3$

$V = \frac{4}{3} \cdot \pi \cdot 1.41^3$

$V = \frac{4}{3} \cdot \pi \cdot 2.803221$

$V = 11.74\ in^3$

$11.74\ in^3 - 9.42\ in^3 = 2.32\ in^3$ is the volume of wool alone.

Part C

$C = \pi \cdot d$

$C = \pi(2.86)$

$C = 8.98\ in$ to

$C = \pi \cdot d$

$C = \pi(2.94)$

$C = 9.23\ in$

$V = \frac{4}{3} \cdot \pi \cdot r^3$

$V = \frac{4}{3} \cdot \pi \cdot (1.43)^3$

$V = \frac{4}{3} \cdot \pi \cdot 2.924207$

$V = 12.25\ in^3$ to

$V = \frac{4}{3} \cdot \pi \cdot r^3$

$V = \frac{4}{3} \cdot \pi (1.47)^3$

$V = \frac{4}{3} \cdot \pi \cdot 3.176523$

$V = 13.31\ in^3$

Part D

$V = \frac{1}{3} \cdot \pi r^2 \cdot h$

$V = \frac{1}{3} \cdot \pi (1.75)^2 \cdot 8$

$V = \frac{1}{3} \cdot \pi \cdot 3.0625 \cdot 8$

$V = 25.65634$

$25.65634 = \frac{1}{3}\pi(3.5)^2 \cdot h$

$\frac{25.65634}{12.82817} = \frac{12.82817 \cdot h}{12.82817}$

$2\ in = h$

The height is 2 inches.

Part E

Maximum = 2.70

The height is 8.1 inches (2.7x3) and the diameter is 2.7 inches.

BALL

$V = \frac{4}{3}\pi r^3$

$V = \frac{4}{3} \cdot \pi \cdot (1.45)^3$

$V = \frac{4}{3}\pi \cdot 3.048625$

$V = 12.77\ in^3$

CAN

$V = \pi r^2 h$

$V = \pi(1.45)^2 8.1$

$V = 53.50\ in^3$

$12.77 \times 3 = 38.31$

$38.31 \div 53.50 = 71.6\%$ of the can is filled.

$53.50 - 38.31 = 15.19$ cubic inches remain.

Chapter 8 Performance Task

PART A

Core: 9.4

PART B

Wool: 11.7

PART C

Ave. Circumference: 9.1

Ave. Volume: 12.7

PART D

H: 4

PART E

D: 2.575

H: 7.725

V = 71.5 balls

V = 160.9 can

Extra: 89.4

Student Work Sample

Page 123 • Make a Run for It

Note to teacher: For this Performance Task, have students survey 32 students about whether they run for exercise or participate in an organized sport. Then have students research Olympic gold medalist times in the men's 100-meter dash from 1900 to the present.

<table>
<tr><td colspan="3">Task Scenario
Students will collect data about sports and Olympic times, display their data in two-way tables and scatter plots, and interpret relative frequencies and a line of best fit.</td></tr>
<tr><td colspan="2">CCSS Content Standard(s)</td><td>8.SP.1, 8.SP.2, 8.SP.3, 8.SP.4</td></tr>
<tr><td colspan="2">Mathematical Practices</td><td>MP1, MP2, MP3, MP4, MP5, MP6, MP7</td></tr>
<tr><td colspan="2">Depth of Knowledge</td><td>DOK2, DOK3, DOK4</td></tr>
<tr><th>Part</th><th>Maximum Points</th><th>Scoring Rubric</th></tr>
<tr><td>A</td><td>3</td><td>Full Credit:
Sample survey data and relative frequencies:
<table>
<tr><th></th><th>Runs</th><th>Does Not Run</th><th>Total</th></tr>
<tr><td>Sport</td><td>11; 0.34</td><td>9; 0.28</td><td>20</td></tr>
<tr><td>No Sports</td><td>5; 0.16</td><td>7; 0.22</td><td>12</td></tr>
<tr><td>Total</td><td>16</td><td>16</td><td>32</td></tr>
</table>
Sample answer:
About 34% of students run and play a sport. The least percentage of students (16%) run but do not play a sport.

Partial credit (1 point) will be given for each of the 3: correct two-way table OR correct relative frequencies OR a correct analysis.

No credit will be given for an incorrect or incomplete answer.</td></tr>
<tr><td>B</td><td>2</td><td>Full Credit:
Sample table and answer:
<table>
<tr><th></th><th>Runs</th><th>Does Not Run</th></tr>
<tr><td>Sport</td><td>0.69</td><td>0.56</td></tr>
<tr><td>No Sports</td><td>0.31</td><td>0.44</td></tr>
</table>
More than two thirds of runners play a sport. Students who do not run are also more likely to play a sport.

Partial Credit (1 point) will be given for correct relative frequencies OR an accurate analysis of the frequencies.

No credit will be given for an incorrect or incomplete answer.</td></tr>
<tr><td>C</td><td>2</td><td>Full Credit:
Sample table and answer:
<table>
<tr><th></th><th>Runs</th><th>Does Not Run</th></tr>
<tr><td>Sport</td><td>0.55</td><td>0.45</td></tr>
<tr><td>No Sports</td><td>0.42</td><td>0.58</td></tr>
</table>
Students who play sports are slightly more likely to run. 42% of students who do not play sports still run for exercise.

Partial Credit (1 point each) will be given for correct relative frequencies OR an accurate analysis of the frequencies.

No credit will be given for an incorrect or incomplete answer.</td></tr>
</table>

Part	Maximum Points	Scoring Rubric
D	3	Full Credit: Data, given as "year, time in seconds": 1900, 11; 1904, 11; 1908, 10.8; 1912, 10.8; 1920, 10.8; 1924, 10.6; 1928, 10.8; 1932, 10.38; 1936, 10.3; 1948, 10.3; 1952, 10.4; 1956, 10.5; 1960, 10.2; 1964, 10; 1968, 9.95; 1972, 10.14; 1976, 10.06; 1980, 10.25; 1984, 9.99; 1988, 9.92; 1992, 9.96; 1996, 9.84; 2000, 9.87; 2004, 9.85; 2008, 9.69; 2012, 9.63 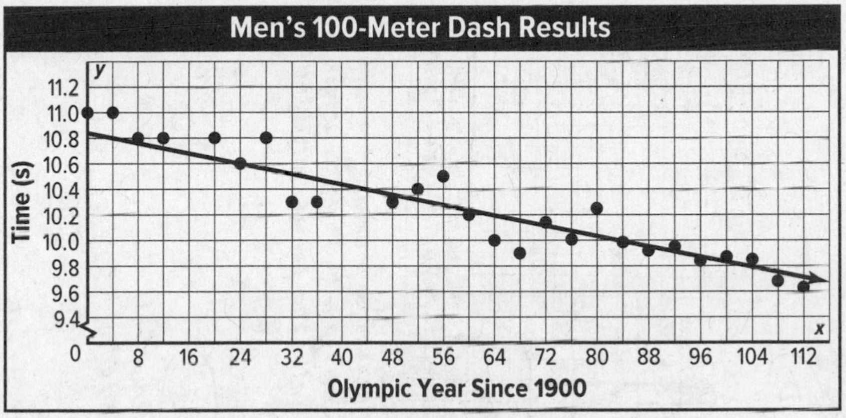 **Men's 100-Meter Dash Results** y-axis: Time (s): 9.4, 9.6, 9.8, 10.0, 10.2, 10.4, 10.6, 10.8, 11.0, 11.2 x-axis: Olympic Year Since 1900: 0, 8, 16, 24, 32, 40, 48, 56, 64, 72, 80, 88, 96, 104, 112 A sample line of fit is shown. Sample answer: As the year increases, the time in seconds decreases, so a negative association exists. The points lie close to the line, so the data appear linear. There are no outliers. Partial Credit (1 point) will be given for each of 3 answers: a correct scatter plot OR an accurate line of best fit OR a description of the associations in the data. No credit will be given for an incorrect or incomplete answer.
E	3	Full Credit: Sample answer: slope = $\frac{10.2 - 10.6}{64 - 24} = -0.01$; $10.6 = -0.01(24) + b$; $b = 10.84$, so y-intercept = 10.84 line of best fit: $y = -0.01x + 10.84$ In 2020: $y = -0.01(120) + 10.84 = 9.64$ s In 2056: $y = -0.01(156) + 10.84 = 9.28$ s The result of the 2020 race should be fairly similar to the 2012 result, but in 2056, the gold medalist is expected to be almost 0.4 second faster than in 2012. Partial Credit (1 point) will be given for each of 3 answers: an accurate equation for the line of best fit OR correct predictions for 2020 and 2056 OR an accurate comparison. No credit will be given for an incorrect and incomplete answer.
TOTAL	13	

Chapter 9 Performance Task

Part A

	Runs		Does not run		Total
Sport	11	0.34	9	0.28	20
No sport	5	0.16	7	0.22	12
Total	16		16		32

About half the students run and half don't.
34% of students who run play a sport.
28% play a sport and don't run.
16% of kids run but play no sports.
22% of kids do neither.

Part B

	Run	No Running
Sports	0.69	0.56
No sports	0.31	0.44

The students who run are likely to play sports because nearly 7 out of 10 do.
For the students who do not run, they are only slightly more likely (a little over 1/2) to play sports.

Part C

	Run	Do not run
Sports	0.55	0.45
No sports	0.42	0.58

students who play sports are slightly more likely to run (55% vs 45%) of students who don't play sports, they are less likely to run. (42% run vs 58% who don't).

Part D

Men's 100-Meter Dash Results

Time (s)

OLYMPIC YEAR SINCE 1900

As the years increase, the time for the 100 m dash decreases. It is a negative association. There are no outliers and all the points are fairly close to the line.

Part E

y-intercept: 11
slope (0,11) (80,10)

$\frac{10-11}{80-0} = \frac{-1}{80} = {}^{-}0.01$

$y = {}^{-}0.01x + 11$

$x = 120 \quad y = {}^{-}0.01(120) + 11$
$y = 9.8$

$x = 156 \quad y = {}^{-}0.01(156) + 11$
$y = 9.44$

In 2012, the results were 9.63. In 2020, the results could be about 0.17 seconds slower at 9.8 sec.
In 2056, the results should be 0.19 sec faster with a result around 9.44 sec.

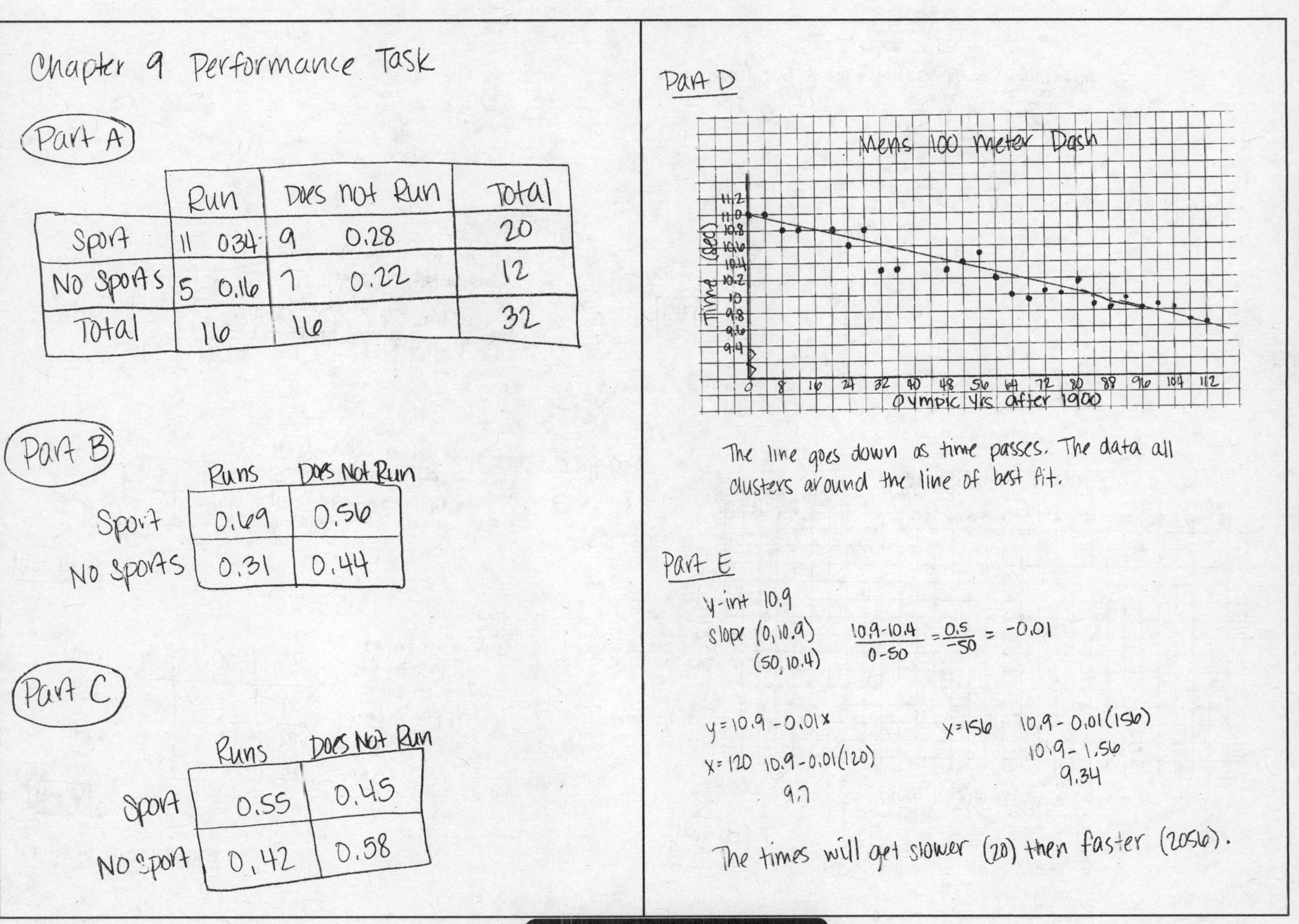

Chapter 9 Performance Task

Part A

	Run	Does not Run	Total
Sport	11 0.34	9 0.28	20
No Sports	5 0.16	7 0.22	12
Total	16	16	32

Part B

	Runs	Does Not Run
Sport	0.69	0.56
No Sports	0.31	0.44

Part C

	Runs	Does Not Run
Sport	0.55	0.45
No Sport	0.42	0.58

Part D

The line goes down as time passes. The data all clusters around the line of best fit.

Part E

y-int 10.9

slope (0, 10.9) (50, 10.4) $\frac{10.9-10.4}{0-50} = \frac{0.5}{-50} = -0.01$

$y = 10.9 - 0.01x$

$x = 120$ $10.9 - 0.01(120)$ 9.7

$x = 156$ $10.9 - 0.01(156)$ $10.9 - 1.56$ 9.34

The times will get slower (20) then faster (2056).

Student Work Sample

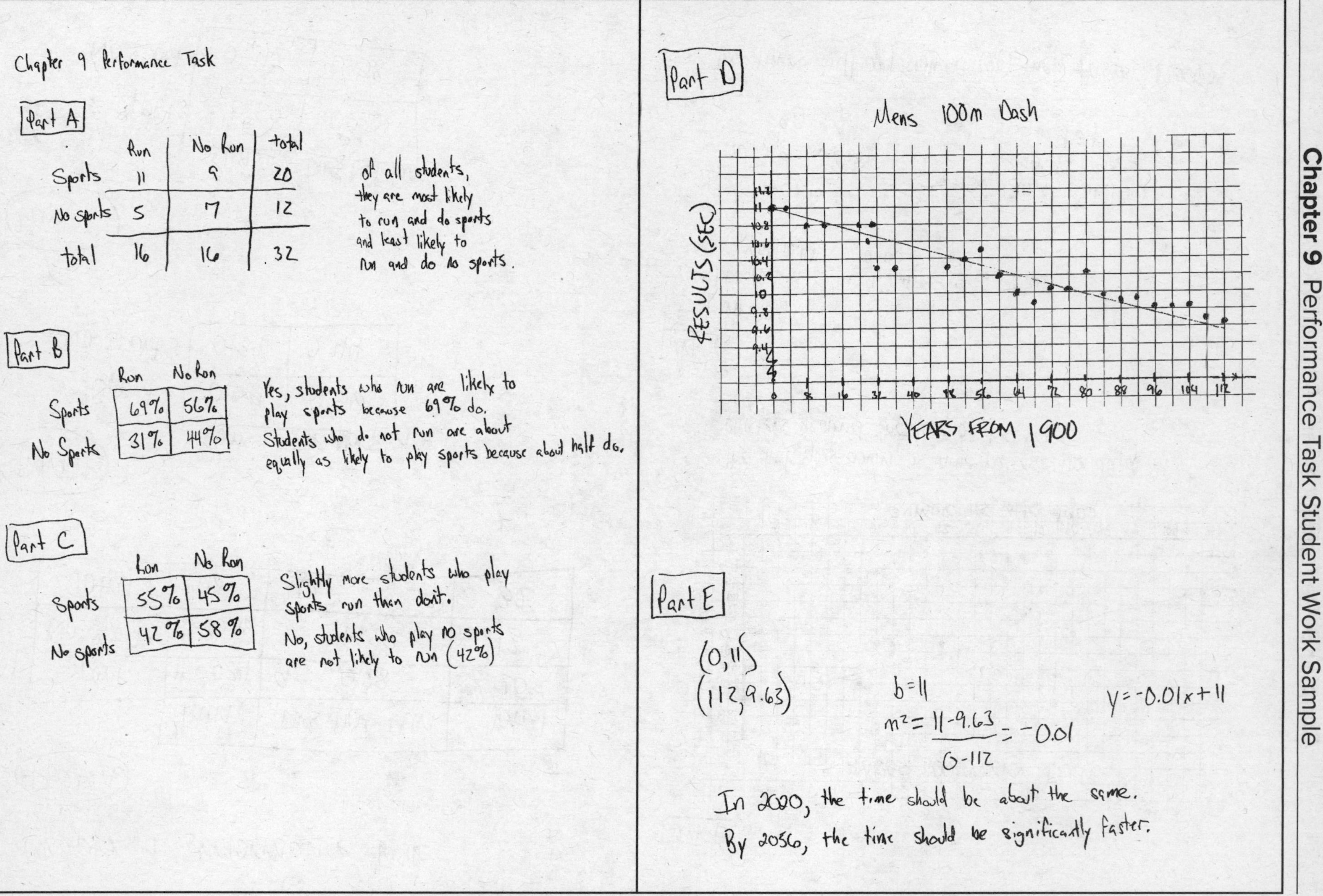
Chapter 9 Performance Task
Part A
Run
No Run
total
Sports
11
9
20
No sports
5
7
12
total
16
16
32
of all students, they are most likely to run and do sports and least likely to run and do no sports.
Part B
Run
No Run
Sports
69%
56%
No Sports
31%
44%
Yes, students who run are likely to play sports because 69% do.
Students who do not run are about equally as likely to play sports because about half do.
Part C
Run
No Run
Sports
55%
45%
No sports
42%
58%
Slightly more students who play sports run than don't.
No, students who play no sports are not likely to run (42%)
Part D
Mens 100m Dash
RESULTS (SEC)
YEARS FROM 1900
Part E
(0,11)
(112,9.63)
b=11
m = 11-9.63 / 0-112 = -0.01
y=-0.01x+11
In 2020, the time should be about the same.
By 2056, the time should be significantly faster.

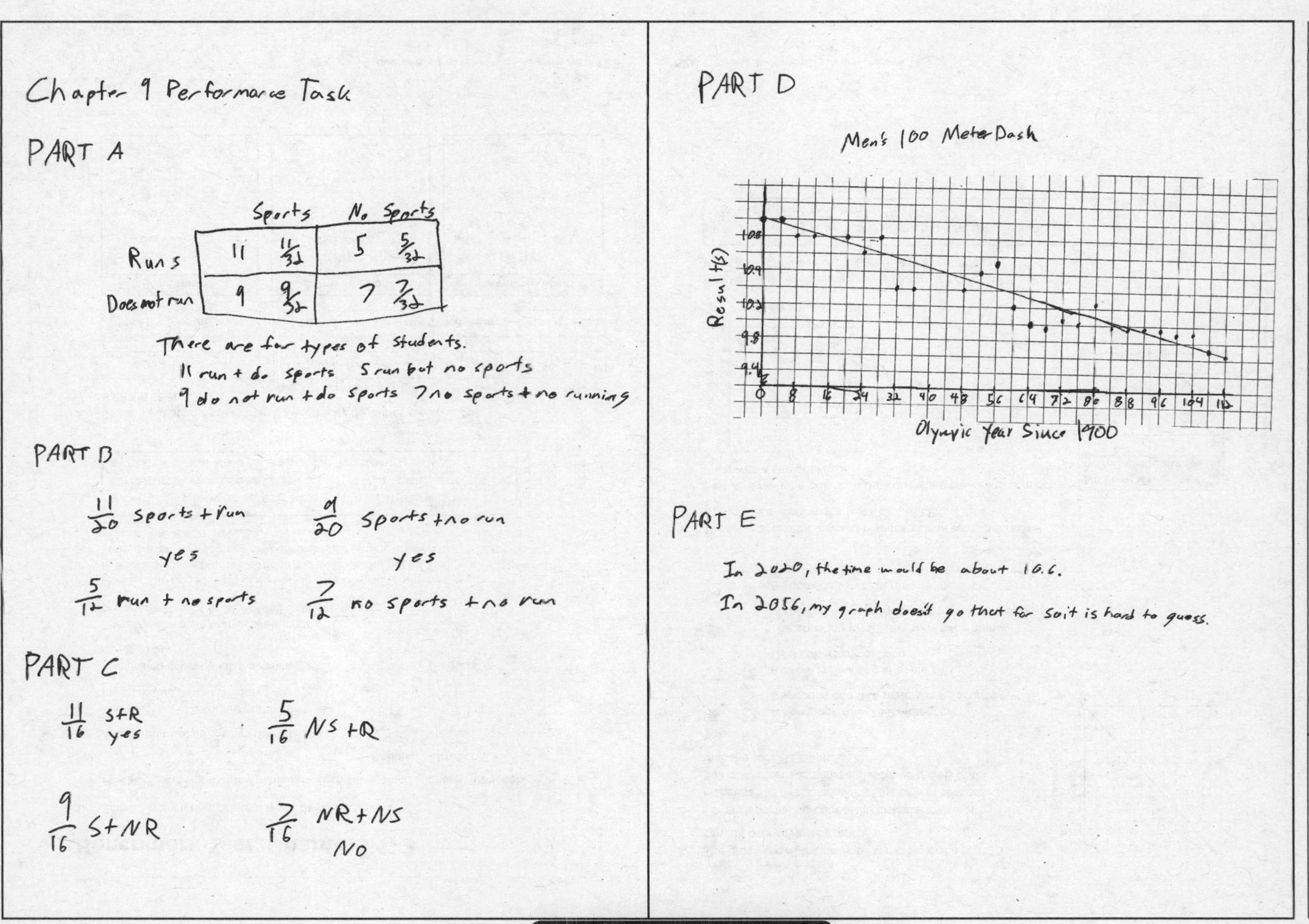
Chapter 9 Performance Task
PART A
Sports
No Sports
Runs
11
11/32
5
5/32
Does not run
9
9/32
7
7/32
There are for types of students.
11 run + do sports 5 run but no sports
9 do not run + do sports 7 no sports + no running
PART B
11/20 sports + run
yes
9/20 sports + no run
yes
5/12 run + no sports
7/12 no sports + no run
PART C
11/16 S+R
yes
5/16 NS + R
9/16 S+NR
7/16 NR+NS
No
PART D
Men's 100 Meter Dash
Result (s)
Olympic Year Since 1900
PART E
In 2020, the time would be about 10.6.
In 2056, my graph doesn't go that far so it is hard to guess.

Student Work Sample

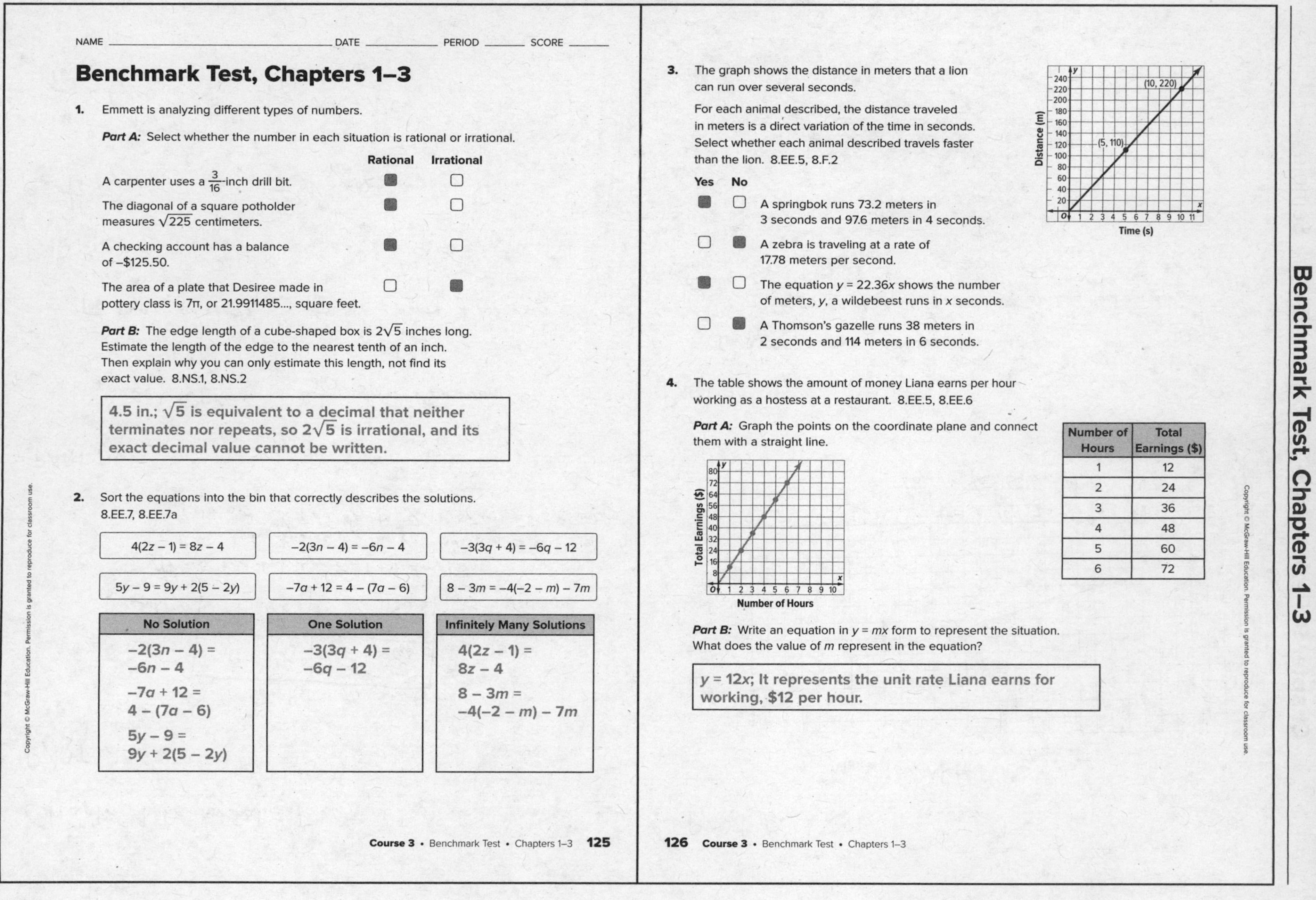

NAME ______________ DATE ________ PERIOD ______ SCORE ______

Benchmark Test, Chapters 1–3

1. Emmett is analyzing different types of numbers.

Part A: Select whether the number in each situation is rational or irrational.

	Rational	Irrational
A carpenter uses a $\frac{3}{16}$-inch drill bit.	■	☐
The diagonal of a square potholder measures $\sqrt{225}$ centimeters.	■	☐
A checking account has a balance of –\$125.50.	■	☐
The area of a plate that Desiree made in pottery class is 7π, or 21.9911485..., square feet.	☐	■

Part B: The edge length of a cube-shaped box is $2\sqrt{5}$ inches long. Estimate the length of the edge to the nearest tenth of an inch. Then explain why you can only estimate this length, not find its exact value. 8.NS.1, 8.NS.2

4.5 in.; $\sqrt{5}$ is equivalent to a decimal that neither terminates nor repeats, so $2\sqrt{5}$ is irrational, and its exact decimal value cannot be written.

2. Sort the equations into the bin that correctly describes the solutions. 8.EE.7, 8.EE.7a

$4(2z - 1) = 8z - 4$	$-2(3n - 4) = -6n - 4$	$-3(3q + 4) = -6q - 12$
$5y - 9 = 9y + 2(5 - 2y)$	$-7a + 12 = 4 - (7a - 6)$	$8 - 3m = -4(-2 - m) - 7m$

No Solution	One Solution	Infinitely Many Solutions
$-2(3n - 4) = -6n - 4$	$-3(3q + 4) = -6q - 12$	$4(2z - 1) = 8z - 4$
$-7a + 12 = 4 - (7a - 6)$		$8 - 3m = -4(-2 - m) - 7m$
$5y - 9 = 9y + 2(5 - 2y)$		

3. The graph shows the distance in meters that a lion can run over several seconds.

For each animal described, the distance traveled in meters is a direct variation of the time in seconds. Select whether each animal described travels faster than the lion. 8.EE.5, 8.F.2

Yes	No	
■	☐	A springbok runs 73.2 meters in 3 seconds and 97.6 meters in 4 seconds.
☐	■	A zebra is traveling at a rate of 17.78 meters per second.
■	☐	The equation $y = 22.36x$ shows the number of meters, y, a wildebeest runs in x seconds.
☐	■	A Thomson's gazelle runs 38 meters in 2 seconds and 114 meters in 6 seconds.

4. The table shows the amount of money Liana earns per hour working as a hostess at a restaurant. 8.EE.5, 8.EE.6

Number of Hours	Total Earnings (\$)
1	12
2	24
3	36
4	48
5	60
6	72

Part A: Graph the points on the coordinate plane and connect them with a straight line.

Part B: Write an equation in $y = mx$ form to represent the situation. What does the value of m represent in the equation?

$y = 12x$; It represents the unit rate Liana earns for working, \$12 per hour.

5. The table shows the total distance Jayden biked each day last week.

Day	Sunday	Monday	Tuesday	Wednesday	Thursday	Friday	Saturday
Distance Biked (km)	11.5	8.7	6.3	9.2	4.5	6.0	13.8

The total distance Jayden biked last week is 1.25 times the distance he biked this week. Write and solve an equation to show how far Jayden biked this week. 8.EE.7, 8.EE.7b

Equation: $1.25x = 60$

Distance biked this week: **48 kilometers**

6. Match each equation to the appropriate graph. 8.EE.8, 8.EE.8c, 8.F.5

$2x - 4y = 8$ $2x + 4y = -8$
$4x - 2y = 8$ $4x + 2y = -8$

$2x + 4y = -8$ | $4x + 2y = -8$ | $2x - 4y = 8$ | $4x - 2y = 8$

7. Manuel purchased a storage cube that has a volume of 9 cubic feet. He wants to put it on a shelf on his wall that is 24 inches below the ceiling. Will the cube fit? Explain your reasoning. 8.EE.2

No, it will not fit. 24 in. = 2 ft, and the cube root of 8 is 2. So the cube root of 9 is greater than 2. The storage cube has a height greater than 2 ft.

8. The expressions represent the number of middle school students who signed up for 4 different spring intramural sports. The number of students signed up for baseball and kickball is equal to the number of students signed up for flag football and soccer. 8.EE.7, 8.EE.7b

Expression	Sport
$8n - 10$	Baseball
$2n + 3$	Flag football
$n + 4$	Kickball
$3(2n - 1)$	Soccer

Part A: Model the situation with an equation by writing the correct expression in each space.

$8n - 10$ + $n + 4$ = $2n + 3$ + $3(2n - 1)$

Part B: Solve the equation. Then identify the number of students signed up for each sport.

$n =$ **6**

Baseball: **38 students** Flag Football: **15 students**

Kickball: **10 students** Soccer: **33 students**

9. The table shows the populations of four South American countries that Lisa visited last summer. Select the correct number to make each statement true. 8.EE.3, 8.EE.4

Country	Population
Argentina	4.1×10^7
Brazil	2.01×10^8
Paraguay	6.8×10^6
Uruguay	3.3×10^6

2 3 5 6
20 30 50 60

The population of Brazil is about **60** times greater than the population of Uruguay.

The population of Argentina is about **6** times greater than the population of Paraguay.

The population of Brazil is about **5** times greater than the population of Argentina.

The population of Paraguay is about **2** times greater than the population of Uruguay.

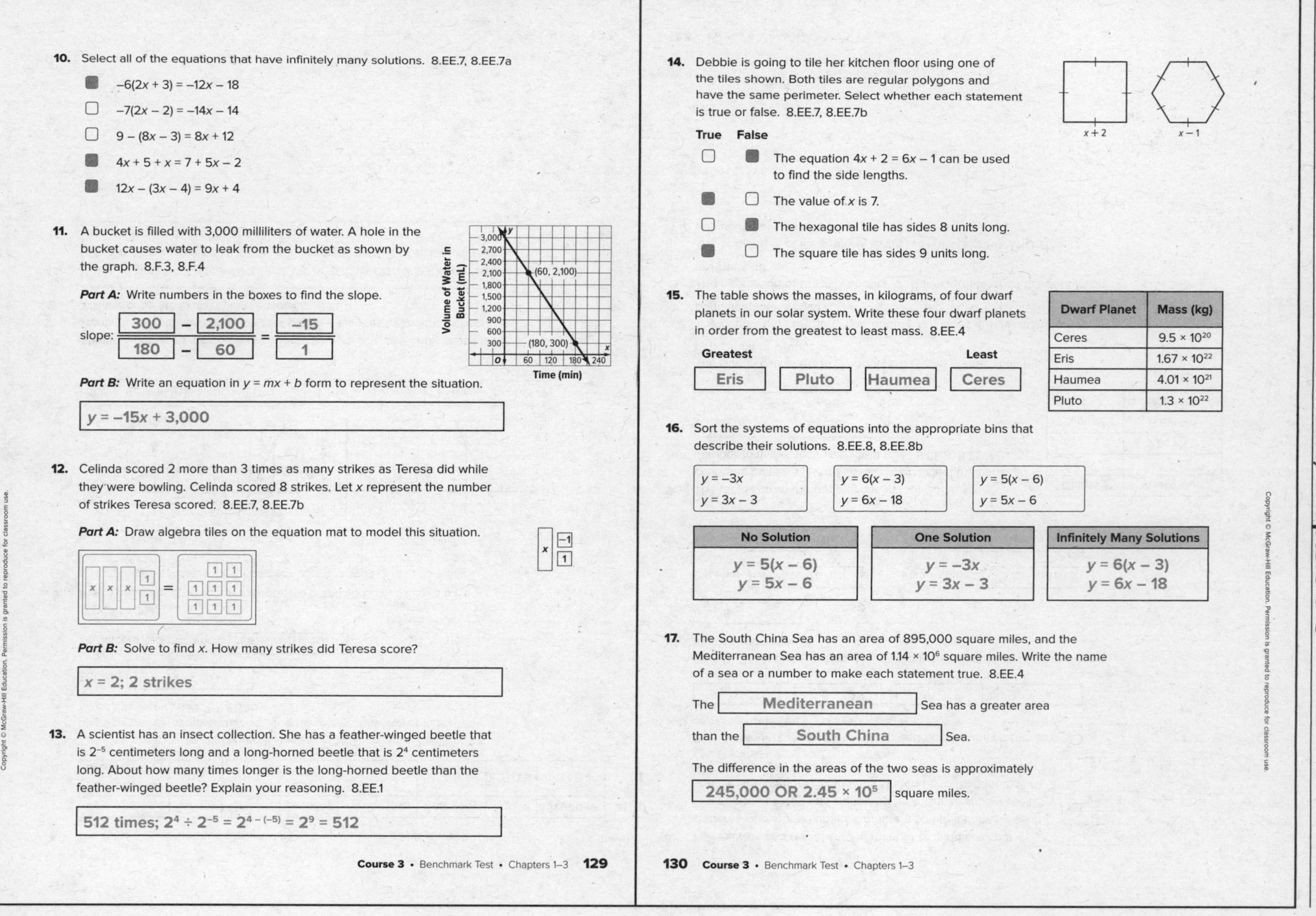

10. Select all of the equations that have infinitely many solutions. 8.EE.7, 8.EE.7a

- ■ $-6(2x + 3) = -12x - 18$
- □ $-7(2x - 2) = -14x - 14$
- □ $9 - (8x - 3) = 8x + 12$
- ■ $4x + 5 + x = 7 + 5x - 2$
- ■ $12x - (3x - 4) = 9x + 4$

11. A bucket is filled with 3,000 milliliters of water. A hole in the bucket causes water to leak from the bucket as shown by the graph. 8.F.3, 8.F.4

Part A: Write numbers in the boxes to find the slope.

slope: $\frac{300 - 2{,}100}{180 - 60} = \frac{-15}{1}$

Part B: Write an equation in $y = mx + b$ form to represent the situation.

$y = -15x + 3{,}000$

12. Celinda scored 2 more than 3 times as many strikes as Teresa did while they were bowling. Celinda scored 8 strikes. Let x represent the number of strikes Teresa scored. 8.EE.7, 8.EE.7b

Part A: Draw algebra tiles on the equation mat to model this situation.

Part B: Solve to find x. How many strikes did Teresa score?

$x = 2$; 2 strikes

13. A scientist has an insect collection. She has a feather-winged beetle that is 2^{-5} centimeters long and a long-horned beetle that is 2^4 centimeters long. About how many times longer is the long-horned beetle than the feather-winged beetle? Explain your reasoning. 8.EE.1

512 times; $2^4 \div 2^{-5} = 2^{4-(-5)} = 2^9 = 512$

14. Debbie is going to tile her kitchen floor using one of the tiles shown. Both tiles are regular polygons and have the same perimeter. Select whether each statement is true or false. 8.EE.7, 8.EE.7b

True	False	
□	■	The equation $4x + 2 = 6x - 1$ can be used to find the side lengths.
■	□	The value of x is 7.
□	■	The hexagonal tile has sides 8 units long.
■	□	The square tile has sides 9 units long.

15. The table shows the masses, in kilograms, of four dwarf planets in our solar system. Write these four dwarf planets in order from the greatest to least mass. 8.EE.4

Dwarf Planet	Mass (kg)
Ceres	9.5×10^{20}
Eris	1.67×10^{22}
Haumea	4.01×10^{21}
Pluto	1.3×10^{22}

Greatest: Eris, Pluto, Haumea, Ceres :Least

16. Sort the systems of equations into the appropriate bins that describe their solutions. 8.EE.8, 8.EE.8b

$y = -3x$, $y = 3x - 3$ | $y = 6(x - 3)$, $y = 6x - 18$ | $y = 5(x - 6)$, $y = 5x - 6$

No Solution	One Solution	Infinitely Many Solutions
$y = 5(x - 6)$ $y = 5x - 6$	$y = -3x$ $y = 3x - 3$	$y = 6(x - 3)$ $y = 6x - 18$

17. The South China Sea has an area of 895,000 square miles, and the Mediterranean Sea has an area of 1.14×10^6 square miles. Write the name of a sea or a number to make each statement true. 8.EE.4

The **Mediterranean** Sea has a greater area than the **South China** Sea.

The difference in the areas of the two seas is approximately **245,000 OR 2.45×10^5** square miles.

18. Carter buys a bus card. The table shows the amount in dollars left on the card after it had been used for several rides. The relationship is graphed on a coordinate plane. Write a number or word to complete the statements. 8.F.4

Number of Rides Taken	0	2	4
Balance on Bus Card ($)	20	15	10

The slope is **−2.5**. The y-intercept is **20**.

The **y-intercept** shows the initial amount on the card in dollars.

The **slope** shows that the amount on the card decreases by $**2.50** each time a ride is taken.

−20	0.40
−5	2.50
−2.5	5
−0.4	20
slope	y-intercept

19. Retta won 4 times as many ribbons at the county fair as Ximena did. Ximena won 6 fewer ribbons than Retta. The number of ribbons won by each friend can be represented by this system of equations. 8.EE.3, 8.EE.8b, 8.EE.8c

$y = 4x$
$y = x + 6$

Part A: Graph these equations on the coordinate plane. Plot the point of intersection.

Part B: What is the solution of the system of equations? What does the solution represent?

(2, 8); Ximena won 2 ribbons, and Retta won 8 ribbons.

20. The formula $t = \sqrt{\frac{h}{16}}$ represents the time in seconds t that it takes an object to fall from a height of h feet. 8.NS.2

Part A: Estimate, to the nearest integer, the time it takes each stone to fall when dropped from the given height.

Stone A: $h = 160$ feet **$t \approx 3$ seconds**

Stone B: $h = 544$ feet **$t \approx 6$ seconds**

Part B: Show on the number line how you estimated each time.

Stone A:

Stone B:

Page 132 • Moving to the City

Note to teacher: For this task, have students research the population, land area, and distance from your school for these cities: New York City, Los Angeles, Chicago, Houston, and Philadelphia.

Task Scenario		
Students will recognize and order rational numbers, write numbers in scientific notation, use functions to model relationships, graph proportional relationships, and write and solve linear equations and systems to discover information about U.S. cities.		
CCSS Content Standard(s)		8.NS.1, 8.EE.3, 8.EE.4, 8.EE.5, 8.EE.7, 8.EE.7a, 8.EE.8, 8.F.3, 8.F.4
Mathematical Practices		MP1, MP2, MP4, MP5, MP6, MP7
Depth of Knowledge		DOK2, DOK3, DOK4
Part	**Maximum Points**	**Scoring Rubric**
A	2	Full Credit: Sample data: **New York:** Population: 8.2×10^6; Land Area: 302.6 mi^2 **Los Angeles:** Population: 3.8×10^6; Land Area: 468.7 mi^2 **Chicago:** Population: 2.7×10^6; Land Area: 227.6 mi^2 **Houston:** Population: 2.1×10^6; Land Area: 599.6 mi^2 **Philadelphia:** Population: 1.5×10^6; Land Area: 134.1 mi^2 Both types of numbers are rational. Population is a whole number and land area is a terminating decimal. Writing population in scientific notation makes comparing large numbers easier. Partial Credit (1 point) will be given for writing the numbers correctly OR providing acceptable explanations. No credit will be given for an incorrect answer.
B	3	Full Credit: Sample answers (Students will choose 3 cities): Population, least to greatest: Philadelphia, Houston, Chicago Population densities (using actual, not rounded, populations): Philadelphia: $\frac{1,526,006}{134.1} \approx 11,380$; Houston: $\frac{2,100,263}{599.6} \approx 3,503$; Chicago: $\frac{2,695,598}{227.6} \approx 11,844$ people per square mile Population density, least to greatest: Houston, Philadelphia, Chicago The orders are not the same. Even though more people live in Houston than Philadelphia, Philadelphia is more densely populated because there is much less space in the city. Partial Credit (1 point) will be given for each of these 3: the correct population densities OR the correct order for population and population density OR an appropriate explanation. No credit will be given for an incorrect answer.

Part	Maximum Points	Scoring Rubric
C	3	Full Credit: Sample answer: Distance from school to city is 1,015 miles. (Indianapolis to Houston): From the graph, it would take about 20 hours to drive. Check: $1{,}015 = 50x$; $20.3 = x$ 20.3 is close to 20, so the estimate is reasonable. Partial Credit (1 point) will be given for each: the correct graph OR the correct estimate of time OR the correct algebraic check of the estimate. No credit will be given for an incorrect answer.
D	2	Full Credit: Sample answer: Total cost of driving: $y = 125x + (1{,}015 \div 30)(3.90)$, or $y = 125x + 131.95$ about 20 hours to drive; So it will take $20 \div 10 = 2$ days. $y = 125(2) + 131.95 = \$381.95$ total cost Partial Credit (1 point) will be given for the correct equation OR the total cost of the trip. No credit will be given for an incorrect answer.
E	2	Full Credit: Sample answer: The distance from Indianapolis to New York is 710 miles. Total cost: $y = 125x + (710 \div 30)(3.90)$, or $y = 125x + 92.3$ The slopes are the same because the meal/lodging cost doesn't change. The y-intercept is different because the distance between cities changes. System: $y = 125x + 131.95$; $y = 125x + 92.3$ Use substitution: $125x + 131.95 = 125x + 92.3$ which simplifies to $131.95 = 92.3$; the system has no solution. No matter how many days you travel, the cost of the trip will never be the same. Driving to Houston will always be more expensive than driving to New York from Indianapolis. Partial Credit (1 point) will be given for the equation for the second city and describing differences between equations OR writing and solving the system of equations and describing the solution. No credit will be given for an incorrect answer.
TOTAL	**12**	

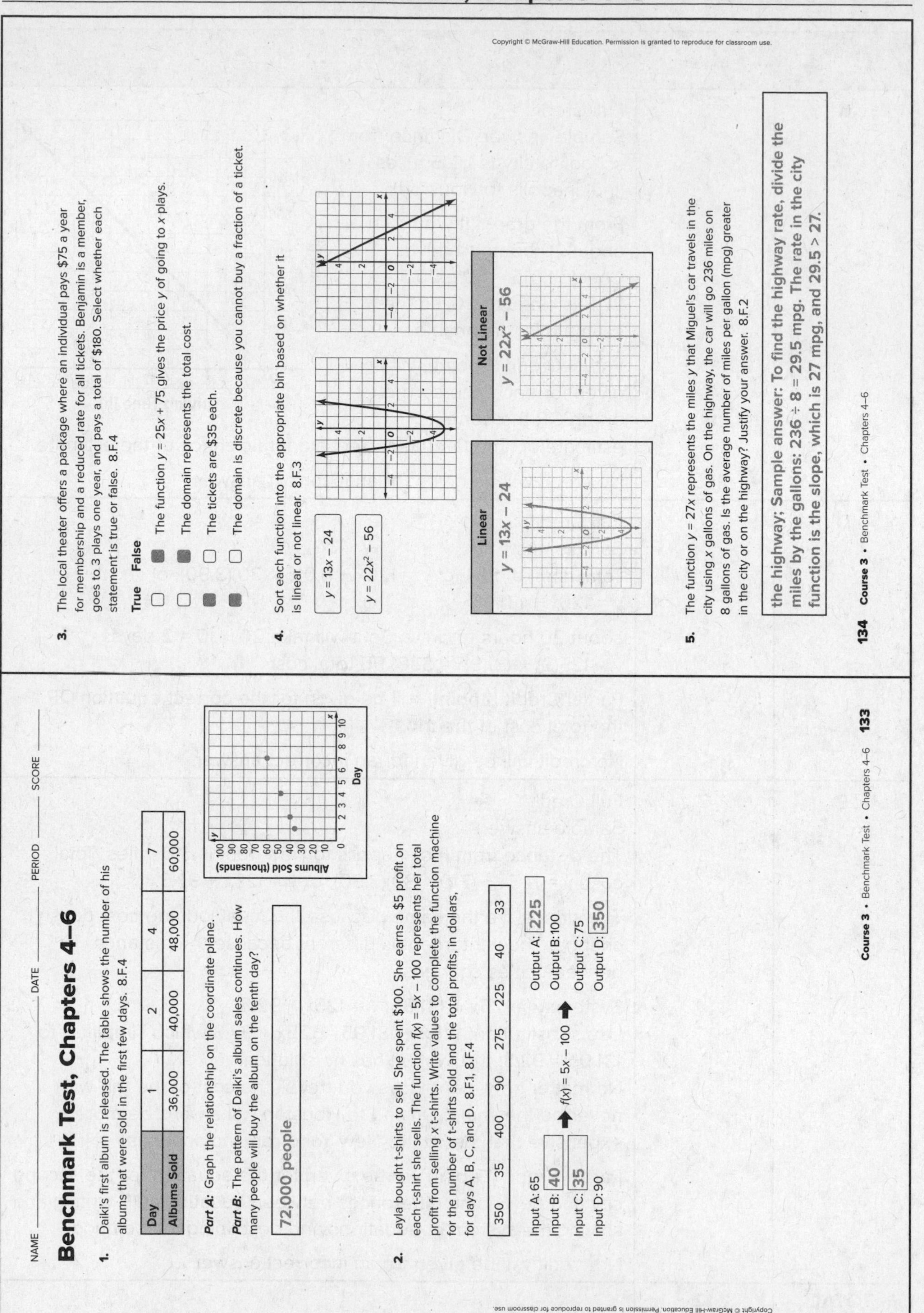

NAME ________________ DATE ________ PERIOD ______ SCORE ______

Benchmark Test, Chapters 4–6

1. Daiki's first album is released. The table shows the number of his albums that were sold in the first few days. 8.F.4

Day	1	2	4	7
Albums Sold	36,000	40,000	48,000	60,000

Part A: Graph the relationship on the coordinate plane.

Part B: The pattern of Daiki's album sales continues. How many people will buy the album on the tenth day?

72,000 people

2. Layla bought t-shirts to sell. She spent $100. She earns a $5 profit on each t-shirt she sells. The function $f(x) = 5x - 100$ represents her total profit from selling x t-shirts. Write values to complete the function machine for the number of t-shirts sold and the total profits, in dollars, for days A, B, C, and D. 8.F.1, 8.F.4

350 35 400 90 275 225 40 33

Input A: 65 → Output A: 225
Input B: 40 → Output B: 100
Input C: 35 → $f(x) = 5x - 100$ → Output C: 75
Input D: 90 → Output D: 350

3. The local theater offers a package where an individual pays $75 a year for membership and a reduced rate for all tickets. Benjamin is a member, goes to 3 plays one year, and pays a total of $180. Select whether each statement is true or false. 8.F.4

True	False	
☐	■	The function $y = 25x + 75$ gives the price y of going to x plays.
☐	■	The domain represents the total cost.
■	☐	The tickets are $35 each.
■	☐	The domain is discrete because you cannot buy a fraction of a ticket.

4. Sort each function into the appropriate bin based on whether it is linear or not linear. 8.F.3

$y = 13x - 24$

$y = 22x^2 - 56$

Linear	Not Linear
$y = 13x - 24$	$y = 22x^2 - 56$

5. The function $y = 27x$ represents the miles y that Miguel's car travels in the city using x gallons of gas. On the highway, the car will go 236 miles on 8 gallons of gas. Is the average number of miles per gallon (mpg) greater in the city or on the highway? Justify your answer. 8.F.2

the highway; Sample answer: To find the highway rate, divide the miles by the gallons: $236 \div 8 = 29.5$ mpg. The rate in the city function is the slope, which is 27 mpg, and $29.5 > 27$.

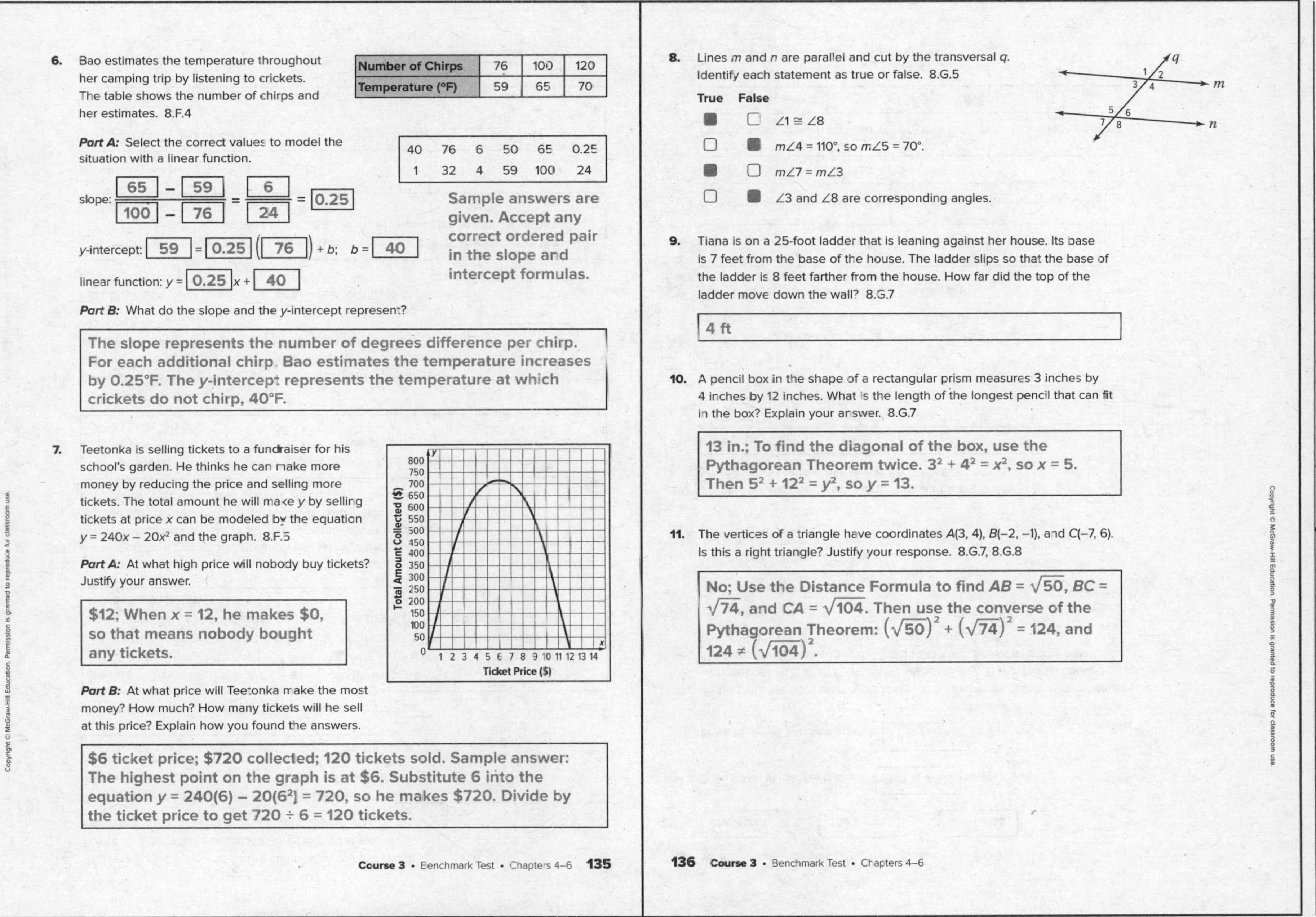

6. Bao estimates the temperature throughout her camping trip by listening to crickets. The table shows the number of chirps and her estimates. 8.F.4

Number of Chirps	76	100	120
Temperature (°F)	59	65	70

Part A: Select the correct values to model the situation with a linear function.

40	76	6	50	65	0.25
1	32	4	59	100	24

slope: $\frac{65 - 59}{100 - 76} = \frac{6}{24} = 0.25$

y-intercept: $59 = 0.25(76) + b$; $b = 40$

linear function: $y = 0.25x + 40$

Sample answers are given. Accept any correct ordered pair in the slope and intercept formulas.

Part B: What do the slope and the *y*-intercept represent?

The slope represents the number of degrees difference per chirp. For each additional chirp, Bao estimates the temperature increases by 0.25°F. The *y*-intercept represents the temperature at which crickets do not chirp, 40°F.

7. Teetonka is selling tickets to a fundraiser for his school's garden. He thinks he can make more money by reducing the price and selling more tickets. The total amount he will make *y* by selling tickets at price *x* can be modeled by the equation $y = 240x - 20x^2$ and the graph. 8.F.5

Part A: At what high price will nobody buy tickets? Justify your answer.

\$12; When $x = 12$, he makes \$0, so that means nobody bought any tickets.

Part B: At what price will Teetonka make the most money? How much? How many tickets will he sell at this price? Explain how you found the answers.

\$6 ticket price; \$720 collected; 120 tickets sold. Sample answer: The highest point on the graph is at \$6. Substitute 6 into the equation $y = 240(6) - 20(6^2) = 720$, so he makes \$720. Divide by the ticket price to get $720 \div 6 = 120$ tickets.

8. Lines *m* and *n* are parallel and cut by the transversal *q*. Identify each statement as true or false. 8.G.5

True	False	
■	☐	$\angle 1 \cong \angle 8$
☐	■	$m\angle 4 = 110°$, so $m\angle 5 = 70°$.
■	☐	$m\angle 7 = m\angle 3$
☐	■	$\angle 3$ and $\angle 8$ are corresponding angles.

9. Tiana is on a 25-foot ladder that is leaning against her house. Its base is 7 feet from the base of the house. The ladder slips so that the base of the ladder is 8 feet farther from the house. How far did the top of the ladder move down the wall? 8.G.7

4 ft

10. A pencil box in the shape of a rectangular prism measures 3 inches by 4 inches by 12 inches. What is the length of the longest pencil that can fit in the box? Explain your answer. 8.G.7

13 in.; To find the diagonal of the box, use the Pythagorean Theorem twice. $3^2 + 4^2 = x^2$, so $x = 5$. Then $5^2 + 12^2 = y^2$, so $y = 13$.

11. The vertices of a triangle have coordinates *A*(3, 4), *B*(–2, –1), and *C*(–7, 6). Is this a right triangle? Justify your response. 8.G.7, 8.G.8

No; Use the Distance Formula to find $AB = \sqrt{50}$, $BC = \sqrt{74}$, and $CA = \sqrt{104}$. Then use the converse of the Pythagorean Theorem: $(\sqrt{50})^2 + (\sqrt{74})^2 = 124$, and $124 \neq (\sqrt{104})^2$.

Benchmark Tests

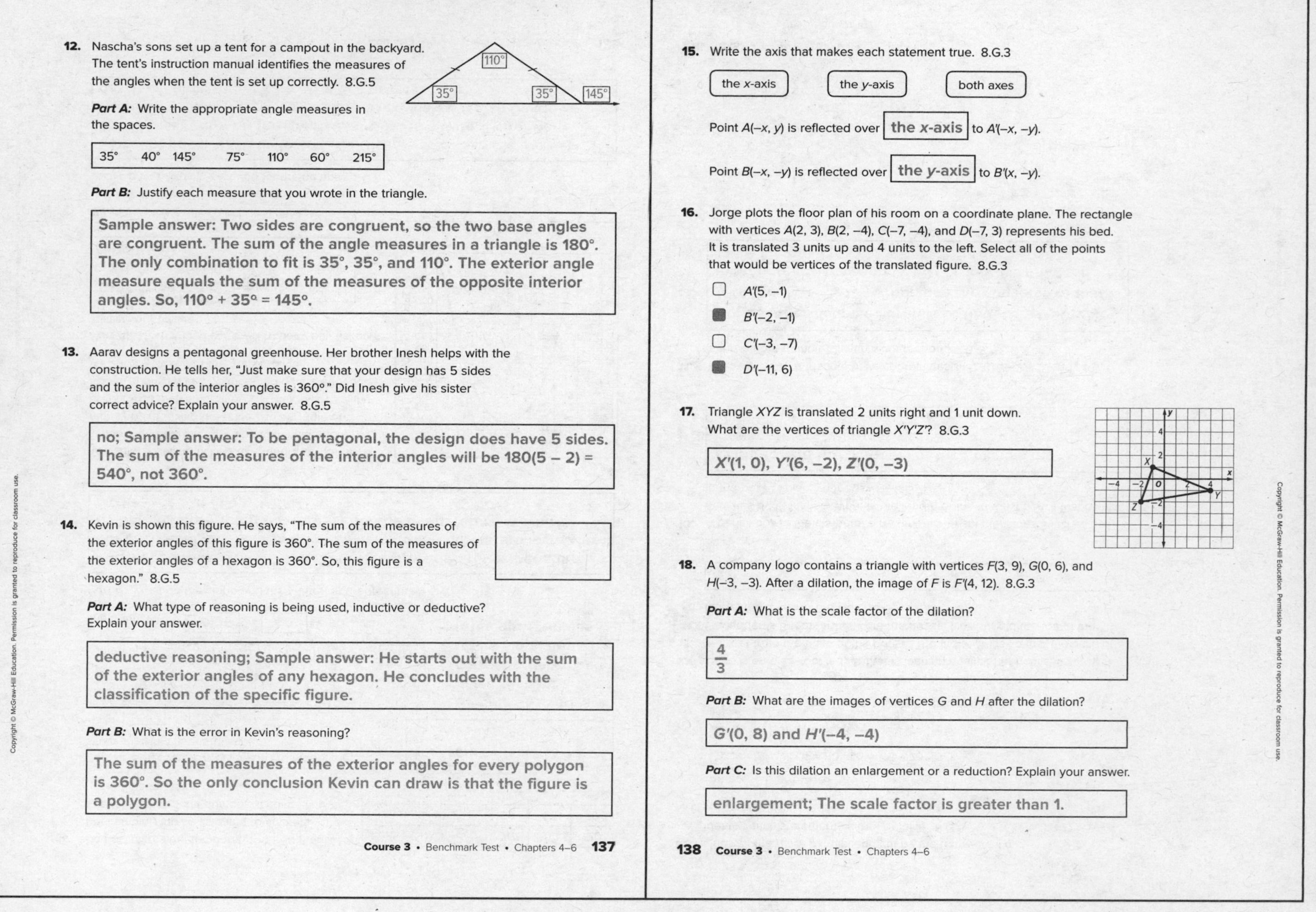

12. Nascha's sons set up a tent for a campout in the backyard. The tent's instruction manual identifies the measures of the angles when the tent is set up correctly. 8.G.5

Part A: Write the appropriate angle measures in the spaces.

35°	40°	145°	75°	110°	60°	215°

Part B: Justify each measure that you wrote in the triangle.

Sample answer: Two sides are congruent, so the two base angles are congruent. The sum of the angle measures in a triangle is 180°. The only combination to fit is 35°, 35°, and 110°. The exterior angle measure equals the sum of the measures of the opposite interior angles. So, 110° + 35° = 145°.

13. Aarav designs a pentagonal greenhouse. Her brother Inesh helps with the construction. He tells her, "Just make sure that your design has 5 sides and the sum of the interior angles is 360°." Did Inesh give his sister correct advice? Explain your answer. 8.G.5

no; Sample answer: To be pentagonal, the design does have 5 sides. The sum of the measures of the interior angles will be 180(5 – 2) = 540°, not 360°.

14. Kevin is shown this figure. He says, "The sum of the measures of the exterior angles of this figure is 360°. The sum of the measures of the exterior angles of a hexagon is 360°. So, this figure is a hexagon." 8.G.5

Part A: What type of reasoning is being used, inductive or deductive? Explain your answer.

deductive reasoning; Sample answer: He starts out with the sum of the exterior angles of any hexagon. He concludes with the classification of the specific figure.

Part B: What is the error in Kevin's reasoning?

The sum of the measures of the exterior angles for every polygon is 360°. So the only conclusion Kevin can draw is that the figure is a polygon.

15. Write the axis that makes each statement true. 8.G.3

the *x*-axis | the *y*-axis | both axes

Point $A(-x, y)$ is reflected over **the *x*-axis** to $A'(-x, -y)$.

Point $B(-x, -y)$ is reflected over **the *y*-axis** to $B'(x, -y)$.

16. Jorge plots the floor plan of his room on a coordinate plane. The rectangle with vertices $A(2, 3)$, $B(2, -4)$, $C(-7, -4)$, and $D(-7, 3)$ represents his bed. It is translated 3 units up and 4 units to the left. Select all of the points that would be vertices of the translated figure. 8.G.3

- ☐ $A'(5, -1)$
- ■ $B'(-2, -1)$
- ☐ $C'(-3, -7)$
- ■ $D'(-11, 6)$

17. Triangle *XYZ* is translated 2 units right and 1 unit down. What are the vertices of triangle $X'Y'Z'$? 8.G.3

$X'(1, 0)$, $Y'(6, -2)$, $Z'(0, -3)$

18. A company logo contains a triangle with vertices $F(3, 9)$, $G(0, 6)$, and $H(-3, -3)$. After a dilation, the image of *F* is $F'(4, 12)$. 8.G.3

Part A: What is the scale factor of the dilation?

$\frac{4}{3}$

Part B: What are the images of vertices *G* and *H* after the dilation?

$G'(0, 8)$ and $H'(-4, -4)$

Part C: Is this dilation an enlargement or a reduction? Explain your answer.

enlargement; The scale factor is greater than 1.

19. D'Andrea draws plans for a park on a coordinate plane. She includes a community table *ABCDE*. She changes the location of the table by reflecting it over the *x*-axis. Graph the reflection. 8.G.3

20. The position of a lab table shaped like a parallelogram is shown on the coordinate plane. The table is then rotated 270° clockwise about the origin. Select whether each point is a vertex of the rotated image. 8.G.3

Yes	No	
■	☐	$A'(-2, -1)$
■	☐	$B'(-2, 3)$
☐	■	$C'(-1, -2)$
☐	■	$D'(-1, 2)$

Page 140 • Soaking Up a Storm

Note to teacher: Prior to completing this task, have students research and write down the record high 1-minute rainfall and the record high 1-hour rainfall for the United States.

<table>
<tr><td colspan="3">Task Scenario
Students will use functions, tables, graphs, equations, and the Pythagorean Theorem to solve problems about the effects of a rainstorm.</td></tr>
<tr><td colspan="2">CCSS Content Standard(s)</td><td>8.EE.2, 8.F.1, 8.F.3, 8.F.4, 8.F.5, 8.G.1, 8.G.7</td></tr>
<tr><td colspan="2">Mathematical Practices</td><td>MP1, MP2, MP4, MP6, MP7</td></tr>
<tr><td colspan="2">Depth of Knowledge</td><td>DOK2, DOK3, DOK4</td></tr>
<tr><th>Part</th><th>Maximum Points</th><th>Scoring Rubric</th></tr>
<tr><td>A</td><td>4</td><td>Full Credit:
Data: 1-minute rainfall record = 1.23 inches in Unionville, Maryland, in 1956
<table>
<tr><th>Time (min)</th><td>1</td><td>2</td><td>3</td><td>4</td></tr>
<tr><th>Rainfall (in.)</th><td>1.23</td><td>2.46</td><td>3.69</td><td>4.92</td></tr>
</table>
The function is $f(m) = 1.23m$ or $r = 1.23m$.
Rainfall (in.)
Time (min)
The function is continuous because the time and rainfall can be measured using any positive number, such as 2.5 minutes or 1.23 inches.
Partial Credit (1 point) will be given for each of these 4 answers: a correct table OR a correct function OR a correct graph based on either a correct or incorrect table/function OR an accurate description of the function.
No credit will be given for an incorrect answer.</td></tr>
</table>

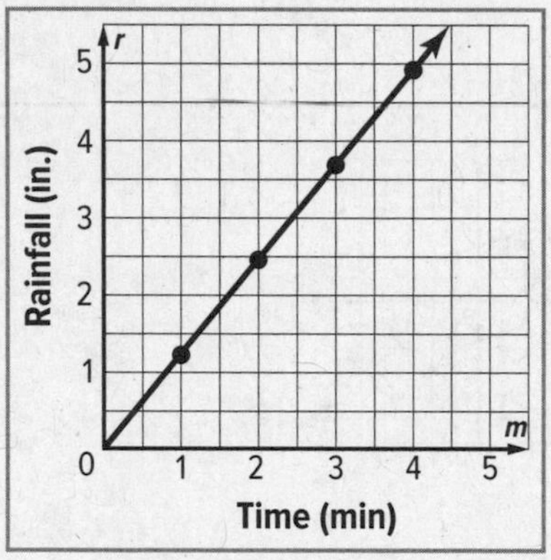

Part	Maximum Points	Scoring Rubric
B	2	Full Credit: Data: 1-hour rainfall record is 12 inches in Holt, Missouri, in 1947. Substitute 12 for r in the function $r = 1.23m$. $12 = 1.23m$ $m \approx 9.76$, so it would take about 9.76 minutes to reach the record 1-hour rainfall at the 1-minute rate. Substitute 60 minutes for m In the function $f(m) = 1.23m$. $f(60) = 1.23(60) = 73.8$, so 73.8 inches of rain would have fallen in an hour at the 1-minute rate. Partial Credit (1 point) will be given for the correct amount of time OR the correct amount of rainfall. No credit will be given for an incorrect answer.
C	1	Full Credit: Sample answer: The wind gradually picked up speed and then suddenly slowed down and stopped for a while. The wind started back up with a quick increase in speed and then slowed down a bit, before the wind increased to its greatest speed. After it peaked, it gradually decreased in speed but did not completely stop. No credit will be given for an incorrect answer.
D	2	Full Credit: A right triangle can be drawn with hypotenuse AB. The hypotenuse c is the length of segment AB. $c^2 = 5^2 + 12^2$ $c^2 = 25 + 144$ $c^2 = 169$ $c = \sqrt{169} = 13$ The distance to the ground is 13 feet. Before the tree broke, it had line, or reflectional, symmetry. The vertical line through the middle of the tree was the line of symmetry, dividing the tree into congruent parts that were mirror images of each other. Partial Credit (1 point) will be given for the correct distance the branch treetop traveled to the ground OR an accurate description of the symmetry. No credit will be given for an incorrect answer.
TOTAL	**9**	

NAME ____________ DATE ________ PERIOD ______ SCORE ______

Benchmark Test A, Chapters 1–9

1. Luis is creating a solar system with a star called Shine. Luis made a table to show the size of this solar system. Express your answers in scientific notation whenever possible. 8.EE.3, 8.EE.4

Luis' Solar System		
Planets	Distance from Shine (mi)	Diameter (ft)
Abba	3.525×10^{16}	3.525×10^{7}
Berta	7.008×10^{18}	4.748×10^{8}
Canni	2.263×10^{19}	7.003×10^{9}

How many more miles is Canni from Shine than Abba is? **2.259×10^{19} mi**

Approximately how many times bigger is the diameter of Canni than the diameter of Abba? **200**

How many more miles is Canni from Shine than Berta is? **1.562×10^{19} mi**

2. Box A has a length of 8 inches and its width and height are equal. Its volume is 1,656 cubic inches. Estimate the height of Box A. Write the volume formula to find the height. Then locate the height between two perfect squares. Finally estimate the height to the nearest whole number and explain why. 8.NS.2, 8.EE.2

Volume formula: **$1,656 = 8h^2$ OR $h^2 = 207$**

Height between perfect squares: $\sqrt{196} < \sqrt{207} < \sqrt{225}$.

Height estimate: **14 in., because 207 is closer to 196 than it is to 225.**

3. Select whether each statement is true or false. 8.NS.1, 8.EE.1

True	False	
■	□	The number $\sqrt{5}$ is an irrational number because its decimal expansion does not repeat.
■	□	The number $6.\overline{6}$ is a rational number because its decimal expansion repeats.
□	■	The number 1,785.2 is a rational integer.
□	■	$2^3 \cdot \sqrt{2} = 2^3 \cdot 2^{-2} = 2$
■	□	$\frac{4^5}{4^2} \cdot \frac{4^{-1}}{4^{-3}} = 4^5 \cdot 4^3 \cdot 4^{-1} \cdot 4^{-2} = 4^8 \cdot 4^{-3} = 4^5$

4. Jackson bought an equal number of notebooks and binders. The notebooks cost \$1.25 each, and the binders cost \$3.50 each. He spent a total of \$28.50. 8.EE.7, 8.EE.7b

Deanna's solution:

Let x be the number of notebooks.

$1.25x + 3.5x = 28.50$
$4.75x = 28.50$
$x = 6$

Jackson purchased 6 notebooks.

Part A: Select whether each statement is true or false.

True	False	
□	■	Deanna correctly used x to represent the number of notebooks Jackson bought.
■	□	Deanna added the coefficients correctly.
■	□	Deanna computed $28.50 \div 4.75$ accurately.
■	□	Deanna is correct that Jackson purchased 6 notebooks.

Part B: How many binders did Jackson buy? What was their cost?

6 binders; \$21.00

5. Sort the equations into the bin that correctly describes the solution. 8.EE.7, 8.EE.7a

$6a + 19 = 2(3a + 5) + 9$	$0.3(a - 8) = 0.2(a + 4)$	$0.25(24 - 12a) = -3a + 6$
$2(5a + 4) = 4a + 8$	$3(2a + 1) - a = 6 + 5a$	$2(a - 2) = 2(a - 3) - 2$

No Solution	One Solution	Infinitely Many Solutions
$2(a - 2) = 2(a - 3) - 2$	$2(5a + 4) = 4a + 8$	$6a + 19 = 2(3a + 5) + 9$
$3(2a + 1) - a = 6 + 5a$	$0.3(a - 8) = 0.2(a + 4)$	$0.25(24 - 12a) = -3a + 6$

6. A cell phone company has two price plans for their service. Select whether each statement is true or false. 8.EE.7, 8.EE.7b

	Monthly Charge	Minute Limit	Over Limit Price per Minute
Plan A	\$26	1,000	\$0.20
Plan B	\$12	500	\$0.48

True	False	
■	□	The plans cost the same when the over-limit minutes are 50.
□	■	Plan B costs more than Plan A when over-limit minutes are less than 50.
■	□	A customer would choose Plan B over Plan A when he or she plans on using under 500 minutes a month.

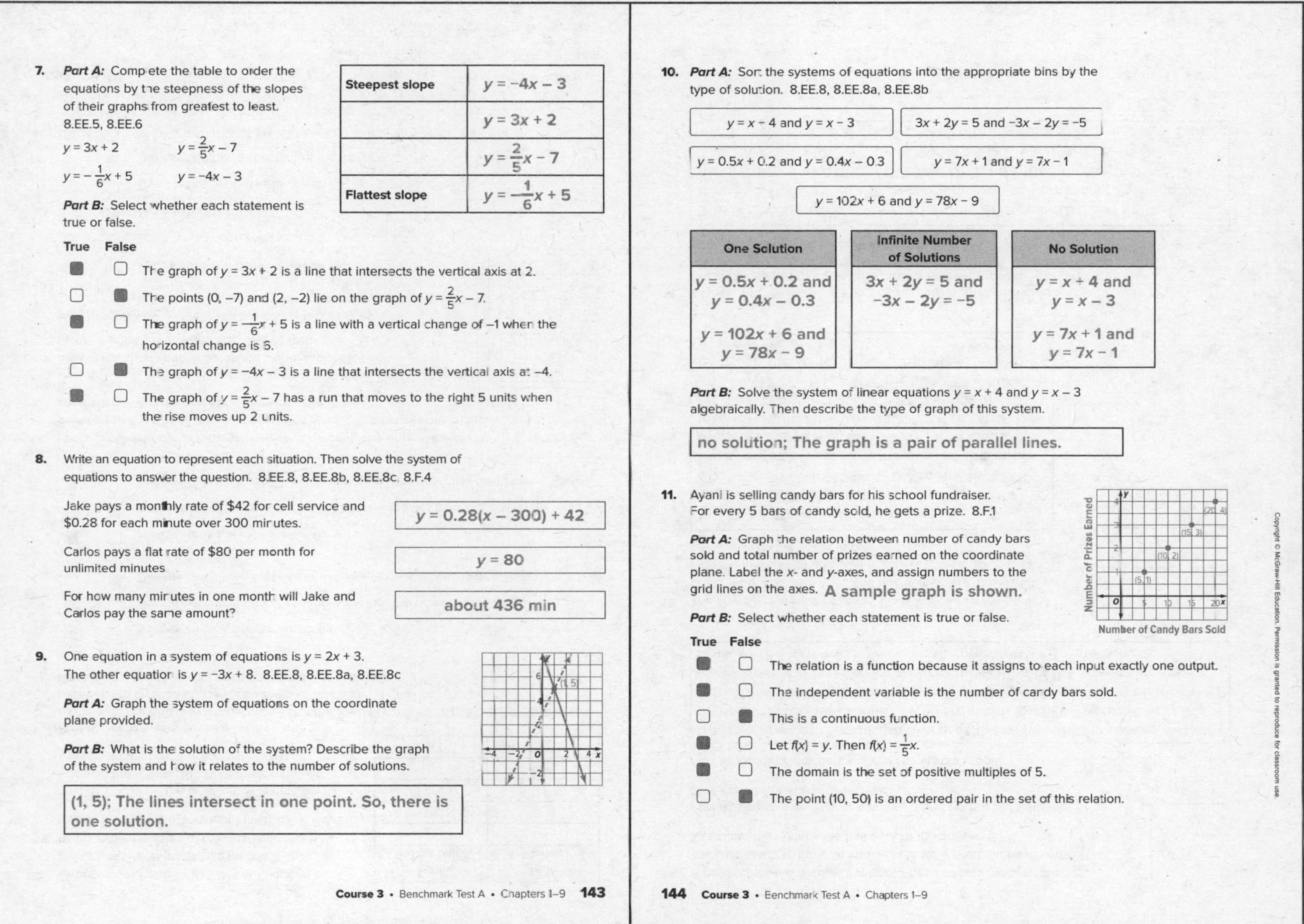

7. *Part A:* Complete the table to order the equations by the steepness of the slopes of their graphs from greatest to least. 8.EE.5, 8.EE.6

$y = 3x + 2$ $y = \frac{2}{5}x - 7$

$y = -\frac{1}{6}x + 5$ $y = -4x - 3$

Steepest slope	$y = -4x - 3$
	$y = 3x + 2$
	$y = \frac{2}{5}x - 7$
Flattest slope	$y = -\frac{1}{6}x + 5$

Part B: Select whether each statement is true or false.

True	False	
■	□	The graph of $y = 3x + 2$ is a line that intersects the vertical axis at 2.
□	■	The points (0, –7) and (2, –2) lie on the graph of $y = \frac{2}{5}x - 7$.
■	□	The graph of $y = -\frac{1}{6}x + 5$ is a line with a vertical change of –1 when the horizontal change is 6.
□	■	The graph of $y = -4x - 3$ is a line that intersects the vertical axis at –4.
■	□	The graph of $y = \frac{2}{5}x - 7$ has a run that moves to the right 5 units when the rise moves up 2 units.

8. Write an equation to represent each situation. Then solve the system of equations to answer the question. 8.EE.8, 8.EE.8b, 8.EE.8c, 8.F.4

Jake pays a monthly rate of $42 for cell service and $0.28 for each minute over 300 minutes. **$y = 0.28(x - 300) + 42$**

Carlos pays a flat rate of $80 per month for unlimited minutes **$y = 80$**

For how many minutes in one month will Jake and Carlos pay the same amount? **about 436 min**

9. One equation in a system of equations is $y = 2x + 3$. The other equation is $y = -3x + 8$. 8.EE.8, 8.EE.8a, 8.EE.8c

Part A: Graph the system of equations on the coordinate plane provided.

Part B: What is the solution of the system? Describe the graph of the system and how it relates to the number of solutions.

(1, 5); The lines intersect in one point. So, there is one solution.

10. *Part A:* Sort the systems of equations into the appropriate bins by the type of solution. 8.EE.8, 8.EE.8a, 8.EE.8b

$y = x - 4$ and $y = x - 3$ | $3x + 2y = 5$ and $-3x - 2y = -5$ | $y = 0.5x + 0.2$ and $y = 0.4x - 0.3$ | $y = 7x + 1$ and $y = 7x - 1$ | $y = 102x + 6$ and $y = 78x - 9$

One Solution	Infinite Number of Solutions	No Solution
$y = 0.5x + 0.2$ and $y = 0.4x - 0.3$	$3x + 2y = 5$ and $-3x - 2y = -5$	$y = x + 4$ and $y = x - 3$
$y = 102x + 6$ and $y = 78x - 9$		$y = 7x + 1$ and $y = 7x - 1$

Part B: Solve the system of linear equations $y = x + 4$ and $y = x - 3$ algebraically. Then describe the type of graph of this system.

no solution; The graph is a pair of parallel lines.

11. Ayani is selling candy bars for his school fundraiser. For every 5 bars of candy sold, he gets a prize. 8.F.1

Part A: Graph the relation between number of candy bars sold and total number of prizes earned on the coordinate plane. Label the x- and y-axes, and assign numbers to the grid lines on the axes. **A sample graph is shown.**

Part B: Select whether each statement is true or false.

True	False	
■	□	The relation is a function because it assigns to each input exactly one output.
■	□	The independent variable is the number of candy bars sold.
□	■	This is a continuous function.
■	□	Let $f(x) = y$. Then $f(x) = \frac{1}{5}x$.
■	□	The domain is the set of positive multiples of 5.
□	■	The point (10, 50) is an ordered pair in the set of this relation.

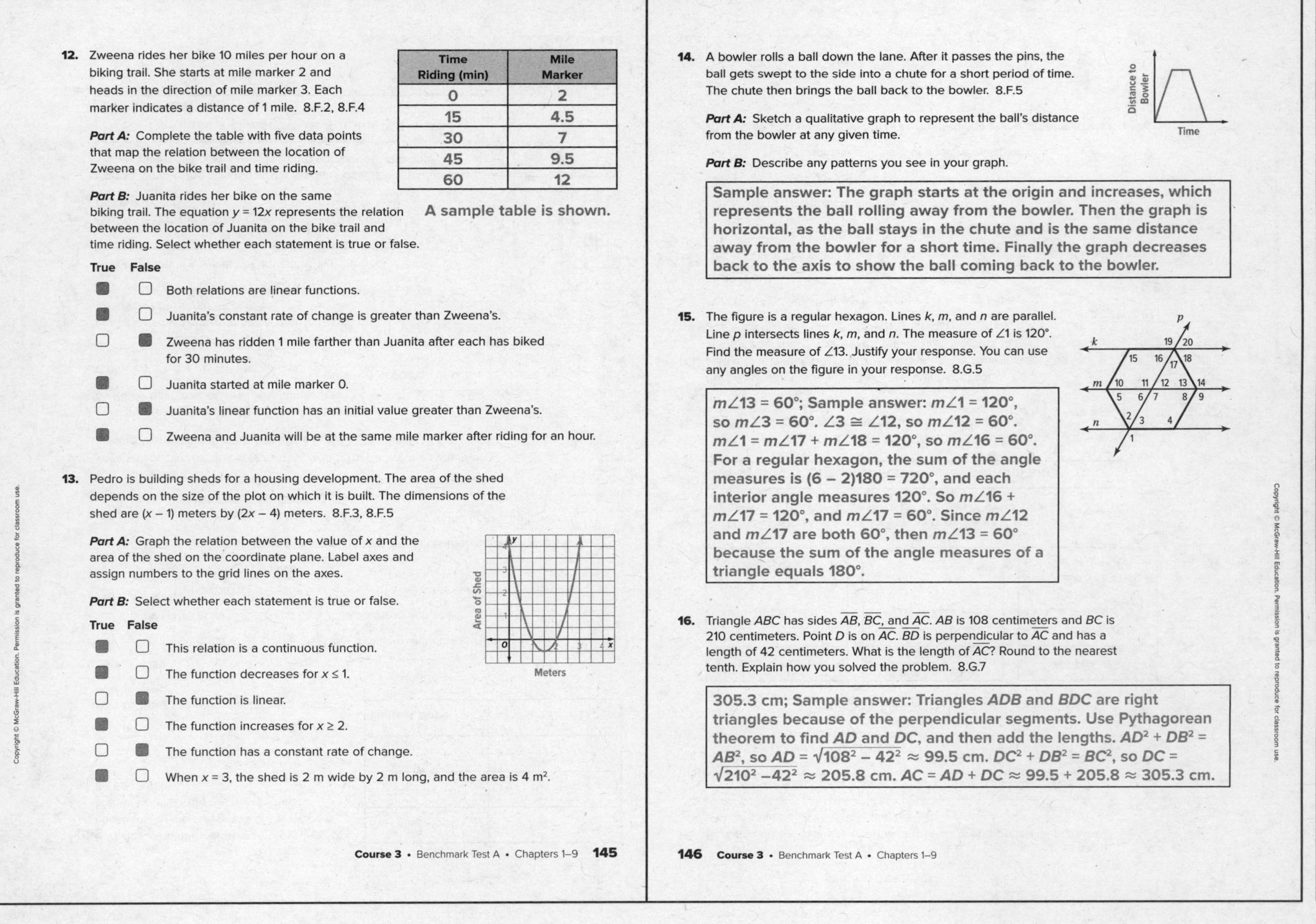

12. Zweena rides her bike 10 miles per hour on a biking trail. She starts at mile marker 2 and heads in the direction of mile marker 3. Each marker indicates a distance of 1 mile. 8.F.2, 8.F.4

Part A: Complete the table with five data points that map the relation between the location of Zweena on the bike trail and time riding.

Time Riding (min)	Mile Marker
0	2
15	4.5
30	7
45	9.5
60	12

A sample table is shown.

Part B: Juanita rides her bike on the same biking trail. The equation $y = 12x$ represents the relation between the location of Juanita on the bike trail and time riding. Select whether each statement is true or false.

True	False	
■	□	Both relations are linear functions.
■	□	Juanita's constant rate of change is greater than Zweena's.
□	■	Zweena has ridden 1 mile farther than Juanita after each has biked for 30 minutes.
■	□	Juanita started at mile marker 0.
□	■	Juanita's linear function has an initial value greater than Zweena's.
■	□	Zweena and Juanita will be at the same mile marker after riding for an hour.

13. Pedro is building sheds for a housing development. The area of the shed depends on the size of the plot on which it is built. The dimensions of the shed are $(x - 1)$ meters by $(2x - 4)$ meters. 8.F.3, 8.F.5

Part A: Graph the relation between the value of x and the area of the shed on the coordinate plane. Label axes and assign numbers to the grid lines on the axes.

Part B: Select whether each statement is true or false.

True	False	
■	□	This relation is a continuous function.
■	□	The function decreases for $x \le 1$.
□	■	The function is linear.
■	□	The function increases for $x \ge 2$.
□	■	The function has a constant rate of change.
■	□	When $x = 3$, the shed is 2 m wide by 2 m long, and the area is 4 m².

14. A bowler rolls a ball down the lane. After it passes the pins, the ball gets swept to the side into a chute for a short period of time. The chute then brings the ball back to the bowler. 8.F.5

Part A: Sketch a qualitative graph to represent the ball's distance from the bowler at any given time.

Part B: Describe any patterns you see in your graph.

Sample answer: The graph starts at the origin and increases, which represents the ball rolling away from the bowler. Then the graph is horizontal, as the ball stays in the chute and is the same distance away from the bowler for a short time. Finally the graph decreases back to the axis to show the ball coming back to the bowler.

15. The figure is a regular hexagon. Lines k, m, and n are parallel. Line p intersects lines k, m, and n. The measure of $\angle 1$ is 120°. Find the measure of $\angle 13$. Justify your response. You can use any angles on the figure in your response. 8.G.5

$m\angle 13 = 60°$; Sample answer: $m\angle 1 = 120°$, so $m\angle 3 = 60°$. $\angle 3 \cong \angle 12$, so $m\angle 12 = 60°$. $m\angle 1 = m\angle 17 + m\angle 18 = 120°$, so $m\angle 16 = 60°$. For a regular hexagon, the sum of the angle measures is $(6 - 2)180 = 720°$, and each interior angle measures 120°. So $m\angle 16 + m\angle 17 = 120°$, and $m\angle 17 = 60°$. Since $m\angle 12$ and $m\angle 17$ are both 60°, then $m\angle 13 = 60°$ because the sum of the angle measures of a triangle equals 180°.

16. Triangle ABC has sides $\overline{AB}$, $\overline{BC}$, and $\overline{AC}$. AB is 108 centimeters and BC is 210 centimeters. Point D is on $\overline{AC}$. $\overline{BD}$ is perpendicular to $\overline{AC}$ and has a length of 42 centimeters. What is the length of $\overline{AC}$? Round to the nearest tenth. Explain how you solved the problem. 8.G.7

305.3 cm; Sample answer: Triangles ADB and BDC are right triangles because of the perpendicular segments. Use Pythagorean theorem to find AD and DC, and then add the lengths. $AD^2 + DB^2 = AB^2$, so $AD = \sqrt{108^2 - 42^2} \approx 99.5$ cm. $DC^2 + DB^2 = BC^2$, so $DC = \sqrt{210^2 - 42^2} \approx 205.8$ cm. $AC = AD + DC \approx 99.5 + 205.8 \approx 305.3$ cm.

17. Select whether the statements describe similar figures. 8.G.4, 8.EE.6

Yes	No	
■	☐	A square has an area of 16 ft² and another square has an area of 81 ft².
■	☐	The slope of a right triangle's hypotenuse is 3 and the slope of another right triangle's hypotenuse is –3.
☐	■	The perimeter of a hexagon is 30 in. and the perimeter of another hexagon is 60 in.
■	☐	A pentagon is reflected over the *y*-axis and then dilated by a scale factor of 0.4.
☐	■	The slope of a right triangle's hypotenuse is 4 and the slope of another right triangle's hypotenuse is 0.25.

18. The beads on a loom line up in an array of rows and columns just like on a coordinate plane. You can make a pattern by performing a transformation of the shaded box with vertices at (2, 0), (4, 0), (2, 2), and (4, 2). 8.G.1, 8.G.3

Part A: Perform $(x, y) \rightarrow (x + 2, y + 2)$ and shade in the result. Then perform $(x', y') \rightarrow (x' - 2, y' + 2)$ and shade in the result.

Part B: What type of transformations did you perform? Explain.

Translations; The coordinates of the figure were changed by adding or subtracting numbers to *x* and *y*.

19. Triangle *ABC* with vertices *A*(0, 0), *B*(0 –5), and *C*(–4, –5) is transformed 3 separate times. Starting with triangle ABC each time, complete the table with a description of the three transformations on triangle *ABC*. 8.G.1 8.G.3

Transformation 1	**A clockwise 90° (or counterclockwise 270°) rotation about the origin.**
Transformation 2	**A clockwise (or counterclockwise) 180° rotation about the origin.**
Transformation 3	**A clockwise 270° (or counterclockwise 90°) rotation about the origin.**

20. A trapezoid *ABCD* has vertices *A*(0, 0), *B*(8, 0), *C*(6, 4), and *D*(2, 4). 8.G.3

Part A: The trapezoid is dilated by a scale factor of 0.5 and then translated 6 units right and 8 units up. Find the coordinates of trapezoid *A″B″C″D″*.

***A″*(6, 8), *B″*(10, 8), *C″*(9, 10), *D″*(7, 10)**

Part B: The translation is performed first and then the dilation. Will you get the same set of coordinates as in Part A? Explain.

No; *A″*(3, 4), *B″*(7, 4), *C″*(6, 6), *D″*(4, 6), because the operations of division and addition are not commutative with each other.

21. Ana is 5.5 feet tall. Her shadow is 2.4 feet long. The hot-air balloon on the ground next to her is casting a 26.4-foot-long shadow. A nearby flagpole is 42 feet tall. Find each measure to the nearest tenth. 8.G.4, 8.G.7

height of the hot-air balloon: **60.5 ft**

length of the shadow of the flagpole: **18.3 ft**

22. The sliding board at a pool has a height of 14 feet and a horizontal length from ladder to bottom of slide of 12 feet. The amusement park sliding board has a height of 40 feet and a horizontal length from ladder to bottom of slide of 32 feet. Select whether each statement is true or false. 8.G.7, 8.EE.6

True	False	
■	☐	The slope of the pool sliding board is $\frac{7}{6}$ ft.
☐	■	The slope of the amusement park sliding board is $\frac{4}{5}$ ft.
■	☐	The amusement park sliding board is steeper but not by much.

23. Hernando is mountain biking and maps his route on a coordinate plane. He starts at the origin and then rides 6 miles east, 3 miles north, 2 miles east again, and 8 miles south. 8.G.8

What are the coordinates of Hernando's endpoint? **(8, –5)**

What is the shortest distance back to where Hernando started? Round to the nearest tenth.

9.4 miles

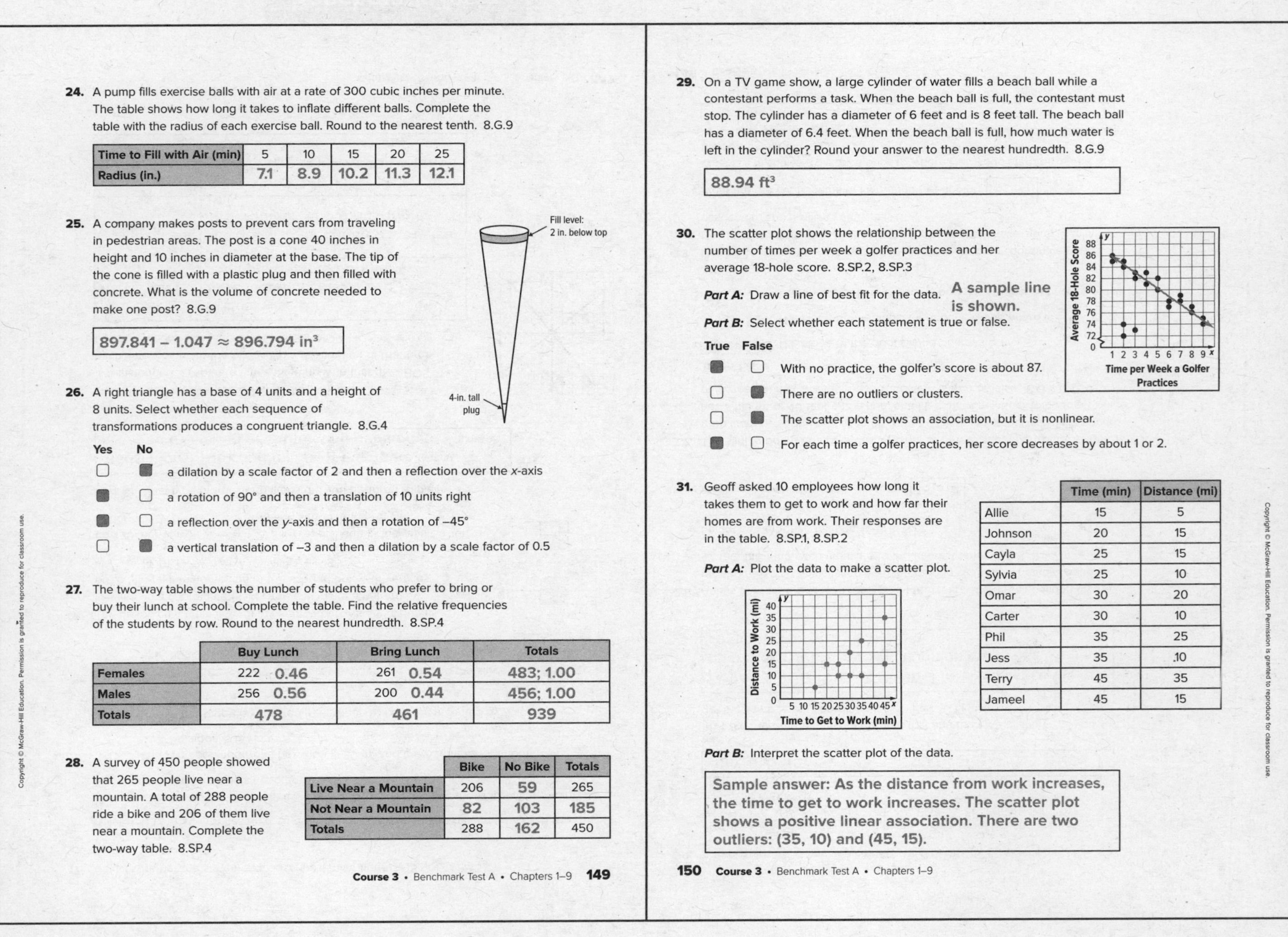

24. A pump fills exercise balls with air at a rate of 300 cubic inches per minute. The table shows how long it takes to inflate different balls. Complete the table with the radius of each exercise ball. Round to the nearest tenth. 8.G.9

Time to Fill with Air (min)	5	10	15	20	25
Radius (in.)	7.1	8.9	10.2	11.3	12.1

25. A company makes posts to prevent cars from traveling in pedestrian areas. The post is a cone 40 inches in height and 10 inches in diameter at the base. The tip of the cone is filled with a plastic plug and then filled with concrete. What is the volume of concrete needed to make one post? 8.G.9

897.841 – 1.047 ≈ 896.794 in³

26. A right triangle has a base of 4 units and a height of 8 units. Select whether each sequence of transformations produces a congruent triangle. 8.G.4

Yes	No	
☐	■	a dilation by a scale factor of 2 and then a reflection over the *x*-axis
■	☐	a rotation of 90° and then a translation of 10 units right
■	☐	a reflection over the *y*-axis and then a rotation of –45°
☐	■	a vertical translation of –3 and then a dilation by a scale factor of 0.5

27. The two-way table shows the number of students who prefer to bring or buy their lunch at school. Complete the table. Find the relative frequencies of the students by row. Round to the nearest hundredth. 8.SP.4

	Buy Lunch	Bring Lunch	Totals
Females	222 0.46	261 0.54	483; 1.00
Males	256 0.56	200 0.44	456; 1.00
Totals	478	461	939

28. A survey of 450 people showed that 265 people live near a mountain. A total of 288 people ride a bike and 206 of them live near a mountain. Complete the two-way table. 8.SP.4

	Bike	No Bike	Totals
Live Near a Mountain	206	59	265
Not Near a Mountain	82	103	185
Totals	288	162	450

29. On a TV game show, a large cylinder of water fills a beach ball while a contestant performs a task. When the beach ball is full, the contestant must stop. The cylinder has a diameter of 6 feet and is 8 feet tall. The beach ball has a diameter of 6.4 feet. When the beach ball is full, how much water is left in the cylinder? Round your answer to the nearest hundredth. 8.G.9

88.94 ft³

30. The scatter plot shows the relationship between the number of times per week a golfer practices and her average 18-hole score. 8.SP.2, 8.SP.3

Part A: Draw a line of best fit for the data. **A sample line is shown.**

Part B: Select whether each statement is true or false.

True	False	
■	☐	With no practice, the golfer's score is about 87.
☐	■	There are no outliers or clusters.
☐	■	The scatter plot shows an association, but it is nonlinear.
■	☐	For each time a golfer practices, her score decreases by about 1 or 2.

31. Geoff asked 10 employees how long it takes them to get to work and how far their homes are from work. Their responses are in the table. 8.SP.1, 8.SP.2

	Time (min)	Distance (mi)
Allie	15	5
Johnson	20	15
Cayla	25	15
Sylvia	25	10
Omar	30	20
Carter	30	10
Phil	35	25
Jess	35	10
Terry	45	35
Jameel	45	15

Part A: Plot the data to make a scatter plot.

Part B: Interpret the scatter plot of the data.

Sample answer: As the distance from work increases, the time to get to work increases. The scatter plot shows a positive linear association. There are two outliers: (35, 10) and (45, 15).

Page 151 • It's All Downhill From Here!

Task Scenario		
Students will use their understanding of how to map the relationship between two quantities in a real-world situation to interpret and analyze the data that Sisay and Mika collect on the ski runs.		
CCSS Content Standard(s)		8.EE.5, 8.EE.8, 8.EE.8a, 8.EE.8b, 8.F.4, 8.G.7, 8.SP.4
Mathematical Practices		MP1, MP2, MP3, MP4, MP5, MP6, MP7
Depth of Knowledge		DOK2, DOK3
Part	**Maximum Points**	**Scoring Rubric**
A	2	Full Credit: Sample answer: Sisay's average speed = $\frac{12.6 - 8.4}{3 - 2} = 4.2$ m/s Mika's average speed = $\frac{7.0 - 3.5}{2 - 1} = 3.5$ m/s $4.2 > 3.5$, so Sisay's speed is faster. Partial Credit (1 point) will be given for the correct speed for one person OR for the correct answer about who is faster, without the speeds. No credit will be given for an incorrect answer.
B	3	Full Credit: Total cost for a day, where x is the number of hours of service from a ski guide: Powder Fresh's total cost: $y = 48x + 62$ Got Snow's total cost: $y = 43x + 70$ When the functions are equal, the total cost for skiing for the day at both resorts is the same. Set the functions equal to each other, and solve for x. $48x + 62 = 43x + 70$ $5x = 8$ $x = 1.6$ $y = 48(1.6) + 62 = 138.8$ or $y = 43(1.6) + 70 = 138.8$ The cost to ski for one day and use a ski guide for 1.6 hours is $138.80 at both ski resorts. Partial Credit (2 points) will be given for the correct functions and values of x and y OR the correct functions and an appropriate explanation of the functions being equal OR the correct values of x and y and an appropriate explanation of the functions being equal. Partial Credit (1 point) will be given for the correct functions OR the correct values of x and y OR an appropriate explanation of the functions being equal. No credit will be given for an incorrect answer.

<table>
<tr><th>Part</th><th>Maximum Points</th><th>Scoring Rubric</th></tr>
<tr><td>C</td><td>2</td><td>
Full Credit:
<table>
<tr><th></th><th>400 m long</th><th>550 m long</th><th>Totals</th></tr>
<tr><td>Elevation: 150 m</td><td>$\frac{22}{25}$; 0.88</td><td>$\frac{3}{25}$; 0.12</td><td>25; 1.00</td></tr>
<tr><td>Elevation: 300 m</td><td>$\frac{2}{21}$; 0.10</td><td>$\frac{19}{21}$; 0.90</td><td>21; 1.00</td></tr>
</table>
Sample answer: It is very likely that a ski run with an elevation of 150 m will have a length of 400 m. It is highly likely that a ski run with an elevation of 300 m will have a length of 550 m.
Partial Credit (1 point) will be given for the correct relative frequencies OR a correct interpretation of the relative frequencies.
No credit will be given for an incorrect answer.
</td></tr>
<tr><td>D</td><td>3</td><td>
Full Credit:
Use the Pythagorean Theorem to find the base length of each ski run.
elevation^2 + base^2 = length^2
$150^2 + b^2 = 400^2$; $b^2 = 137{,}500$; approx. 371 m
$300^2 + b^2 = 400^2$; $b^2 = 70{,}000$; approx. 265 m
$150^2 + b^2 = 550^2$; $b^2 = 280{,}000$; approx. 529 m
$300^2 + b^2 = 550^2$; $b^2 = 212{,}500$; approx. 461 m
<table>
<tr><th>Length (m)</th><th>Elevation (m)</th><th>Ski Run Grade</th><th>Steepness</th></tr>
<tr><td>400</td><td>150</td><td>$\frac{150}{371} \approx 40\%$</td><td>third steepest</td></tr>
<tr><td>400</td><td>300</td><td>$\frac{300}{265} \approx 113\%$</td><td>steepest</td></tr>
<tr><td>550</td><td>150</td><td>$\frac{150}{529} \approx 28\%$</td><td>least steep</td></tr>
<tr><td>550</td><td>300</td><td>$\frac{300}{461} \approx 65\%$</td><td>second steepest</td></tr>
</table>
Partial Credit (2 points) will be given for correct base lengths and grades OR correct grades and comparison of steepness.
Partial Credit (1 point) will be given for correct base lengths OR correct grades OR correct comparison of steepness of the ski runs.
No credit will be given for an incorrect answer.
</td></tr>
<tr><td>TOTAL</td><td>10</td><td></td></tr>
</table>

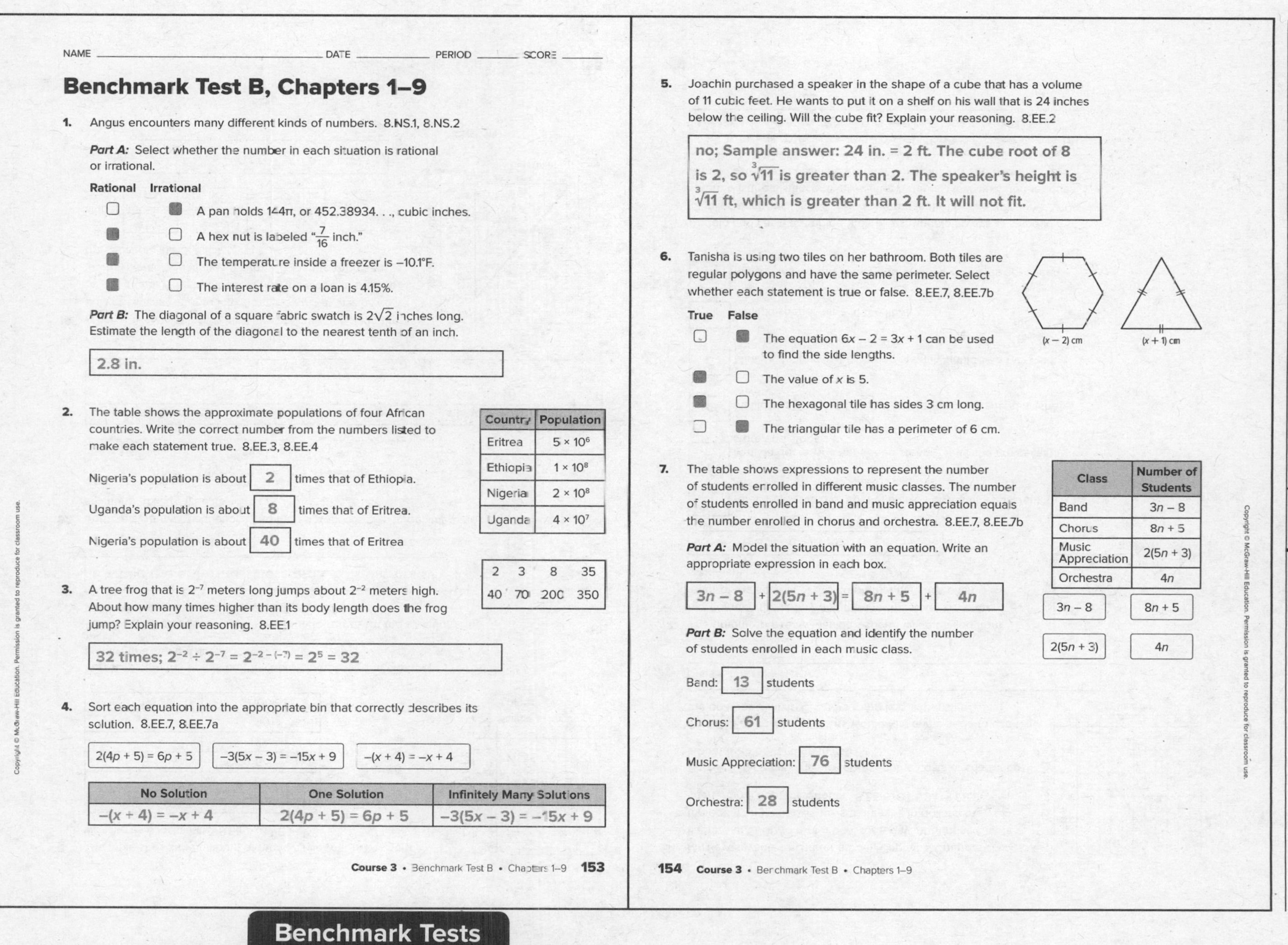

NAME ______________ DATE ________ PERIOD ______ SCORE ______

Benchmark Test B, Chapters 1–9

1. Angus encounters many different kinds of numbers. 8.NS.1, 8.NS.2

Part A: Select whether the number in each situation is rational or irrational.

Rational	Irrational	
□	■	A pan holds 144π, or 452.38934. . ., cubic inches.
■	□	A hex nut is labeled "$\frac{7}{16}$ inch."
■	□	The temperature inside a freezer is –10.1°F.
■	□	The interest rate on a loan is 4.15%.

Part B: The diagonal of a square fabric swatch is $2\sqrt{2}$ inches long. Estimate the length of the diagonal to the nearest tenth of an inch.

2.8 in.

2. The table shows the approximate populations of four African countries. Write the correct number from the numbers listed to make each statement true. 8.EE.3, 8.EE.4

Country	Population
Eritrea	5×10^6
Ethiopia	1×10^8
Nigeria	2×10^8
Uganda	4×10^7

Nigeria's population is about **2** times that of Ethiopia.

Uganda's population is about **8** times that of Eritrea.

Nigeria's population is about **40** times that of Eritrea

2	3	8	35
40	70	200	350

3. A tree frog that is 2^{-7} meters long jumps about 2^{-2} meters high. About how many times higher than its body length does the frog jump? Explain your reasoning. 8.EE.1

32 times; $2^{-2} \div 2^{-7} = 2^{-2-(-7)} = 2^5 = 32$

4. Sort each equation into the appropriate bin that correctly describes its solution. 8.EE.7, 8.EE.7a

$2(4p + 5) = 6p + 5$ | $-3(5x - 3) = -15x + 9$ | $-(x + 4) = -x + 4$

No Solution	One Solution	Infinitely Many Solutions
$-(x + 4) = -x + 4$	$2(4p + 5) = 6p + 5$	$-3(5x - 3) = -15x + 9$

5. Joachin purchased a speaker in the shape of a cube that has a volume of 11 cubic feet. He wants to put it on a shelf on his wall that is 24 inches below the ceiling. Will the cube fit? Explain your reasoning. 8.EE.2

no; Sample answer: 24 in. = 2 ft. The cube root of 8 is 2, so $\sqrt[3]{11}$ is greater than 2. The speaker's height is $\sqrt[3]{11}$ ft, which is greater than 2 ft. It will not fit.

6. Tanisha is using two tiles on her bathroom. Both tiles are regular polygons and have the same perimeter. Select whether each statement is true or false. 8.EE.7, 8.EE.7b

(x – 2) cm

(x + 1) cm

True	False	
□	■	The equation $6x - 2 = 3x + 1$ can be used to find the side lengths.
■	□	The value of x is 5.
■	□	The hexagonal tile has sides 3 cm long.
□	■	The triangular tile has a perimeter of 6 cm.

7. The table shows expressions to represent the number of students enrolled in different music classes. The number of students enrolled in band and music appreciation equals the number enrolled in chorus and orchestra. 8.EE.7, 8.EE.7b

Class	Number of Students
Band	$3n - 8$
Chorus	$8n + 5$
Music Appreciation	$2(5n + 3)$
Orchestra	$4n$

Part A: Model the situation with an equation. Write an appropriate expression in each box.

$3n - 8$ + **$2(5n + 3)$** = **$8n + 5$** + **$4n$**

$3n - 8$ | $8n + 5$ | $2(5n + 3)$ | $4n$

Part B: Solve the equation and identify the number of students enrolled in each music class.

Band: **13** students

Chorus: **61** students

Music Appreciation: **76** students

Orchestra: **28** students

Benchmark Tests

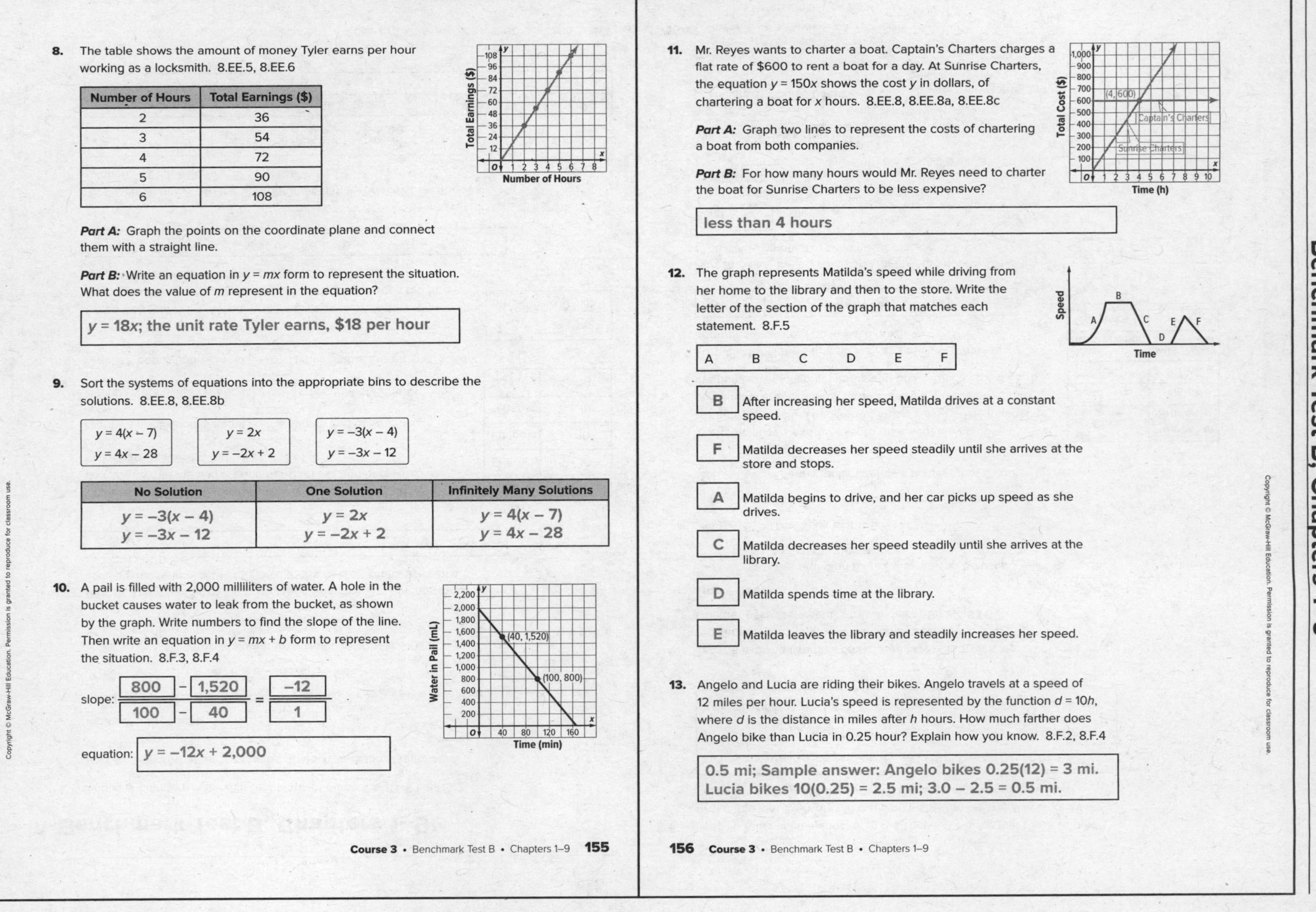

8. The table shows the amount of money Tyler earns per hour working as a locksmith. 8.EE.5, 8.EE.6

Number of Hours	Total Earnings ($)
2	36
3	54
4	72
5	90
6	108

Part A: Graph the points on the coordinate plane and connect them with a straight line.

Part B: Write an equation in $y = mx$ form to represent the situation. What does the value of m represent in the equation?

$y = 18x$; the unit rate Tyler earns, $18 per hour

9. Sort the systems of equations into the appropriate bins to describe the solutions. 8.EE.8, 8.EE.8b

$y = 4(x - 7)$, $y = 4x - 28$ | $y = 2x$, $y = -2x + 2$ | $y = -3(x - 4)$, $y = -3x - 12$

No Solution	One Solution	Infinitely Many Solutions
$y = -3(x - 4)$ $y = -3x - 12$	$y = 2x$ $y = -2x + 2$	$y = 4(x - 7)$ $y = 4x - 28$

10. A pail is filled with 2,000 milliliters of water. A hole in the bucket causes water to leak from the bucket, as shown by the graph. Write numbers to find the slope of the line. Then write an equation in $y = mx + b$ form to represent the situation. 8.F.3, 8.F.4

slope: $\frac{800 - 1{,}520}{100 - 40} = \frac{-12}{1}$

equation: **$y = -12x + 2,000$**

Course 3 • Benchmark Test B • Chapters 1–9 155

11. Mr. Reyes wants to charter a boat. Captain's Charters charges a flat rate of $600 to rent a boat for a day. At Sunrise Charters, the equation $y = 150x$ shows the cost y in dollars, of chartering a boat for x hours. 8.EE.8, 8.EE.8a, 8.EE.8c

Part A: Graph two lines to represent the costs of chartering a boat from both companies.

Part B: For how many hours would Mr. Reyes need to charter the boat for Sunrise Charters to be less expensive?

less than 4 hours

12. The graph represents Matilda's speed while driving from her home to the library and then to the store. Write the letter of the section of the graph that matches each statement. 8.F.5

A B C D E F

B After increasing her speed, Matilda drives at a constant speed.

F Matilda decreases her speed steadily until she arrives at the store and stops.

A Matilda begins to drive, and her car picks up speed as she drives.

C Matilda decreases her speed steadily until she arrives at the library.

D Matilda spends time at the library.

E Matilda leaves the library and steadily increases her speed.

13. Angelo and Lucia are riding their bikes. Angelo travels at a speed of 12 miles per hour. Lucia's speed is represented by the function $d = 10h$, where d is the distance in miles after h hours. How much farther does Angelo bike than Lucia in 0.25 hour? Explain how you know. 8.F.2, 8.F.4

0.5 mi; Sample answer: Angelo bikes 0.25(12) = 3 mi. Lucia bikes 10(0.25) = 2.5 mi; 3.0 – 2.5 = 0.5 mi.

156 Course 3 • Benchmark Test B • Chapters 1–9

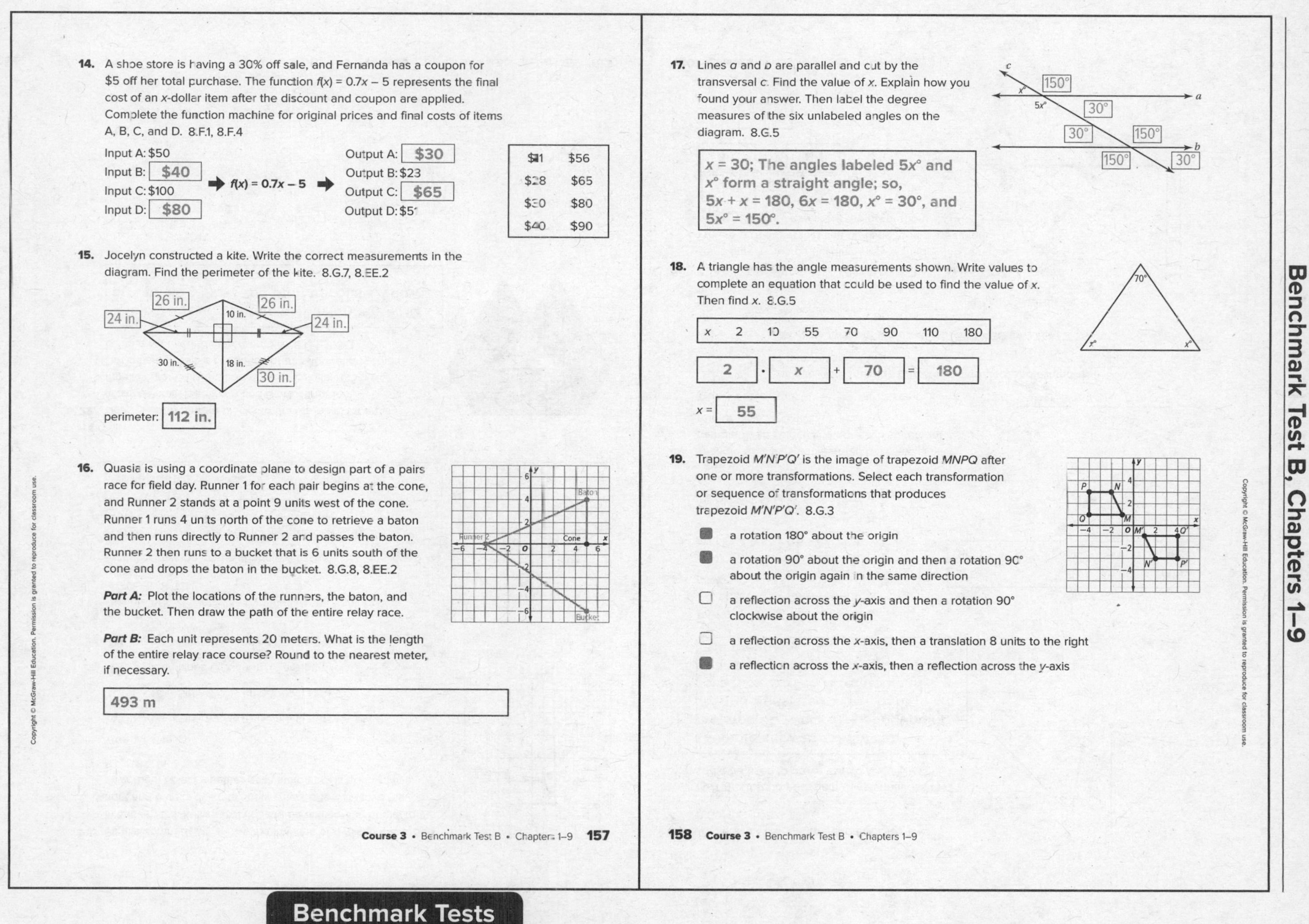

14. A shoe store is having a 30% off sale, and Fernanda has a coupon for \$5 off her total purchase. The function $f(x) = 0.7x - 5$ represents the final cost of an x-dollar item after the discount and coupon are applied. Complete the function machine for original prices and final costs of items A, B, C, and D. 8.F.1, 8.F.4

Input A: \$50 | Input B: \$40 | Input C: \$100 | Input D: \$80

→ $f(x) = 0.7x - 5$ →

Output A: \$30 | Output B: \$23 | Output C: \$65 | Output D: \$51

\$[illegible]1	\$56
\$28	\$65
\$30	\$80
\$40	\$90

15. Jocelyn constructed a kite. Write the correct measurements in the diagram. Find the perimeter of the kite. 8.G.7, 8.EE.2

perimeter: 112 in.

16. Quasia is using a coordinate plane to design part of a pairs race for field day. Runner 1 for each pair begins at the cone, and Runner 2 stands at a point 9 units west of the cone. Runner 1 runs 4 units north of the cone to retrieve a baton and then runs directly to Runner 2 and passes the baton. Runner 2 then runs to a bucket that is 6 units south of the cone and drops the baton in the bucket. 8.G.8, 8.EE.2

Part A: Plot the locations of the runners, the baton, and the bucket. Then draw the path of the entire relay race.

Part B: Each unit represents 20 meters. What is the length of the entire relay race course? Round to the nearest meter, if necessary.

493 m

17. Lines a and b are parallel and cut by the transversal c. Find the value of x. Explain how you found your answer. Then label the degree measures of the six unlabeled angles on the diagram. 8.G.5

$x = 30$; The angles labeled $5x°$ and $x°$ form a straight angle; so, $5x + x = 180$, $6x = 180$, $x° = 30°$, and $5x° = 150°$.

18. A triangle has the angle measurements shown. Write values to complete an equation that could be used to find the value of x. Then find x. 8.G.5

x	2	10	55	70	90	110	180

2 · x + 70 = 180

$x =$ 55

19. Trapezoid $M'N'P'Q'$ is the image of trapezoid $MNPQ$ after one or more transformations. Select each transformation or sequence of transformations that produces trapezoid $M'N'P'Q'$. 8.G.3

- [x] a rotation 180° about the origin
- [x] a rotation 90° about the origin and then a rotation 90° about the origin again in the same direction
- [ ] a reflection across the y-axis and then a rotation 90° clockwise about the origin
- [ ] a reflection across the x-axis, then a translation 8 units to the right
- [x] a reflection across the x-axis, then a reflection across the y-axis

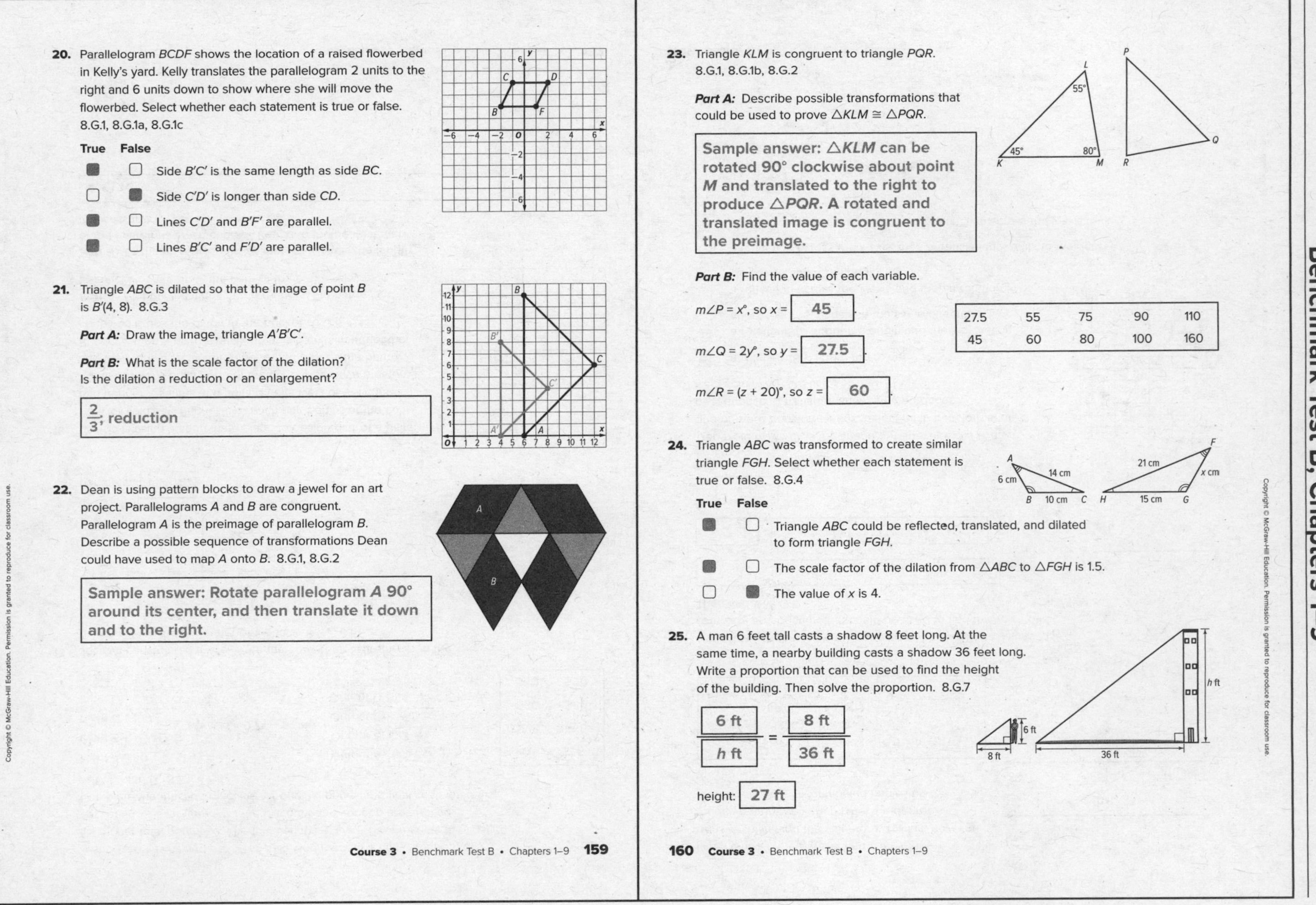

20. Parallelogram *BCDF* shows the location of a raised flowerbed in Kelly's yard. Kelly translates the parallelogram 2 units to the right and 6 units down to show where she will move the flowerbed. Select whether each statement is true or false. 8.G.1, 8.G.1a, 8.G.1c

True	False	
■	☐	Side $B'C'$ is the same length as side BC.
☐	■	Side $C'D'$ is longer than side CD.
■	☐	Lines $C'D'$ and $B'F'$ are parallel.
■	☐	Lines $B'C'$ and $F'D'$ are parallel.

21. Triangle *ABC* is dilated so that the image of point *B* is $B'(4, 8)$. 8.G.3

Part A: Draw the image, triangle $A'B'C'$.

Part B: What is the scale factor of the dilation? Is the dilation a reduction or an enlargement?

$\frac{2}{3}$, reduction

22. Dean is using pattern blocks to draw a jewel for an art project. Parallelograms *A* and *B* are congruent. Parallelogram *A* is the preimage of parallelogram *B*. Describe a possible sequence of transformations Dean could have used to map *A* onto *B*. 8.G.1, 8.G.2

Sample answer: Rotate parallelogram *A* 90° around its center, and then translate it down and to the right.

23. Triangle *KLM* is congruent to triangle *PQR*. 8.G.1, 8.G.1b, 8.G.2

Part A: Describe possible transformations that could be used to prove $\triangle KLM \cong \triangle PQR$.

Sample answer: $\triangle KLM$ can be rotated 90° clockwise about point *M* and translated to the right to produce $\triangle PQR$. A rotated and translated image is congruent to the preimage.

Part B: Find the value of each variable.

$m\angle P = x°$, so $x =$ **45**

$m\angle Q = 2y°$, so $y =$ **27.5**

$m\angle R = (z + 20)°$, so $z =$ **60**

27.5	55	75	90	110
45	60	80	100	160

24. Triangle *ABC* was transformed to create similar triangle *FGH*. Select whether each statement is true or false. 8.G.4

True	False	
■	☐	Triangle *ABC* could be reflected, translated, and dilated to form triangle *FGH*.
■	☐	The scale factor of the dilation from $\triangle ABC$ to $\triangle FGH$ is 1.5.
☐	■	The value of *x* is 4.

25. A man 6 feet tall casts a shadow 8 feet long. At the same time, a nearby building casts a shadow 36 feet long. Write a proportion that can be used to find the height of the building. Then solve the proportion. 8.G.7

$$\frac{6 \text{ ft}}{h \text{ ft}} = \frac{8 \text{ ft}}{36 \text{ ft}}$$

height: **27 ft**

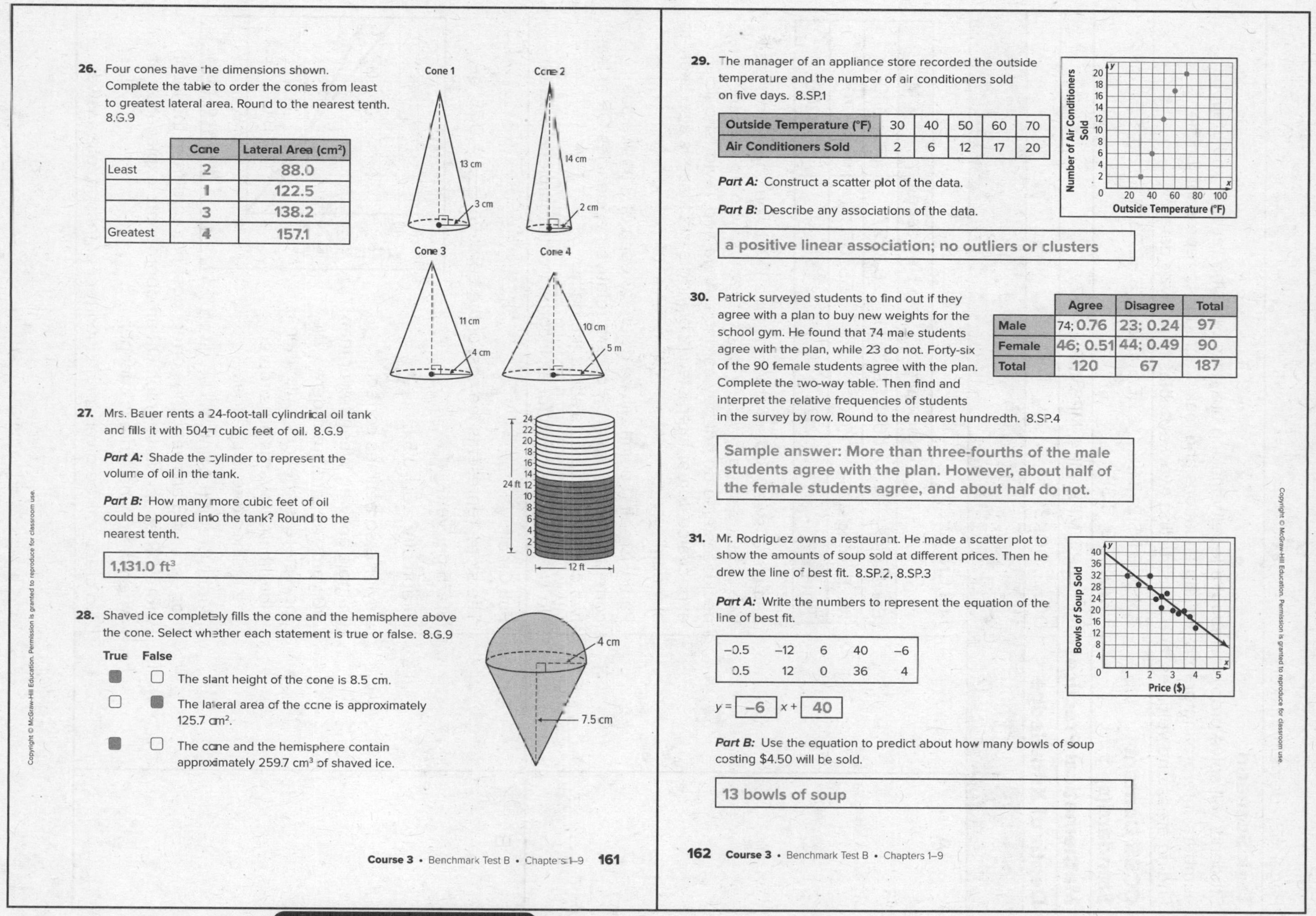

26. Four cones have the dimensions shown. Complete the table to order the cones from least to greatest lateral area. Round to the nearest tenth. 8.G.9

	Cone	Lateral Area (cm^2)
Least	2	88.0
	1	122.5
	3	138.2
Greatest	4	157.1

27. Mrs. Bauer rents a 24-foot-tall cylindrical oil tank and fills it with 504π cubic feet of oil. 8.G.9

Part A: Shade the cylinder to represent the volume of oil in the tank.

Part B: How many more cubic feet of oil could be poured into the tank? Round to the nearest tenth.

1,131.0 ft^3

28. Shaved ice completely fills the cone and the hemisphere above the cone. Select whether each statement is true or false. 8.G.9

True	False	
■	□	The slant height of the cone is 8.5 cm.
□	■	The lateral area of the cone is approximately 125.7 cm^2.
■	□	The cone and the hemisphere contain approximately 259.7 cm^3 of shaved ice.

29. The manager of an appliance store recorded the outside temperature and the number of air conditioners sold on five days. 8.SP.1

Outside Temperature (°F)	30	40	50	60	70
Air Conditioners Sold	2	6	12	17	20

Part A: Construct a scatter plot of the data.

Part B: Describe any associations of the data.

a positive linear association; no outliers or clusters

30. Patrick surveyed students to find out if they agree with a plan to buy new weights for the school gym. He found that 74 male students agree with the plan, while 23 do not. Forty-six of the 90 female students agree with the plan. Complete the two-way table. Then find and interpret the relative frequencies of students in the survey by row. Round to the nearest hundredth. 8.SP.4

	Agree	Disagree	Total
Male	74; 0.76	23; 0.24	97
Female	46; 0.51	44; 0.49	90
Total	120	67	187

Sample answer: More than three-fourths of the male students agree with the plan. However, about half of the female students agree, and about half do not.

31. Mr. Rodriguez owns a restaurant. He made a scatter plot to show the amounts of soup sold at different prices. Then he drew the line of best fit. 8.SP.2, 8.SP.3

Part A: Write the numbers to represent the equation of the line of best fit.

−0.5	−12	6	40	−6
0.5	12	0	36	4

$y =$ −6 $x +$ 40

Part B: Use the equation to predict about how many bowls of soup costing $4.50 will be sold.

13 bowls of soup

Benchmark Tests

Page 163 • Jewelry Makers

Task Scenario

Students will solve problems about a jewelry-making business by using rational and irrational numbers, interpreting graphs, writing equations and making graphs to represent functions, finding areas and volumes, and constructing two-way tables to analyze data.

CCSS Content Standard(s)	8.NS.1, 8.NS.2, 8.EE.2, 8.EE.5, 8.EE.8, 8.EE.8a, 8.EE.8b, 8.F.1, 8.F.2, 8.F.4, 8.G.9, 8.SP.4
Mathematical Practices	MP1, MP2, MP3, MP4, MP5, MP6, MP7
Depth of Knowledge	DOK2, DOK3

Part	Maximum Points	Scoring Rubric
A	3	See below
B	3	See below

Part A — Maximum Points: 3

Full Credit:

	Necklace	No Necklace	Total
Earrings	110; 0.88	20; 0.27	130
No Earrings	15; 0.12	55; 0.73	70
Total	125	75	200

Sample answer: 88% of students who like to buy necklaces also like to buy earrings, while 73% of students who do not buy necklaces also do not buy earrings. Anya and Taylor should expect a customer interested in buying a necklace is also likely to buy earrings.

Partial Credit (1 point) will be given for each of 3 answers: a correct two-way table OR correct relative frequencies OR at least two correct statements about the data.

No credit will be given for an incorrect or incomplete answer.

Part B — Maximum Points: 3

Full Credit:

The slope represents the cost of the cord: $\frac{30 - 7.5}{40 - 10} = 0.75$, or $0.75 per yard.

Graph of $y = 5 + 0.5x$:

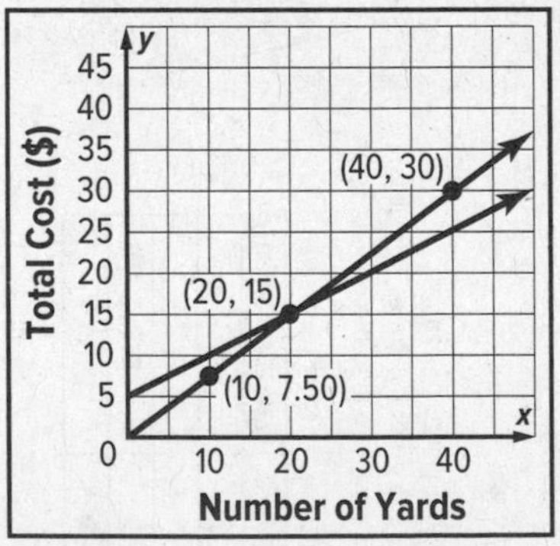

Taylor is sometimes correct.

Sample answer: When fewer than 20 yards of cord are ordered, the local store is cheaper; but, when more than 20 yards are ordered, the online store is cheaper.

Partial Credit (1 point) will be given for each of 3 answers: the correct cost per yard from the local store OR an accurate graph OR an appropriate explanation of when the online store is cheaper.

No credit will be given for an incorrect or incomplete answer.

<table>
<tr><th>Part</th><th>Maximum Points</th><th>Scoring Rubric</th></tr>
<tr><td>C</td><td>2</td><td>Full Credit:
volume of 1 bead = volume of large cylinder – volume of hole:
$\pi(1.5^2)(8) - \pi(1^2)(8) = 18\pi - 8\pi = 10\pi \approx 31.4159$ mm^3
volume of 100 beads: $100(31.4159) \approx 3{,}141.6$ mm^3
Partial Credit (1 point) will be given for the correct volume of one bead OR the correct volume of 100 beads.
No credit will be given for an incorrect or incomplete answer.</td></tr>
<tr><td>D</td><td>2</td><td>Full Credit:
area of wooden square: $s^2 = 7$
$s = \sqrt{7} \approx 2.65$, so the side length is 2.65 cm.
Sample answer: The length is an estimate. It is not possible to find an exact length because $\sqrt{7}$ is irrational. An irrational number is a non-terminating, non-repeating decimal.
Partial Credit (1 point) will be given for the correct side length OR a correct explanation of why the side length is an estimate.
No credit will be given for an incorrect or incomplete answer.</td></tr>
<tr><td>E</td><td>2</td><td>Full Credit:
50% of c is $0.50c$, so after the markup, the selling price is $c + 0.5c = 1.5c$.
function: $P = 1.5c - 1$
<table><tr><th>Cost of Making One Piece of Jewelry, c ($)</th><td>$4.00</td><td>$6.00</td><td>$11.00</td><td>$14.00</td></tr><tr><th>Amount Earned from That Sale, P ($)</th><td>$5.00</td><td>$8.00</td><td>$15.50</td><td>$20.00</td></tr></table>
Partial Credit (1 point) will be given for the correct function OR a completed table with the correct costs.
No credit will be given for an incorrect and incomplete answer.</td></tr>
<tr><td>TOTAL</td><td>12</td><td></td></tr>
</table>

Performance Task Rubrics